INORGANIC CHEMISTRY

DATE DUE

Mar 30 '65		
May 13 '65		
May 5 '67		
May 22 '67		
Sep 25 '68		
May 5 '69		
Mar 7 '72		
May 23 '72		
Apr 30 '82		

| | |

SOLE DISTRIBUTORS FOR THE UNITED STATES AND CANADA

AMERICAN ELSEVIER PUBLISHING COMPANY, INC.

52 Vanderbilt Avenue, New York 17, N.Y.

INORGANIC CHEMISTRY

A Guide to Advanced Study

by

R. B. HESLOP

Lecturer in Chemistry,
The Manchester College of Science and Technology

and

P. L. ROBINSON

Emeritus Professor in the University of Durham;
formerly Professor of Inorganic Chemistry,
King's College, Newcastle upon Tyne
and later Principal Scientific Officer,
Atomic Energy Research Establishment, Harwell

SECOND, REVISED EDITION

ELSEVIER PUBLISHING COMPANY
AMSTERDAM   LONDON   NEW YORK
1963

Library of Congress Catalog Card Number 62–13774

With 292 figures and 136 tables

First impression April 1960

Second impression September 1960

Third impression December 1960

Fourth impression November 1961

Fifth impression February 1962

Second Edition 1963

PRINTED IN THE NETHERLANDS BY
N.V. DRUKKERIJ G. J. THIEME, NIJMEGEN

Preface

This book is addressed to students and intended to provide in a single small volume an outline of current inorganic chemistry sufficient for basic reading up to honours degree standard. The approach is general and reasonably fundamental, so that some of the material is suitable for advanced level and scholarship pupils in schools and for non-specialist students in universities and technical colleges. Suggestions are made for further reading. Teachers may find it useful in planning their instruction to classes at all stages. An endeavour has been made to select factual matter of topical interest and to present the theoretical foundations rigorously enough to make advance possible by addition rather than correction.

Inorganic chemistry is descriptive in the sense that many branches of chemistry remain essentially descriptive. But the emphasis falls increasingly upon a description of its phenomena in terms of the discoveries of atomic physics, quantum mechanics, and theoretical and physical chemistry. Accordingly the earlier chapters seek to provide a minimum background for the rational understanding of chemical observations. The information is not intended to take the place of specific reading and instruction in physical and theoretical chemistry, but simply to give a handy, coherent synopsis of ideas which should enrich the appreciation of the chapters which follow.

These constitute the main body of the work which has three objects. First to provide clear-cut, readily assimilated information about the elements, presented in a comparative way, usually, but not exclusively, under the appropriate periodic sub-groups; secondly to cross-link related material by short discussions of particular topics; and thirdly to emphasise, by reiteration and repeated page reference, applications of theory developed in the earlier chapters. By these modes of association, it is hoped the student will both acquire a useful body of information and appreciate the growing integration which now characterises inorganic chemistry. Although short, and intended as a framework for planning his study, this book includes something on most aspects of the subject. Its character makes direct reference to original literature out of place; but, in some instances, authors' names and the year of publication have been given.

The varied and interesting experimentation pursued in modern inorganic chemistry has been outlined elsewhere; the brief reference that has been possible here will, it is hoped, suggest that inorganic chemistry is an actively experimental subject.

As is inevitable in a new text-book on an old subject, we have, besides drawing on our own experience, consulted many original papers, articles and books; without the efforts of their authors we could not have written these pages. To Dr. T. G. Pearson and Dr. B. A. Scott we are very grateful, for they undertook the considerable and unenviable task of reading the first draft, and their stimulating criticisms and valuable suggestions were most acceptable. We are especially indebted to Dr. R. McWeeny who actively collaborated in the writing of chapters 4, 5, 6 and 8, and largely brought them to their final form. He also read and criticised the remaining chapters, and his influence on the presentation of theoretical topics throughout the book is very cordially acknowledged. For the text in its final form we accept responsibility.

We thank Mr. J. Routledge who prepared the diagrams, all specially drawn for this work, and Mrs. A. Bartrope who typed the manuscript and gave much other help.

January 1960   R. B. HESLOP

                                                          P. L. ROBINSON

Preface to the Second Edition

Four further impressions of this book have been called for since it was published in April 1960. This fact and much encouraging comment suggest that the selection of material and the manner of its presentation have met with general approval. We are grateful for many helpful criticisms—made personally and in reviews—all of which have been carefully considered. Wherever possible, modifications to meet them have been made in this second edition.

The original aim, which remains unchanged, was a text-book of modest size and price that did not presume to be a substitute for oral instruction or seek to deal with the special topics which give individuality to advanced courses. Extending its scope to include even a selection of these topics would have destroyed the character of the book; hence the only major additions are a description of phosphonitrilic compounds, a section on complexes in aqueous solution, and a short chapter on inorganic polymers. In other parts the treatment has been modified to bring it into line with the results of recent research.

We have suggested useful sources of information on p. 3 and still feel that the further direction of reading should rest with the teacher.

We thank Dr. T. N. Bell, Professor N. N. Greenwood, Dr. M. F. Lappert, Dr. L. E. J. Roberts, Dr. A. G. Sharpe, Professor E. H. Wiebenga and Dr. W. Wild for the helpful suggestions they were kind enough to make.

September 1962   R. B. H.

                                                           P. L. R.

Contents

Chapter 1

An Approach to Inorganic Chemistry

A resurgence in inorganic chemistry, the oldest discipline in chemistry, is evident; not only is the subject exciting more interest as a topic of pure and applied research, it is finding manifold applications in industry. Inorganic chemistry forms the foundation of vast endeavour in fine and heavy chemicals, in ceramics, and in extraction metallurgy. The last, once restricted to a few, is now extended to most metals. It is concerned with the preparation of catalysts, and its ramifications in the field of atomic energy are extensive and growing. This book will have failed of its purpose if something of the enthusiasm and confidence now inspiring inorganic chemists has not been reflected in its pages. Distinguished exponents of the subject have recently called attention to much that awaits investigation. Apart from research, the calls of industry for inorganic chemists, at present inadequately met, grow.

In this opening chapter we shall try to show what constitutes inorganic chemistry, why we think it desirable to adopt a modification of the usual approach to the subject, how we believe this book can best be used and, finally, what symbols and contractions we have used to get all we wished within these 576 pages.

Inorganic chemistry

The ambit of inorganic chemistry is well established; it comprises the natural occurrence and artificial preparation of the elements, their properties and reactions, and those of their compounds, together with a rational correlation and theoretical interpretation of the phenomena. Most of the compounds of carbon lie outside this purview, though interest in organic ligands widens.

Having been the first of the major divisions of classical chemistry to be treated didactically and, consequently, earliest a subject for text-books, inorganic chemistry has suffered the pioneer's penality in its exposition. The historical approach, so natural and rewarding at the beginning, has been too long retained. Because facts are more readily recognised than their significance, accumulation has tended to outrun selection. Systematisation of the accumulated material became possible much later, relatively, than in either organic or physical chemistry. As a result inorganic chemistry has tended to be presented as a mass of arbitrarily chosen facts which have been brought into some relationship by the Periodic Table.

Modern inorganic chemistry remains essentially descriptive and pictorial, though the pictures increase in precision and the descriptions become less and less qualitative. The historical approach, formerly much favoured, is now inappropriate because a point has been reached in the development of the subject from which it is easier and less confusing to enter it at the level of present theoretical and physico-chemical knowledge. This book attempts to provide such an entry.

Departure from custom

It is customary in text-books of inorganic chemistry to discuss, sometimes at length, two topics which belong more properly to general and historical chemistry, namely the earlier work on the structure of the atom culminating in the atomic model of Bohr, and the development of the idea of periodicity in the properties of the elements with details of its tabular presentation. Both have been omitted from this book because they hamper a rapid, lively development of the subject which stimulates interest in the student.

Approach to the subject

Quantum theory has provided a picture of the atom that allows an immediate approach to valency and molecular structure while furnishing a far more secure basis for the periodic arrangement of the elements than selected physical and chemical properties. This is not to denigrate the achievements of Thomson, Rutherford and Bohr in atomic structure, or of Newlands, Lothar Meyer, Mendeleeff, Bohr and others in evolving the Periodic Law, but rather to seize upon developments which their prescient work made possible. Readers will find it easier to assimilate and remember the facts embodied in the Periodic Classification when these are seen to emerge from the systematic development of electronic structure with increasing atomic number.

The description of atoms and molecules which has been adopted—that of one or more positive nuclei surrounded by a cloud of electrons which, for many purposes, is equivalent to a smeared-out negative charge—presents in pictorial form the results of thirty years of quantum mechanics. All available evidence suggests that this general picture is unlikely to suffer substantial modification. Theoretical chemistry accepts the Schrödinger equation and is largely concerned with finding the most direct mathematical path to a unified and transparent explanation of the physico-chemical properties of molecules. The adoption of this kind of description is therefore believed to be both desirable and opportune. The nucleus itself forms a useful starting point in this approach, not only because its charge and mass determine the extranuclear structure of the atom, but because it is the seat of radioactivity and the source of nuclear energy.

The reason why chemical reactions take place and the mechanism by which they operate are matters of increasing interest and call for some knowledge of thermodynamics and kinetics. The brief excursions into these subjects are synoptic and intended to provide the reader with no more than he will need in pursuing the main part of the book. Information about the kinetics of inorganic reactions is still sparse, but there is a wealth of thermodynamical data, standard electrode potentials and dissociation constants and the student must acquire facility in using these figures.

So much of inorganic matter is crystalline that once a means of investigating the structure of solids became available it was eagerly applied. The result has made it necessary to include a short account of the solid state. With this goes a little about the growth of crystals and the way atoms in their lattices suffer dislocation.

Suggestions

This book is a brief epitome of modern inorganic chemistry and the reader may usefully begin where his interest lies. Liberal cross-references provide a constant link with definitions and underlying theory. The earlier chapters need not be mastered before the rest of the book can be understood, but their assimilation by repeated reference will be repaid by a fuller appreciation of what follows. It is idle to suppose that a real appreciation of any branch of chemistry can be had without two things—adequate theory and sufficient facts. The best way to grasp theory is to apply it constantly, and the easiest way to remember facts is to seek their theoretical relationship. To continue from the stage reached in this book the student has a great choice of reading.

There are the larger standard texts, the books including many topics or dealing with one, a number of articles in *Quarterly Reviews of the Chemical Society*, some monographs of the *Royal Institute of Chemistry* and many other excellent presentations of current inorganic topics in *Chemistry and Industry*, the *School Science Review* and the *Journal of Chemical Education*. Other standard sources of reference and some account of laboratory methods will be found in *Experimental Inorganic Chemistry* by R. E. Dodd and P. L. Robinson.

Symbols and Abbreviations

1. Chemical symbols and formulae have been frequently used in place of names to save space and often to secure clarity. Where an arrow ($\rightarrow$) from the donor atom appears, it does not imply that the bond is different from the rest.
2. Where there can be no confusion as to the temperature scale, °C is indicated by the degree sign only after a number.
3. For pressure, mm signifies mm of mercury.
4. The numerical values of properties are intended for comparative purposes; they are given to no greater accuracy than this requires.
5. Atomic radius, density and atomic volume data are for the form stable at 25° and 1 atmosphere, except where otherwise stated.
6. Symbols which appear frequently are:

Avogadro's number	N	Heat capacity	C (cal mole^{-1} deg^{-1})
Gas constant	R (cal mole^{-1})	Internal energy	U (cal)
Faraday's constant	F (coulombs)	Entropy	S (cal deg^{-1})
		Heat content	H (cal)
Charge on an electron	$-$e (coulombs)	Gibbs free energy	G (cal)
		Atomic number	Z
Planck's constant	h (erg sec)	Atomic mass number	A
		Concentration of X	[X] moles l.$^{-1}$
Frequency	ν (sec^{-1})	Activity of X	a_x or $\{X\}$
Wave number	λ^{-1} (cm^{-1})	Specific reaction rate	k
		Equilibrium constant	K
Wave length	λ (Ångstrom units)	Activation energy	E (cal)

Subscripts and superscripts when used with these symbols, are explained in the text. The units of k and K are variable.

7. The most frequently used abbreviations are:

g	gram	mole	gram molecule
kg	kilogram	h.c.p.	hexagonal close-packed
l.	litre	b.c.c.	body-centred cubic
ml	millilitre	f.c.c.	face-centred cubic
cc	cubic centimetre	At. Vol.	atomic volume
cm	centimetre	A.M.U.	atomic mass unit
Å	Ångstrom unit (10^{-8} cm.)	b.p.	boiling point
V	volt	m.p.	melting point
eV	electron volt	u.v.	ultraviolet
MeV	million electron volts	i.r.	infrared
$I(1)$	ionisation potential (first)	atm.	atmosphere (pressure)
$E_h^\circ(M^+/M)$	standard electrode potential for M$^+$/M couple in volts	dens.	density
		s.g.	specific gravity
e.m.f.	electromotive force (volts)	°K	degree Kelvin
cal	calorie	Gp. II. etc.	Periodic Group Two etc.
kcal	kilocalorie	ln x	logarithm of x to base e

Chapter 2

The Atomic Nucleus: Genesis of the Elements

The chemical properties of an element depend on the nature of its atoms, and many advances in chemistry are directly attributable to advances in atomic physics during the last half century.

An atom comprises a positively charged, central *nucleus* which occupies about 10^{-15} of its volume, has a radius of $\sim 10^{-13}$ cm, and accounts for nearly all its mass, surrounded by a region of negative charge produced by the *electrons*, the whole unit being electrically neutral. The nucleus contains positive *protons* and uncharged *neutrons*, both particles having about the same mass. Other particles are known to emerge from the nucleus (*e.g.* electrons, p. 17, and positrons, p. 18) but are not regarded as primary constituents and are only observable in a transient sense. This apparent paradox is a manifestation of the Uncertainty Principle (p. 44): if the position of an electron is known within extremely narrow limits (as in a nucleus) its momentum can be known only within extremely wide limits; this means an electron known to be within a nucleus at one instant has a high probability of escaping during the next instant, *i.e.* it cannot be regarded as a permanent constit-

TABLE 1

CONSTITUTION OF SOME NUCLEI

Element	Z	N	A	Symbols		Properties
Hydrogen	1	0	1	$^{1}_{1}\text{H}$	p	Stable
Deuterium	1	1	2	$^{2}_{1}\text{H}$	d	Stable
Tritium	1	2	3	$^{3}_{1}\text{H}$	t	Radioactive
Helium	2	1	3	$^{3}_{2}\text{He}$		Stable
	2	2	4	$^{4}_{2}\text{He}$	α	Stable
Lithium	3	3	6	$^{6}_{3}\text{Li}$		Stable
	3	4	7	$^{7}_{3}\text{Li}$		Stable
Sodium	11	11	22	$^{22}_{11}\text{Na}$		Radioactive
	11	12	23	$^{23}_{11}\text{Na}$		Stable
	11	13	24	$^{24}_{11}\text{Na}$		Radioactive

uent. The number of protons in the nucleus determines the nature of an
element; it equals the number of electrons which in turn fixes the chemical
character. An atom with eight protons is oxygen, one with seventeen protons
chlorine. This, the *atomic number Z*, fixes the place of the element in the
Periodic Table. Except for hydrogen, all nuclei also contain a number of
neutrons, N. The sum of Z and N is the *mass number*, A. Protons and
neutrons being known collectively as *nucleons*, A is the number of nucleons.

An atom has three noteworthy features: (*i*) the enormous density of the
nucleus, about 5×10^{12} times as dense as uranium; (*ii*) the small volume of
the nucleus, about 10^{-15} of that of the atom, (*iii*) the large volume of the
negatively charged cloud, about 10^{15} times that of the nucleus. Nevertheless
atoms have diameters which do not differ greatly, the largest being only
five times greater than the smallest.

TABLE 2

APPROXIMATE DATA FOR NUCLEUS, ELECTRON CLOUD AND ATOM

	Nucleus	*Electron Cloud*	*Atom*
Charge (coulombs)	$+1.6 \times 10^{-19} Z$	$-1.6 \times 10^{-19} Z$	—
Mass	A	$Z/1837$	A
Diameter (cm)	$1.5 \times 10^{-13} A^{\frac{1}{3}}$	10^{-8}	10^{-8}
Density (g/cc)	10^{14}	$2 \times 10^{-4} Z$	$0.4 A$
Charge density (coulombs/cm³)	5×10^{18}	$4 \times 10^{4} Z$	—

Isotopes

There are three types of hydrogen atoms and, unlike any other isotopes,
they have names: *protium, deuterium, tritium*. In the commonest, protium,
the nucleus is a proton. Terrestrial hydrogen is usually combined with other
elements, and one atom of hydrogen in six thousand has a nucleus containing
a neutron as well as a proton. This isotope, deuterium, was separated from
ordinary hydrogen in 1931 (Urey, Brickwedde and Murphy) and has
somewhat different properties from the latter. The third isotope, tritium,
is produced by bombarding lithium ($^{6}_{3}$Li) with slow neutrons. Tritium is
unstable, its atom reverting to helium of the same mass by loss of a *β-particle*
(p. 17), an electron, in this instance, of nuclear origin:

$$^{3}_{1}\text{H} \longrightarrow {}^{3}_{2}\text{He} + \beta.$$

In a process of this kind the neutron decays into a proton and an electron.
The respective hydrogen isotopes are designated $^{1}_{1}$H, $^{2}_{1}$H and $^{3}_{1}$H the superscript being the mass number, A, and the subscript the atomic number, Z.

These isotopes occupy the same place as hydrogen in the Periodic Table. Helium has two natural isotopes $^3_2$He and $^4_2$He, the former very rare, and lithium also two, $^6_3$Li and $^7_3$Li, occurring in the ratio of about 1:13. Though the mass number precedes the symbol, the isotopes are spoken of as lithium-*six* and lithium-*seven*. There is only one natural isotope of sodium, $^{23}_{11}$Na; the other two, $^{22}_{11}$Na and $^{24}_{11}$Na, are artificial and unstable, the lighter emitting positrons (p. 18) and the heavier electrons.

Besides *isotope*, there are two other useful terms: atoms with the same mass number and different atomic numbers are called *isobars;* those with the same number of neutrons, *isotones*.

TABLE 3
ISOTOPE, ISOBAR AND ISOTONE

	Z	A	N	Examples	
Isotope	Same	Different	Different	$^{31}_{15}$P	$^{32}_{15}$P
Isobar	Different	Same	Different	$^3_1$H	$^3_2$He
Isotone	Different	Different	Same	$^2_1$H	$^3_2$He

Though it is proper to refer to phosphorus-31 and phosphorus-32 as isotopes of phosphorus, an individual atomic species should be called a *nuclide*. The hundred or so elements have furnished about twelve hundred nuclides.

Isotopes were first recognised in the natural radioactive series which comprise heavy elements, but positive ray analysis (Thomson, 1912) showed that light elements also had isotopes and the development of the mass spectrograph (Aston, 1927) enabled all the elements to be investigated. The operation of the mass spectrograph is based on the deflection of collimated beams of positively charged particles, cations, in electric and magnetic fields of known strength. The ions are formed as an anode ray by evaporation from a hot filament or, as in Aston's earliest apparatus, by passing a discharge through a vapour. Adjustment of the strength of the fields enables particles of the same charge to mass ratio to be focussed as slit images. With such a beam from an element possessing isotopes, the several images are brought to different foci, and from their positions the masses of the individual isotopes may be determined with an accuracy of 0.01% or better.

Molecules have rotational and vibrational energies (p. 119) which are quantised, taking only certain discrete values which depend in magnitude on the masses of the atoms involved and are therefore different for molecules containing different isotopes of the same element, for instance ^{1}H^{35}Cl and ^{1}H^{37}Cl. Changes in rotational energy are characterised by the absorption of radiation in the far infrared, and in vibrational energy by absorption in the near infrared; they give rise to lines in these spectral regions. Particular lines which occur singly when one nuclide is present appear in groups when there are several nuclides. From the small differences in frequency both the presence and relative masses of the nuclides may be inferred. By this sensitive method Giauque and Johnson (1929) showed that oxygen contained molecules of $^{16}O^{17}O$ and $^{16}O^{18}O$. The existence of oxygen-17 and 18 had not been revealed by the mass spectrograph.

Natural isotopic ratios — Atomic mass standard

The mass spectrometer is a mass spectrograph in which the ions are produced at a steady rate and the photographic plate, by means of which the positions of the ion images were formerly observed, is replaced by a slit behind which is a collector connected to devices for amplifying and measuring the ion current. The slit scans the spectrum and the ion current shows as a series of peaks. Every peak indicates an isotope and its height represents the relative number of ions (Fig. 1). The design of these instruments now

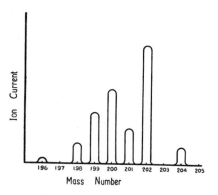

Fig. 1. Ion current peaks in the mass spectrograph of mercury.

allows an accuracy of 0.001%, making the method better than that of chemical analysis for the determination of atomic mass—the weighted mean of the masses of the isotopes.

The relative abundance of isotopes from different sources may vary a little. Atmospheric oxygen is slightly richer in oxygen-18 than the combined oxygen in sea water, and the relative abundance in water from different sources is not constant. Elementary sulphur in the Texas deposits has a different isotopic composition from that of the combined sulphur in the surrounding rocks. A range of 3.8% has been observed in the ratio of boron-10 and 11 from various sources (Briscoe and Robinson, 1925), but no difference in the ratio of silicon-28, 29 and 30 in material of widely spaced terrestrial origin (Robinson and Smith, 1926).

Atomic masses have been expressed with the naturally occurring mixture of oxygen isotopes as a standard value of 16 (the chemical scale); a later scale was that based on the mass of the nuclide $^{16}_{8}O$ (the physical scale). Because of the two heavier isotopes present in ordinary oxygen, atomic masses on the physical scale are 1.000275 times greater than those on the chemical scale.

It is now recommended by the International Union of Pure and Applied Chemistry that the nuclide $^{12}_{6}C$ should be used as the basis of a unified scale. To bring them to the carbon-12 scale, atomic masses on the chemical scale must be reduced by 43 parts per million (multiplied by 0.999957). No atomic mass is changed by more than 4 in the last place quoted in the 1957 table, and few of these have been established with certainty to better than 5 in the last place. The carbon-12 scale is very suitable for expressing the masses of nuclides and has the advantage that very few of the present figures are affected by as much as their limits of error.

The Mole

In keeping with this rationalisation of the atomic mass standard, Guggenheim (1961) has proposed a definition of the mole which includes not only molecular species but atoms, radicals, ions and electrons. *"The Mole* is the amount of substance containing the same number of molecules (or atoms, or radicals, or ions, or electrons as the case may be) as there are atoms in 12 g of ^{12}C".* Mole has been used in this sense throughout this book.

Separation of isotopes

(i) Gaseous diffusion

Gases of different density, ϱ, diffuse at different rates: rate $\propto 1/\sqrt{\varrho}$. Uranium hexafluoride made from natural uranium contains one part of $^{235}UF_6$ in 140 parts of $^{238}UF_6$. The ratio of the densities is 1.0086, of diffusion rates 1.0043. A process of successive diffusion through a series of porous partitions was developed at Oak Ridge, Tennessee (1945), and has been modified elsewhere. In these the lighter fraction passes a barrier and becomes the feed for a later stage while the heavier fraction is returned to an earlier stage.

(ii) Thermal diffusion

When two gases of different densities are in a vertical tube which is cool and has an electrically heated wire down the axis, the lighter gas diffuses preferentially towards the hot wire where it rises in a convection current, while the heavier streams downwards on the surface of the tube. The principle is applicable to isotopes and, with a column of 100 feet and a temperature difference of 600°, Clusius and Dickel (1938) effected an almost complete separation of ^{35}Cl from ^{37}Cl.

(iii) Electromagnetic method

A perfect separation is possible with a mass spectrograph in which the positive ions of the different isotopes pass into collectors, but the quantities would be small. About 1943, however, a large-scale apparatus, the calutron, was constructed in which an ideal rigorous separation was sacrificed to yield, since the ions in beams of heavy current repel one another and cause spreading. The method has been further refined and is extensively used.

(iv) Molecular distillation

Brönsted and Hevesy (1921) partially separated the isotopes of mercury by distillation in a high vacuum with a distance between the evaporating and condensing surfaces equal to about the mean free path of the atoms. The rates at which the isotopes evaporate is inversely proportional to the square roots of their masses so that the condensate is a little richer in the lighter isotopes.

(v) Chemical methods

Isotopes are not expected to be absolutely identical in chemical properties (p. 247), but the difference is observable only in the light elements where the ratio of the mass of the isotopes is large, for instance ^{1}H and ^{2}H. Thode and Urey (1939) concentrated nitrogen-15 in ammonium nitrate, to the extent of 70%, by allowing a solution of the salt to flow down a column against a counter current of ammonia. The equilibrium constant (p. 178) for

$$^{15}NH_3(g) + {}^{14}NH_4{}^+(aq) \rightleftharpoons {}^{14}NH_3(g) + {}^{15}NH_4{}^+(aq)$$

has a value of about 1.033.

(vi) Gas chromatography

This technique enables gases to be separated by the selective adsorption of one or more from a mixture on a suitable packing in a column. The adsorbed gas, should that be required, may be subsequently recovered by elution or other means. Though only partially successful when applied to the isotopes of neon because the difference in their adsorption coefficient on charcoal is small, the method has enabled deuterium to be separated from a 1 : 1 deuterium-hydrogen mixture (Glueckauf and Kitt, 1956). The column is packed with palladium-black on asbestos which preferentially adsorbs the hydrogen and allows the deuterium to pass on.

Exact masses of nuclides

Precise determinations of the masses of nuclides have shown that they are not simply the sums of the individual masses of their component protons and neutrons. When these units or nucleons combine to form a nucleus there is a change of potential and kinetic energy which appears as a change in mass. Einstein showed the energy created by the destruction of mass and the mass destroyed to be related thus:

$$E = mc^2.$$

The velocity of light c is $\sim 3 \times 10^{10}$ cm.sec^{-1} and a mass of 1 g is thus equivalent to about 9×10^{20} ergs.

A unit of energy, the *electron-volt*, is used in discussing energy changes in nuclei. It is the kinetic energy acquired by an electron in falling through a potential difference of 1 V.

$$1 \text{ eV} = 1.60 \times 10^{-12} \text{ ergs,}$$
$$1 \text{ million eV, } 1 \text{ MeV} = 1.60 \times 10^{-6} \text{ ergs,}$$
$$\therefore \text{ a mass of 1 g} = 5.61 \times 10^{26} \text{ MeV.}$$

An obvious result of Einstein's deduction is that the separate principles of conservation of mass and conservation of energy are replaced by the single principle of conservation of mass-energy. Furthermore, both mass and energy may be expressed in electron-volts, ergs or grams.

A convenient unit for the measurement of the masses of nuclides is the *atomic mass unit*, AMU, which is defined as one twelfth of the mass of the ^{12}C nuclide. The AMU $= 1.6604 \times 10^{-24}$ g; this is the reciprocal of the Avogadro number, 6.0228×10^{23} molecules per mole. It is equivalent to 931 MeV. The atomic mass or exact mass, M, of a nuclide is the weight of its atom, which includes the extra-nuclear electrons, in AMU. M is very slightly different from the mass number, A, in every instance except the standard, carbon-12. With sulphur-32, for instance, $M = 31.982183$ AMU, the difference $A - M$ (0.017817 AMU) being the mass defect. The *mass defect* formerly used as a guide to the stability of a nucleus has been replaced for this purpose by the more precise concept of *binding energy*.

Binding energy

When nucleons coalesce into a nucleus there is a loss of energy, shown as an equivalent decrease in mass; the binding energy, *BE*, is given by

$BE = \Delta M$

    $= Z \times$ (mass of proton) $+ N \times$ (mass of neutron) $-$ Mass of nucleus

    $= Z \times$ (mass of H atom) $+ N \times$ (mass of neutron) $-$ Mass of atom (M)

The mass of the hydrogen atom $= 1.008142$ AMU.

The mass of the neutron $= 1.008982$ AMU.

For oxygen 16, $Z = N = 8$,   and $M = A = 16$,

$BE = 8(1.008142) + 8(1.008982) - 16$,

    $= 0.136992$ AMU $= 0.136992 \times 931$ MeV,

    $= 128$ MeV.

Thus the BE per nucleon $= \frac{128}{16} = 8$ MeV.

The nuclear binding forces are strong attractive forces, independent of charge and of very short range. Just as an individual extra-nuclear energy level holds two electrons (Pauli principle (p. 59)) so an individual nuclear energy level appears to hold two protons and two neutrons. This probably accounts for the stability of the α-particle (p. 16), the $_2^4$He nucleus, and those nuclides with even numbers of protons and neutrons. Oxygen-16 and carbon-12 are outstanding examples, and the majority of the stable (non-radio-active) nuclides are further instances.

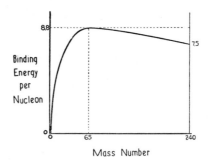

Fig. 2. Relation between binding energy and mass number.

TABLE 4

CONSTITUTION AND STABILITY OF NUCLIDES

Z	N	A	*Number of stable nuclides*
Even	Even	Even	164
Even	Odd	Odd	55
Odd	Even	Odd	50
Odd	Odd	Even	4

Nuclear shell structure

The energy of a system of nucleons is capable of taking only certain discrete values, *i.e.* it is *quantised*; the possible values of the energy cannot be reliably calculated by quantum mechanics, however, because the exact nature of the nuclear forces is unknown. In this respect the situation is less satisfactory than in the case of extra-nuclear electrons bound to the nucleus by electrostatic forces, where the possible energies can be calculated with reasonable accuracy (p. 57).

Nevertheless, there is strong empirical evidence, set out below, for a shell structure associated with the special stability of nuclei containing 2, 8, 20, 50, 82, or 126 of either protons or neutrons (Elsasser, 1934), the so-called magic number nuclides. This rests upon the following facts:

(i) The elements with unusually large numbers of stable isotopes and with the greatest range of mass are calcium and tin, which have the stable isotopes:

$$^{40}_{20}\text{Ca}, \ ^{42}_{20}\text{Ca}, \ ^{43}_{20}\text{Ca}, \ ^{44}_{20}\text{Ca}, \ ^{46}_{20}\text{Ca}, \ \text{and} \ ^{48}_{20}\text{Ca}$$

and

$$^{112}_{50}\text{Sn}, \ ^{114}_{50}\text{Sn}, \ ^{115}_{50}\text{Sn}, \ ^{116}_{50}\text{Sn}, \ ^{117}_{50}\text{Sn}, \ ^{118}_{50}\text{Sn}, \ ^{119}_{50}\text{Sn}, \ ^{120}_{50}\text{Sn}, \ ^{122}_{50}\text{Sn}, \ \text{and} \ ^{124}_{50}\text{Sn}.$$

Similarly lead, $Z = 82$, is the final stable isotope of all the natural radioactive series.

(ii) Energies of radioactive decay products show the BE of neutrons to have a 2.2 MeV discontinuity at 126 neutrons, and the BE of protons to have a discontinuity of 1.6 MeV at 82 protons.

(iii) Nuclei with 50 or 82 neutrons are particularly abundant.

(iv) $^{87}_{36}\text{Kr}$ and $^{137}_{54}\text{Xe}$ are neutron emitters—very few are known. They have 51 and 83 neutrons respectively. The last neutron is evidently weakly held.

(v) Neutrons are absorbed with difficulty—the absorption cross sections are low—by nuclei with 50, 82 or 126 neutrons.

(vi) Experimental nuclear masses and semi-empirically calculated ones often differ. The largest of these differences can be explained by assuming nuclei with 50 and 82 neutrons to be particularly stable.

Acceptance of a shell model implies an assumption that each nucleon moves in an *average* central field provided by all the others, rather as the extra-nuclear electrons move in the electrostatic field of the whole nucleus.

Deviations in binding energy per nucleon

For a sufficiently large nucleus, nuclear forces alone would give a constant binding energy per nucleon and lead to stable nuclei with any number of protons and neutrons. But the normal electrostatic forces between protons in the heavier nuclei reduce the binding energy per nucleon below the average and lead the stable nuclides to have fewer protons than neutrons. However, in the lighter nuclei, where the ratio of surface to mass becomes high, the surface energy reduces the binding energy per nucleon below the average. The binding energy per nucleon in deuterium is 1.1 and in tritium 2.8 whereas it is 7 MeV in helium; fusion of very light nuclei thus involves an increase in binding energy and the release of energy.

Energy is also released when the heavy nucleus uranium-235 suffers fission to xenon and strontium.

$$^{235}_{92}\text{U} \rightarrow {}^{143}_{54}\text{Xe} + {}^{90}_{38}\text{Sr} + 2{}^{1}_{0}\text{n}.$$

Radioactivity

The manifestations of radioactivity are the emission from the nucleus of α-particles ($^{4}_{2}\text{He}$ nuclei moving with high kinetic energies), β^{-}-particles (electrons of nuclear origin) and β^{+}-particles (positrons, p. 18); the emissions are often accompanied by γ-radiation (electromagnetic waves of very high frequency). The energies involved in a radioactive change are so great as to be unaffected in rate by changes of temperature of several thousand degrees. Individual reactions are governed by statistical laws, and are accompanied by a characteristic radiation.

The probability of a nucleus distintegrating in unit time is the *decay constant*, λ. For N nuclei

$$\frac{dN}{dt} = -\lambda N, \quad \text{and} \quad N = N_0 e^{-\lambda t},$$

where N_0 is the original number of nuclei and N the number left after time t (in convenient units). The *activity*, A, of a specimen is the number of disintegrations in unit time.

$$A = \frac{dN}{dt} = -\lambda N, \quad \text{and} \quad A = A_0 e^{-\lambda t}.$$

A useful constant is the half-life, $t_{\frac{1}{2}}$, the time taken to halve the number of atoms of the nuclide.

Substituting $\dfrac{N}{N_0} = \dfrac{A}{A_0} = \frac{1}{2}$ in either equation above:

$$\lambda = \frac{\ln 2}{t_{\frac{1}{2}}} = \frac{0.693}{t_{\frac{1}{2}}}.$$

The specific activity, S, is the activity per gram,

$$S = \frac{0.693N}{At_{\frac{1}{2}}} \text{ disintegrations in unit time,}$$

where N is Avogadro's number and A the atomic mass number.

The standard used for measuring the activity of radioactive species is the *curie;* it is the activity of 1 g of radium, for which $A = 226$ and $t_{\frac{1}{2}} = 1622$ years. It represents 3.7×10^{10} disintegrations per second.

Generally for any nuclide,

$$S = \frac{1622 \times 226}{t_{\frac{1}{2}} \times A} \text{ curies per g} = \frac{3.67 \times 10^5}{t_{\frac{1}{2}} \times A} (t_{\frac{1}{2}} \text{ being expressed in years).}$$

The activity of a specimen is measured by comparing the number of impulses which it produces per minute in a Geiger counter with that produced by a substance of known specific activity, say uranium oxide, in the same position in the same counting equipment.

Natural radioactivity

There is no difference between the principles governing natural and artificial radioactivity. The classical disintegration series stem from radio-nuclides with long half-lives, exceeding 10^8 years. Their decay is almost entirely by α- and β-emissions.

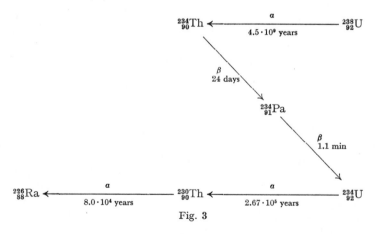

Fig. 3

This is the beginning of the Uranium series, designated the $4n + 2$ series because the expression, with n integral, gives the mass number.

TABLE 5

THE DISINTEGRATION SERIES

Series	Parent nuclide	Half life of parent	Type
Thorium	^{232}Th	1.4×10^{10} years	$4n$ (natural)
Neptunium	^{237}Np	2.25×10^{6} years	$4n + 1$ (not natural)
Uranium	^{238}U	4.5×10^{9} years	$4n + 2$ (natural)
Actinium	^{235}U	7.0×10^{8} years	$4n + 3$ (natural

Radioactive elements

At. No.	Name	Symbol	Isotope	$t_{\frac{1}{2}}$	Disintegration
43	Technetium	Tc	99*	2.2×10^{5} y	β^-
61	Promethium	Pm	147*	2.6 y	β^-
84	Polonium	Po	210*	140 d	α
85	Astatine	At	210	8.3 y	α
86	Radon	Rn	222	3.8 d	α
87	Francium	Fr	223	21 min	β^-
88	Radium	Ra	226	1622 y	α
89	Actinium	Ac	227	22 y	β^-, α
90	Thorium	Th	232	1.4×10^{10} y	α
91	Protactinium	Pa	231	3.4×10^{4} y	α
92	Uranium	U	238	4.5×10^{9} y	α
93	Neptunium	Np	237	2.2×10^{6} y	α
94	Plutonium	Pu	242	3.8×10^{5} y	α
95	Americium	Am	243	7.6×10^{3} y	α
96	Curium	Cm	247	4×10^{7} y	α
97	Berkelium	Bk	249*	290 d	β^-
98	Californium	Cf	251*	660 d	β^-
99	Einsteinium	Es	254	280 d	α
100	Fermium	Fm	253	4.5 d	α
101	Mendelevium	Md	256	0.5 h	Spontaneous fission
102	Nobelium	No		~ 10 min	

* Indicates the isotope most commonly known but not that of longest $t_{\frac{1}{2}}$. Rest are of longest $t_{\frac{1}{2}}$.

α-Emission

The α-particle is a helium atom which has lost two electrons and become He^{2+}. Its emission depends on the probability of the α-particle penetrating the potential energy barrier arising from the nuclear interactions. Thus the greater the energy of the particle in relation to the energy barrier the higher the decay constant. The energy of the emitted particle is given by the empirical formula

$$\log \lambda = A \log E + B,$$

A and B being constants for a particular series (Geiger-Nuttall rule, 1912). The energies of α-particles, though not identical for a particular species, usually lie within a narrow range and are high, generally greater than 4.5 MeV. Because of their size and charge, α-particles do not penetrate far into matter. Their energies can be roughly assessed by observing their penetration, or can be measured from their response to magnetic and electric fields.

Following Rutherford and Wood's (1916) observation that thorium C' produced some α-particles of exceptionally long range, it has been established that a number of nuclides give α-particles of different energies. For instance, ThC emits five groups with energies 6.084, 6.044, 5.762, 5.620 and 5.601 MeV, the first group comprising 27% and the second 70% of the total. Such *spectra* are accounted for by the existence of definite energy levels in the atomic nucleus. ThC is ordinarily in its ground state, but the emission of an α-particle gives, according to its energy, ThC'' in the ground state *or* in one of its four excited states.

β-Emission: isobaric change

The energy of a β-particle, or electron of nuclear origin, on emission can be calculated approximately from the mass lost in the disintegration producing it.

In the nuclear change $^{14}_{6}C \rightarrow {}^{14}_{7}N + \beta +$ neutrino:

$$M \text{ for } {}^{14}_{6}C = 14.007682 \text{ AMU}$$
$$M \text{ for } {}^{14}_{7}N = 14.007515 \text{ AMU}$$
$$\text{Difference} = 0.000167 \text{ AMU}$$
$$= 0.000167 \times 931 \text{ MeV}$$
$$= 0.155 \text{ MeV}$$

Thus the change is accompanied by the release of 0.155 MeV, as kinetic energy of β-particle and neutrino. The neutrino, which has no charge and a very small mass, shares the available energy with the β-particle; hence the energy of β-particles from a particular type of nuclide can vary. A neutrino has spin which enables the angular momentum to be conserved in the disintegrating process. The energy is approximately assessed by the depth the particle penetrates into aluminium. Sometimes the β-emission is accompanied by γ-emission.

$$^{198}\text{Au} \xrightarrow[0.96 \text{ MeV}]{\beta^-} \boxed{\begin{array}{c}\text{Unstable}\\\text{nuclide}\end{array}} \xrightarrow[0.41 \text{ MeV}]{\gamma} {}^{198}\text{Hg}.$$

In these circumstances an unstable nucleus is generally produced by the first change and stabilised by the second. The γ-radiation can be measured, after filtering out the β-particles with aluminium foil, by either its ionising or penetrating effects.

Alternative processes often occur such as the one illustrated in Fig. 4 in which chlorine-38 produces three β-particles, in the proportions and of the energies shown. Conversion to a stable argon atom is completed by low energy β-emission being followed by γ-radiation; but this is not necessary after high energy β-emission.

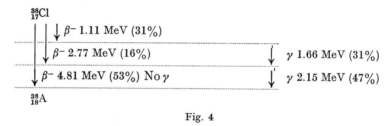

Fig. 4

Frequently disintegration processes are far more complicated.

Positrons

Dirac (1928) showed theoretically that a particle of the mass of an electron may have an energy less than $-mc^2$ or greater than $+mc^2$ but not of an intermediate value, and proposed the following hypothesis. The negative states are normally all filled and give an all-pervading, uniform density of negative charge whose presence cannot be detected experimentally: for otherwise ordinary electrons would spontaneously disappear by falling into the lower energy states and taking on the properties of particles of negative mass (negative kinetic energy). Such particles would, for instance, move *against* an applied force instead of with it. A perfect vacuum is thus a *sea* of negative energy electrons and only *changes* in this background are observable. If, however, a particle in the sea is given enough energy

($> 2mc^2$) it can go into a positive energy state and is observed as an ordinary electron; at the same time it leaves a "hole" and this is also observed as something with positive energy (for to fill it up, and make it disappear, negative energy must be added) and with positive *charge* (being a missing negative charge in the uniform sea). Excitations of this kind are actually observed, with energy absorption of at least $2mc^2$ or 1.02 MeV, and the process is described as *pair production*. The hole behaves like a positive 'electron' and is called a positron. The reverse process also occurs, an electron and a positron annihilating each other with the liberation of a similar amount of energy. Both processes require the presence of a nucleus—as 'catalyst'—in order that momentum conservation conditions are satisfied.

Anderson (1932) discovered the positron in a study of cosmic rays, using the Wilson cloud chamber. Blackett (1933) confirmed his findings.

Curie and Joliot obtained positron-electron pairs from heavy metals bombarded with high energy (5 MeV) γ-rays derived from beryllium mixed with polonium. The average life of the positron is about 10^{-9} sec. On colliding with an electron both are annihilated and γ-radiation—the annihilation radiation—is emitted. The formation and annihilation of a positron-electron pair is thus represented.

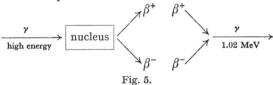

Fig. 5.

β^+-Emission: isobaric change

The energy of a β^+-particle at the instant of emission can be found by using copper-64. This, in one of its transitions, emits a positron with a maximum energy of 0.66 MeV, giving nickel-64.

For Cu 64	M = 63.9491	AMU
Ni 64	M = 63.9473	AMU
Difference	ΔM = 0.0018	AMU
	= 1.68	MeV
Energy required to create a β^+	= 1.02	MeV
Maximum kinetic energy available to the positron =	0.66	MeV.

Electron capture: isobaric change

Besides β^- and β^+-emissions, a third form of isobaric change is possible in which the nucleus captures an extra-nuclear, usually a K,electron. This is not accompanied by radiation unless the daughter nucleus emits a γ-ray, all the energy of transition being retained.

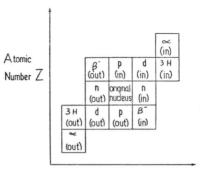

Fig. 6. Diagram illustrating nuclear changes. Movement vertically represents unit change in atomic number, and horizontally unit change in neutron number.

Nuclear reactions

(i) α-Induced reactions

Rutherford (1919) noticed that high energy α-particles from bismuth-214, on passing through nitrogen gas, produced protons of long range:

$$^{14}_{7}N + ^{4}_{2}He \rightarrow ^{17}_{8}O + ^{1}_{1}H.$$

This nuclear reaction, in which an α-particle induces the loss of a proton, is known as an (α,p) reaction and represented by $^{14}_{7}N(\alpha,p)^{17}_{8}O$.

For ^{14}N	$M =$	14.007524 AMU
^{4}He	$M =$	4.003860 AMU
Total mass		18.011384 AMU

For ^{17}O	$M =$	17.004507 AMU
^{1}H	$M =$	1.008142 AMU
Mass after reaction		18.012649 AMU

Since the mass is increased by 0.001265 AMU (1.18 MeV), only high energy α-particles are capable of bringing about the change. All elements from boron to potassium, except carbon and oxygen, undergo α-induced reactions. Heavy nuclei repel the α-particles more strongly but some of these have been broached by α-particles highly energised (up to 300 MeV) in the cyclotron. An example is

$$^{75}As\,(\alpha,n)\,^{78}Br.$$

(ii) Proton-induced reactions

Cockcroft and Walton (1932) disrupted lithium with low energy protons ($\sim 10^5$ eV, *cf.* natural α-particles $\sim 10^7$ eV) produced in a linear accelerator:

$$^{7}_{3}\text{Li} + ^{1}_{1}\text{H} \rightarrow ^{4}_{2}\text{He} + ^{4}_{2}\text{He}.$$

This reaction liberated 17.3 MeV, the mass afterwards being 0.0186 AMU less than before. Beryllium, fluorine, sodium and magnesium provide nuclides which undergo proton-induced reactions. Nitrogen-14 yields carbon-11, a positron-emitter with a half-life of twenty minutes.

$$^{14}_{7}\text{N} + ^{1}_{1}\text{H} \rightarrow ^{11}_{6}\text{C} + ^{4}_{2}\text{He} \quad [^{14}\text{N}(p,\alpha)^{11}\text{C}].$$

(iii) Neutron-induced reactions

Chadwick (1932) produced neutrons by bombarding beryllium with natural α-particles:

$$^{9}_{4}\text{Be} + ^{4}_{2}\text{He} \rightarrow ^{12}_{6}\text{C} + ^{1}_{0}\text{n}.$$

The yield is very small, thirty neutrons per million α-particles. As the neutron is non-ionising it is detected by its action on a nuclide such as boron-10,

$$^{10}_{5}\text{B} + ^{1}_{0}\text{n} \rightarrow ^{7}_{3}\text{Li} + ^{4}_{2}\text{He},$$

the α-particle produced being readily observable. This is an (n,α) reaction. The neutron is a versatile participator in nuclear reactions; its freedom from charge enables it to penetrate into nuclei resistant to high-energy α-particles and protons. Fermi discovered the three main types of neutron-induced reactions illustrated.

(a) (n,α) $^{27}_{13}\text{Al} + ^{1}_{0}\text{n} \rightarrow ^{24}_{11}\text{Na} + ^{4}_{2}\text{He}.$

(b) (n,p) $^{27}_{13}\text{Al} + ^{1}_{0}\text{n} \rightarrow ^{27}_{12}\text{Mg} + ^{1}_{1}\text{H}.$

(c) (n,γ) $^{27}_{13}\text{Al} + ^{1}_{0}\text{n} \rightarrow ^{28}_{13}\text{Al} + \gamma.$

Fast neutrons favour the first (a), medium speed, the second (b), and slow, the third (c). The capture reaction (c) is important in the heavy elements (p. 437).

(iv) Reactions induced by high energy γ-rays

One of the best-known of these is

$$^{9}_{4}\text{Be} + h\nu \rightarrow ^{8}_{4}\text{Be} + ^{1}_{0}\text{n}.$$

It takes place when antimony 124, which emits γ-rays of 2.04 MeV, is intimately mixed with powdered beryllium, and furnishes an easily accessible source of neutrons.

(v) Deuteron-induced reactions

Deuterons may be sufficiently accelerated in the cyclotron to cause nuclear reaction:

$$^{9}_{4}\text{Be} + {}^{2}_{1}\text{H} \rightarrow {}^{10}_{5}\text{B} + {}^{1}_{0}\text{n},$$
$$^{12}_{6}\text{C} + {}^{2}_{1}\text{H} \rightarrow {}^{13}_{7}\text{N} + {}^{1}_{0}\text{n}.$$

Stellar energy

The recognition of the enormous energy set free in nuclear reaction has suggested the source from which the stars draw their energy. At the exceedingly high temperatures prevailing ($\sim 10^{8}\,^{\circ}\text{C}$) the nuclei are stripped of electrons and attain velocities comparable with those of particles from the cyclotron, thus making possible thermonuclear reactions. Weizsäcker and Bethe independently (1938) proposed the *carbon cycle* of six reactions in the sequence shown (Fig. 7), in which four protons are converted into one alpha particle, a process accompanied by the release of 30 MeV.

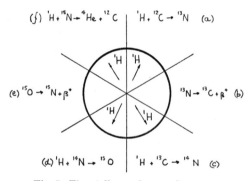

Fig. 7. The stellar carbon cycle.

On the other hand the energy of cooler stars like the sun ($\sim 10^{7}\,^{\circ}\text{C}$) appears to emerge from a proton-proton cycle:

$$^{1}_{1}\text{H} + {}^{1}_{1}\text{H} = {}^{2}_{1}\text{H} + \beta^{+} + 0.42\ \text{MeV},$$
$$^{1}_{1}\text{H} + {}^{2}_{1}\text{H} = {}^{3}_{2}\text{He} + \gamma + 5.5\ \text{MeV},$$
$$^{3}_{2}\text{He} + {}^{3}_{2}\text{He} = {}^{4}_{2}\text{He} + 2{}^{1}_{1}\text{H} + 12.8\ \text{MeV}.$$

Four protons are converted into an α-particle with the release of 26.6 MeV, including the annihilation energy of an electron-positron pair.

Artificial radioactivity

(i) α-Bombardment

Curie and Joliot (1934) produced a radioactive light element by bombarding aluminium with α-particles.

$$^{27}_{13}Al + ^{4}_{2}He \rightarrow ^{30}_{14}Si + ^{1}_{1}H \ (95\%)$$
(stable)

$$^{27}_{13}Al + ^{4}_{2}He \rightarrow ^{30}_{15}P + ^{1}_{0}n \ (5\%)$$
(radioactive)

The silicon is inactive but phosphorus-30 is a β^{+}-emitter. When the irradiated aluminium is dissolved in hydrochloric acid, all the radioactivity goes with the hydrogen, presumably as phosphine. Aqua regia oxidises it to phosphoric acid which can be precipitated as radioactive zirconium phosphate.

Many of the lighter nuclides including potassium-39 undergo this (α,n) transformation to give radionuclides.

$$^{24}_{12}Mg + ^{4}_{2}He \rightarrow ^{1}_{0}n + ^{27}_{14}Si \ (\beta^{+}\text{-emitter, } 7 \text{ min}),$$

$$^{10}_{5}B \ \ + ^{4}_{2}He \rightarrow ^{1}_{0}n + ^{13}_{7}N \ (\beta^{+}\text{-emitter, } 11 \text{ min}).$$

It is also possible for α-bombardment of these light elements to cause (α,p) changes.

$$^{7}_{3}Li \ \ + ^{4}_{2}He \rightarrow ^{1}_{1}H + ^{10}_{4}Be \ (\beta^{-}\text{-emitter, } 2.7 \times 10^{6}\text{y}),$$

$$^{25}_{12}Mg + ^{4}_{2}He \rightarrow ^{1}_{1}H + ^{28}_{13}Al \ (\beta^{-}\text{-emitter, } 2 \text{ min}).$$

(ii) Neutron bombardment

Most of the light radioactive nuclides which are being produced for radiochemical work are made by the action of neutrons on suitable materials in an atomic pile (p. 436). In such a reactor there is a high flux of slow and fast neutrons and also abundant γ-rays. Fast neutrons cause (n,α) and (n,p), and the slow ones (n,γ) reactions. As a rule the products are β^{-} -emitters. In (n,γ) reactions the nuclide produced is isotopic with the parent, and cannot be separated therefrom, so the latter acts as a diluent or carrier,

$$^{23}_{11}Na \ (n,\gamma) \ ^{24}_{11}Na \ (\beta^{-} \text{ and } \gamma, \ 15.1 \text{ h}).$$

$$^{63}_{29}Cu \ (n,\gamma) \ ^{64}_{29}Cu \ (\text{complex, } \beta^{-}, \ \beta^{+} \text{ and K-capture, } 12.8 \text{ d}).$$

(n,p) Reactions brought about by fast neutrons, however, give non-isotopic products which may be separated chemically and produced almost carrier-free.

$$^{32}_{16}S \ (n,p) \ ^{32}_{15}P \ (\beta^{-}, \ 14.3 \text{ d}).$$

$$^{14}_{7}N \ (n,p) \ ^{14}_{6}C \ (\beta^{-}, \ 5,600 \text{ y}).$$

A nitrate, for example, is converted into a ^{14}C carbonate from which $^{14}CO_2$ may be liberated by acid.

(n,α) Reactions occur only to a limited extent even with fast neutrons. Chemical separation again produces a carrier-free product of high specific activity.

(*iii*) *Bombardment with deuterons or protons (from cyclotron)*

Some radioactive nuclides which do not result from neutron attack can be made in the cyclotron by bombarding suitable targets with deuterons or protons.

$$^{24}_{12}\text{Mg} + ^2_1\text{H} \rightarrow ^4_2\text{He} + ^{22}_{11}\text{Na} \ (\beta^+, \ 2.6 \text{ years}),$$

$$^{56}_{26}\text{Fe} + ^2_1\text{H} \rightarrow ^4_2\text{He} + ^{54}_{25}\text{Mn} \ (\beta^+ \text{ and K-capture, } 310 \text{ days}).$$

(*iv*) *Fission products*

When a uranium-235 atom undergoes neutron-induced fission two atoms are produced, one of mass about 95, the other about 140, together with neutrons.

The actual nuclides formed may be $^{92}_{36}\text{Kr}$ and $^{142}_{56}\text{Ba}$,

$$^{235}_{92}\text{U} + ^1_0\text{n} \rightarrow ^{92}_{36}\text{Kr} + ^{142}_{56}\text{Ba} + 2^1_0\text{n};$$

but these reactions usually release two or three neutrons. The nuclides have high A/Z ratios and undergo β^- changes which increase their stability. This applies to all the fission products:

$$^{92}_{36}\text{Kr} \xrightarrow[3.6 \text{ sec}]{\beta^-} {}^{92}_{37}\text{Rb} \xrightarrow[3.0 \text{ sec}]{\beta^-} {}^{92}_{38}\text{Sr} \xrightarrow[2.7 \text{ h}]{\beta^-} {}^{92}_{39}\text{Y} \xrightarrow[5.5 \text{ h}]{\beta^-} {}^{92}_{40}\text{Zr} \text{ (stable)}$$

While a reactor is working the uranium-235 or plutonium-239 is slowly converted into fission products. The materials are intensely radioactive. Some of them capture thermal neutrons and thus diminish the efficiency of the pile. It is therefore necessary to take out the fuel rods from time to time and remove the fission products. For this purpose they are kept about 100 days to allow the short-lived radioelements to decay and then dissolved in nitric acid. Nitrous acid ensures that all the plutonium is in the Pu^{4+} form. The reactions, with H^+ written for H_3O^+ (p. 194), are

$$\text{Pu}^{3+} + \text{HNO}_3 + \text{H}^+ \rightarrow \text{Pu}^{4+} + \text{NO}_2 + \text{H}_2\text{O},$$

$$\text{Pu}^{6+} + \text{HNO}_2 + \text{H}_2\text{O} \rightarrow \text{Pu}^{4+} + \text{NO}_3^- + 3\text{H}^+.$$

From this liquid the uranium and plutonium can be extracted by tri-*n*-butyl phosphate (TBP) dissolved in kerosene, leaving the fission products in the nitric acid solution.

$$\text{UO}_2(\text{NO}_3)_2 + 2\text{TBP} \rightarrow \text{UO}_2(\text{NO}_3)_2.2\text{TBP}$$

$$\text{Pu}(\text{NO}_3)_4 + 2\text{TBP} \rightarrow \text{Pu}(\text{NO}_3)_4.2\text{TBP}.$$

The plutonium, when reduced in the presence of dilute nitric acid to Pu^{3+}, passes into the aqueous phase and is thus separated from the uranium which remains in the TBP complex (p. 573).

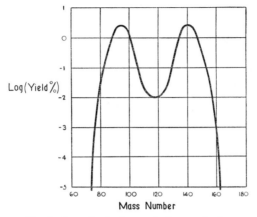

Fig. 8. Spread of primary fission products.

The yield of primary fission products in relation to their mass number is shown in Fig. 8. Most of the radioactive fission products have short half-lives, but some decay slowly; technetium-99 has $t_{\frac{1}{2}}$ 2.2 × 10⁵ yr and promethium-147, 2.6 yr. Two of the most useful fission products obtained in the operation of a pile are caesium-137 (β^-, 33 yr) and strontium-90 (β^+, 22 yr). The former is used in medicine and the latter in medicine and industry; both are separated from shorter-lived material.

(v) *The breeder reactor*

Plutonium-239 extracted from a graphite-moderated pile is used to produce more of the element from ^{238}U in a breeder reactor. The core of this reactor is uranium mixed with ^{239}Pu. There is no moderator. Cooling may be achieved by circulating liquid sodium. Surrounding the core is a 'blanket' of natural uranium in which the neutrons from the plutonium lose their energy gradually by colliding with the heavy atoms present, not quickly as in the graphite-moderated pile. Deflection of neutrons back into the core also occurs. The neutrons eventually reach energy levels at which they undergo *resonance capture* by ^{238}U with the subsequent formation of ^{239}Np and ^{239}Pu. As a high proportion of the neutrons set free by plutonium fission are re-captured by ^{238}U, and as a plutonium fission produces two or three neutrons, the amount of plutonium in the reactor increases. This is a 'breeding' process. It offers a useful way of helping to satisfy the demand for industrial energy as such a reactor not only produces energy but, at the same time, more fuel.

(vi) *Mesons*

In an attempt to explain the stability of atomic nuclei, Yukawa (1935) suggested the existence of particles carrying unit positive or negative charge and having masses about 100 to 200 times that of the electron but average lives of only about a ten thousandth of a second. Both positive and negative mesons with a variety of masses and lifetimes have since been detected (Neddermeyer and Anderson, 1937) in the course of observations on the cosmic rays reaching the earth's surface from outer space.

The very large accelerating machines such as the cosmotron at Long Island and the bevatron in California are capable of producing mesons with masses 273 times that of the electron. The capture of these by atomic nuclei causes nuclear explosions in which many protons and neutrons are set free. By this means arsenic-75 gives copper-64, among other nuclides, indicating a loss of up to four protons and seven neutrons. The suggested explanation is that the meson rest mass, equivalent to about 140 MeV, is imparted to a limited number of nucleons which escape before sharing their energies with the whole nucleus. Nitrogen, oxygen, zinc, bromine, iodine and mercury have also been studied as target atoms. About 1% of the mesons captured by mercury produce this type of disintegration: similar results have been obtained with protons of 150 MeV.

(vii) *Estabished elementary particles*

It is generally believed (Salam, 1959) that all matter and energy (except gravitation) consist of sixteen fundamental entities. They are the photon, the electron, the proton, the neutron, six species of hyperon (charged particles with masses greater than the proton), four species of meson (charged particles with masses between the mass of the proton and electron), the muon and the neutrino. With the exception of the mesons all the particles have spin. Only four, however, are stable, namely, the photon, electron, proton and neutron. The free neutron (half-life $\sim$ 20 min) decays to a proton, an electron and a neutrino.

A number of particles with properties opposite in some respect to those mentioned are known, for instance the positron (electron) and the anti-proton. More of these anti-particles are likely to be observed when the high power ($\sim 10^{10}$ eV) accelerators come into operation.

Genesis and abundance of the elements

Many estimates have been made of the relative abundance of the elements in the Universe, notably by Goldschmidt (1931), Brown (1949) and Urey (1952). The logarithm of the estimated abundance, taking log $A_{Si} = 6$ as

standard, is plotted against atomic number in the diagram (Fig. 9). The points of interest are:
  (i) the higher abundance values for the even elements,
  (ii) the rapid fall in abundance with atomic number up to element 45 after which the variations are smaller,
  (iii) the surprisingly low abundance of Li, Be and B,
  (iv) the high values for elements with Z near 26, 54 and 78,
  (v) the abnormal abundance of iron.

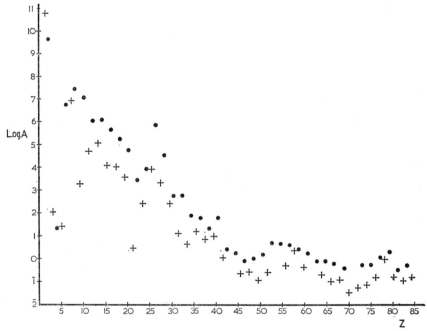

Fig. 9. Cosmic abundance of elements compared with silicon (10^6) (Suess and Urey).
⊕ Even atomic numbers.
+ Odd atomic numbers.

Various theories have been advanced to explain the relative abundance of the elements. In recent years knowledge has accumulated of the types of nuclear transformations occurring in stars. A continuous process of synthesis and consumption of elements (Burbidge, Burbidge, Fowler and Hoyle, 1957) accounts for the observed differences in composition of stars of different ages and also such abnormalities as the presence of technetium in S-type stars.

Except in catastrophic phases a star has a self-governing energy balance, the temperature attained depending on the nuclear fuel available. The consumption of hydrogen is responsible for the production of energy on a large scale, and the nuclear reactions employed in the changes do not require such a high temperature as other stellar processes. Cyclic processes synthesise He and those isotopes of C, N, O, F, Ne and Na not produced by He consumption or α-processes:

$$p + p \rightarrow d + \beta^+ + \text{antineutrino} + 0.421 \text{ MeV}$$

and, probably,

$$2 d \rightarrow {}^4_2\text{He} + 25.38 \text{ MeV}.$$

The conversion of helium to ^{12}C, ^{16}O and ^{20}Ne occurs in stars whose temperatures are about 10^8 °C.

$$^4\text{He} + {}^4\text{He} \rightarrow {}^8\text{Be},$$
$$^8\text{Be} + {}^4\text{He} \rightarrow {}^{12}\text{C*} \rightarrow {}^{12}\text{C} + \gamma \; etc.$$

At temperatures of about 2×10^8 °C the so-called α-process also becomes possible. Under these conditions the γ-rays produced in the helium consumption are sufficiently energetic to bring about the change

$$^{20}\text{Ne} + \gamma \rightarrow {}^{16}\text{O} + \alpha$$

and for the α-particle released to have the energy necessary for such reactions as ^{20}Ne$(\alpha,\gamma)^{24}$Mg and ^{24}Mg$(\alpha,\gamma)^{28}$Si, in which the α-addition goes on certainly as far as ^{40}Ca, and possibly to ^{48}Ti. The high abundance of nuclei with mass numbers divisible by four compared with that of their neighbours is due to the remarkable efficiency of the He consumption and α-processes. The C,N cycle (p. 22) belongs to this stage; it results in the catalytic conversion of hydrogen into helium until the hydrogen is exhausted.

Elements of the first transitional period are synthesised at about 3×10^9 °C ;n the so-called e-process. The nuclear reactions operating are of many types (γ,α) (γ,p) (γ,n) (α,γ) (p,γ) (n,γ) (p,n) but they always lead to a preponderance of elements belonging to the iron group. The strongly-marked peak in the abundance curve at ^{56}Fe is due to the e-process, which occurs when stellar evolution is at an advanced stage.

Two nuclear reactions involving neutron capture are responsible for the production of the majority of nuclides. The s-process, in which (n,γ) reactions occur on a time-scale of 10^2 to 10^5 years per neutron capture, gives rise to most of the nuclides in the mass-range 23–46 which are not formed in the α-process, together with a large proportion of those in the range 63 to 209. The s-process is responsible for peaks in the abundance curve at mass numbers 90, 138 and 208. The r-process also involves (n,γ) reactions but with a time-scale of 0.01 to 10 sec per neutron capture. It is responsible for very many nuclides in the mass range 70 to 209, and for Th and U. Peaks in the abundance curve are produced at mass numbers 80, 138 and 194. The advanced stage of stellar evolution necessary to build up elements of such high mass numbers is uncommon in the Universe and accordingly the heavier elements are relatively rare.

The p-process is one of proton capture (p,γ) or of gamma-ray absorption with neutron emission (γ,n), and is responsible for many proton-rich nuclides of low abundance, generally derived from iron-group elements. Finally, an x-process is responsible for the synthesis of D, Li, Be and B which are unstable at the temperatures reached inside stars, where they are converted to helium by a large number of processes including $^2D(p.\gamma)^3He$, $^6Li(p,\alpha)^3He$ and $^{11}B(p,\alpha)^8Be \rightarrow 2\ ^4He$.

The rarity of D, Li, Be and B compared with H, He, C, N, and O is due partly to the inefficiency of their production and partly to their consumption in processes such as those just set out.

The composition of the Earth differs from that of the Universe by having a much lower proportion of hydrogen and helium; these elements comprise about 90% and 9% respectively of the currently accepted grand total of matter. The small planets, Venus, Mercury and Mars, appear to have compositions similar to that of the Earth. Presumably their masses are too small for them to attract and retain the lighter particles in the form of an atmosphere as they move through space. Jupiter, however, has a core of iron and siliceous material surrounded by ice, solid methane and ammonia and finally by hydrogen and helium.

Apart from the small values for hydrogen and helium, the Earth's composition is not remarkable, the percentages by weight of the commonest elements, taking hydrosphere and lithosphere together, are:

O	49.20	Mg	1.93	C	0.08
Si	25.67	H	0.87	S	0.06
Al	7.50	Ti	0.58	Ba	0.04
Fe	4.71	Cl	0.19	N	0.03
Ca	3.39	P	0.11	F	0.03
Na	2.63	Mn	0.08	Sr	0.02
K	2.40			All others	0.47

The composition of the atmosphere at sea level in moles per million moles is:

N_2	7.8×10^5	Ne	1.8×10^1	N_2O	0.5
O_2	2.1×10^5	He	5.2	H_2	0.5
Ar	9.3×10^3	CH_4	1.5	O_3	0.4
CO_2	3×10^2	Kr	1	Xe	0.08

Relative abundance of naturally–occurring isotopes

(Hydrogen to Nickel)

Z	Element	Nuclide	Percentage	Z	Element	Nuclide	Percentage
1.	Hydrogen	^{1}H	99.985	17.	Chlorine	^{35}Cl	75.4
		^{2}H	0.015			^{37}Cl	24.6
		* ^{3}H	~ 0	18.	Argon	^{36}Ar	0.34
2.	Helium	^{3}He	0.00013			^{38}Ar	0.06
		^{4}He	~ 100			^{40}Ar	99.60
3.	Lithium	^{6}Li	7.4	19.	Potassium	^{39}K	93.08
		^{7}Li	92.6			*^{40}K	0.012
4.	Beryllium	^{9}Be	100			^{41}K	6.91
5.	Boron	^{10}B	18.7	20.	Calcium	^{40}Ca	96.92
		^{11}B	81.3			^{42}Ca	0.64
6.	Carbon	^{12}C	98.9			^{43}Ca	0.13
		^{13}C	1.1			^{44}Ca	2.13
		*^{14}C	~ 10^{-10}			^{46}Ca	0.0032
						^{48}Ca	0.18
7.	Nitrogen	^{14}N	99.63				
		^{15}N	0.37	21.	Scandium	^{45}Sc	100
8.	Oxygen	^{16}O	99.76	22.	Titanium	^{46}Ti	8.2
		^{17}O	0.037			^{47}Ti	7.4
		^{18}O	0.20			^{48}Ti	73.4
9.	Fluorine	^{19}F	100			^{49}Ti	5.6
10.	Neon	^{20}Ne	90			^{50}Ti	5.4
		^{21}Ne	0.3	23.	Vanadium	^{50}V	0.25
		^{22}Ne	9.7			^{51}V	99.75
11.	Sodium	^{23}Na	100	24.	Chromium	^{50}Cr	4.4
12.	Magnesium	^{24}Mg	79.0			^{52}Cr	83.7
		^{25}Mg	10.0			^{53}Cr	9.5
		^{26}Mg	11.0			^{54}Cr	2.4
13.	Aluminium	^{27}Al	100	25.	Manganese	^{55}Mn	100
14.	Silicon	^{28}Si	92.18	26.	Iron	^{54}Fe	5.9
		^{29}Si	4.70			^{56}Fe	91.6
		^{30}Si	3.12			^{57}Fe	2.2
15.	Phosphorus	^{31}P	100			^{58}Fe	0.33
16.	Sulphur	^{32}S	95.04	27.	Cobalt	^{59}Co	100
		^{33}S	0.74	28.	Nickel	^{58}Ni	67.9
		^{34}S	4.24			^{60}Ni	26.2
		^{36}S	0.017			^{61}Ni	1.2
						^{62}Ni	3.7
						^{64}Ni	1.0

* Radioactive isotopes.

Chapter 3

Radiochemistry

The operation, since 1945, of nuclear reactors has made available radio-isotopes of most elements. The isotopes are useful in a variety of chemical investigations, including those concerned with solubility, diffusion, reaction mechanism and structure. They have given rise to new analytical techniques, such as isotopic dilution and radioactivation analysis. In industry also, they have a wide and rapidly expanding application. All this is made possible by the ease with which small quantities of the nuclides can be detected, often remotely, and quantitatively determined by commercially available and easily operated equipment.

Detection

The most common measurement is β-counting with a Geiger-Muller tube. A potential difference of some hundreds of volts is applied between an axial wire and the cylindrical wall. When an ionising particle enters through the mica end-window the gas inside, usually neon, is ionised; acceleration of the ions towards the electrodes, causing further ionisation, gives rise to a pulse which is amplified and finally counted by a suitable electronic device. The thickness of the window prevents penetration by β-particles of low energy and gas-counting techniques must be used for counting such particles from ^{14}C and ^{3}H, compounds like $^{14}CO_2$ or $^{3}H_2O$ being introduced at about 2 mm. pressure into the tube itself.

Scintillation methods are increasing in importance. A γ-photon falling on a single sodium iodide crystal produces a flash of light which causes emission of photo-electrons from the light-sensitive surface, or photocathode, of a photomultiplier tube. Suitable voltages applied to the intermediate electrodes, or dynodes, of the tube cause electron multiplication and the current pulses so produced are counted by a scalar circuit. The energy as well as the intensity of radiation can be recorded, and a mixture of several γ-emitters can be resolved into its components, without chemical separation, by means of a γ-scintillation spectrometer. The sodium iodide phosphor can be replaced by ZnS for α-counting or an anthracene crystal for β-counting.

An activity of about 10^{-9} curie can be detected by ordinary counting equipment. The quantity of radioactive material corresponding to this activity

depends on the specific activity, and hence the half-life, of the nuclide involved. Phosphorus-32 (β^-, 14.3 days) has a specific activity of 3.3×10^7
curies per gram; 10^{-16} g of this nuclide gives about 300 counts per minute
with equipment of moderate efficiency. A comparison of this limit of measurement with those of other methods shows its advantage.

Gravimetric analysis	10^{-6} g.
Emission spectroscope	10^{-8} g.
Polarography	10^{-10} g.
Radiochemical	10^{-16} g.

Production

Radioactive nuclides are produced principally in the nuclear reactor as the
result of (n, γ), (n, p) and (n, d) reactions (p. 23). When a high specific
activity is required an (n, γ) preparative reaction is unsuitable because the
product is necessarily diluted by the parent isotope, from which separation is
always difficult and generally impossible, as in the ^{23}Na(n, γ) ^{24}Na conversion.
^{18}F is conveniently made by irradiating LiOH in a reactor:

$$^6_3\text{Li} + ^1_0\text{n} \rightarrow ^3_1\text{H} + ^4_2\text{He},$$
$$^3_1\text{H} + ^{16}_8\text{O} \rightarrow ^{18}_9\text{F} + ^1_0\text{n}.$$

Another useful source of radionuclides, particularly those with mass
number from 80 to 140, is the fission occurring in uranium fuel in a reactor.
From the fission products ^{90}Sr of high specific activity is obtainable. Certain
nuclides can, however, only be made by proton or deuteron bombardment in
the cyclotron. An example is ^{24}Mg(d, α) ^{22}Na (2.6 yr); and another route to
^{18}F is provided, ^{18}O(p, n) ^{18}F (112 min).

Tracers: suitability of nuclides

For physical and chemical investigation by means of radioactive material
minute quantities of the active isotopes, termed *tracers*, are used. Generally
the nuclide employed is isotopic with the inactive atoms whose behaviour is
to be studied.

The choice of tracer for a particular experiment depends upon three things:
1. Whether the radionuclide must be isotopic with an element in the system
under investigation. In the absence of this requirement the choice of tracer
is widened considerably.
2. The duration of the experiment. A nuclide with a half-life shorter than this
is clearly unsuitable. This limitation is marked with nitrogen and oxygen
whose longest-lived active isotopes are the cyclotron-produced ^{13}N (10.1
min) and ^{15}O (2.1 min). For these elements the stable ^{15}N and ^{18}O are used,

their behaviour being followed by the mass-spectrograph. Helium, boron and aluminium are other elements without active isotopes suitable for tracer work.

3. Whether the radiation emitted by the tracer is suitable for measurement under the conditions of the experiment. For instance ^{35}S cannot be used when the experiment would call for a liquid counter, since the β energy (max. 0.17 MeV) is too low to penetrate the glass walls of the counter. Again the very low β energy of ^{3}H (0.018 MeV) excludes all but gas-counting techniques.

Separation of tracers from non-isotopic fission products

The non-isotopic products of (n, p) and (n, α) reactions, usually from high-energy neutrons, are separable from the parent. Many methods are available.

(*i*) *Solvent extraction.* Cobalt-59 reacts with fast neutrons to give iron-59. The metals are converted to $FeCl_3$ and $CoCl_2$, the former being quantitatively extractable with ether (p. 572).

(*ii*) *Volatilisation.* Iodine-132 is produced spontaneously by tellurium -132, a fission product of uranium, and is readily volatilised from the involatile parent:

$$^{132}_{52}Te \longrightarrow {}^{132}_{53}I + \beta^-.$$

(*iii*) *Electrodeposition.* Copper-64 is made from zinc-64 by an (n, p) reaction. Electrolysis of a sulphate solution deposits the copper preferentially.

(*iv*) *Ion exchange.* Carrier-free material can be obtained by this method. Harris and Tompkins (1947) separated ^{143}Pr from cerium by absorbing the dilute chloride solution on Dowex 50 in its ammonium form. Elution with 5% nitrate buffered at pH 3 gave, in the first 4 litres of eluate, 94% of the praseodymiun and no cerium (p. 426).

(*v*) *Precipitation.* These methods of separation are usually carried out with the aid of carriers.

Carriers

Most of the radionuclides produced in the pile have high specific activities. One millicurie of ^{32}P represents only about 10^{-8} g of phosphate. A safely-handled quantity of this nuclide would be the amount adsorbed on the surface of the containing vessel. About 10^{-4} g of inert phosphate is added as an isotopic carrier for each millicurie of activity, and, in subsequent chemical operations, the ^{32}P accompanies the added phosphorus.

The *hold-back* carriers are those used to prevent adsorption on precipitates. For instance in the separation of ^{90}Sr and ^{140}La from fission products, precipitation of the ^{90}Sr as sulphate takes place only when sufficient inert strontium ion has been added to exceed the solubility product. But, under these conditions, nearly all the lanthanum would also be removed from solution as ions adsorbed on the precipitate; to avoid this ordinary lanthanum ions must be added to provide a non-active adsorbate and thereby 'hold back' in solution most of the ^{140}La.

Non-isotopic carriers have their uses as may be judged by the following example. ^{89}Sr is made from ^{89}Y by an (n, p) reaction. The addition of a lead salt followed by fuming nitric acid precipitates lead and strontium together as nitrates and leaves the yttrium in solution. The lead, having thus acted as a non-isotopic carrier, may be precipitated as sulphide from a solution of the lead and strontium salts. Here again a hold-back carrier of inactive strontium ions is necessary to prevent adsorption of most of the ^{89}Sr on the PbS.

Precipitates such as iron(III) hydroxide, with a large specific surface, adsorb certain ions preferentially. Thus phosphate ion can be separated from sulphate ion by adding a soluble iron(III) salt to the solution and then precipitating as hydroxide. The method is used to separate $^{32}PO_4^{3-}$ from $^{35}SO_4^{2-}$, the former being completely, and the latter but slightly adsorbed. Such precipitates as this hydroxide are known as *scavenging* carriers.

Chemical applications of tracers

(*i*) *Diffusion.* Radioactive tracers are particularly suitable for studying self-diffusion in both liquids and solids. Wang and Kennedy (1950) observed the rate of diffusion of sodium ions from sodium iodide solution in capillary tubes. Two tubes with sodium iodide solution of the same concentration, but with ^{22}Na in one, were held end to end for a known time and the rate of diffusion was measured by separating them and taking counts on each. Corresponding observations were also made of the diffusion of the iodide ion.

The rate of self-diffusion in solids has also been measured by means of tracers. Gold containing active ^{198}Au when pressed against inactive gold was shown to diffuse, the extent being found by machining successive thin slices from the originally inactive metal and making counts. Similarly, Rollin (1939) obtained self-diffusion rates for copper of 4×10^{-11} cm^2/sec at 830° and 2.8×10^{-9} cm^2/sec at 1030°. Moutlock and Tomlin (1956) measured the rate of diffusion at 1053° of ^{51}Cr plated on to the flat end of one titanium bar and pressed for 24 h against another of the same material. The diffusion coefficient of chromium into titanium was measured either by machining or dissolving off thin layers and making counts, or by autoradiography.

(*ii*) *Solubility and Partition.* Solubility studies are facilitated by tracer techniques. The solid is labelled, usually by precipitation from a solution containing active material (*e.g.* strontium sulphate from a solution containing some $^{90}Sr^{2+}$) and the specific activity of the dry solid is determined.

It is then shaken with the solvent until equilibrium is established, when the solution shows an activity proportional to the solubility.

Measurement of partition coefficients of immiscible layers is particularly easy; an example is the addition of ^{131}I to inactive iodine to observe the distribution between an organic solvent and water. The partition coefficient, K = activity per cc in the aqueous layer/activity per cc in the organic layer.

(iii) *Precipitation and entrainment in precipitates.* The completeness of the separation of, say, a phosphate can be found by precipitating from a phosphate carrier solution containing some ^{32}P phosphate. A count-rate is made on the original solution and on a solution obtained by dissolving the precipitate after filtration, appropriate volumes and the same liquid counter being used. The efficiency of the separation = count-rate from redissolved precipitate/count-rate from original solution. The method is especially useful for assessing the efficacy of different reagents; in this instance magnesia mixture, molybdate, and zirconium nitrate, or the same reagent under different conditions of perhaps pH and temperature.

The entrainment of other materials in precipitates may also be measured. For example a precipitate of tin(II) sulphide carries down some cobalt ions when they are present, and the extent of this can be ascertained by means of a trace of ^{60}Co and the comparative count-rates of the original solution and the redissolved precipitate.

Exchange reactions

Isotopic exchange is possible in both homogeneous and heterogeneous conditions and the commonest form is represented by

$$AX + B*X \longrightarrow A*X + BX.$$

A knowledge of the rate is necessary in tracer investigations since it should be negligible in relation to the duration of the experiments.

The free-energy change (p. 171) in an isotopic exchange reaction is always negative since

$$\Delta G = \Delta H - T\Delta S,$$

in which ΔH is zero because there is no chemical change and ΔS is positive because there is an increasing randomness in the distribution of the isotopic atoms. Nevertheless, exchange reactions are often extremely slow on account of the high entropy of formation of the activated complex.

Exchange rates are found by mixing the two species AX and BX, one labelled with a suitable radioisotope of X, taking portions at suitable time intervals, separating the two species, analysing the fractions and counting the activities. The separation may be made by (i) precipitation, (ii) solvent extraction, or (iii) ion exchange. But it has to be remembered that chemical reaction may induce exchange by producing a labile species. Haissinski (1951) points out that when studying exchange reactions in which there is a change in charge number of a metal, the lower oxidation state should be the one precipitated so as to reduce the chance of intermediate (possibly labile) stages in the formation of the solid. That the particular precipitant used is also significant is illustrated by the change

$$Tl^{3+} + *Tl^+ \longrightarrow Tl^+ + *Tl^{3+}.$$

When the extent of exchange is measured by precipitating Tl^{3+} as $Tl(OH)_3$, it appears great; but, when measured by precipitating Tl^+ as $TlCrO_4$, it appears slight. Evidently a rapid exchange occurs during the actual precipitation of the Tl^{III} compound.

For the reaction

$$AX + B*X \longrightarrow A*X + BX,$$

the rate can be obtained from the equation

$$\ln (1 - F) = -Rt \frac{a + b}{ab}$$

where a and b are the total concentrations of both active and inactive X in AX and BX respectively at time t, and R is the rate of exchange of X.

$$F \text{ (the fractional change at time } t) = \frac{\text{specific activity of AX at time } t}{\text{specific activity of AX at equilibrium}} .$$

For the time of half-exchange, $t_{\frac{1}{2}}$,

$$R = \frac{ab}{a + b} \times \frac{0.693}{t_{\frac{1}{2}}} .$$

Exchange between inorganic ions of different charge is often rapid: examples are Cu^+, Cu^{2+}; Fe^{2+}, Fe^{3+}; Co^{2+}, Co^{3+}; MnO_4^-, MnO_4^{2-}; $Fe(CN)_6^{3-}$ $Fe(CN)_6^{4-}$. In other instances, the time of half-reaction is measurable and sometimes long: Mn^{2+}, Mn^{3+} ($t_{\frac{1}{2}} = 20$ sec); $Co(en)_3^{2+}$, $Co(en)_3^{3+}$ ($t_{\frac{1}{2}} = 30$ h); Ce^{3+}, Ce^{4+} ($t_{\frac{1}{2}} = 11$ min); $Co(NH_3)_6^{2+}$, $Co(NH_3)_6^{3+}$ ($t_{\frac{1}{2}} = 80$ days). Other ions present in solution may affect the speed of reaction; thus at corresponding concentrations for Tl^+, Tl^{3+} in HCl, $t_{\frac{1}{2}} = 10$ days and in $HClO_4$, $t_{\frac{1}{2}} = 25$ min.

In trying to explain exchange between ions of the same sign it is always necessary to seek a mechanism which allows of electron-transfer without demanding contact between the ions. The possible intermediates are: (i) solvent molecules, (ii) ions of opposite sign, and (iii) neutral molecules.

Haissinski (1951) believes (ii) to be the most important of these, the change of charge number being effected within the ionic atmosphere:

$$\begin{matrix} Cl \\ \\ Cl \end{matrix} \!\!\!\diagdown\!\!\!\diagup \overset{*}{Mn}{}^{III}\!\!-\!\!Cl \cdots\cdots \rightarrow \cdots\cdots Mn^{II} \!\!\!\diagup\!\!\!\diagdown \begin{matrix} Cl \\ \\ Cl \end{matrix}$$

It is likely that the high exchange rate of Tl^+ and Tl^{3+} in the presence of ClO_4^- ions is of the same character.

Exchange rates between ions and neutral molecules also vary widely. Chlorine exchanges with aqueous Cl^- ion too rapidly for measurement, but not at all with ClO_3^- or ClO_4^- ions in slightly acid solution. The rapidity with Cl^- is probably due to the ready formation of a complex ion:

$$*Cl^- + Cl_2 \rightarrow *Cl\!-\!Cl\!-\!Cl^- \rightarrow *Cl_2 + Cl^-.$$

A similar mechanism is advanced for the rapid exchange between dissolved sulphur and S^{2-} ions in polysulphide solutions. The fast exchange between HF and interhalogen fluorides has been accounted for by ionisation:

$$HF + Br*F_3 \rightleftharpoons H*F_2^- + BrF_2^+.$$

Heterogeneous exchange processes are more complicated. Solid-liquid interchange depends not only on the rate of exchange between the solution and the solid surface, but also on the slower rate of diffusion into the solid, and, to a lesser extent, on any recrystallisation which is proceeding. Kolthoff (1934), studying the ageing of precipitates, found an aged precipitate, with its small specific surface area and more perfect lattice, undergoes exchange more slowly than a fresh precipitate.

Freshly precipitated lead sulphate exchanged lead ions completely with lead nitrate (^{212}Pb tracer) solution in about 3 minutes. But after the precipitate had stood in its mother liquor 48 hr exchange in the same time was only 35% of the previous value, presumably because of a decrease in available surface (Kolthoff and Rosenblum, 1934).

Finding the course of reaction by radioactive tracer

Suppose A_1 and A_2 are possible precursors of B in a reaction chain:

$$\begin{array}{c} \cdots\cdots -A_1 \diagdown^{k_1} \\ B \xrightarrow{k'} C \\ \cdots\cdots -A_2 \diagup_{k_2} \end{array}$$

To the reaction mixture is added labelled A_1 and unlabelled B. The specific activity of A_1 should decrease and that of B increase if B is formed from A_1.

The specific activity of B eventually reaches a maximum, a_1; if the specific activity of A_1 is a_1, then $k_2 = O$, showing that B is formed only from A_1, not from A_2.

Margolis and Roginsky (1955) investigated the oxidation of ethylene over metallic oxides at 220° and found both ethylene oxide and carbon dioxide to be products. When ^{14}C-labelled ethylene was used the CO_2 formed had a higher specific activity than the ethylene oxide, showing the CO_2 to be produced, not from ethylene oxide, but from the ethylene itself.

The labelling of compounds with radioactive atoms has enabled the course of reactions to be followed. The reaction between P_4O_{10} and PCl_5 forms an excellent route to pyrophosphoryl chloride, $P_2O_3Cl_4$. The manner in which the yield depends on the $P_4O_{10}:PCl_5$ ratio suggested that the P—O—P links were not formed during the reaction and that the phosphorus atoms of pyrophosphoryl chloride were derived entirely from the phosphorus(V) oxide. This has been confirmed by the use of [32]PCl_5 and inactive P_4O_{10}; the $P_2O_3Cl_4$ produced was inactive (Crofts, Downie and Heslop, 1960).

$$P_4O_{10} + 4\ ^{32}PCl_5 \rightarrow 2\ P_2O_3Cl_4 + 4\ ^{32}POCl_3.$$

The uses of natural radionuclides

(i) *Emanation.* Solids have been investigated by incorporating a source of radon or thoron in them. The latter is introduced either by co-precipitation with [228]Th, or by mixing the dry solids with a thorium compound so that the thoron is distributed by recoil.

$$^{228}\text{Th} \xrightarrow[\text{1.9y}]{\alpha} {}^{224}\text{Ra} \xrightarrow[\text{3.6d}]{\alpha} {}^{220}\text{Rn} \xrightarrow[\text{54 sec.}]{\alpha} {}^{216}\text{Po.}$$

Emanating power is defined as the fraction of radioactive gas atoms which escapes and is measured by the ratio of rate of escape to rate of formation.

Hahn (1931) applied the method to studies of the ageing of precipitates. The emanating power of freshly formed, dry iron(III) hydroxide is high and falls by only about 2% a year. Digestion in water quickly reduces the emanating power, indicating a rapid ageing.

Structural changes in a solid can be detected by changes in emanating power. For instance, that of anhydrous $BaCl_2$ increases with temperature to 540° and then falls a little, but again begins to rise and reaches a maximum at 925°. The first maximum is associated with the change from a porous form to the monoclinic α-form, the second with one from the monoclinic α-form to the cubic β-form (Lieber, 1939).

Emanation has also been used to detect compound-formation between solids. Thus Tagitsch (1936) found a rapid fall in the emanating power of SiO_2 when it is heated with PbO at 700°, due to the formation, under these conditions, of lead silicate which has a low emanating power.

(ii) *Geochronometry*. With the great improvement in the precision of physico-chemical measurements, rapid advances are being made in the use of natural radionuclides for the dating of natural objects and artifacts. Some of the radioactive clocks, as they may be termed, with remote ranges are based on the extent to which the following changes have been found to have occurred: $^{87}Rb \rightarrow {}^{87}Sr$; $^{40}K \rightarrow {}^{40}Ar$; U, Th $\rightarrow$ Pb.

In the first, a mineral is chosen containing rubidium but unlikely, at formation, to have contained strontium in its lattice. With a knowledge of the Rb:Sr ratio and the radioactive constant of Rb, it is possible to determine the age. The last comprises four clocks in one, (1) $^{238}U \rightarrow {}^{206}Pb$, (2) $^{235}U \rightarrow {}^{207}Pb$, (3) $^{232}Th \rightarrow {}^{208}Pb$, (4) the ratio $^{206}Pb : {}^{207}Pb : {}^{208}Pb$. Of these, (4) enables the age of a mineral to be determined even when some of the lead has been leached out of it, because the isotopic ratio is independent of amount, depending only upon the time during which the lead has been produced.

Radiocarbon dating has attracted considerable attention. Carbon-14 is produced in the upper atmosphere by cosmic-ray bombardment of nitrogen-14. It is oxidised to carbon dioxide and eventually absorbed and incorporated in the tissues of plants and animals. The time taken for a carbon atom to complete such a carbon-cycle and return to the upper atmosphere is, on average, about 500 years. As the half-life of ^{14}C is 5568 years, the specific activity of carbon in the carbon cycle is roughly constant. But carbon removed from this life-embracing cycle by conversion to, and retention in, a solid such as wood, bone or shell loses activity at a rate determined by the decay constant for ^{14}C. Thus the specific activity of carbon in a rock, a fossil plant or bone, or ancient artifact gives its age (Libby, 1951). Measurements are not easy because of the low specific activities but are of considerable and improving accuracy.

Tritium has been used similarly, since water, free to move to and from the upper atmosphere had also a constant specific activity. The position is however changing with the release of tritium from nuclear reactions. Because of its shorter half-life (12.5y) it is adopted for shorter-range dating, such as finding the age of a wine.

Measurement with carbon assumes that the rate of cosmic activation has remained constant over the period involved. Though doubts have been cast on this assumption, there is no evidence that it is not a safe one to make; the times found have agreed well with those fixed by other scales.

Radiochemical methods of analysis

(*i*) *Radiometric analysis*. This is used for finding the amount of a nuclide of long half-life and known specific activity in a material; it is based on the premise that the mass present is proportional to the activity. Because it is impossible to observe all disintegrations the count-rate from a sample is compared with that from the same weight of a standard, the same geometry being ensured by the use of the same counting equipment.

The potassium content of a fertiliser can be determined by comparing its activity with a pure potassium salt. However, as ^{40}K, about 0.01% of natural potassium, has a specific activity of only 7×10^{-6} curies/g, the count-rate is low (20 c.p.m. for 1 g of K_2SO_4), and the background-count must be reduced to a minimum.

(*ii*) *Isotope dilution analysis*. This has been used for the determination of amino acids in protein hydrolysates, and it has also been applied to the analysis of mixtures of lanthanides. In both instances quantitative separation into pure species is wellnigh impossible. But when an active specimen of one of the species is uniformly incorporated in the original and some of the mixture is put through the purification process, then

$$\frac{\text{specific activity of additive}}{\text{specific activity of purified specimen}} = \frac{\text{weight of species originally present}}{\text{weight of additive}}.$$

For the protein hydrolysate a ^{14}C acid is added which suffers dilution by the inactive acid already present. The extent of the dilution, measured radiometrically, indicates the amount of the particular acid in the hydrolysate.

By adding in turn an active form of all the amino acids present a complete analysis is possible.

(*iii*) *Radioactivation analysis*. This requires a reactor or other strong neutron source. It is specially useful for measuring trace impurities; an example is copper in aluminium. The aluminium under examination and a pure copper standard are irradiated together and subsequently dissolved, the solution of the latter being diluted up to 10^5 times. Portions of both solutions, after the addition of a copper carrier, are precipitated. (Sometimes a hold-back carrier is required at this stage to remove high-activity products which would interfere in the counting of the copper activity). The two precipitates are dried and weighed and their activities are compared. Then

$$\frac{\text{activity of copper in aluminium}}{\text{activity in standard}} = \frac{\text{mass of copper in aluminium}}{\text{mass in standard}}.$$

The method enables impurities to be assessed with an accuracy greater than one part per million without recourse to micro methods. Care must be exercised in its application, for in a high neutron flux spurious impurities may arise.

The estimation of traces of arsenic in germanium provided problems of this kind (Smales, 1951). Irradiation of ^{75}As with neutrons gives rise to the 27 hour β-emitter ^{76}As:

$$^{75}_{33}\text{As} + ^{1}_{0}\text{n} \longrightarrow ^{76}_{33}\text{As}.$$

But both this nuclide and the 40 hour ^{77}As can arise from the irradiation of the germanium itself:

(i) $^{74}_{32}\text{Ge} + ^{1}_{0}\text{n} \rightarrow ^{75}_{32}\text{Ge} \xrightarrow[\text{80 min}]{\beta^-} ^{75}_{33}\text{As} \ (\text{n}, \gamma) \ ^{76}_{33}\text{As};$

(ii) $^{76}_{32}\text{Ge} + ^{1}_{0}\text{n} \rightarrow ^{77}_{32}\text{Ge} \xrightarrow[\text{60 sec}]{\beta^-} ^{77}_{33}\text{As}.$

The amount of spurious ^{76}As is small because of the comparative complexity of process (i), but considerable amounts of ^{77}As can be produced. The interference of ^{77}As has been overcome by the use of proportional counting techniques which distinguish between the different β-energies, 0.7 MeV for ^{77}As and 3.1 MeV for ^{76}As. Choice of suitable time of irradiation and neutron flux can minimise the yield of spurious ^{76}As, making possible the determination of as little as 0.01 ppm As in GeO_2.

Neutron activation analysis without chemical separation is possible when the contaminating element and the principal constituent have

(i) large differences in their cross-section for neutron capture,

(ii) large differences in the half-life of the products of irradiation,

(iii) product-nuclides with very different emission characteristics.

As an example of (i) gold has a cross-section of 96 barns for slow-neutron capture, lead of only 5×10^{-4} barns. Irradiation, while hardly affecting the lead, changes the gold into an active form. The gold content of lead can thus be found.

Traces of osmium in rhodium can be determined because of (ii). Irradiation produces $^{193}_{76}\text{Os}$ (32 hr) and $^{104}_{45}\text{Rh}$ (4.4 min). If the irradiated specimen is kept for some hours the activity due to the rhodium decays and makes possible the measurement of the osmium activity.

The estimation of iridium in palladium is possible because of (iii). All the isotopes of palladium are pure β-emitters but $^{194}_{77}\text{Ir}$ produces γ radiation as well as β particles. Measurement of the γ activity after absorption of the β radiation gives the iridium content.

Chapter 4

Electronic Structures of Atoms. The Periodic Table

The experimental basis of wave mechanics

Two main sets of experimental phenomena are inconsistent with classical physics. (i) Changes in the internal energy of an atom accompanying emission or absorption of light are not continuous but occur in discrete amounts. Similarly spectroscopic evidence shows an atom exists only in certain discrete energy states characteristic of the element. The change from an energy state E to one E' is accompanied by emission $(E > E')$ or absorption $(E < E')$ of light, whose frequence ν is related to the energy change:

$$|E - E'| = h\nu$$

h (Planck's constant) $= 6.624 \times 10^{-27}$ erg sec (the dimensions of action). (ii) A beam of electrons shows interference effects exactly as does a beam of light. A diffraction pattern is obtained when light is reflected or diffracted from a grating. The regularly spaced atoms in a crystal provide a grating which diffracts not only X-rays but also electron beams. Hence wave properties must be associated with the electron.

The occurrence of discrete energy states of a 'bound' electron in an atom and the co-existence of wave and particle properties in a free electron, can be accounted for on the basis of *wave mechanics* (Schrödinger, 1926). Observation of the diffraction patterns produced when electrons of known energy encounter crystals of known atomic spacing shows that the wave length, λ, associated with an electron of velocity, v, is given by

$$\lambda = h/mv.$$

Wave and particle properties can then be reconciled by the following argument.

Normally, a wave motion is a disturbance which varies at any point with a *frequency*, ν, and is propagated with some *phase velocity*, u. The *wavelength*, λ, is then given by the relationship $\lambda\nu = u$, and represents the distance, along the direction of propagation, between points where the variation is exactly similar or *in phase*. A train of waves of this kind extends over all space as long as the source goes on emitting energy; it describes a steady state.

But if a wave is to be associated with a localised particle, it is necessary to consider a travelling *pulse* or *wave packet*. Such a pulse can be described only by combining a group of wave trains whose phase velocities (and hence also wave lengths) depend on frequency, varying slightly about their mean values: it travels with a *group velocity*, v_g, given by

$$v_g = \frac{dv}{d\left(\dfrac{1}{\lambda}\right)}.$$

Now for the electron, $\lambda = h/mv$ (experimentally) and therefore

$$v_g = \frac{h}{m}\frac{dv}{dv};$$

but if the wave packet, which carries the energy, is always to stay with the particle, v_g must be the same as the actual particle velocity v and the frequency v must then satisfy the equation

$$\frac{dv}{dv} = \frac{m}{h}v.$$

The solution is simply $v = E/h$, where $E = \frac{1}{2}mv^2$ is the energy of the particle. Planck's law relating the energy of a pulse of radiation, a *light quantum*, to its frequency thus acquires a more general significance; it enables us to associate a wave packet with a *material particle*, its frequency being similarly related to the energy of the particle. Such a wave has to be associated with a particle simply in order to describe its behaviour; it is not necessarily real in the same sense as an electromagnetic wave. Its interpretation must now be examined.

Interpretation

Let ψ be the amplitude, varying from point to point in space, of the wave associated with a moving particle. Relative amplitudes at different points can then be calculated just as in optical diffraction theory; and in all diffraction experiments the degree of darkening of a photographic plate at different points depends on the relative values of ψ^2, the *intensity*, at these points. Now, on a particle picture, this effect must depend on the *number of particles* landing at the different points, and since one particle can arrive only at one point, it is necessary to make a *statistical* interpretation. The *probability* of a particle being found in a given small region is proportional to the square of the amplitude of the associated *wave function* in that region. Since this probability is also proportional to the size of the region the actual probability must be $\psi^2 d\tau$, where $d\tau$ is the volume element and ψ^2 is a *probability density*.

In the diffraction of a free particle, the probability density changes with time as the wave packet progresses, but the interpretation turns out to be quite general. In other situations, where the particle is bound within a certain region of space, *stationary patterns* occur (like the standing waves on a vibrating string, where the actual profile is fixed, instead of travelling along the string as it does in a whip), and again ψ^2 determines the probability of finding the particle at a given point. Stationary patterns are of supreme importance in molecular theory since they describe an electron bound in an atom or molecule. They are invoked throughout this book and their calculation is taken up in a later section.

The Uncertainty Principle

The need to associate a wave packet with a moving particle has another important consequence. In the one-dimensional case of plane waves representing a particle moving in the x-direction, the extension of the wave packet (Δx, say) is determined by the range of wavelengths admitted in the packet and this in turn, by the momentum range (Δp_x, say). It can then be shown (Heisenberg, 1927) that

$$\Delta x \, \Delta p_x \sim h.$$

This is one consequence of the famous Uncertainty Principle, which relates the simultaneous uncertainties in certain pairs of measurable quantities. Similar relationships exist for the y and z co-ordinates and momentum components. If the wave packet is very compact (Δx small) it must be very 'impure', containing a mixture of wave trains corresponding to a considerable range of momenta (Δp_x large); it is then known fairly accurately where the particle is at a given time, but only roughly what momentum to associate with it. And if the momentum is measured more precisely, the width of the wave packet must increase, with a corresponding loss of precision in knowledge of its position. Since h is very small, these uncertainties are often negligible—but this is not so in atomic physics. The position of a particle weighing 1 g can be determined optically without sensibly disturbing its momentum, but even in principle this is not true for an electron.

The wave equation

Any disturbance Ψ (*e.g.* the displacement of an elastic string or the height of a water wave) which is propagated along the x-direction with velocity u, satisfies a simple partial differential equation, the *wave equation:*

$$\frac{\partial^2 \Psi}{\partial x^2} = \frac{1}{u^2} \cdot \frac{\partial^2 \Psi}{\partial t^2}.$$

Here Ψ depends on both position and time, $\Psi = \Psi(x,t)$. More generally for a three-dimensional disturbance,

$$\nabla^2\Psi = \frac{\partial^2\Psi}{\partial x^2} + \frac{\partial^2\Psi}{\partial y^2} + \frac{\partial^2\Psi}{\partial z^2} = \frac{1}{u^2}\cdot\frac{\partial^2\Psi}{\partial t^2},$$

where $\Psi = \Psi(x,y,z,t)$. Proceeding immediately to the stationary patterns, a particular type of one-dimensional solution is, for example,

$$\Psi(x,t) = \psi(x)\sin 2\pi\nu t,$$

where $\psi(x)$ is the amplitude, which depends only on position, and the disturbance at a point varies between $+\psi(x)$ and $-\psi(x)$, oscillating ν times per unit time owing to the time-dependent factor which has extreme values ± 1. In this case substitution in the wave equation shows that $\psi(x)$ must satisfy a time-independent amplitude equation:

$$\frac{d^2\psi}{dx^2} = \frac{4\pi^2\nu^2}{u^2}\psi.$$

It is customary to call ψ the 'wave function', though strictly it is only the amplitude of the wave function Ψ, the time-dependent quantity. Provided the medium is uniform, so that u is constant, the last equation has solutions of the form

$$\sin\frac{2\pi\nu}{u}x \quad \text{and} \quad \cos\frac{2\pi\nu}{u}x,$$

and these stationary patterns (standing waves) are repeated when x increases by $\lambda = u/\nu$, the wave length.

Returning to the case of an electron with kinetic energy E, the associated *wave function* is known to have a wavelength

$$\lambda = \frac{h}{mv} = \frac{h}{\sqrt{2mE}},$$

and the amplitude equation then becomes

$$\frac{d^2\psi}{dx^2} + \frac{8\pi^2mE}{h^2}\psi = 0.$$

In the first instance, this applies only to a particle with constant kinetic energy. Nevertheless, it shows with unexpected clarity the origin of *quantisation*—when a particle is bound within a certain region of space it can exist only in certain discrete energy states. For if the particle is now confined to a certain region, by means of barriers a distance l apart, ψ must vanish at and outside the end points and these 'boundary conditions' require that the region contains an integral number of half waves, *i.e.* $n\left(\frac{1}{2}\lambda\right) = l$. Substituting for λ, the only possible values of E are

$$E = \frac{h^2}{8ml^2}\,n^2, \qquad \text{where } n = 1,\ 2,\ 3,\ \ldots$$

A particle moving back and forth within definite limits can exist in states described by a stationary probability pattern only for certain discrete values of the energy.

The Schrödinger equation (1926) represents a generalisation to the case in which there is an external potential field and the kinetic energy is no longer constant. The kinetic energy, which might be expected to take the place of E in the above equation, is now (classically) $E - V$, where E is the total energy and $V = V(x)$ is the potential energy, which in general varies from place to place. The final wave equation for determining the stationary wave patterns associated with a particle in an arbitrary potential field is then

$$\nabla^2 \psi + \frac{8\pi^2 m}{h^2}\,(E - V)\,\psi = 0.$$

Although the historical derivation sketched above depends largely on suggestive analogies, more profound derivations have since been given, and the equation itself is now regarded as entirely satisfactory so long as extremely small relativistic effects are neglected. On physical grounds (ψ^2 has a physical meaning) it is assumed that the only solutions which mean anything are well-behaved (*i.e.* everywhere finite, smoothly varying, and vanishing at infinity). This requirement alone leads automatically to the quantisation so foreign to classical physics. Sometimes the wave equation is rewritten in the form

$$\left[\frac{1}{2m}\left(\frac{-h^2}{4\pi^2}\right)\nabla^2 + V(x,\,y,\,z)\right]\psi = E\psi.$$

The quantity in square brackets is an 'operator'—the Hamiltonian operator. All *eigenvalue equations* have this form; and solutions ψ occur only for certain *eigenvalues* of the factor E on the right hand side. This form immediately suggests the final generalisation from 1 to n electrons. Since the classical energy expression is

$$E = \tfrac{1}{2}mv^2 + V(xyz) = \frac{1}{2m}\,(p_x^2 + p_y^2 + p_z^2) + V(xyz)$$

where $p_x = mv_x$ etc. are components of momentum, the 1-electron equation may be obtained by replacing p_x^2 etc. by the differential operators

$$-\frac{h^2}{4\pi^2}\,\frac{\partial^2}{\partial x^2},\ \text{etc.}$$

letting the resultant operator (in square brackets above) operate on a wave function ψ, and equating the result to $E\psi$. The same recipe, applied to a system of N particles with masses $m_1, m_2, m_3 \ldots m_N$, gives

$$\left[\frac{1}{2m_1} \left(\frac{-h^2}{4\pi^2} \right) \nabla^2_{(1)} + \frac{1}{2m_2} \left(\frac{-h^2}{4\pi^2} \right) \nabla^2_{(2)} + \ldots V \right] \psi = E\psi,$$

where V and ψ are now functions of the co-ordinates of all the particles and there is a ∇^2 for every particle. $\psi^2 d\tau_1, d\tau_2 \ldots d\tau_n$ is then the probability of simultaneously finding particle 1 in volume element $d\tau_1$, particle 2 in volume element $d\tau_2$, etc.

The hydrogen atom

In the hydrogen atom, an electron of charge $-e$ moves about a proton of charge $+e$. If the distance between them is r,

$$V = -\frac{e^2}{r}$$

and

$$\nabla^2\psi + \frac{8\pi^2 m}{h^2} \left(E + \frac{e^2}{r} \right) \psi = 0.$$

One type of solution follows on taking $\psi = f(r)$ and assuming that, as the potential is spherically symmetrical, there must be a solution dependent only on r; in which case

$$\frac{\partial \psi}{\partial x} = \frac{d\psi}{dr} \frac{\partial r}{\partial x} \text{ etc.}$$

Then since

$$r = \sqrt{x^2 + y^2 + z^2}, \qquad \left(\frac{\partial r}{\partial x} \right)_{yz} = \frac{1}{2} \frac{2x}{\sqrt{x^2 + y^2 + z^2}} = \frac{x}{r}$$

and

$$\frac{\partial \psi}{\partial x} = \frac{x}{r} \frac{d\psi}{dr}.$$

Differentiating again:

$$\frac{\partial^2 \psi}{\partial x^2} = \frac{1}{r} \frac{d\psi}{dr} - \frac{x^2}{r^3} \frac{d\psi}{dr} + \frac{x^2}{r^2} \frac{d^2\psi}{dr^2}.$$

$\dfrac{\partial^2 \psi}{\partial y^2}$ and $\dfrac{\partial^2 \psi}{\partial z^2}$ may be found similarly. Adding, and using $x^2 + y^2 + z^2 = r^2$,

$$\nabla^2\psi = \frac{3}{r} \frac{d\psi}{dr} - \frac{1}{r} \frac{d\psi}{dr} + \frac{d^2\psi}{dr^2} = \frac{2}{r} \frac{d\psi}{dr} + \frac{d^2\psi}{dr^2}.$$

As $\nabla^2\psi$ reduces to this form if ψ is a spherically symmetrical function, it follows that spherically symmetrical solutions must satisfy the equation

$$\frac{d^2\psi}{dr^2} + \frac{2}{r}\frac{d\psi}{dr} + \frac{8\pi^2 m}{h}\left(E + \frac{e}{r^2}\right)\psi = 0.$$

A standard trial solution is $\psi = e^{-ar}$, for the exponential factor remains on differentiation, and can be extracted as a common factor.
Thus

$$\frac{d\psi}{dr} = -a\,e^{-ar} \quad \text{and} \quad \frac{d^2\psi}{dr^2} = +a^2 e^{-ar},$$

and substitution gives

$$e^{-ar}\left[a^2 - \frac{2}{r}a + \frac{8\pi^2 m}{h^2}\left(E + \frac{e^2}{r}\right)\right] = 0.$$

If this is to be true for all values of r the constant term and the term in $\frac{1}{r}$ must both vanish: thus

$$a^2 + \frac{8\pi^2 mE}{h^2} = 0, \quad \text{and} \quad -2a + \frac{8\pi^2 me^2}{h^2} = 0, \qquad \therefore a = \frac{4\pi m^2 e^2}{h^2};$$

and the E value for this state is $E_1 = \dfrac{-a^2 h^2}{8\pi^2 m} = -\dfrac{2\pi^2 me^4}{h^2}.$

E_1 is negative and the electron is bound. E_1 is expressed in terms of universal constants and is itself a useful constant. $-E_1$ is the ionisation energy necessary to remove the electron entirely from the hydrogen atom. The actual value, 13.60 eV, agrees with that calculated.

Since the probability of finding an electron in volume element $d\tau$ is $\psi^2 d\tau$*, and ψ here depends only on r, the probability of its being at a distance between r and dr from the nucleus (*i.e.* in a shell of volume $4\pi r^2 dr$) is $4\pi r^2\psi^2 dr$. The 'radial probability density', $4\pi r^2\psi^2$, is plotted in Fig. 10, and has a maximum at $r = 1/a$.

It can be calculated in terms of m, e and h and equals $h^2/4\pi^2 me^2 = 0.5292$ Å. This is the Bohr radius of the semiclassical approach (1913) and is often adopted as the atomic unit of length. The electron has a maximum probability of being at this distance from the nucleus but a good chance of being anywhere within a very considerable volume.

The probability density ψ^2 is commonly represented pictorially by density

* Actually ψ is multiplied by a constant to make $\int\psi^2 d\tau = 1$ (the probability of the electron being *somewhere*): ψ is then *normalised*.

of shading (Fig. 11) or, more simply, by sketching a bounding contour (on which all points have the same value of ψ^2) enclosing, say, 95% of the density. The ψ-function, indicated by this bounding surface, is called an *atomic orbital*, being the wave-mechanical counterpart of the classical orbit (Fig. 12).

An electron whose orbital is spherically symmetrical is called an s electron.

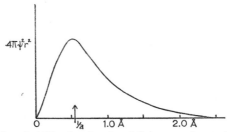

Fig. 10. Radial probability density, $4\pi\psi^2 r^2$, in ground state hydrogen atom.

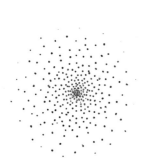

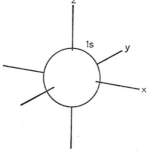

Fig. 11. Electron probability density represented by density of shading.

Fig. 12. Atomic orbital represented by spherical bounding surface.

In addition to the state of lowest energy E_1, there are *excited states* with greater energies $E_2, E_3, \ldots E_n$, for which it can be shown that

$$E_n = \frac{-2\pi^2 me^4}{h^2}\frac{1}{n^2} = \frac{E_1}{n^2},$$

n being an integral quantum number. When n is very large, E_n approaches zero. For the free electron $E \geqslant 0$.

The energy set free when an electron falls from an energy level n to the energy level 2 is

$$E_n - E_2 = -\frac{2\pi^2 me^4}{h^2}\left(\frac{1}{n^2} - \frac{1}{2^2}\right),$$

$$= +\frac{2\pi^2 me^4}{h^2}\left(\frac{1}{2^2} - \frac{1}{n^2}\right).$$

In this form the equation relates the wave number of lines in the visible hydrogen spectrum (Balmer, 1885) to the change in energy state of the electron. The wave number λ^{-1} is simply the number of waves per unit length:

$$\lambda^{-1} = \frac{1}{\lambda} = \frac{\nu}{c},$$

where c is the velocity of light. Since

$$E_n - E_2 = \Delta E = h\nu = h\lambda^{-1}c,$$

$$h\lambda^{-1}c = \frac{2\pi^2 me^4}{h^2}\left(\frac{1}{2^2} - \frac{1}{n^2}\right),$$

$$\lambda^{-1} = \frac{2\pi^2 me^4}{h^3 c}\left(\frac{1}{2^2} - \frac{1}{n^2}\right) = R\left(\frac{1}{2^2} - \frac{1}{n^2}\right).$$

The constant R agrees, within the limits of experimental error, with the empirical one found by Rydberg (1889).

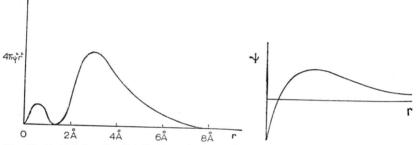

Fig. 13. Radial density distribution of charge for   Fig. 14. Relation of ψ to r for
electron of energy E_2.   electron of energy E_2.

The radial density distribution of the charge of an electron of energy E_2 is shown by plotting $4\pi\psi^2 r^2$ against r, as in Fig. 13. The corresponding

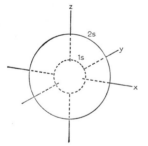

Fig. 15. Boundary surface for 2s electron, compared with that for 1s.

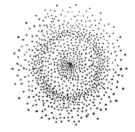

Fig. 16. Representation of probability density for electron of energy E_2.

relationship of ψ itself to r is shown in Fig. 14. Alternative pictorial representations of both ψ and ψ^2 are given in Fig. 15 and Fig. 16, the former obscuring the details but indicating schematically the general size and shape of the orbital. The shapes are intended only to show where ψ is large.

p Functions

Though the potential V in the Schrödinger equation depends only on r, there are solutions which depend on x, y and z separately, e.g. $\psi = xf(r)$. Wave functions of this type are p functions and there are three solutions for the same energy value. As a result of the spherical symmetry of the potential V, the orbitals which are not themselves spherically symmetrical occur in groups, the members of a given group having the same value of E but quite independent ψ-patterns. Solutions in the same group are described as *degenerate*, their number being the *degree of degeneracy*, and different orbitals of the same group are often said to be *equivalent*, that is energetically alike.

For the special case where $V(r) = -e^2/r$, substitution in the Schrödinger equation shows the p-type solution of lowest energy to give

$$E = \frac{-2\pi^2me^4}{h^2}\frac{1}{2^2} = E_2,$$

the energy of the second-lowest s state. This energy level is fourfold degenerate in the hydrogen atom, corresponding to one s and three p orbitals. In all other atoms an electron moves, roughly speaking, in the field created by the nucleus and the other electrons together. This field is not of a simple inverse-distance form, and in such atoms p electrons and s electrons differ in energy.

The number of higher energy solutions is infinite, their 'atomic' character disappearing for $E \rightarrow 0$, when the electron becomes free. Some of the higher atomic orbitals are represented by boundary surfaces including most of the probability density in Figs. 17 and 18. The figures do not strictly show surfaces of constant ψ (ψ vanishes at the nucleus) but rather their general disposition in relation to one another and for clarity the different parts of the separate lobes are joined up into a single pattern. This indicates simply the sign of ψ and the regions where it is large, the different regions being separated by nodal surfaces in which $\psi = 0$. Sevenfold degenerate f states are less easy to represent pictorially. The terminology, s, p, d, f, ... is a legacy from the Bohr theory which attempted to classify the 'sharp', 'principal', 'diffuse' and 'fundamental' series of classical spectroscopy.

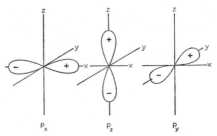

Fig. 17. Boundary surfaces for p electrons.

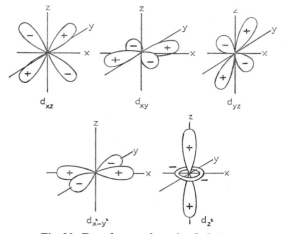

Fig. 18. Boundary surfaces for d electrons.

Orbital angular momentum

The *angular momentum* of a particle about a point O is a quantity $M = pmv$ where p is the perpendicular distance from O to the line of motion and mv is the ordinary momentum; the quantity is associated with an axis through O, namely the normal to the plane in which the motion is taking place (Fig. 19). The angular momentum is thus a vector quantity and can be described in terms of components parallel to the three axes. The magnitude of the vector is

$$M = \sqrt{M_x^2 + M_y^2 + M_z^2},$$

and the direction (*i.e.* the axis) makes angles

$$\cos^{-1}\frac{M_x}{M}, \qquad \cos^{-1}\frac{M_y}{M}, \qquad \cos^{-1}\frac{M_z}{M}$$

with the three co-ordinate axes. Here for instance $M_x = y\,(mv_z) - z(mv_y)$ and is seen from Fig. 20 to be the total momentum of the y and z momentum components about the x axis, the contributions being counted positive for anticlockwise and negative for clockwise motion. M_y and M_z follow by cyclic rearrangement, $xyz \rightarrow yzx \rightarrow zxy$.

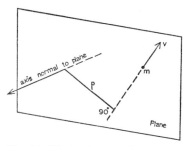

Fig. 19. Illustrating angular momentum.

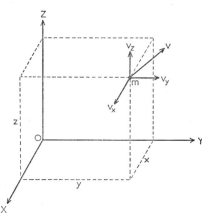

Fig. 20. Components of angular momentum.

Now M and its three components are all observable dynamical quantities just as is the energy E. It turns out that, in a definite energy state, M and *one* of its components can simultaneously have definite, quantised values. Thus if a particular direction in space is singled out, by means of an applied magnetic field for example, the component in this direction can take only certain quantised values, while the other two components must remain uncertain. It is customary to call the particular axis the z axis. The definite allowed values of M_z are then integral multiples of $h/2\pi$,

$$M_z = m_l\,(h/2\pi) \quad m_l = 0,\ \pm 1,\ \pm 2,\ \dots \pm l$$

those of M itself being

$$M = \sqrt{l(l+1)}\ \frac{h}{2\pi} \quad l = 0, 1, 2, \dots$$

The s, p, d, f, ... electrons have angular momenta corresponding to $l = 0, 1, 2, 3, \dots$ respectively, and the different degenerate states can be classified according to the simultaneously definite values of M_z. There are three p orbitals, corresponding to $m_l = -1, 0, +1$; five d orbitals, corresponding to $m_l = -2, -1, 0, +1, +2$; and in general $(2l + 1)$ orbitals, corresponding to $m_l = -l, \dots 0 \dots + l$, for an angular momentum M with quantum number l. This classification suggests a *vector model* (Fig. 21) in which different states correspond to different settings of a vector of length l, representing the angular momentum. This model goes back to the early days of quantum theory, when it was found empirically necessary to assume the rather curious angular momentum value $\sqrt{l(l+1)}$ (in units $h/2\pi$) instead of the l employed in the semi-classical vector diagram. The wave mechanical treatment is in fact capable of bringing theoretical and experimental results into perfect agreement.

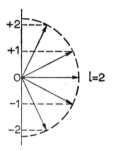

Fig. 21. Representation of angular momenta.

The quantisation of angular momentum components in a given direction is experimentally realised in the Zeeman effect. Here the unique direction is fixed by an applied magnetic field; the states with different electronic angular momentum components in this direction correspond to slightly different energy values since the circulating charge behaves like a small magnet, whose component along the field is proportional to m_l. The splitting of the initially degenerate level, due to the different coupling energies, is spectroscopically observable. Quantitative discussion of this magnetic effect will be deferred (p. 63). The Zeeman effect does, however, provide a very powerful tool in the interpretation of atomic spectra.

At this stage, it must be stressed that any mixture of two or more degenerate solutions is also a solution of the wave equation, and is an equally satisfactory description of an electron with a given energy and angular momentum; but, for example, an equal mixture of solutions with common E and l but with $m_l = +1$ and -1, respectively, would describe a state in which M_z was uncertain and, if observed, would be equally likely to yield either result. This arbitrariness disappears only if the spherical symmetry of the problem is destroyed by fixing an axis (*e.g.* by an applied field); for when this is done the only stationary states are those compatible with this axis of symmetry, and such states correspond to definite values of the third characteristic, M_z. To make this clear, consider the three p orbitals, describing electrons with the same energy, and with $l = 1$, but with $m_l = -1, 0, +1$. These orbitals, which are called p_{-1}, p_0 and p_{+1}, describe the stationary states when a feeble magnetic field (just sufficient to reduce the symmetry) is applied along the z axis; but they may be *mixtures* of the p orbitals p_x, p_y, and p_z, which were introduced before any reference was made to symmetry or angular momentum. In fact p_z which is symmetrical about the z axis, does coincide with p_0: but p_{-1} and p_{+1} are mixtures of p_x and p_y (and *vice versa*) which can be interpreted, somewhat naively, as permitting the 'jumping' of an electron from one orbital to the other, so as to give respectively clockwise or anticlockwise circulation. On the other hand, p_x and p_y correspond to standing waves (this time 'rotational') built up from p_{-1} and p_{+1} which are oppositely directed travelling waves. The same situation arises with the d electrons. Five 'travelling wave' solutions can be used which all give electron distributions completely symmetrical about a particular axis, or five standing wave solutions which are less symmetrical but more easily visualized. This ambiguity need cause no alarm; the freedom of choice simply means it is possible to work with those orbitals most suitable for a given application. In describing the spectroscopic states of free atoms (spherical symmetry), and of linear molecules (axial symmetry), it is often advantageous to employ the functions which correspond to definite M_z values; but this is not so in systems of lower symmetry in which there is no such thing as quantised angular momentum. And in discussing molecular structure where the atomic orbitals are employed only as 'building bricks' for constructing molecular wave functions, it is usually quite immaterial which type of orbital is used. The mixtures such as p_x, p_y, p_z, have, however, an important practical advantage. Unlike the travelling wave solutions, they can be directly represented by stationary patterns with a fixed orientation in space, and permit a pictorial approach to the construction of molecular wave functions.

Electron spin. Fine structure

The interpretation of the Zeeman effect provided by the theory of orbital angular momentum is incomplete. Anomalous Zeeman splittings are observed (indeed, the so-called 'normal' splitting is found to be the exception) and require a further development of the theory. The difficulty first arises in the one-electron (hydrogen-like) system already considered, for even an s electron, with *no* angular momentum, is found to have two accessible energy states in the presence of a magnetic field. This led Goudsmit and Uhlenbeck (1925) to postulate an intrinsic angular momentum due to *spin* of the electron itself. Treating this on the same footing as orbital angular momentum the observed *doublet splitting* of an s state requires a spin quantum number, $s = \frac{1}{2}$, such that there would be two possible z components (separated by an integral multiple of $h/2\pi$) namely $+\frac{1}{2}$ and $-\frac{1}{2}$ (*cf.* Fig. 21).

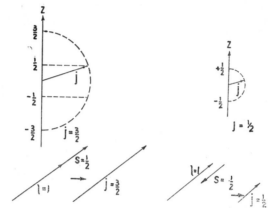

Fig. 22. Vector addition of orbital and spin angular momenta.

The general interpretation of the Zeeman effect for a one-electron system then calls for an extension of the vector picture. Consider an electron in a p state, denoting z components of the orbital and spin angular momenta, in units of $h/2\pi$, by m_l and m_s respectively. The possibilities are $m_l = -1, 0, +1$ and $m_s = -\frac{1}{2}, +\frac{1}{2}$; thus the possible values of the total angular momentum z components are $(-1 \pm \frac{1}{2})$, $(0 \pm \frac{1}{2})$, $(+1 \pm \frac{1}{2})$. These correspond to different z components of total angular momentum with quantum number j, where j can take the values $1 + \frac{1}{2} = \frac{3}{2}$ and $1 - \frac{1}{2} = \frac{1}{2}$. The two vector diagrams for the allowed states are shown in Fig. 22, along with the pictorial composition of the orbital and spin vectors, the spin being parallel or anti-parallel to the orbital vector. The method of composition is applicable for arbitrary orbital angular momentum with quantum number l, j taking values $l + \frac{1}{2}$ and $l - \frac{1}{2}$. The alternative couplings of orbital and spin angular momentum give rise to another experimentally observable phenomenon. The magnetic field associated with l performs in effect a Zeeman experiment on the spinning electron and even in the absence of an external field, the two couplings correspond to slightly different energies which are revealed in the fine structure of spectral lines. Thus p, d, f ... states are always resolved into doublets by the electron spin, while the s state is single, being unresolved because the orbital magnetic moment is then zero. Further resolutions should occur when an external field is applied and these are in complete accord with the observed Zeeman splittings. A rigorous justification of this semi-classical vector model again comes from quantum mechanics. The pictorial interpretation must not be taken too literally (in getting quantative results, for instance, angular momenta with quantum numbers l, j etc. have magnitudes $\sqrt{l(l+1)}$, $\sqrt{j(j+1)}$ etc.); nevertheless, the pictorial model is extremely useful in the general classification and understanding of spectra.

Many-electron systems

The wave equation for several electrons in the presence of a central nucleus may be taken over from p. 47—where now $m_1 = m_2 = \ldots = m$, the electron mass. Abbreviating the co-ordinates of the electrons from (x_1, y_1, z_1), (x_2, y_2, z_2),... to 1, 2 ... the wave function is then $\Psi(1, 2, \ldots N)$, and $V(1, 2, \ldots N)$ contains the potential energy of each electron in the field of the nucleus together with interaction terms representing the mutual repulsion of the electrons. This partial differential equation cannot be solved in closed form (*i.e.* to give formulae for wave functions and energy levels) even for the helium atom; but highly developed approximation methods yield numerical values of the energy in essentially perfect agreement with experiment (1 part in 50,000). This leaves little doubt of the general validity of the wave equation itself.

When approximate solutions are extended to heavier atoms and to molecules, it is necessary to be content with a rather lower accuracy (*e.g.* 1 to 2%). The most fruitful approximation method is that of Hartree (1928), later justified and refined by Slater (1930) and Fock (1930). This is suggested by first neglecting the electron repulsion and observing that the probability function $P(1, 2, \ldots N)$ must then be approximated by the product $P_1(1)$ $P_2(2) \ldots P_N(N)$, for then the probability of any configuration of the electrons is a product of the probabilities of N independent events. Since $P = \Psi_1^2$, this means the many-electron wave function must also be a product

$$\Psi(1, 2, \ldots N) = \psi_1(1)\, \psi_2(2) \ldots \psi_N(N),$$

in which electron 1 is described by orbital ψ_1 and probability pattern $P_1 = \psi_1^2$, electron 2 by orbital ψ_2 and probability pattern $P_2 = \psi_2^2$, and so on. Pictorially, each electron occupies its own orbital, as if it alone were being considered. The probability of finding electron 1 at a given point (x, y, z) is proportional to $P_1(x, y, z)$, that of finding electron 2 at the same point is proportional to $P_2(x, y, z)$ and by addition the probability P of finding an electron (*i.e.* any of the N electrons) at the point (x, y, z) is

$$P(x, y, z) = P_1(x, y, z) + P_2(x, y, z) \ldots + P_N(x, y, z).$$

The probability density in the system is thus, to this approximation, obtained simply by pictorially superimposing contributions from individual electrons, each described by its own orbital. The orbitals ψ_1, ψ_2 ... ψ_N are, however, not necessarily the orbitals of the one-electron problem in which all electrons but one are literally ignored, for it is possible to choose all the orbitals in such a way that the resultant wave function closely approaches the exact solution. These best orbitals then represent the motion of an electron in an *effective* field (the Hartree field) due to the nucleus together with the remaining electrons, each regarded as a smeared-out negative charge with a density which is that of its probability function.

Certain restrictions are imposed on this picture by the fact that electrons are indistinguishable and by the existence of electron spin. Indistinguishability implies that P (1, 2 ... N) shall be unchanged in value if the positions of any two particles are interchanged, and this in turn implies that ψ can at most change sign. For electrons, the wave function must be an anti-symmetric sum of products,

$$C[\psi_1(1)\,\psi_2(2)\,\psi_3(3) \ldots \psi_N(N) - \psi_1(2)\,\psi_2(1)\,\psi_3(3) \ldots \psi_N(N) + \ldots]$$

whose sign reverses in any interchange (the constant C being chosen to normalise the probability function so that the chance of finding all particles somewhere is unity). Fortunately, this does not destroy the simplicity of the picture; the electron probability density $P(x, y, z)$ is given by exactly the same sum-rule as for a single product. But there is now a fundamental restriction on the choice of orbitals. It might have been expected that every electron added to a nucleus would, in the lowest energy or ground state, be described by the lowest energy solution of the one particle wave equation. However the requirement of antisymmetry rules out this possibility because an antisymmetric Ψ vanishes if any two orbitals (*e.g.* ψ_1, ψ_2 above) are identified. The orbitals occupied by the electrons must therefore all be different and in the ground state the tendency will be for N electrons to occupy the first $\frac{1}{2}$N orbitals, in ascending energy order, of the one-electron problem.

The existence of spin calls for a further slight modification. An orbital such as ψ_1 describes the spatial distribution of an electron in a given energy state. If, in addition to given energy, a particle has one of two given spin components, this must also be indicated in its orbital description by adding a factor α, which is unity if the particle has spin $s_z = \frac{1}{2}$ and vanishes otherwise, or β, which is likewise unity or 0 according as $s_z = -\frac{1}{2}$ or not. The set of orbitals is therefore in effect duplicated, becoming $\psi_1\alpha$, $\psi_1\beta$, $\psi_2\alpha$, $\psi_2\beta$ .... At the same time $\psi_1\alpha$ and $\psi_1\beta$, having the same spatial part ψ_1, lead to identical contributions to the electron density.

The effect of indistinguishability, which denies the occupation of two orbitals which are alike in every respect (including now the spin), may consequently be stated in modified form. Any orbital ψ can be empty or occupied by either 1 or 2 electrons, appearing once with each spin factor in the second instance, but not by more than 2. The conclusion is that the electron density is of the form

$$P\left(x, y, z\right) = n_1 P_1\left(x, y, z\right) + n_2 P_2\left(x, y, z\right) + \ldots n_N P_N\left(x, y, z\right),$$

where each of the 'occupation numbers' $n_1, n_2, \ldots$ may be 1 or 2, and an orbital is said to be 'filled' when it is 2. This is the wave-mechanical form of the Pauli exclusion principle.

Electronic configurations of atoms

In the ground states of atoms the lowest energy orbitals are doubly occupied but some of those of higher energy, which may be degenerate, may be only singly occupied. Later it will be seen that the occupied orbitals of highest energy are the *valence orbitals*, responsible for the chemical behaviour of the atom. Whereas the lower energy orbitals are tightly localised about the nucleus, the higher ones are much more diffuse, and when a whole set of orbitals is occupied the resultant density falls into 'shells' (Fig. 23), giving the wave-mechanical analogue of the shells of

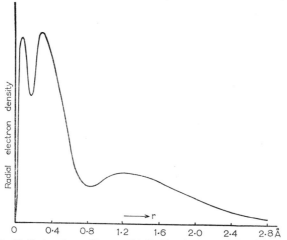

Fig. 23. Shell structure. Charge distribution in argon (after Hartree).

Bohr theory. The shells are determined by the *principal* quantum number n, and orbitals in the same shell are distinguished by the *subsidiary* quantum numbers l and m_l. (When the orbitals are not strictly hydrogen-like, n can still be defined as the number of nodes in an orbital minus one.) This classification is general, depending only on the spherical symmetry of the system, but it must be stressed that orbitals in the same shell but with different l values do not have quite the same 'spread', and for $n \geqslant 3$ the division into shells is not very clear-cut.

The nature of the departures from hydrogen-like form must now be discussed. It is the essence of the Hartree method that each orbital describes one electron in the field of the nucleus *and* all the other electrons (each regarded as 'smeared out' according to its orbital). Thus when there are two electrons in a 1s orbital and one in a 2s orbital, outside a nucleus of charge $+3e$, the 2s electron will 'feel', roughly speaking, an effective nuclear charge of little more than $+1e$. The simplest way of improving hydrogen-like orbitals, in order to take into account electron repulsion, is to use 'screening rules' (Slater, 1931) to estimate an effective nuclear charge for each orbital. In better approximation, the orbitals are obtained by numerical solution of the equations given by Hartree and Fock. But since each depends, through the field arising from the charge distribution, upon the forms of *all* the occupied orbitals, tedious repetition is necessary to get a *self-consistent field*. Fortunately, the main features of atomic orbitals can be understood in terms of the screening due to various groups of electrons and the non-Coulombic form of the resultant field. In particular, this is responsible for a separation of the energy levels of orbitals in the same shell but with different l values, the order becoming s < p < d < f ....

It is now possible to predict the electron configurations of simple atoms by adding Z electrons to a central nucleus, filling the available orbitals in ascending energy order in accordance with the Pauli principle. This is because the total electronic energy is a sum of the characteristic energies of the occupied orbitals (counted once or twice according to occupation) along with a smaller electron interaction term. Consequently the normal or *ground state* occurs when the electrons occupy the orbitals of lowest energy, with not more than 2 in each. Thus, the atoms from H to B have electron configurations which may be indicated by H ($1s^1$), He ($1s^2$), Li ($1s^2\,2s^1$), Be ($1s^2\,2s^2$), B ($1s^2\,2s^2\,2p^1$). At this point a difficulty arises. In the next atom, carbon, there are 2 electrons outside the $1s^2\,2s^2$ group, but there are three 2p orbitals of equal energy (6 counting the spin) into which they may go. This ambiguity is admitted by writing the configuration C ($1s^2\,2s^2\,2p^2$) without specifying which of the equivalent 2p orbitals are occupied. Corresponding to such a configuration there are several states whose energies differ somewhat. We are interested primarily in the lowest of these, which is the ground state, and in its spectroscopic character. Before proceeding further in 'building up' the atoms of the Periodic Table it is therefore necessary to classify the states associated with a given electron configuration and to decide which is lowest.

Spectroscopic states

After specifying the configuration in terms of the occupation of orbitals of given (n, l), without reference to m_l which labels different equivalent orbitals, the possible states may be classified according to angular momentum. We shall therefore summarise and extend the vector scheme (p. 56), using the carbon $1s^2 \, 2s^2 \, 2p^2$ configuration in illustration.

(1) s, p, d, ... orbitals describe electrons with angular momentum quantum numbers 0, 1, 2 .... For any value of l there are $2l + 1$ equivalent orbitals, corresponding to z-components of $m_l = l, l - 1, \ldots -l$.

2) Each electron has a spin with quantum number $s = \frac{1}{2}$ and possible z-components $m_s = +\frac{1}{2}, -\frac{1}{2}$.

(3) The orbital and spin vectors may be separately combined to give *total* angular momenta with orbital and spin quantum numbers (for 2 electrons) $L = (l_1 + l_2), (l_1 + l_2 - 1) \ldots (l_1 - l_2)$ and $S = s_1 + s_2 (= 1)$, $s_1 + s_2 - 1 (= 0)$; and z-components $M_L = L, L - 1, \ldots -L$ and $M_S = S, S - 1, \ldots -S$. The possibilities are indicated, for carbon, in Fig. 24. The greatest possible L is simply the maximum value of M_L, which is $m_{l_1} + m_{l_2}$; but the latter has a maximum value $l_1 + l_2$ and the greatest possible L is thus $L = l_1 + l_2 = 2$. The other L values correspond to different couplings in which $M_{L(max)}$ and hence L are reduced by unit steps. The allowed total angular momenta therefore correspond to $L = 2, 1, 0$, each with its $2L + 1$ possible z-components. Atomic states are classified according to L value in essentially the same way as orbitals in terms of l value. Those in which L has the value 0, 1, 2, 3, ... are called S, P, D, F, ... states. For instance, S, P and D states are associated with the $1s^2 \, 2s^2 \, 2p^2$ configuration of carbon.

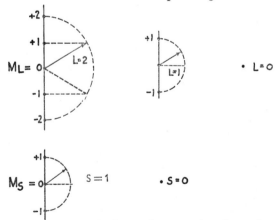

Fig. 24. Resultant orbital and spin angular momentum for configuration $2p^2$.

(4) The total orbital angular momentum and the total spin, described by L and S, may be coupled exactly as in the one-electron case (p. 56). Their resultant total angular momentum is described by a quantum number J, with possible values $L + S, L + S - 1, \ldots L - S$; and for each J there are $2J + 1$ possible z-components $M_J = J, J - 1, \ldots - J$. There are $2S + 1$ possible couplings of L and S if $S < L$ (or $2L + 1$ if $L < S$) and, since these introduce slightly different coupling energies, a state of given L is always a *multiplet*, with multiplicity $2S + 1$ (or $2L + 1$ if $L < S$). Since for carbon, $S = 1$ or 0, we expect S, P and D states of multiplicity 1 and 3 to appear. It is customary to indicate these singlet and triplet states by ¹S, ¹P, ¹D and ³S, ³P, ³D. Not all these states occur. Thus ³D would require two electrons in the same orbital with the same spin and this, by the Pauli principle, is inadmissible. In fact only ¹S, ³P and ¹D are found. The individual states of a multiplet may be labelled (when necessary) by adding their J values as subscripts. The states comprising the triplet P level of carbon are ³P₂, ³P₁, ³P₀. States of given J are not resolved further (according to M_J) unless a magnetic field is applied, when each shows a Zeeman splitting into $2J + 1$ components.

By the use of this vector model it is possible to recognise and classify observed atomic states and to associate them with definite electron configurations. It will be noticed that mention has not been made of the doubly occupied orbitals of closed shells; these together give a zero contribution to the angular momenta, and consequently spectral data provide direct information about the outer, singly-occupied orbitals. Later this will be seen to be of the utmost importance. Briefly, the valency of an atom, that is the number of *covalent* bonds in which it can participate (p. 85), is the number of singly occupied outer orbitals, and this is shown by the fact that a configuration with n such orbitals gives rise to states with a maximum multiplicity of $p = 2S + 1 = n + 1$. Hence the valency of an atom whose electron configuration gives states of maximum multiplicity p is $p - 1$. Even at this stage, important conclusions can be drawn. Thus, the lowest energy configuration of carbon is observed to give states of maximum multiplicity $p = 3$. Carbon is not however bivalent; and the implication is that the normal quadrivalence must in some way involve an excitation, from a ground state with *two* singly occupied orbitals (the theoretically expected 1s² 2s² 2p²) to an excited state with *four*. The energy order of the various states cannot be predicted from the vector model, but rules are available for this purpose.

Finally, it must be remembered that the vector model gives only an approximate description of the electronic structure. According to (4) the present picture is one of *L-S* (or Russell-Saunders) coupling. For heavy atoms this picture is often inadequate, the *L-S* coupling being broken (*cf.* p. 79).

Hund's rules. The Landé g-factor

The order of the energy levels arising from any configuration can be predicted, in the case of *L-S* coupling, by rules due to Hund (1925):

(1) The state of maximum multiplicity lies lowest. The electrons then occupy equivalent orbitals singly, as far as possible, with parallel spins.

(2) For a given multiplicity, the state of maximum *L* lies lowest.

(3) For a given *S* and *L*, the state of maximum or minimum *J* lies lowest, according as the set of equivalent orbitals is more or less than half filled.

The first two rules are of greatest chemical importance. From them it follows immediately that the lowest energy states of the carbon atom lie in the order ^3P, ^1D, ^1S; carbon has a ^3P ground state.

At a later stage we shall also need to know precisely what magnetic moment is associated with an atom in a given angular momentum state, this determining the Zeeman splitting of the levels. The magnetic moment is proportional to the angular momentum, but experiment indicates that the proportionality factor is twice as great for spin as for orbital angular momentum. When both contributions occur, the formula for the effective magnetic moment, μ, is consequently rather complicated: it is found to be

$$\mu = g \sqrt{J(J+1)}\, \mu_B$$

where
$$g = 1 + \frac{J(J+1) + S(S+1) - L(L+1)}{2J(J+1)},$$

and
$$\mu_B = \frac{eh}{4\pi mc} = 9.273 \times 10^{-21} \text{ erg/gauss}$$

is the *Bohr magneton*. This *g-factor* was first proposed on experimental grounds by Landé and later derived theoretically.

The 'Aufbau' principle and the Periodic Table

It is now possible to work through the Periodic Table, predicting ground state electronic configurations and spectroscopic states, by adding *Z* electrons to each nucleus, filling the available orbitals in ascending energy order and observing the Pauli principle and Hund's rules. The principles already discussed, upon which this process is based, are known collectively as the *aufbau principle*. It is, of course, necessary to known the energy order of the orbitals, but fortunately their relative positions change gradually and systematically throughout the Periodic Table. The variation results mainly from the screening effect of electrons near the nucleus and is clearly revealed in the ionisation potentials, which are numerically equal to the orbital energies. Thus, in filling the shell with principal quantum number $n = 2$, we start with Li, whose $1s^2$ 'core' is roughly equivalent to a charge $3 - 2 = 1$ and end with Ne, whose 2s and 2p electrons move outside a core of effective charge roughly $10 - 2 = 8$, their mutual screening effects being much smaller than that of the core itself. Thus ionisation potentials tend to increase as each shell is filled, increasing from $I = 5.4$ eV for Li to $I = 21.6$ eV for Ne. For the same reason, a second ionisation is much more difficult to achieve than the first. On the other hand, nearly filled shells usually accept an extra electron quite readily owing to the relatively small change in screening which results. Thus, F readily accepts one electron but F⁻ has a closed shell and repels a second electron which could only be accommodated outside; consequently fluorine forms only a singly-charged anion.

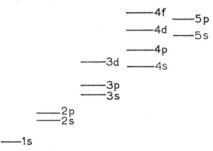

Fig. 25. Energy levels in a heavy atom.

The energies associated with the occupied orbitals of a typical heavy atom follow the trend shown in Fig. 25. The separations depend upon atomic number, but the *order* of the levels rarely differs from that shown. It should be noticed that the energy levels associated with different shells overlap after $n = 2$. For instance, the 4s orbital has a lower energy than the 3d, and this is a general feature of the atoms of the fourteen elements from nitrogen to calcium inclusive. It is simply a result of the different shapes of the 4s and 3d orbitals and their different degrees of penetration into the inner shells, a 4s electron spending considerably more time within the *L*-shell (where screening is relatively small and binding high) than a 3d electron. The fact that the order of the energy levels is preserved in going from one atom to another, with only a few exceptions, means that the order of filling, as z is increased and electrons are added, is pre-determined. This order is indicated in Fig. 26. The diagram is slightly over-simplified; in fact one 5d electron is found in lanthanum before the 4f orbitals begin to fill, and there are one or more 6d electrons in actinium (and possibly in Th and Pa) before any 5f. Fig. 27 gives a more detailed picture of the building-up process, but again the order is not adhered to strictly. A chromium atom in its ground state has five 3d electrons and only one 4s, and a copper atom has ten 3d electrons and only one 4s, a half-filled or completely filled subsidiary shell, that is a set of equivalent orbitals, giving a particularly stable state.

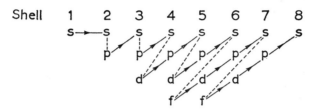

Fig. 26. Order of filling orbitals.

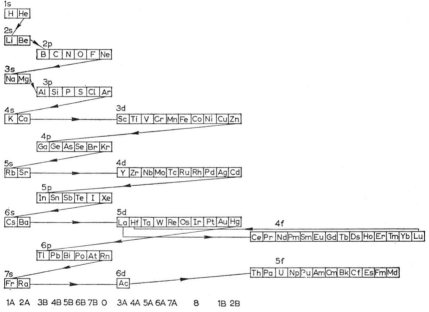

Fig. 27. The 'Aufbau' principle.

Various types of structure can be distinguished:

(i) In the inert gases He, Ne, A, Kr, Xe, Rn all the sets of p, d, f orbitals which occur are filled to capacity, radon for example having the structure

$$1s^2 \, 2s^2 \, 2p^6 \, 3s^2 \, 3p^6 \, 3d^{10} \, 4s^2 \, 4p^6 \, 4d^{10} \, 4f^{14} \, 5s^2 \, 5p^6 \, 5d^{10} \, 6s^2 \, 6p^6.$$

The $ns^2 \, np^6$ arrangement is common to all the inert gases except helium and confers particularly great stability on the atom. Such atoms have spherically symmetrical electron distributions and ^{1}S ground states.

(ii) The 'representative' elements of Gps. IA, IIA and Gps. IIIB to VIIB have atoms in which singly occupied orbitals are confined to the outermost shell. All the underlying levels are filled to capacity. This type includes all the non-metals.

(iii) In the transition elements of Gps. IIIA to VIII, the hitherto empty d orbitals of an inner shell begin to fill. These elements would be expected to have an outer electronic structure ranging from $(n-1)\mathrm{d}ns^2$ to $(n-1)\mathrm{d}^9ns^2$, but there is not a rigid adherence to ns^2. Chromium and copper, already mentioned, and gold have reasonably stable ns^1 states. These also occur in the second transition series; zirconium has $4\mathrm{d}^2\,5s^2$ but its successor niobium has $4\mathrm{d}^4\,5s^1$, and after that the d orbitals continue to fill up to ruthenium with $4\mathrm{d}^8\,5s^1$. Palladium differs from the rest in having no electron in the 5s level. The third transition series is regular, though it is interrupted between La and Hf by the development, within it, of an inner transition series—the lanthanides.

(iv) Inner transition elements, the lanthanides and actinides, contain not only unfilled d orbitals, but unfilled f orbitals as well, the latter filling as the two series develop (Table 6).

TABLE 6

58 Ce	$4f^2$	$5s^2$	$5p^6$		$6s^2$
59 Pr	$4f^3$	$5s^2$	$5p^6$		$6s^2$
	4f shell filling up to Yb				
70 Yb	$4f^{14}$	$5s^2$	$5p^6$		$6s^2$
71 Lu	$4f^{14}$	$5s^2$	$5p^6$	$5d^1$	$6s^2$

Again, configurations in which all orbitals of an equivalent set are either singly or doubly occupied are particularly stable. Thus the $4f^7$ and $4f^{14}$ shells in Eu and Yb tend to persist in the elements which follow them, for instance Gd has $4f^7\,5d^1$ rather than $4f^8$. The similarity of the configurations of the outermost energy levels causes the transition elements, and particularly the inner transition elements, to have very similar properties.

Electron configurations of the elements

Ground states of the free atoms

Atomic No.	Element	K	L		M			N			
		1s	2s	2p	3s	3p	3d	4s	4p	4d	4f
1	H	1									
2	He	2									
3	Li	2	1								
4	Be	2	2								
5	B	2	2	1							
6	C	2	2	2							
7	N	2	2	3							
8	O	2	2	4							
9	F	2	2	5							
10	Ne	2	2	6							
11	Na	2	2	6	1						
12	Mg	2	2	6	2						
13	Al	2	2	6	2	1					
14	Si	2	2	6	2	2					
15	P	2	2	6	2	3					
16	S	2	2	6	2	4					
17	Cl	2	2	6	2	5					
18	Ar	2	2	6	2	6					
19	K	2	2	6	2	6		1			
20	Ca	2	2	6	2	6		2			
21	Sc	2	2	6	2	6	1	2			
22	Ti	2	2	6	2	6	2	2			
23	V	2	2	6	2	6	3	2			
24	Cr	2	2	6	2	6	5	1			
25	Mn	2	2	6	2	6	5	2			
26	Fe	2	2	6	2	6	6	2			
27	Co	2	2	6	2	6	7	2			
28	Ni	2	2	6	2	6	8	2			
29	Cu	2	2	6	2	6	10	1			
30	Zn	2	2	6	2	6	10	2			
31	Ga	2	2	6	2	6	10	2	1		
32	Ge	2	2	6	2	6	10	2	2		
33	As	2	2	6	2	6	10	2	3		
34	Se	2	2	6	2	6	10	2	4		
35	Br	2	2	6	2	6	10	2	5		
36	Kr	2	2	6	2	6	10	2	6		
		2	8		18						

(continued)

Electron configurations of the elements *(continued)*
Ground states of the free atoms

Atomic No.	Element	K	L	M	N				O				P
					4s	4p	4d	4f	5s	5p	5d	5f	6s
37	Rb	2	8	18	2	6			1				
38	Sr	2	8	18	2	6			2				
39	Y	2	8	18	2	6	1		2				
40	Zr	2	8	18	2	6	2		2				
41	Nb	2	8	18	2	6	4		1				
42	Mo	2	8	18	2	6	5		1				
43	Tc	2	8	18	2	6	6		1				
44	Ru	2	8	18	2	6	7		1				
45	Rh	2	8	18	2	6	8		1				
46	Pd	2	8	18	2	6	10						
47	Ag	2	8	18	2	6	10		1				
48	Cd	2	8	18	2	6	10		2				
49	In	2	8	18	2	6	10		2	1			
50	Sn	2	8	18	2	6	10		2	2			
51	Sb	2	8	18	2	6	10		2	3			
52	Te	2	8	18	2	6	10		2	4			
53	I	2	8	18	2	6	10		2	5			
54	Xe	2	8	18	2	6	10		2	6			
55	Cs	2	8	18	2	6	10		2	6			1
56	Ba	2	8	18	2	6	10		2	6			2
57	La	2	8	18	2	6	10		2	6	1		2
58	Ce	2	8	18	2	6	10	1	2	6	1		2
59	Pr	2	8	18	2	6	10	2	2	6	1		2
60	Nd	2	8	18	2	6	10	3	2	6	1		2
61	Pm	2	8	18	2	6	10	4	2	6	1		2
62	Sm	2	8	18	2	6	10	5	2	6	1		2
63	Eu	2	8	18	2	6	10	6	2	6	1		2
64	Gd	2	8	18	2	6	10	7	2	6	1		2
65	Tb	2	8	18	2	6	10	8	2	6	1		2
66	Dy	2	8	18	2	6	10	9	2	6	1		2
67	Ho	2	8	18	2	6	10	10	2	6	1		2
68	Er	2	8	18	2	6	10	11	2	6	1		2
69	Tm	2	8	18	2	6	10	12	2	6	1		2
70	Yb	2	8	18	2	6	10	13	2	6	1		2
71	Lu	2	8	18	2	6	10	14	2	6	1		2

32

Electron configurations of the elements *(continued)*

Ground states of the free atoms

Atomic No.	Element	K	L	M	N	O				P			Q
						5s	5p	5d	5f	6s	6p	6d	7s
72	Hf	2	8	18	32	2	6	2		2			
73	Ta	2	8	18	32	2	6	3		2			
74	W	2	8	18	32	2	6	4		2			
75	Re	2	8	18	32	2	6	5		2			
76	Os	2	8	18	32	2	6	6		2			
77	Ir	2	8	18	32	2	6	9					
78	Pt	2	8	18	32	2	6	9		1			
79	Au	2	8	18	32	2	6	10		1			
80	Hg	2	8	18	32	2	6	10		2			
81	Tl	2	8	18	32	2	6	10		2	1		
82	Pb	2	8	18	32	2	6	10		2	2		
83	Bi	2	8	18	32	2	6	10		2	3		
84	Po	2	8	18	32	2	6	10		2	4		
85	At	2	8	18	32	2	6	10		2	5		
86	Rn	2	8	18	32	2	6	10		2	6		
87	Fr	2	8	18	32	2	6	10		2	6		1
88	Ra	2	8	18	32	2	6	10		2	6		2
89	Ac	2	8	18	32	2	6	10		2	6	1	2
90	Th	2	8	18	32	2	6	10		2	6	2	2
91	Pa	2	8	18	32	2	6	10	2	2	6	1	2
92	U	2	8	18	32	2	6	10	3	2	6	1	2
93	Np	2	8	18	32	2	6	10	4	2	6	1	2
94	Pu	2	8	18	32	2	6	10	6	2	6		2
95	Am	2	8	18	32	2	6	10	7	2	6		2
96	Cm	2	8	18	32	2	6	10	7	2	6	1	2
97	Bk	2	8	18	32	2	6	10	9	2	6		2
98	Cf	2	8	18	32	2	6	10	10	2	6		2

The Periodic Classification

The above considerations give rise to the Periodic Law, established empirically by Mendeleev, and determine the modern form of the Periodic Table (Table 7).

TABLE 7

THE PERIODIC TABLE

The First Two Periods							
s orbitals filling		p orbitals filling					
1	2	3	4	5	6	7	0
H						(H)	He
Li	Be	B	C	N	O	F	Ne
Na	Mg	Al	Si	P	S	Cl	Ar

All the Periods																	
		d orbitals filling										p orbitals filling					
1A	2A	3A	4A	5A	6A	7A	8	8	8	1B	2B	3B	4B	5B	6B	7B	0
H																(H)	He
Li	Be											B	C	N	O	F	Ne
Na	Mg											Al	Si	P	S	Cl	Ar
K	Ca	Sc	Ti	V	Cr	Mn	Fe	Co	Ni	Cu	Zn	Ga	Ge	As	Se	Br	Kr
Rb	Sr	Y	Zr	Nb	Mo	Tc	Ru	Rh	Pd	Ag	Cd	In	Sn	Sb	Te	I	Xe
Cs	Ba	La*	Hf	Ta	W	Re	Os	Ir	Pt	Au	Hg	Tl	Pb	Bi	Po	At	Rn
Fr	Ra	Ac†															

* Lanthanides Ce Pr Nd Pm Sm Eu Gd Tb Dy Ho Er Tm Yb Lu
† Actinides   Th Pa U Np Pu Am Cm Bk Cf Es Fm Md No Lr

This particular tabulation of the elements is one of the many proposed, all of which possess advantages and disadvantages. The form affords quick reference to the groups and periods; it also shows the transition elements in their true relation to the rest. Hydrogen and helium are obviously different from all the other elements in that there are no p orbitals in the $n = 1$ shell. They are also analogous to F and Ne and, by reason of their chemical properties, H is allotted to both Gp. 1 and Gp. 7, and He to Gp. 0. Except for La and Ac the lanthanides and actinides are shown separately.

It is assumed that the use of the Periodic Table as a basis of study of the properties of the elements is understood. Its value for this purpose stems from the fact that atoms with similar electron configurations lie in the same columns. For example, excluding completely filled inner shells, the configurations of the atoms C, Si, Ge, Sn, Pb are $2p^2$, $3p^2$, $4p^2$, $5p^2$ and $6p^2$ respectively: all the elements have the same spectroscopic ground state as carbon, namely ^3P, and the similarity of their outermost structure is responsible for a family relationship in chemical properties.

Atomic radii

The nature of the electron cloud about the nucleus makes it difficult to define the size of an atom. However, the distance between a nucleus and its nearest neighbour is a precisely measurable quantity. Internuclear distances in solids and bond lengths in molecules can be determined by a variety of methods such as X-ray or electron diffraction and band spectroscopy. Inter-nuclear distances in solids depend to some extent on the way the atoms are packed. In diamond, however, the C—C distance (1.542 Å) is very nearly the same as it is in a saturated hydrocarbon (1.52 to 1.55 Å). In unsaturated hydrocarbons the C—C bonds are shorter and evidently indicate a different type of linkage. The atomic radius, or covalent radius, of carbon for tetrahedral bonding is thus 0.77 Å. In silicon the Si—Si distance is 2.34 Å, indicating a covalent radius of 1.17 Å. Thus the C—Si distance in a compound should be $0.77 + 1.17 = 1.94$ Å, which proves to be the measured value in tetramethyl silane, $Si(CH_3)_4$. The covalent radius of hydrogen has been determined in many compounds; the values are in H_2 0.37, CH_4 0.32, NH_3 and H_2O 0.31, HCl 0.29 Å. The radii of many non-metal atoms can be obtained in this way from covalent compounds. Pauling has observed the inter-nuclear distance in a metal to be approximately twice the covalent radius of its atoms, and values are now available for most elements.

TABLE 8

COVALENT RADII Å

Li	Be											B	C	N	O	F
1.33	0.89											0.80	0.77	0.74	0.74	0.72
Na	Mg											Al	Si	P	S	Cl
1.57	1.36											1.25	1.17	1.10	1.04	0.99

K	Ca	Sc	Ti	V	Cr	Mn	Fe	Co	Ni	Cu	Zn	Ga	Ge	As	Se	Br
2.03	1.74	1.44	1.32	1.22	1.17	1.17	1.16	1.16	1.15	1.17	1.25	1.25	1.22	1.21	1.17	1.14

Rb	Sr	Y	Zr	Nb	Mo	Tc	Ru	Rh	Pd	Ag	Cd	In	Sn	Sb	Te	I
2.16	1.91	1.61	1.45	1.34	1.29		1.24	1.25	1.28	1.34	1.41	1.50	1.41	1.41	1.37	1.33

Cs	Ba	La	Hf	Ta	W	Re	Os	Ir	Pt	Au	Hg	Tl	Pb	Bi	Po	At
2.35	1.98	1.69	1.44	1.34	1.30	1.28	1.26	1.26	1.29	1.34	1.44	1.55	1.54	1.52	1.52	

Ce	Pr	Nd	Pm	Sm	Eu	Gd	Tb	Dy	Ho	Er	Tm	Yb	Lu
1.65	1.65	1.64		1.66	1.85	1.61	1.59	1.59	1.58	1.57	1.56	1.70	1.56

Ionic radii

Bragg (1912) showed a sodium chloride crystal to consist, not of discrete molecules of NaCl, but of Na^+ ions and Cl^- ions arranged in an indefinitely extended cubic lattice (Fig. 28, exterior view; Fig. 84 on p. 138 shows co-ordination); X-ray analysis (p. 141) gave the internuclear distance as 2.81 Å. Most alkali metal halides have the same type of crystal lattice but the inter-ionic distances differ.

	KCl	3.14	NaCl	2.81	Difference	0.33 Å
	KF	2.66	NaF	2.31		0.35 Å
Difference		0.48		0.50 Å		

Such results cannot give absolute ionic sizes. Three methods are used for obtaining this information.

(i) Landé's method (1920) rests on the idea that in a lattice of mixed ions those of the element with the larger size may be considered to touch, though those of the element with a smaller size need not. MnS and MgS have the same crystal lattice (NaCl) and the same inter-ionic distance (2.594 Å). If the S^{2-} ions of radius r be assumed to touch (Fig. 29), $\sqrt{2}r = 2.59$ Å and $r = 1.84$ Å.

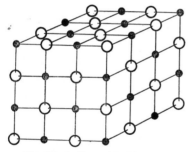

Fig. 28. Sodium chloride lattice.

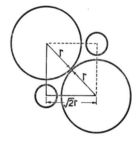

Fig. 29. Relation of anionic radius to interionic distance.

(ii) Wasastjerna's method (1922) depends on the theoretical relation, $R \propto r^3$, between the molar refractivity and ionic radius for ions of inert gas structure. Assuming ionic refractivities to be additive in aqueous solution,

$$R_{HCl} = R_{H_3O^+} + R_{Cl^-}$$

and

$$R_{NaCl} = R_{Na^+} + R_{Cl^-}.$$

On the assumption that H_3O^+ has the same molar refractivity as water, the radii of many ions have been estimated.

TABLE 9

IONIC RADII (6 CO-ORDINATION) IN Å

Charge number	−2	−1	+1	+2	+3	+4
		H 1.45	Li 0.78	Be 0.31	B 0.20	
	O 1.40	F 1.36	Na 0.98	Mg 0.65	Al 0.50	Si 0.43
	S 1.84	Cl 1.81	K 1.33	Ca 0.99	Sc 0.81	Ti 0.68
	Se 1.98	Br 1.95	Rb 1.48	Sr 1.13	Y 0.93	Zr 0.74
	Te 2.21	I 2.16	Cs 1.69	Ba 1.35	La 1.22	Ce 1.01

Charge number			+1	+2	+3	+4
			Cu 0.96	Zn 0.74	Ga 0.62	Ge 0.53
			Ag 1.26	Cd 0.97	In 0.81	Sn 0.71
			Au 1.37	Hg 1.10	Tl 0.95	Pb 0.84

(iii) Pauling (1927) used the concept of effective nuclear charge, defined as the actual charge reduced by the screening effect of electrons in the inner shells. He considered the distance between two isoelectronic ions to be divided in the inverse ratio of their effective nuclear charges. The ions K^+ and Cl^- have equal numbers of electrons ($1s^2\ 2s^2\ 2p^6\ 3s^2\ 3p^6$), but whereas in K^+ the nucleus has an excess of one unit of positive charge, in Cl^- there is an excess of one electron. Appropriate division of the K^+ —Cl^- distance (3.14 Å) gives ionic radii K^+ 1.33 Å and Cl^- 1.81 Å.

Like the atomic size, the ionic radius varies a little with the way the ions are arranged in the crystal. The figures given in Table 9 are for 6 co-ordination, as in the NaCl structure, where each ion is surrounded octahedrally by 6 others of opposite charge (Fig. 30).

As will appear later, ions with integral charges seldom exist in compounds, the binding always involving some sharing of the outer electrons. For this reason the charge numbers in Table 9 are formal in that they refer to a model

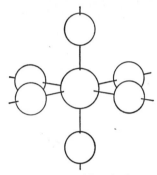

Fig. 30. Arrangement of ions in 6 co-ordination.

in which the electrons are somewhat artificially allocated. But this does not detract from the value of the table as an empirical guide.

Trends in covalent and ionic radii

An atom is larger than its cation,

Na	1.57	Na$^+$	0.98 Å
Ca	1.74	Ca^{2+}	0.99 Å,

but smaller than its anion,

O	0.74	O^{2-}	1.40 Å
Cl	0.99	Cl$^-$	1.81 Å.

When a positive ion is formed the effective nuclear charge is increased and the electron cloud is drawn in. Conversely the reduction in the effective nuclear charge in an anion allows the electron cloud to expand. For corresponding reasons a 2-positive cation is larger than a 3- or 4-positive one:

Fe^{2+}	0.75	Fe^{3+}	0.60 Å,
Pb^{2+}	1.32	Pb^{4+}	0.84 Å.

Down a column of the Periodic Table, the size of atoms and ions with comparable electronic structure increases with atomic number; the effect of the electrons added to outer orbitals outweighs the overall shrinkage due to increasing nuclear charge.

Atomic radii	Be	0.89	Mg	1.36	Ca	1.74	Sr	1.91	Ba	1.98 Å
Ionic radii	Be^{2+}	0.31	Mg^{2+}	0.65	Ca^{2+}	0.99	Sr^{2+}	1.13	Ba^{2+}	1.35 Å

Across the short periods, the size of the atom decreases with atomic number because the increase in nuclear charge is not accompanied by an increase in screening, since the electron addition takes place within the same shell. In the transition series where electrons are entering an inner d shell there is a small decrease in size. The element immediately following a transition series shows an increase in size through the screening of the nucleus by the completed d shell.

$$\text{Pd} \quad 1.28 \rightarrow \text{Ag} \; 1.34 \; \text{Å}$$
$$\text{Pt} \quad 1.29 \rightarrow \text{Au} \; 1.34 \; \text{Å}$$

In the lanthanides an increase of 14 in atomic number occurs without change in occupation of the outermost orbital, 6s, and without a comparable increase in d shell screening effect. The atomic radii fall from La (1.69) to Lu (1.56) and the ionic radii of the M^{3+} ions even more, from 1.06 to 0.85 Å. This *lanthanide contraction* affects the size of the subsequent atoms and ions in the Periodic Table.

Ionisation potentials

The energy required to withdraw an electron from an atom against the attraction of the nuclear charge is the first *ionisation energy* of the atom. (Although this is, properly speaking, an energy, expressed in eV, the term *ionisation potential* is often used for it and has been adopted in this book.) It is usually measured spectroscopically. Atomic size and ionisation potential are related, decrease in size and increase in ionisation potential both resulting from an increase in effective nuclear charge due to a reduction in screening. A small atom like lithium loses an electron less easily than a large one; the first ionisation potential of Li is 5.39 and of Rb 4.18 eV. The corresponding potentials in Gp. II A are Be 9.32 and Sr 5.69 eV, showing a similar correlation with decreasing atomic size in passing from Gp.IA to Gp.IIA. It has already been pointed out that the energy of an electron, and hence the first ionisation potential, is also affected by the extent to which the orbital of the particular electron penetrates the inner shells. Thus, the s, p and d electrons of given principal quantum number are increasingly easy to remove.

The energy required to remove a second electron from a unipositive ion is the second ionisation potential. For Gp.IIA metals it is about twice the first ionisation potential.

$$\text{Be}^+ \rightarrow \text{Be}^{2+} \quad 18.21 \; \text{eV}$$
$$\text{Sr}^+ \rightarrow \text{Sr}^{2+} \quad 10.98 \; \text{eV}$$

This is because the effective nuclear charge has been increased by the removal of the first electron. For Gp.IA elements the second ionisation potentials are very large indeed (Li 75.62, Rb 27.36 eV) on account of the difficulty of abstracting an electron from a complete shell.

The Gp. IA metals have the lowest first ionisation potentials (~ 5 eV) and the inert gases the highest (15 to 25 eV). The halogens have high values too (I ~ 10, F ~ 17 eV). Though there is a general increase along a short period from Gp. I to the inert gas, there is a drop between Gp. II and Gp. III.

Be	9.32 eV	B	8.30 eV
Mg	7.64 eV	Al	5.98 eV

This is because the p electron introduced at this point is well shielded and easy to remove once the s orbital has been filled.

For transition and inner transition elements there is little variation (7.4 $\pm$ 0.6 eV for a transition series and 5.9 $\pm$ 0.3 for the lanthanides). The metals following the lanthanides are exceptions to the general rule of decreasing ionisation potential down a group. In them the screening effect of the rather diffuse d shell is outweighed by the increasing nuclear charge; and, as in the lanthanide contraction, orbital size tends to decrease and binding energy to increase.

Ag	7.87 eV	Cd	8.99 eV
Au	9.22 eV	Hg	10.43 eV

Elements of B subgroups have higher ionisation potentials than those of the corresponding A subgroups.

K	4.34 eV	Cu	7.72 eV
Ca	6.11 eV	Zn	9.39 eV

The increased binding of the electron due to the penetration of its orbital is greater with 18 than with 8 electrons immediately beneath it, since it comes into the region of a positive charge greater by 10 units.

Electron affinities

The energy drop when an extra electron is taken up by an atom is its electron affinity. This is generally estimated indirectly by applying the Born-Haber cycle to ionic compounds (p. 92).

In the halogens, except for fluorine, the smaller the atom the greater the electron affinity and the ease of anion formation:

F 3.74, Cl 4.02, Br 3.78, I 3.44 eV.

In Gp. 6 the values for two electrons are

O -7.28 S -3.44 Se -4.21 eV.

Once an electron has been received the uninegative ion repels further electrons; hence the negative affinities displayed by oxide, sulphide and selenide 2-negative ions.

Magnetic properties

A few materials, termed *ferromagnetic*, attract a magnetic field very strongly and can themselves become magnetic, for example iron, cobalt alloys, magnetite. With these we are not further concerned here.

Other substances are *diamagnetic*, tending to move to the weakest part of a non-uniform magnetic field, or *paramagnetic*, tending to move to the strongest part (Fig. 31).

The *magnetic permeability*, μ, is the ratio of the flux (*i.e.* number of lines of force per unit cross section) in the substance to that in a vacuum. The ratio is greater than unity for a paramagnetic substance and less, but not much less, than unity for a diamagnetic one (Fig. 32).

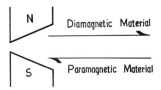

Fig. 31. Movement of diamagnetic and paramagnetic materials in a non-uniform field.

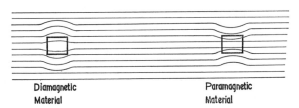

Diamagnetic Material

Paramagnetic Material

Fig. 32. Lines of force through diamagnetic and paramagnetic materials.

The *volume susceptibility*, $\varkappa$, is related to μ:

$$\mu = 1 + 4\pi\varkappa$$

A quantity $\varkappa/\varrho = \chi$, where ϱ is the density, is the *gram susceptibility*, but in magnetochemistry the most useful quantities are χ_M, χ_A and χ_I the susceptibility for molecule, atom and ion respectively. These are obtained by multiplying the gram susceptibility by the molecular or atomic weight.

The value of χ is independent of field strength. It may be found by many methods, for instance by suspending the material from a balance in a non-uniform magnetic field increasing vertically to $\sim 10^4$ oersteds, and measuring the apparent change in weight.

The fact that an electron in an orbital produces a magnetic field proportional to its angular momentum has already been discussed. The application of an external field causes, in classical language, a precession which produces a field opposed to that originally applied. This results in the negative susceptibility which characterises a diamagnetic material, though all atoms exhibit this effect. Diamagnetic susceptibility increases numerically with atomic number but is always small compared with paramagnetic susceptibilities. It is independent of temperature.

Paramagnetism, on the other hand, is restricted to certain materials; when it occurs it completely overshadows the relatively feeble diamagnetism. In general, paramagnetism arises from the presence of a permanent (*i.e.* not induced) magnetic moment associated with a state of definite angular momentum. The magnetic moment arising from total angular momentum with quantum number J may be represented pictorially by a vector of length $Jg\mu_B$, where μ_B is the Bohr magneton and g the Landé g-factor (p. 63), although, as usual, a strict analysis gives $\sqrt{J(J+1)}$ instead of J. The components of magnetic moment along the field direction can take only the values $M_J g$ ($M_J = J, J-1, \ldots -J$) and when the field strength is H these $(2J+1)$ energy levels are separated by intervals $g\mu_B H$.

For atoms in S states, $L = 0$, $J = S$, and therefore $g = 2$; but in all other states $g < 2$. Consequently observed g values indicate whether the paramagnetic moment arises from both orbital and spin momentum or from spin only. In the latter instance, observation of the maximum J arising from a given electron configuration indicates the number, N, of unpaired spins, $J_{\max} = S_{\max} = \frac{1}{2} N$.

Since the magnetic moment of an assembly of atoms depends on statistical averaging over all possible z components, thermal agitation opposing regular orientation, the relationship between μ and the observed quantity χ_A must involve the temperature. For $\mu H \ll kT$, it can be shown that $\chi_A \propto 1/T$ (Curie's law) and that $\mu = 2.839 \sqrt{\chi_A T}$. More accurately $\chi_A \propto 1/(T - \theta)$, a result due to Weiss, where θ is the *Curie temperature* and is small for most paramagnetics. When other small effects are taken into account (*e.g.* the small opposing diamagnetism) magnetic moments determined in this way agree well with those inferred from spectroscopy.

There are three principal types of paramagnetic ion.

(i) The rare earths, in which the separation between states with different J values is large compared with kT (strong L-S coupling). For these ions

$$\mu = g \sqrt{J(J+1)} \quad \text{(in Bohr magnetons)}.$$

(ii) The iron group, in which the orbital contribution to the magnetic moment is 'quenched', owing to the destruction of spherical symmetry by the strong field of neighbouring ions. This occurs only when the unpaired electrons occupy the outermost orbitals. The moment is calculated from the 'spin-only' formula with n singly occupied orbitals:

$$\mu = \sqrt{4S(S + 1)} = \sqrt{n(n + 2)}.$$

Thus for the Fe^{3+} ion, with a $3d^5$ configuration, $\mu = \sqrt{5(5 + 2)} = 5.9$ Bohr magnetons in agreement with experiment.

(iii) Ions in which the separation of states with different J values is small compared with kT (weak L-S couplings). Here the orbital contribution is not quenched but is 'uncoupled' from the spin so that a resultant J does not occur. The resultant moment is

$$\mu = \sqrt{4S(S + 1) + L(L + 1)}.$$

The 2-positive ions Co^{2+} and Fe^{2+} are of this type and the good agreement with experiment confirms that orbital angular momentum contributes to the permanent moment.

Finally, it must be stressed that Hund's rules (and indeed the whole L-S coupling picture) do not generally apply well to heavy atoms. However, magnetic measurements confirm their approximate validity in the transition series Sc to Fe. The occupation of the 3d and 4s orbitals is indicated in the following scheme:

To summarise, magnetic measurements confirm and supplement spectroscopic data on the electronic configuration of atoms and ions, particularly in regard to the occupation of the outermost orbitals upon which valency depends.

Chapter 5

Valency

Nature and Classification of Chemical Bonding

Introduction

In principle, the existence of stable compounds could be predicted by solving the wave equation for systems of nuclei (masses M_1, M_2, ...) and electrons (mass m). Solutions would occur for certain most probable nuclear configurations, and would correspond to lower energy values than when the systems were separated into neutral atoms at rest. This has never been attempted. Fortunately it is not necessary because the large mass ratio (usually $> 10,000:1$) of nuclei and electrons makes it permissible to discuss separately the electron distribution and the relatively sluggish motion of the nuclei. To an exceedingly good approximation, the nuclei may be regarded as moving in a 'cloud' of electrons whose distribution is determined by a wave function depending on the instantaneous positions of the nuclei. This general picture is adopted universally in the electronic interpretation of valency, the stability of different configurations being discussed as though the nuclei were at rest. Another guiding principle of great value was derived theoretically by Feynman and Hellmann (1939). It states that the forces which hold together the positive nuclei in a molecule or crystal are just those which they would experience if they were embedded in a static distribution of negative charge of density P, $P(x, y, z)$ being the probability density for finding an electron at the point x, y, z.

This principle at once provides immediate physical insight into the nature of bonding and its classification, and emphasises the similarity rather than the diversity of different bond types. Briefly, all bonds can be interpreted electrostatically in terms of a charge cloud, provided this is determined wave-mechanically rather than classically. Usually, the form of the charge cloud is inferred from experimental, intuitive and theoretical considerations.

When internuclear distances are large, every nucleus has its normal complement of electrons fairly tightly localised about it. At molecular distances, the inner shells remain so, but the outermost electrons are affected in varying degrees, ranging from a slight distortion of their orbitals to a redistribution by transfer from one atom to another. The following types of bond may be broadly distinguished: *ionic* (or *electrovalent*); *covalent* (or *electron-pair*); *non-localised* and *metallic*; *Van der Waals* and *long-range*.

The ionic or electrovalent bond

This is the limiting case in which the electron distribution goes over almost completely into one describing a set of *ions*, Fig. 33(a). Classical ionic theory, in which the ions are regarded as charged spheres, is then fairly satisfactory. Such binding occurs only when an atom loses electrons easily (low ionisation potential) and another accepts electrons readily (positive electron affinity). If carbon could achieve quadrivalency by losing four electrons in this way, so as to be able to hold four singly charged anions, the ionisation would require about 150 eV. Accordingly carbon does not form ionic bonds. As, on the other hand, only about 1 eV is required to transfer an electron from a sodium to a fluorine atom, this expenditure of energy is more than offset by the resultant electrical forces which lead to a strong attraction and a net energy decrease, giving an ionic bond.

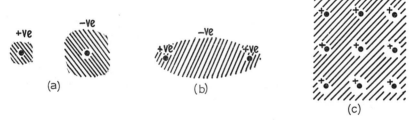

Fig. 33. (a) Ionic. (Electron transferred from one atom to another.)
 (b) Covalent. (One electron from each atom in the 'bond region'.)
 (c) Metallic. (One or more electrons from each atom in a common 'pool'.)

The covalent or electron-pair bond

Bonding of this kind entails a 'sharing' of the outermost electrons of the bonded atoms, Fig. 33(b). Two electrons are associated with every such bond, and the electron density shows a considerable 'piling up' of charge in the bond region. In a normal covalent bond, one electron is supplied by each atom; but sometimes one atom is able to provide both electrons, and then the bond is frequently called *dative* or *co-ordinate*, the atoms which it unites being distinguished as *donor* and *acceptor*. Though often for convenience this is indicated by → instead of — between donor and acceptor atoms, dative bonds are essentially similar to normal covalent bonds; in both the two electrons are most likely to be found between the nuclei. The binding forces consist of attractions between the individual positive ions and the negative charge cloud in the bond, rather than between one positive and one negative ion.

Non-localised and metallic bonds

In metals, and also in many organic molecules, some or all of the valency electrons may form a fairly uniform 'sea', spreading about all the positive ions instead of falling into localised electron-pair bonds, Fig. 33(c). It is the essentially non-localised nature of the charge distribution which is responsible for electrical conductivity and other typically metallic properties whenever these appear.

Van der Waals and long-range bonds

When two atoms approach there is a weak attraction between them long before their electron clouds overlap appreciably. This is a manifestation of various effects: the *electrostatic interaction* between their separate charge distributions; the mutual *polarisation*, each charge cloud inducing slight changes in the other; and the so-called *dispersion forces*, which arise from *correlation* of the electronic motions on the two atoms and resemble the forces between rapidly varying electric dipoles. These various forces are always relatively weak and are masked at the internuclear distances found in compounds by strong covalent or repulsive forces. But they give rise to the Van der Waals attraction between atoms or molecules in a gas, and also to weak binding between well-separated units in a crystal, for example that between adjacent layer planes in graphite (where the C—C distance is ~ 3.8 Å instead of the normal 1.42 Å). It is now widely believed that the *hydrogen bond*, for instance in ice, between a hydrogen atom in one molecule and the oxygen in another (in which the O—H distance is ~ 1.8 Å instead of the normal ~ 1.0 Å) is also predominantly of this type (p. 232).

Although the above classification of bonding is very useful, it must be stressed that it is not rigid and that there is a continuous gradation from one type to another. To understand this, it is necessary to examine the electronic description in more detail.

Electronic Theory of Bonding

The Aufbau approach

The simplest of all molecules is the ion H_2^+ since it possesses two nuclei and but one electron. If orbitals can be found to describe the states of the one electron in a two-centre field of this kind, it should be possible to develop an aufbau theory of diatomic molecules, exactly as in the one-centre instance (p. 57). And there is no reason why this should not be extended to a many-centre example. The one-electron orbitals, which extend over all nuclei, are called *molecular orbitals*; or in the case of a crystal, *crystal* or *Bloch* orbitals (after Bloch who first used them). In the aufbau approach, the available molecular orbitals are filled in ascending energy order and the resultant electron density is, in this approximation, again just a sum of the orbital contributions. And again, as in the Hartree method, the picture will be a good one when each orbital is chosen so as to take account of the various nuclear charges, the screening effect of electrons in inner orbitals, and the average disposition of electrons in the other molecular orbitals.

Forms of molecular orbitals

In 1927 Burrau determined accurately the molecular orbital of lowest energy for the system H_2^+ and found, by considering a range of internuclear distances, that at 1.06 Å there was an energy minimum 2.777 eV lower than that of a system comprising a normal H atom and a distant proton. This bond length and the theoretical dissociation energy agree excellently with spectroscopic values. The electron density calculated by Burrau is indicated in Fig. 34; it clearly substantiates the Feynman-Hellman principle by showing a considerable piling up of charge in the bond region. Burrau's results form the true starting point of an aufbau theory of molecular structure. They were, however, almost immediately overshadowed by those of Heitler and London, who considered the normal hydrogen molecule and later developed a general theory of two-electron bonds so closely in accord with the accepted ideas of G. N. Lewis (1916) that it won universal popularity. It was not for some time that the relationship between the two approaches was appreciated.

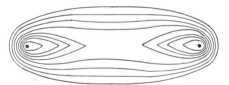

Fig. 34. Electron density in H_2^+ (after Burrau).

Since accurate calculations are not usually feasible, it is necessary to find means of securing fair approximations to *molecular orbitals* and of estimating their relative energies. The simplest way is to build them up out of *atomic orbitals*, taking

$$\psi = c_1\varphi_1 + c_2\varphi_2 + c_3\varphi_3 + \ldots.$$

where the φ's are suitable atomic orbitals put together with numerical coefficients $c_1, c_2, \ldots$ This is called the *linear combination of atomic orbitals* approximation. Using abbreviations, we employ an LCAO approximation to the MO's. Returning to H_2^+, an approximate MO would be $\psi = c_a\varphi_a + c_b\varphi_b$, where φ_a and φ_b are 1s orbitals on the nuclei a and b. Since the AO's fall off exponentially, ψ at a point near nucleus a will be essentially $c_a\varphi_a$, that is a solution of the wave equation for an electron of atom a. In the same way ψ behaves correctly when the electron is near b. It remains to determine the values of c_a and c_b in order to get as good an approximation of this form as possible. There are standard mathematical methods for this, which give sets of coefficients and energies, not only for the lowest state, but for as many states as there are AO's. Here, however, where the two centres are identical, $P = \psi^2$ is symmetrical which means that $c_a = \pm c_b$. The two solutions are then

$$\psi_1 = N_1(\varphi_a + \varphi_b) \quad \text{and} \quad \psi_2 = N_2(\varphi_a - \varphi_b),$$

where the constants N_1 and N_2 are chosen so that the functions are correctly normalised (p. 48). The shapes of these MO's are indicated in Fig. 35, and it is clear that ψ_1 must approximate to Burrau's ground state solution and ψ_2 represents an excited state. In fact ψ_1, in error by only a few percent, still suffices to predict a stable molecule; but the excited state, giving repulsion at all internuclear distances, indicates spontaneous dissociation. The two MO's are described as *bonding* and *anti-bonding* partners; they are designated by $\sigma 1s$ and σ^*1s, being built out of $1s$ AO's, where σ indicates their symmetry about the molecular axis and the asterisk distinguishes the anti-bonding from the bonding MO.

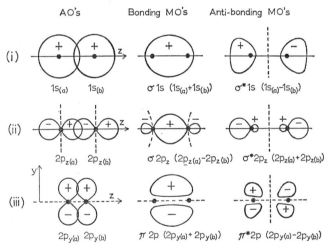

Fig. 35. Molecular orbitals in LCAO approximation (nodes indicated by broken lines)

As with AO's, the set of solutions of the *two*-centre wave equation is infinite; $\sigma 1s$ and σ^*1s are the two of lowest energy. Some of the solutions would lead to certain MO's with more than one node across the bond, others with nodal planes through both nuclei, and so on. The main features of all these MO's can be quite well reproduced in LCAO approximation, as is indicated schematically in Fig. 35, where the names of the orbitals are also given. The symmetry of an MO is specified by the number of nodal planes containing the molecular axis. The types with 0, 1, 2, ... such planes are designated by σ, π, δ, ... by analogy with the AO notation s, p, d, ... Again, these numbers correspond to quantised values of the angular momentum—momentum around the molecular axis—$\lambda(h/2\pi)$, where $\lambda = 0, \pm 1, \pm 2, \ldots$. Orbitals other than those of σ type thus occur in degenerate pairs, corresponding to circulation in one sense or the other; and MO's such as $\pi 2p_x$ and $\pi 2p_y$ are mixtures of equal parts of those representing states of definite angular momentum ($\lambda = \pm 1$), and are the counterparts of the AO's $2p_x$ and $2p_y$ which were adopted in place of $2p_{+1}$ and $2p_{-1}$ (p. 54). There is thus a close similarity throughout with the classification of AO's though this extends only to linear molecules. The LCAO MO method can in fact be applied to any polyatomic molecule or crystal.

Nature of the two-electron bond

The two lowest energy MO's of a homonuclear diatomic molecule are $\sigma 1s$ and $\sigma^* 1s$. According to the aufbau approach, the electronic configuration of the normal molecule H_2 would be written $H[(\sigma 1s)^2]$. The charge cloud would be very similar to that in H_2^+, only twice as dense and, by exerting a correspondingly greater attraction upon the nuclei, would lead to a shorter and stronger bond. But, on the other hand, further addition of electrons would weaken the bond. Thus the hypothetical molecule He_2 would have the structure $He[(\sigma 1s)^2(\sigma^* 1s)^2]$ and the bonding effect of the $\sigma 1s$ electrons would be offset by the anti-bonding effect of the others. If the charge clouds (cf. Fig. 35) are superimposed, it turns out that there is no accumulation of charge in the bond region, the final density being roughly that of two unmodified helium atoms. More precisely, there is a slight repulsion which grows rapidly when the closed shells are pushed together. The saturation property of chemical binding is thus immediately interpreted: an atom with one or more *singly* occupied orbitals has a corresponding number of valencies, but one with only *doubly* occupied orbitals is inert.

Nearly all strong chemical bonds are *two-electron bonds*, and in the aufbau picture both electrons occupy a bonding MO whose antibonding partner is empty. All two-electron bonds can be explained in this way, but their characters and strengths vary widely according to the form of the charge density. The bonding MO, whatever its type, gives a density contribution

$$\psi^2 = c_a^2 \varphi_a^2 + c_b^2 \varphi_b^2 + 2c_a c_b \varphi_a \varphi_b,$$

where the first two terms are AO charge clouds with 'weight factors' c_a^2 and c_b^2. The third term is best described as an overlap density, since it can be large only in the 'overlap region' between the atoms where both φ_a and φ_b are large. Now when c_a and c_b are roughly equal (they are exactly so for all homonuclear systems) the charge will spread more or less evenly over the two atoms and the binding will arise mainly from the attraction exerted by the overlap density between them. This density depends jointly on the *amount* of charge described by the overlap function $\varphi_a\varphi_b$ and upon its weight factor $2c_ac_b$; the amount is clearly greater the greater the overlap of the AO's, but the weight-factor (fixed so that ψ is normalised) is not very sensitive to overlap. Consequently, in a 'homopolar' situation ($c_a \simeq c_b$), the strength of a bond involving two given AO's is determined largely by their overlap, the larger the overlap the stronger the bond. This conclusion, embodied in the *principle of maximum overlap*, is corroborated by a great weight of chemical evidence. When, however, the bonded atoms have very different electron affinities, c_a and c_b may be of different orders of magnitude, describing the much greater chance of finding an electron on one nucleus rather than on the other. The change of bond type can be seen from the limiting case $c_a \to 1$, $c_b \to 0$: for then the MO degenerates into an AO φ_a and this acquires both electrons of the two-electron bond; the overlap density of the covalent bond disappears and the charge cloud becomes that of two oppositely charged ions. There is clearly a perfectly smooth transition from covalent to ionic binding, the amount of ionic character being reflected in the disparity between the MO coefficients and in a 'lopsided' bond orbital.

To summarise: two-electron bonds occur when the singly occupied AO's of different atoms overlap in pairs; these bonds are strong when the overlap is large. The combination of AO's which are doubly occupied, or which overlap only weakly, need not in general be considered. The bonding MO's lean towards the more electronegative atom, approaching the form of an AO of that atom in extreme cases.

These principles, as will be seen later, apply with little modification to polyatomic molecules and crystals, the only difference being that strong overlapping is not confined to *one pair* of AO's.

Heitler-London theory

Although the aufbau approach of MO theory is adequate in all that follows, it may be useful for the sake of completeness to mention the rather more complicated method developed by Heitler, London, Slater, Pauling and others, and to stress that the two theories do not conflict. Both lead to approximations to the same charge density; the difference is superficial and the same Feynman-Hellman interpretation applies in each case. To appreciate this, it is sufficient to consider the molecule H_2. From the MO standpoint, the full two-electron wave function would be the product

$$\Psi(1, 2) = N^2 [\varphi_a(1) + \varphi_b(1)] [\varphi_a(2) + \varphi_b(2)],$$

i.e. $\Psi(1, 2) = N^2 [\varphi_a(1)\varphi_a(2) + \varphi_b(1)\varphi_b(2) + \varphi_a(1)\varphi_b(2) + \varphi_a(2)\varphi_b(1)].$

Every one of the four products represents an AO configuration. The first describes both electrons on nucleus a; the second, both on nucleus b; and the two others, one electron on each of a and b. The first two terms describe ionic situations and might be expected to occur in a more accurately derived wave function with only very little weight. Heitler and London simply used the function in which they were missing altogether, namely

$$\Psi(1, 2) = N' [\varphi_a(1)\varphi_b(2) + \varphi_a(2)\varphi_b(1)]$$

which is not just a simple product but a mixture of two AO products in which the electrons have changed places. When electron spin is taken into account, this function must be supplemented by a spin factor (exactly as in the atomic case). The wave function will be properly antisymmetric (p. 58) when the spin factor is itself antisymmetrical, the orbital part clearly being symmetrical in 1 and 2. This wave function, which describes anti-parallel or *paired* spins, is often referred to as an *electron-pair* or *paired-spin* function: but this does not imply that the binding arises from non-classical forces associated with the spins. What is important, is to recognise that the paired-spin function can go only with a *symmetric* orbital function, and that this always leads to the high internuclear charge density characteristic of a covalent bond. The charge density is, in fact, identical in form with that given by the MO method, differing only in the numerical values of the weight factors.

Another common source of confusion arises from the use of the term 'exchange energy' to describe the energy decrease resulting from the mixing of terms with 'exchanged' electrons. It is often wrongly stated that this has no classical interpretation; it does, in fact, contain the usual electrostatic energy of nuclei and charge cloud. A more non-committal and less misleading term for binding energy of this kind might be 'overlap energy', since it occurs in both theories whenever electron density appears in the region of overlap of two AO's. It should now be clear that, for descriptive purposes, it is quite immaterial which theory is applied: a covalent bond is simply associated with two overlapping AO's which together contribute two electrons whose probability density then contains a substantial overlap term.

The Ionic Bond

Energy changes in the formation of ionic bonds

Suppose that the electronegativities of two atoms a and b are so different that the singly occupied AO's φ_a and φ_b give a bonding MO which is almost purely φ_a. The electron configuration in the molecule then contains φ_a^2 instead of $\varphi_a^1\varphi_b^1$. A typical ionic bond arising in this way is indicated in Fig. 36. The binding force in these circumstances comes predominantly from the attraction of oppositely charged ions, whose outer orbitals are all doubly occupied. The equilibrium position occurs when these filled orbitals begin to interpenetrate, the situation then resembling that in a hypothetical molecule such as He_2 (p. 85). The repulsive force which arises is of short

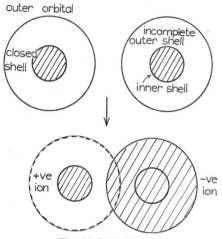

Fig. 36. Ionic binding.

range, corresponding to a potential energy which can be represented fairly well by a term $a\exp(-r/\varrho)$, where ϱ and a are suitably chosen constants. Because when one atom loses z_1 electrons and the other gains z_2 the Coulomb potential energy is $-z_1z_2e^2/r$, the net interaction energy of the two ions at distance r is

$$E_{int} = -z_1z_2e^2/r + a\exp(-r/\varrho).$$

To take a specific example: the energy of formation from free atoms of the bond in $Na^+ - Cl^-$ is

$$\Delta E = (E_{Na^+} + E_{Cl^-} + E_{int}) - (E_{Na} + E_{Cl}),$$

and, since $E_{Na^+} - E_{Na} = I_{Na}$ (ionisation potential) and $E_{Cl} - E_{Cl^-} = A_{Cl}$ (electron affinity), the energy *decrease* (energy of formation) is

$$-\Delta E = (A_{Cl} - I_{Na}) + e^2/r - a\exp(-r/\varrho).$$

If this is positive, binding occurs. In an ionic crystal the interaction energy is *lattice energy* which involves geometrical factors, but the energy change is still of the form $E_{ionisation} + E_{interaction}$.

Factors determining the formation of ions

A simple anion is formed when a non-metal accepts one or two electrons:

$$X \rightarrow X^- \quad (X = H, F, Cl, Br, I),$$
$$X \rightarrow X^{2-} \quad (X = O, S, Se).$$

Anions formed from single atoms all have the inert gas structures $1s^2$ or np^6. On the other hand, cations are formed when a metal loses one, two, three or even four electrons. Various electron configurations occur (see Table 10).

TABLE 10

CONFIGURATIONS OF CATIONS

Kinds of ion				Electron configuration (term in brackets indicates an inert gas inner shell)				
(i) No electrons	H^+							
(ii) Two electrons	Li^+,	Be^{2+}		$1s^2$				He type
(iii) '8-electron' structures	Na^+,	Mg^{2+},	Al^{3+}	$1s^2$	$2s^2$	$2p^6$		Ne type
	K^+,	Ca^{2+},	Sc^{3+}	(Ne)	$3s^2$	$3p^6$		Ar type
(iv) '18-electron' structures	Rb^+, Sr^{2+},	Y^{3+},	Zr^{4+}	(Ar)	$3d^{10}$	$4s^2$	$4p^6$	Kr type
	Cs^+, Ba^{2+},	La^{3+},	Ce^{4+}	(Kr)	$4d^{10}$	$5s^2$	$5p^6$	Xe type
	Cu^+,	Zn^{2+},	Ga^{3+}	(Ar)	$3d^{10}$			
	Ag^+,	Cd^{2+},	In^{3+}	(Kr)	$4d^{10}$			
	Au^+,	Hg^{2+},	Tl^{3+}	(Xe)	$5d^{10}$			
(v) 'Inert pair' structures	In^+,	Sn^{2+},	Sb^{3+}	(Kr)	$4d^{10}$	$5s^2$		
	Tl^+,	Pb^{2+},	Bi^{3+}	(Xe)	$5d^{10}$	$6s^2$		
(vi) Transition ions	V^{3+}			(Ar)	$3d^2$			
	Fe^{3+}			(Ar)	$3d^5$			
	Fe^{2+}			(Ar)	$3d^6$			
	Ni^{2+}			(Ar)	$3d^8$			

Anions and cations are both stable when they have a closed shell (or sub-shell, e.g., nd^{10}) of electrons, as is expected since the electrons outside such a shell are heavily screened from the nuclear charge and therefore loosely bound. Moreover, as the effective nuclear charge upon the outer electrons is increased by the removal of electrons and decreased by their addition, successive ionisations become increasingly difficult. Finally, there is a correlation between size of an atom and ease of ionisation. Again, this would be expected because both depend on the attraction exerted upon the outer electrons. The situation may be represented as in Fig. 37.

Small atom, strongly bound electrons, tightly localised orbitals.
Large ionisation energy (I) (difficult to form +ve ion); large electron affinity (easy to form −ve ion)

Large atom, weakly bound electrons, diffuse orbitals. Small ionisation energy (I) (easy to form +ve
ion); small electron affinity (difficult to form −ve ion)

Fig. 37. Orbital energies.

To summarise: the conversion of atom to ion is easiest when
(i) the ion has a stable electron configuration (*e.g.* closed shell);
(ii) the charge on the ion is small;
(iii) the atom from which it is derived is large for a cation and small for an
anion.

These are Fajans rules (1924); they were originally empirical deductions.

Of the various types of cation, those with the inert gas structure are by far
the most stable. They do not show appreciable tendency to share their
electrons with other atoms or ions. Cations with the '18-electron' configuration are moderately stable, although the Cu^+ ion can lose a second
electron to form Cu^{2+}, a transition type of coloured ion with $3s^2\ 3p^6\ 3d^9$
structure. But the $3d^{10}$ group is stabilised by an increase of nuclear charge,
and the further ionisation of zinc from Zn^{2+} to Zn^{3+} does not occur. The unexpected, though not great, stability of the 'inert pair' structures is due to
the outer s electrons penetrating the rather diffuse 18-electron shell immediately beneath them. The effect increases with higher shells; thus the ions of
the third long period show greater stability than those of the second; Pb^{2+} is,
for instance, much more stable than Sn^{2+}. However, large singly charged ions
with an inert pair, such as Tl^+, show some of the properties of the alkali
metals, though the bonds they form are by no means purely ionic. The least
stable ions are those of the transition metals, and variable charge number
is common (see Table 11). Cobalt ($3s^2\ 3p^6\ 3d^7\ 4s^2$) forms cobalt(II), Co^{2+}, and,
less easily, cobalt(III), Co^{3+}, ions, but nickel ($3s^2\ 3p^6\ 3d^8\ 4s^2$) only Ni^{2+}, the
tendency to lose 3d electrons falling with increasing nuclear charge. The
more highly charged ions, particularly of the transition elements, are frequently invoked in describing molecular complexes (p. 130); but then the
purely ionic picture is not very satisfactory as the bonds often possess
considerable covalent character.

TABLE 11

VARIABLE CHARGE NUMBERS OF
TRANSITION ELEMENT IONS

Ion	Configuration		
V^0	(Ar)	$3d^3$	$4s^2$
V^{2+}	(Ar)	$3d^3$	
V^{3+}	(Ar)	$3d^2$	
Cr^0	(Ar)	$3d^5$	$4s^1$
Cr^{2+}	(Ar)	$3d^4$	
Cr^{3+}	(Ar)	$3d^3$	
Fe^0	(Ar)	$3d^6$	$4s^2$
Fe^{2+}	(Ar)	$3d^6$	
Fe^{3+}	(Ar)	$3d^5$	

Lattice energies of ionic crystals

The energy of a system of spherical ions is at a minimum when each is surrounded by as many others of opposite charge as possible; this number of nearest neighbours is the crystallographic *co-ordination number* of the ion. Thus in sodium chloride (Fig. 84, p. 141) the ions lie on a regular 'lattice' and each has the co-ordination number 6.

When N ions of each kind are brought together in a crystal the interaction energy is clearly not just that of N ion pairs. The formula on p. 88 is replaced by

$$E_{int} = -z_1 z_2 e^2 N A_a / r + b \exp(-r/\varrho),$$

where A_a, the Madelung constant, depends on the crystal geometry, and the exponential term again represents the total repulsion energy. Now the equilibrium value of r, the separation of the two kinds of ion, occurs when E_{int} is a minimum: putting

$$\frac{dE_{int}}{dr} = 0,$$

the exponential term may be eliminated, and the drop in energy on assembling the ions in the crystal (*i.e.* $-E_{int}$) is then seen to be (Born and Mayer, 1932)

$$U = \frac{z_1 z_2 e^2 N A_a}{r} \left(1 - \frac{\varrho}{r}\right).$$

This is the *lattice energy*. A_a may be chosen so that U is given directly in kcal/mole when e is in e.s.u. and r in Å. Some representative values are:

NaCl lattice, $A_a = 1.748$; Wurtzite lattice, $A_a = 1.641$; Corundum, $A_a = 25.03$.

The value $\varrho = 0.345$ Å gives satisfactory results for all alkali halides. The inter-ionic distance r and the type of lattice are found from determinations of crystal structure (p. 118).

Pauling (1940) related ionic size to co-ordination number, and Kapustinskii (1943) used the relationship to eliminate the Madelung constant and obtained an approximate general result:

$$U = 287.2(\Sigma_m) \left(\frac{z_1 z_2}{r_C + r_A} \right) \left(1 - \frac{0.345}{r_C + r_A} \right) \text{kcal/mole},$$

where Σ_m is the number of ions per molecule (in the vapour phase) and r_C and r_A are the atomic radii for 6 co-ordination.

The lattice energy may be determined experimentally from thermo-chemical data by considering a suitable cycle of changes (Born and Haber, 1919). The cycle for formation of sodium chloride is:

$$\text{Na(solid)} + \tfrac{1}{2}\text{Cl}_2\text{(gas)} \xrightarrow{\;\;\Delta H_s + \frac{1}{2}\Delta H_d\;\;} \text{Na(g)} + \text{Cl(g)}$$

$$\downarrow \Delta H_f \qquad\qquad\qquad\qquad\qquad \downarrow I_{Na} \qquad \downarrow -A_{Cl}$$

$$\text{NaCl(s)} \xleftarrow{\qquad -U \qquad} \text{Na}^+\text{(g)} + \text{Cl}^-\text{(g)}$$

The energy changes occurring at each step are shown alongside the arrows: ΔH_s and ΔH_d are heats of sublimation (sodium to free atoms) and dissociation (chlorine molecules to free atoms) and, with the ionisation potential and electron affinity (I_{Na} and A_{Cl}), refer to one mole of material. By Hess's law (p. 168) the change of H is independent of the path and the heat of formation is thus:

$$\Delta H_f = \Delta H_s + \tfrac{1}{2}\Delta H_d + I_{Na} - A_{Cl} - U.$$

Therefore

$$U = \Delta H_s + \tfrac{1}{2}\Delta H_d + I_{Na} - A_{Cl} - \Delta H_f.$$

Interpretation of lattice energies

The experimental (Born-Haber) and theoretical (Born-Mayer) estimates of lattice energy agree well for typically ionic compounds such as the Gp.IA halides, and show that the theoretical picture of complete electron transfer is satisfactory. Values for salts of '18-electron' type cations, however, often show considerable discrepancies. Representative differences between U_{expt} and U_{calc} are: RbI, 4 kcal; CdI_2, 86 kcal; PbO_2, 212 kcal. These indicate a gradual departure from the purely ionic condition; the small cations tend to retain some hold on their electrons and the binding acquires considerable covalent character.

Deviations of this kind used to be ascribed to the 'polarisation' of the large anions by the small cations, the charge density of the former being deformed by the strong electric field of the latter. Although such effects undoubtedly occur, the deviations can most readily be accounted for along lines already indicated (p. 86). The electron transfer from a small cation which has a correspondingly great electron-attracting power is never complete, and the bonds that such a cation forms may exhibit considerable covalent character. Nevertheless, the term 'polarisation' is convenient and continues to be used to describe this effect. The effect, always accompanied by an abnormally high heat of formation and lattice energy, is not confined to '18-electron' ions. Thus, although there is no discrepancy between U_{expt} and U_{calc} for BaO, the difference for MgO is 20 kcal, in accord with the smaller size and higher electron-attracting power of the Mg^{2+} ion.

Lattice energy and solubility

Water consists of polar molecules (dipole moment 1.8 D) with a strong tendency to form hydrogen bonds, and has a high dielectric constant ($\sim$ 78). Its molecules can orient themselves around cations with the oxygen atoms pointing inwards, the complex so formed being stabilised by a *hydration energy* arising from electrostatic attraction between the cation and the excess of negative charge on the oxygen. Consequently, water is a good solvent for ionic compounds but a poor one for non-electrolytes whose molecules are without strong charges. The process of dissolution is easier the higher the dielectric constant; for, in an ideal (continuous) medium, of dielectric constant ε, the solvation or hydration energy of an ion of radius r and charge e would be $(e^2/r)\,(1 - 1/\varepsilon)$.

Crystals also dissolve more easily in water the more ionic the character of the bonds in them. Where there is considerable polarisation, the spreading out of the electron cloud, which accompanies the increase in covalence, leads to a screening of the positive-ion field and a weakening of the effect on the water molecules.

The Covalent Bond

Simple diatomic molecules

The electron configuration of simple diatomic molecules can be discussed quite simply in terms of the MO's described on p. 84. It is only necessary, in the aufbau approach, to know the energy order of the various orbitals, and for most homonuclear molecules (taking the bond as the z axis) this is:

$$\sigma 1s < \sigma^* 1s < \sigma 2s < \sigma^* 2s < \sigma 2p_z < \begin{pmatrix} \pi 2p_x \\ \pi 2p_y \end{pmatrix} < \begin{pmatrix} \pi^* 2p_x \\ \pi^* 2p_y \end{pmatrix} < \sigma^* 2p_z \cdots$$

A more flexible but less explicit notation, due to Mulliken, is also employed. Here the MO's are simply labelled z, y, x, w, v, u, ..., in ascending energy order, the symmetry symbols σ, π, δ, ... being added as required. Thus, for example, $z\sigma$ is used for the $\sigma 2s$ MO, inner shells being omitted. With this notation and the principles already put forward, electronic structures may be described along the following lines:

Lithium. $2\text{Li}(1s^2\ 2s^1) \rightarrow \text{Li}_2(\text{KK } z\sigma^2)$

Here the two 'K-shell' (1s) electrons on each nucleus are indicated in the molecular configuration simply by the two K's, the inner shells being more or less undisturbed, and the two valence electrons give a typical single bond.

Nitrogen. $2\text{N}(1s^2\ 2s^2\ 2p^3) \rightarrow \text{N}_2(\text{KK } z\sigma^2\ y\sigma^2\ x\sigma^2\ w\pi^4)$

Here $z\sigma$ is bonding and $y\sigma$ is its anti-bonding partner, so there is little net effect from this pair of MO's. The first bonding effect comes from $x\sigma^2$, which is a $\sigma 2p$ MO (Fig. 35) formed from 2p AO's pointing towards each other and describing an electron density which is greatest along the bond axis. $w\pi^4$ comprises two pairs of electrons in the two degenerate (equivalent) $2p\pi$-type bonding MO's; these describe densities which vanish on the axis itself but which have maxima some distance to either side of it (Fig. 35). The two orbitals differ by rotation through 90°, but when put together their density contributions give an axially symmetrical resultant. This is a hollow 'tube' of charge, densest in the region between the nuclei (Fig. 38). Thus, in addition to the σ bond, there are two π bonds; but the latter should be less strong than the former (in accord with experience) because the charge pile-up is smaller (smaller overlap between AO's) and lies off the axis.

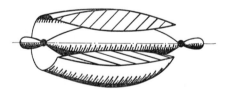

Fig. 38. Diagram showing schematically the general disposition of charge in N_2 (cylindrical density due to two π bonds cut away to reveal σ bond).

Fluorine. $2\text{F}(1s^2\ 2s^2\ 2p^5) \rightarrow \text{F}_2(\text{KK } z\sigma^2\ y\sigma^2\ x\sigma^2\ w\pi^4\ v\pi^4)$

Here the situation resembles that in nitrogen until the last four electrons are added; these fill the $v\pi$ MO's which are the anti-bonding partners of the $w\pi$ MO's. Thus the two π bonds of the nitrogen-like configuration are 'undone' when the extra electrons are provided, and only a single bond remains.

Oxygen. $2O(1s^2\ 2s^2\ 2p^4) \rightarrow O_2(KK\ z\sigma^2\ y\sigma^2\ x\sigma^2\ w\pi^4\ v\pi^2)$

This is intermediate between nitrogen and fluorine; the anti-bonding $v\pi$ orbitals contain only two electrons and leave effectively one π bond. More precisely, by Hund's rules, the two $v\pi$ MO's are each singly occupied, half-cancelling the effect of a $w\pi$ electron pair. There is thus a σ bond and two 'half' π bonds, their resultant density being axially symmetrical as in nitrogen but being much 'thinner'. Since the two odd electrons have parallel spins the molecule is paramagnetic.

Hybridisation

Although simple pairing of the AO's on different atoms suggests MO forms which account surprisingly well for the general properties of many diatomic molecules, its limitations soon become apparent. It must be remembered that the best MO's are solutions of a wave equation and that simple LCAO forms are rather rough approximations only. However, by building an MO out of a number of AO's instead of just a pair, a better approximation can be obtained. It will appear later that this refinement is often quite indispensible, even in qualitative descriptions.

Consider, as a first example, the hydrogen fluoride molecule (Fig. 39).

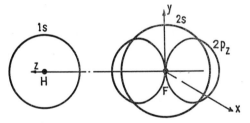

Fig. 39. Atomic orbitals in hydrogen fluoride. The fluorine $2p_x$ and $2p_y$ atomic orbitals, normal to the axis, are omitted for clarity.

Omitting the fluorine K shell, there are eight electrons, and the lowest energy AO's are $1s_H$ (hydrogen), $2s$, $2p_x$, $2p_y$ and $2p_z$ (fluorine). But what are the lowest energy molecular orbitals which may be built from these AO's? Actual calculation yields an answer of the following kind in which the MO's are in ascending energy order:

$$
\overset{z\sigma}{\begin{pmatrix} \text{Mixture of} \\ 1s_H,\ 2s,\ 2p_z \end{pmatrix}}
\quad
\overset{y\sigma}{\begin{pmatrix} \text{Mixture of} \\ 2s,\ 2p_z \end{pmatrix}}
\quad
\overset{x\pi}{\begin{pmatrix} 2p_x \end{pmatrix}}
\quad
\overset{w\pi}{\begin{pmatrix} 2p_y \end{pmatrix}}.
$$

The $z\sigma$ MO is of bonding type, concentrating charge between the nuclei, though it may lean more towards the fluorine atom. The $y\sigma$ MO contains an inappreciable amount of $1s_H$ and is hardly a molecular orbital at all; it leans to the 'rear' of the fluorine atom, away from the hydrogen. The other two orbitals are pure fluorine AO's each of which has its distinctive symmetry and, in the absence of other low-lying AO's of similar type, improved mixtures cannot be formed. The structure is:

$$H(1s) + F(1s^2\ 2s^2\ 2p^5) \rightarrow HF(K\ z\sigma^2\ y\sigma^2\ x\pi^2\ w\pi^2).$$

There is thus a normal σ bond, although it cannot be well represented by less than 3 AO's, which is densest at the fluorine end, and 3 doubly occupied non-bonding orbitals. The latter give a striking picture of the three lone pairs of the octet on the fluorine atom; one projects to the rear while the other two combine to give an axially symmetrical charge distribution, in form something like a doughnut with the fluorine nucleus in the hole (Fig. 40).

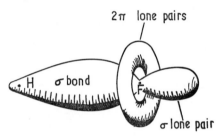

Fig. 40. Principal regions of high charge density in HF (schematic).

By examining the MO's more carefully it is now possible to retrieve the simple picture in which MO's are approximated by overlapping suitable pairs of orbitals derived from the different atoms. For clearly the $z\sigma$ MO could be regarded as being formed by combining the 1s orbital of the hydrogen with a modified fluorine orbital which is itself a *mixture* of the 2s and $2p_z$ on the same (fluorine) atom. Such modified orbitals, which are still essentially atomic though not pure AO's, are called *hybrid* AO's. They are an immense aid to description because they make it possible to retain the pair picture in which bonds are associated with strongly overlapping pairs of AO's (now including hybrid as well as pure AO's), one on each of two atoms. The general forms of the hybrid orbitals which can be achieved by mixing are easily inferred. Thus the 2s and $2p_z$ AO's in the present example yield an infinite range of hybrid pairs, the most symmetrical being

$$h_1 = \frac{1}{\sqrt{2}}(\varphi_{2s} + \varphi_{2p_z}) \qquad \text{and} \qquad h_2 = \frac{1}{\sqrt{2}}(\varphi_{2s} - \varphi_{2p_z}).$$

These are illustrated in Fig. 41 and are called *digonal* sp hybrids; they are exactly similar or 'equivalent' except in orientation. Clearly, a plausible description of the $z\sigma$ MO in HF could be obtained by overlapping h_1 with the hydrogen 1s AO and using h_2 as the lone pair orbital, $y\sigma$. This would not be the best description because there is no reason, here, for choosing a pair of exactly similar hydrids; but it is still qualitatively useful. More generally,

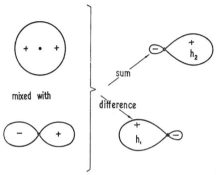

Fig. 41. Representing combination of s and p atomic orbitals to give sp hybrids.

departures from symmetry are permissible, but the most acceptable pairs are related so that they overlap as little as possible. If the 2s content of h_1 is increased and its $2p_z$ content decreased, then the 2s content of h_2 must decrease and its $2p_z$ content increase.

It is probable that sp hybridisation of this kind is significant in a large number of diatomic molecules, but its importance depends on a number of delicately balanced factors. It is favoured by the fact that overlap in a bond region (that is where the electrons are attracted by *two* nuclei) may be increased. It is opposed by, for instance, an increasing p character in a lone pair orbital, and occurs most easily when the p orbital is not much higher in energy than the s. Hybridisation also accounts most readily for the fact that electrons repel one another and tend to stay apart, particularly (owing to the exclusion principle) when each has the same spin. It will be seen later that the forms and disposition of hybrid orbitals can be discussed in terms of repulsions between the different pairs of bonding and lone pair electrons. This more detailed analysis of the electronic energy helps to give some understanding of the factors determining molecular geometry.

Valence states. Promotion

In discussing bonds involving hybrid AO's it is necessary to introduce 'atomic valence states'. If the above description (p. 96) is accepted, the energy of the hydrogen fluoride molecule can be discussed. The bond is formed by overlapping h_1 and $1s_H$, each contributing one electron, where the atoms, supposing they could be taken apart without changing the orbital forms, would be in the respective states

$$H(1s^1) \quad \text{and} \quad F(1s^2\, 2p_x{}^2\, 2p_y{}^2\, h_2{}^2\, h_1{}^1).$$

The hydrogen would be in a 'true atomic' state and the fluorine in a 'valence' state. The latter state is hypothetical, because h_1 and h_2 would, in fact, go smoothly into 2s and $2p_z$ as the nuclei were being separated, but it allows the energy changes to be visualised. As Fig. 42 shows, the net binding energy is the 'gross binding energy' minus the 'valence state excitation energy'. The latter, being characteristic of the valence state considered and constant from one molecule to another, accordingly forms an exceedingly useful datum. The high excitation energy involved is often completely offset by the more satisfactory overlap of the hybrid AO's, so that the net binding energy becomes considerably larger than could be accounted for without invoking hybridisation.

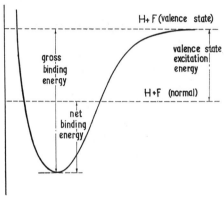

Fig. 42. Energy relationships in HF molecule (energy v distance between nuclei).

There are many instances in which a mixing of the AO's occupied in the ground state of an atom does nothing to improve its capacity for bond formation. Beryllium, for example, has the ground state structure $Be(1s^2\, 2s^2)$ and, being without singly occupied orbitals, should be zero-valent. Carbon, with the structure $C(1s^2\, 2s^2\, 2p^2)$, should be bivalent; mixing the singly occupied 2p orbitals is found merely to change their orientation. The bonds formed by these atoms can best be understood in terms of valence states in which 'electron promotion' has occurred. The promotions envisaged are

$$Be(1s^2\, 2s^2) \;\rightarrow\; Be(1s^2\, 2s^1\, 2p_x{}^1);$$
$$C(1s^2\, 2s^2\, 2p^2) \;\rightarrow\; C(1s^2\, 2s^1\, 2p_x{}^1\, 2p_y{}^1\, 2p_z{}^1);$$

where the x, y, and z directions are chosen in terms of the molecular environment of the atom. These valence states would serve to describe bivalent beryllium and quadrivalent carbon but, since two types of AO appear, would not account for the formation of the sets of *identical* bonds found in the linear molecule $BeCl_2$ and the tetrahedral molecule CH_4. The difficulty disappears when the possibility of hybridisation is introduced; for mixing a 2s and 2p orbital has already been seen to yield, among other possibilities, precisely equivalent hybrid orbitals (Fig. 41) pointing in opposite directions. Promotion and hybridisation are employed freely to set up atomic valence states which give the best account of bond formation in specific molecular situations. With the help of these ideas it is possible usefully to discuss the bonding in really complicated polyatomic molecules.

Localised MO's. Polyatomic molecules

Above (p. 85), the AO's of atoms were paired, according to symmetry and degree of overlap, to yield MO's of various type, all describing a two-electron bond. Essentially similar considerations may be employed in dealing with polyatomic molecules; but then the bonds, instead of being superimposed (*e.g.* σ and π bonds), may lie in different regions of space, uniting different pairs of atoms. If there are 'obvious' pairs of strongly overlapping AO's, or if such pairs can be formed by invoking not unreasonable valence states, it is possible to obtain a fairly satisfactory picture of the molecular electronic structure in terms of the 'localised' MO's which result. As with the diatomic molecule (p. 85), this description does not conflict with the one offered by an appropriate extension of the Heitler-London theory; both approaches succeed in explaining the accumulation of electron density in a number of localised bond regions. The application of these ideas is best illustrated by reference to specific molecules:

Beryllium Chloride, $BeCl_2$. This is a linear molecule in which both Be—Cl bonds are equivalent. The appropriate valence state of the Be atom is thus $Be(1s^2 h_1^1 h_2^1)$, where h_1 and h_2 are the digonal hybrids of Fig. 41. The relevant orbitals on the chlorine atoms are the singly occupied $3p_z$ AO's (z referring to the molecular axis), 3s, $3p_x$ and $3p_y$ containing lone pairs. It is likely also that some digonal hybridisation would occur at the chlorine atoms, the incorporation of some 3s character strengthening the overlap in the bonds and pushing one of the lone pairs to the rear of each chlorine. The resultant situation, shown in Fig. 43, should be compared with that in HF (Fig. 40). Heavier atoms with the same ns^2 ground state configurations, for example zinc, cadmium and mercury, form linear dichlorides and dibromides whose electronic structures must be closely similar.

Acetylene, C_2H_2. This molecule is also linear. Again digonal valence states are appropriate, each carbon having the prepared configuration $C(1s^2\,h_1{}^1\,h_2{}^1\,2p_x{}^1\,2p_y{}^1)$. A σ C—C bond and two σ C—H bonds, all collinear, arise from obvious pairings (Fig. 44); the singly occupied carbon 2p AO's overlap laterally to give two π bonds, exactly as in the diatomic molecule N_2. Consequently, there is a carbon triple bond.

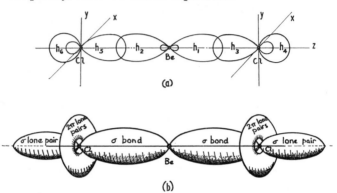

(a)

(b)

Fig. 43. (a) Hybrid orbitals of the σ bonds and σ lone pairs ($2p_x$ and $2p_y$ orbitals omitted). (b) Regions of maximum charge density (schematic).

Water, H_2O. This is a non-linear molecule, the H—O—H angle being about 105°. Hybridisation occurs somewhat less easily in oxygen than in carbon. By neglecting it altogether, it is still possible to get a rough explanation of

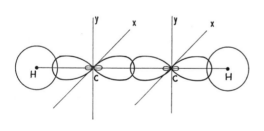

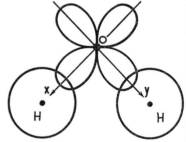

Fig. 44. Hybrid orbitals of the σ bonds in C_2H_2 ($2p_x$ and $2p_y$ orbitals omitted).

Fig. 45. Singly occupied atomic orbitals in oxygen and hydrogens ($2s$, $2p_z$ lone pairs omitted).

the molecular shape. A strong overlap occurs between the singly occupied oxygen 2p orbitals ($2p_x$, $2p_y$, Fig. 45) and the hydrogen 1s AO's and suggests localised MO's at about 90°. But the overlap can be improved and the lone pairs better separated, thus lowering their repulsion energy, by admitting a fair amount of 2s–2p mixing (p. 103).

Boron Trichloride, BCl_3. Here the molecule is planar, with the boron atom at the centre of an equilateral triangle of chlorine atoms (Fig. 46). The valence state must be described in terms of three similar hybrid AO's pointing towards the corners of the triangle. Such orbitals can be formed by mixing 2s and two 2p AO's, $2p_y$ and $2p_z$ say; they lie in the plane of the latter and are precisely equivalent (Fig. 47). If the so-called *trigonal* hybrids are denoted by h_1, h_2 and h_3, the appropriate boron valence state must be $B(1s^2 h_1^1 h_2^1 h_3^1)$. The hybrid AO's overlap chlorine 3p AO's, directed towards the boron atom, to form localised MO's similar to those in beryllium chloride.

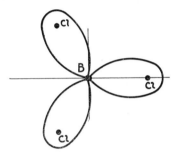

Fig. 46. Localised molecular orbitals in BCl_3.

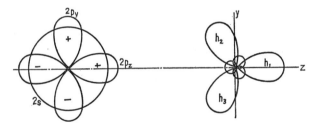

Fig. 47. Mixing of 2s, $2p_y$ and $2p_z$ atomic orbitals to form three equivalent hybrid atomic orbitals, h_1, h_2, h_3. (*Cf.* Fig. 41, except that here the possibilities are super-imposed instead of being shown separately.)

Methyl radical, CH_3. Trigonal hybridisation is indicated whenever an atom forms three identical bonds directed at 120° with each other. In carbon also the valence state entails both promotion and hybridisation: it is $C(1s^2 2p_x^1 h_1^1 h_2^1 h_3^1)$, where the third 2p AO, $2p_x$, is not involved in the mixing and lies perpendicular to the plane of the hybrids. Three C—H bonds are accounted for by an overlap of h_1, h_2 and h_3 with the three hydrogen 1s

AO's, while the free radical character of the system arises from the singly occupied $2p_z$ orbital.

Ethylene, C_2H_4. This molecule is also flat, and the bonds from each carbon atom make very nearly 120° with each other. Assuming the same trigonal valence state as in the methyl radical, four C—H bonds and a central C—C bond are readily accounted for; and, when the two CH_2 groups are rotated about the C—C bond until their singly occupied 2p AO's are parallel, they overlap laterally to give a normal π bond (Fig. 48). The planar configuration is thus stabilised by π bonding and any twisting between the two CH_2 groups is opposed by a reduction in binding energy.

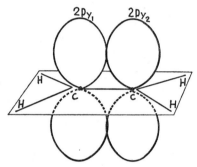

Fig. 48. Formation of a π bond in ethylene (σ bonds omitted). If the two $2p_y$ orbitals are parallel there is substantial lateral overlap (for clarity not shown in the Fig.) giving a π bond: rotation of the CH_2 groups lessens the bonding.

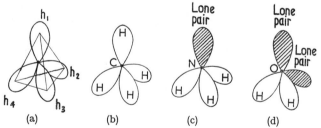

Fig. 49. Tetrahedral hybridisation in a series of iso-electronic molecules.

Methane, CH_4. The hydrogen atoms are at the corners of a regular tetrahedron, with the carbon at the centre. A carbon valence state with four identical, singly occupied hybrid AO's can be set up by allowing the mixing of 2s and *all* the 2p AO's. When they are denoted by h_1, h_2, h_3, and h_4, the carbon valence state is $C(1s^2\ h_1^1\ h_2^1\ h_3^1\ h_4^1)$. The pairing of AO's, describing four identical strong bonds, is then obvious (Fig. 49(a) and (b)). This *tetrahedral* hybridisation occurs whenever carbon forms four single bonds; thus it is appropriate to ethane and indeed to all the paraffins and their derivatives. The possibility of free rotation about the bonds leads to long, flexible chains.

The wide occurrence of hybridisation

Consideration of the bonds formed by atoms with s and p electrons in their valence shells has brought to light three principal types of valence state. Although their realisation may require promotion and hybridisation, it often leads to strongly directed bonds with a very high net binding energy. The principal types of hybrid which occur are:

(i) Digonal or sp hybrids, formed from an s and *one* p orbital and pointing in opposite directions along the axis of the p orbital;

(ii) Trigonal or sp^2 hybrids, formed from an s and *two* p orbitals and inclined at 120° in the plane of the 2p orbitals;

(iii) Tetrahedral or sp^3 hybrids, formed from an s and *three* p orbitals and inclined at about 109.5° (the tetrahedral angle).

It is important to remember that, as already recognised, these types are exactly appropriate only in symmetrical situations (*e.g.* $BeCl_2$, BCl_3, CH_4) and that departures from them are frequent. It is now generally believed that hybridisation is much more widely appropriate than was at first thought. It is interesting to consider, for example, what would happen if one of the protons in CH_4 were transferred to the carbon nucleus. The resulting system, NH_3, is iso-electronic with the original, differing from it only in an increase of 1 in the central charge and a loss of symmetry. But the four C—H MO's have become three N—H MO's together with a lone pair orbital, h_1 say. The tetrahedral valence state is therefore a plausible description of the nitrogen atom in ammonia, although at first sight hybridisation does not appear to be necessary; for the pyramidal form of the molecule (Fig. 49(c)) could be accounted for simply by overlapping three hydrogen orbitals with the three singly occupied 2p orbitals of the nitrogen ground state. The H—N—H angle is, however, 106.7° which is neither the tetrahedral nor the right angle. The hybrid h_1 has increased its s content, thereby lowering the energy of the lone pair electrons (which are no longer attracted by another nucleus), and at the same time decreasing the s content of the other hybrids. This allows their approach towards the right-angled set of three pure p orbitals—an effect which is helped by repulsion from the concentrated lone-pair charge. The equilibrium configuration results from a quite fine energy balance, involving the mutual repulsions of all four electron pairs.

A tetrahedral disposition of four hybrids appears to give a much better description of the actual electronic structure than could be achieved without hybridisation, largely because it puts individual electron pairs in different regions of space. The same is true for H_2O where the simple picture (Fig. 45) suggests a right-angled molecule. But if the system be imagined as formed from the iso-electronic CH_4 by shrinking two protons into the carbon nucleus, a tetrahedral oxygen valence state becomes more reasonable, the two lone pairs being well separated (as in Fig. 49(d)) instead of being superimposed in one 2s and one 2p orbital. The electron donor property of nitrogen and the hydrogen bonding property of oxygen are both connected with the existence of localised and strongly directed lone pairs of this kind. Later (p. 125), it will be seen how a great deal of stereochemistry may similarly be interpreted in terms of a theoretically reasonable distribution of electron pairs.

Covalency maxima

Earliest ideas on covalence were based largely on the view that the atom under consideration attained an inert gas structure by sharing electrons. Faced with such compounds as PCl_5 and SF_6, in which sulphur and phosphorus share 10 and 12 electrons respectively, Sidgwick added the suggestion that every element had a certain maximum covalency which depended on atomic number (see Table 12).

TABLE 12

MAXIMUM COVALENCY AS DEPENDENT ON ATOMIC NUMBER

Atomic number	Element	Maximum number of shared pairs
1	H	1 (2 electrons)
3 — 9	Li to F	4 (8 electrons)
11 — 35	Na to Br	6 (12 electrons)
37 — 92	Rb to U	8 (16 electrons)

The maximum covalency is by no means always reached, being shown by many elements only in their fluorides, and clearly represents the number of orbitals in the outermost, partially filled, shell which might be invoked in forming valence states. It is 1 for hydrogen, 4 for the first short period, 6 for the second short period and 8 for the rest of the elements. The last group, having s, p and d orbitals $(1 + 3 + 5 = 9)$ available might be expected to exhibit a maximum covalency of 9. But the outermost electronic shells become less defined with increasing principal quantum number and the amount of promotion which can take place is restricted. A covalency of 4 is common in the second short period, though there is a limited d orbital participation in spite of the d orbitals being unoccupied in the ground states.

With the admission of d orbitals the number of principal types of hybridisation is increased from 4 (pure p, digonal, trigonal, tetrahedral) to over 40; fortunately only a few of these lead to systems of strong bonds.

Bipyramidal, sp^3d. A typical bipyramidal molecule is phosphorus pentachloride, PCl_5, which is monomeric in the vapour and has the form shown in Fig. 50. The hybridisation in the central plane could be sp^2, giving the three bonds at 120° with one another. And the third p orbital could be mixed with the appropriate d orbital, since both are symmetrical about the central axis, to give one hybrid directed up and another down as in Fig. 51. In these circumstances two chlorines would be expected to be

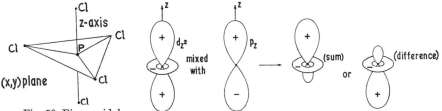

Fig. 50. Bipyramidal structure of PCl_5.

Fig. 51. One type of pd hybridisation.

bound somewhat differently from the other three; the bonds above and below the plane are in fact slightly longer. The corresponding element of the first short period, nitrogen, forms no such compound because there are no 2d AO's and the 3d AO's are too high in energy to allow of appreciable mixing. Thus NF_3 is the highest fluoride.

Octahedral, sp^3d^2. A molecule of this kind is SF_6, which has four bonds lying at right angles in the plane of the sulphur and the other two pointing up and down from the plane (Fig. 52). The two vertical bonds are formed

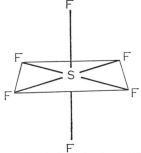

Fig. 52. Octahedral structure of SF_6.

essentially as in a bipyramidal molecule, but the in-plane bonds are best described in terms of hybrids incorporating a second d orbital. The mode of formation of one of the in-plane hybrids is indicated in Fig. 53. Here the four hybrids so formed would not be quite equivalent to the other two, but, if slight mixing is permitted, a strictly equivalent set of six can be found; these point to the corners of a regular octahedron.

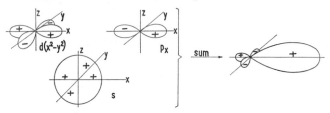

Fig. 53. One type of spd hybridisation.

Plane tetragonal, dsp^2. Certain ions possess the 'square' of the octahedral type without atoms above or below the plane; examples are $Ni(CN)_4^{2-}$ and $PtCl_4^{2-}$. The hybridisation shown in Fig. 53 is again appropriate. In plane ions of this kind, however, it is possible for the primary system of hybrid bonds to be supplemented by a secondary system involving the remaining orbitals of the valence shell. In the plane square instance, the secondary system can be formed from the out-of-plane orbitals (one p and three d) as in Fig. 54. Such orbitals have a node in the molecular

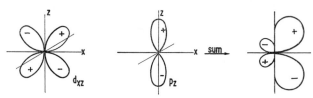

Fig. 54. Secondary hybrid suitable for π-bond formation.

plane and therefore have π character. They can overlap with p orbitals on the atoms to which they point, to give a π bond superimposed on the primary σ bond. Double bonding of this kind is almost certainly important in planar complexes when sufficient electrons are available.

It should be noted that the orbitals which are mixed belong, in the first two examples, to the same quantum shell (3s, 3p, 3d). Often, however, the d orbital belongs to a previous shell (*e.g.* 4s, 4p, 3d) and this is indicated by writing the d orbital first. In the last example (Ni, Pt) we therefore refer to dsp^2 hybridisation.

Compounds in which the maximum covalency is exhibited are naturally very stable. Thus, for instance, CCl_4 and SF_6 are unreactive towards water, whereas $SiCl_4$ and PCl_5 are easily hydrolysed because the valency of each central atom is capable of being increased.

Bond energies

Strictly, what has been said in this discussion of valency refers to an idealised situation in which all the atomic nuclei are at rest in equilibrium positions. Such a situation is not realised even at the absolute zero of temperature, because there still remains the zero-point energy of vibration. The electronic binding energy, the energy required to separate a molecule into its component atoms, in their ground states and at rest, is thus not directly measurable. What can be measured is the 'dissociation energy', which is the energy required for the separation under specified conditions (*e.g.* referred to standard temperature and pressure). The two quantities differ by the energies of vibration, rotation and translation; the latter two are usually small, but the vibrational energy may be a substantial fraction of the binding energy. For a diatomic molecule, the dissociation energy is often called the 'bond energy' and

$$\text{Molecule A—B} + \text{bond energy} \rightarrow \text{atom A} + \text{atom B.}$$

Energies of dissociation can be found by spectroscopic methods (H_2, p. 213), by application of the Van 't Hoff equation ((21), p. 180), from heats of sublimation, and from thermochemical measurements (I_2). For larger molecules the last method is usually employed, heats of reaction being generally used (p. 167). Thus the heat of dissociation of the water molecule can be found from

  (i) the heat of dissociation of H_2 (103.4 kcal/mole),
 (ii) the heat of dissociation of O_2 (118.2 kcal/mole),
(iii) the heat of formation of H_2O (57.8 kcal/mole),

by considering the reactions

$$2H_2 \text{ (g)} \rightarrow 4H \text{ (g)} \qquad \Delta H = \quad 206.8 \text{ kcal (2 moles)}$$
$$O_2 \text{ (g)} \rightarrow 2O\text{(g)} \qquad \Delta H = \quad 118.2 \text{ kcal (1 mole)}$$
$$2H_2 \text{ (g)} + O_2 \text{ (g)} \rightarrow 2H_2O \text{ (g)} \qquad \Delta H = -115.6 \text{ kcal (2 moles).}$$

Subtracting the first two equations from the third

$$4H \text{ (g)} + 2O \text{ (g)} \rightarrow 2H_2O \text{ (g)} \qquad \Delta H = -440.6 \text{ kcal (2 moles).}$$

The heat of dissociation is thus $-\Delta H = 220.3$ kcal/mole. Since in a gas reaction the $p\Delta V$ term in $\Delta H = \Delta U + p\Delta V$ is usually negligible, the energy of dissociation is $D_0 \sim 220.3$ kcal/mole.

Now it is found experimentally that the dissociation energy of a polyatomic molecule can be fairly accurately represented as a sum of bond energies, one for every individual bond broken, and that the energies of the bonds between particular elements do not vary much from one molecule to another. Thus, the dissociation energy of the water molecule is the sum of the two O—H bond energies, $E_{O-H} = 110.2$ kcal/mole. This is a remarkable empirical fact, for the electronic energy of a molecule must depend considerably on its size and shape and the existence of characteristic bond properties must, in a general way, be a consequence of the strong localisation of the orbitals describing individual bonds. Tables of bond energies have been drawn up and have been of considerable value, more particularly in organic chemistry where molecules often contain large numbers of bonds but relatively few different types (e.g. C—H, C—C, C—N, etc.). The additivity rule breaks down when comparing systems whose atoms adopt different valence states; for the gross or 'intrinsic' bond energy (cf. p. 89) will be offset by different excitation energies in different situations. In these circumstances, it would be preferable to use an equation of the form

$$-\Delta U = \Sigma E_{A-B} - \Sigma V_A$$

for the dissociation energy—a sum of intrinsic bond energies minus a sum of atomic valence state excitation energies—but valence state data are at present limited.

The electronegativity scale

In discussing bonds between unlike atoms, it is convenient to associate with every atom a quantity, x, representing its electron-attracting power in a bond, such that the ionic character of a bond P—Q is determined by $x_P - x_Q$. It is clear that the definition $x_P \propto (I_P + A_P)$, in terms of ionisation potential and electron affinity, might be satisfactory; for the ease with which P^+Q^- and P^-Q^+ could be formed would depend (p. 88) on $I_P - A_Q$ and $I_Q - A_P$, respectively. The equality $x_P = x_Q$ would describe a 'pure covalent' situation in which there is no tendency for electron drift in either direction. Mulliken takes $\frac{1}{2}(I + A)$ as the absolute electronegativity of an atom. Now for atoms whose electronegativities are about the same, it is found that the bond energy $E_{P-Q} \sim \sqrt{E_{P-P} E_{Q-Q}}$ (the geometric mean). But for atoms with different electronegativities the bond energy is greater than the geometric mean by an amount proportional to $(x_P - x_Q)^2$. By suitable choice of the proportionality factor it is therefore possible to arrange that the 'ionic stabilisation energy' is given by

$$\Delta_{PQ} = (x_P - x_Q)^2.$$

The x values which best conform with observed bond energies were first given by Pauling (1932) (Table 13), who used a slightly different definition.

TABLE 13

ELECTRONEGATIVITY SCALE

Element	Electro-negativity	Element	Electro-negativity
F	4.0	Ge, Sn	1.7
O	3.5	Ti, Zr	1.6
N, Cl	3.0	Be, Al	1.5
Br	2.8	Sc, Y	1.3
C, S	2.5	Mg	1.2
Se, I	2.4	Li, Ca, Sr	1.0
H, P, Te	2.1	Na, Ba	0.9
B, As	2.0	K, Rb	0.8
Si, Sb	1.8	Cs	0.7

It is also useful to note that the dipole moment of the bond P—Q, in debyes, is usually within a few percent of the difference $x_P - x_Q$. Electronegativity differences determine charge shifts along bonds and this fact will be seen later (p. 128) to be of considerable significance.

The dative bond

Dative bonds involve an atom with a lone pair of electrons, the *donor*, and an electron deficient atom, the *acceptor*. In the example

$$H_3N: + BMe_3 \rightarrow H_3N{\rightarrow}BMe_3$$

the notation indicates the origin of the lone pair. The molecule BMe_3 is trigonal with no electrons occupying the boron 2p AO normal to the plane; it has an incomplete octet. When a nitrogen lone pair approaches along the perpendicular direction the two electrons go into the appropriate localised MO, the difference in electronegativity between B and N being insufficient to resist the sharing.

Dative bonds occur frequently in complex ions, though the designation becomes less significant with increasing complexity. Thus, the $Ni(CN)_4^{2-}$ ion (p. 496) might be regarded as formed by directing carbon lone pairs towards vacant dsp^2 hybrids on a nickel ion. Similarly, the hexacyanoferrate(II) ion might be regarded as formed from an Fe^{2+} ion in an excited singlet state, that is with doubly occupied AO's (spins paired),

leaving vacant d, s and p orbitals which can be used in forming an octahedral valence system by allowing 6 CN^- lone pairs to approach the vacant d^2sp^3 hybrids. Alternatively, however, the system could be regarded as formed by pairing the singly occupied hybrids in a central Fe^{4-} with singly occupied hybrids in 6 neutral radicals. In reality the various ions have no independent existence within the complex, and the term 'dative' refers only to an imaginary method of assembling the complex. The charged groups which surround a central atom in this way are called *ligands*, their number being the *co-ordination number* of the central atom in that particular complex. The term co-ordination number is not used here in its crystallographic sense (cf. p. 91, 141). The binding in complexes cannot strictly be described as *localised covalent* because of the rather diffuse character of the d orbitals and the strong fields imposed by the ligands. Its interpretation is the aim of the 'ligand field theory' (p. 131).

Non-Localised and Metallic Bonding

Non-localised orbitals

It has been possible to represent all the bonds thus far considered by using localised MO's built up from pairs of AO's (or hybrid AO's). But Fig. 55

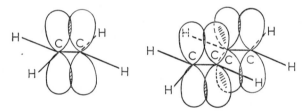

Fig. 55. Singly occupied 2p orbitals in ethylene and butadiene. The σ-bonded frame-work is omitted. (For clarity the greater extent of the actual overlap has not been shown.)

shows that unique pairs cannot always be found. In ethylene there is no ambiguity, the highest occupied orbital providing a normal π bond; but in butadiene, where there is a very similar 'σ-bonded framework', the electrons of the 2p AO's normal to the molecular plane are less easily accommodated. In instances of this kind, which occur throughout organic chemistry, every such AO overlaps *two* or *three* neighbours (end atoms excepted), and if *one* is admitted in a π-type MO then *all* must be admitted. The so-called 'π electrons' must be accommodated in MO's which extend over the whole molecule, the restricted 'pairing' approximation being no longer valid.

The coefficients of the individual AO's, in the LCAO approximation to any π-type MO, can, as always, be determined by standard methods. Fig. 56

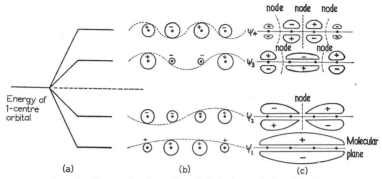

Fig. 56. Energy levels and π-orbitals for a chain of 4 atoms.
(a) MO energies, relative to that of electron confined to one centre.
(b) Coefficients in LCAO approximation—indicated by size of circles.
(c) Regions where ψ is greatest, separated by nodes.

indicates their values in the butadiene MO's and illustrates some general properties of *non-localised MO's*. Clearly the orbitals may be classified as bonding (ψ_1 and ψ_2) or anti-bonding (ψ_3 and ψ_4) on energetic grounds, and their character is reflected in their charge density contributions—the highest energy MO putting a node across every bond, and the lowest leading to a pile-up of charge in every bond. The wave-like pattern followed by the coefficients is also typical; the non-localised orbitals for any long chain would be similar and the allowed energies would behave as in Fig. 57.

Generally, for every energy state of an electron moving about one centre there are n related states in a crystal of n such centres. The energies of these states lie within a *band* whose width depends on the strength of the interaction between neighbours.

Fig. 57. Energy levels for a chain of atoms, showing origin of energy bands.

In foregoing sections the one-centre orbitals have fallen into *pairs*, interaction between different pairs being so small that each pair could be considered by itself, but in conjugated molecules and in metals there is no alternative but to admit complete non-localisation. This non-localisation is essential to an understanding of the characteristic properties of such systems.

Electronic structure of conjugated molecules

Butadiene shows features common to all 'conjugated' molecules, that is those in which the double bonds of classical chemistry cannot be uniquely allocated. According to the aufbau approach, its electronic structure, apart from that of the σ-bonded framework, would be $(\psi_1)^2(\psi_2)^2$. The extra stabilisation due to these 'mobile' π electrons is in fact greater than that which could be provided by two ethylenic π bonds. The difference in the stabilisation which accompanies the increased delocalisation of the same number of electrons, is the 'resonance' energy. If the system is twisted about its centre link it does indeed, from the point of view of the π electrons, break into two ethylenic halves, because interaction between the central 2p AO's diminishes to zero as they are rotated (*cf.* Fig. 48). It is accordingly the resonance energy which keeps such systems flat.

More insight into the π-electronic structure can be gained from the coefficients indicated in Fig. 56. As stated earlier (p. 85), the squares of these coefficients, and therefore the *areas* of the circles in Fig. 56 (b), represent the amounts of charge associated with corresponding atoms in each MO. The electrons in ψ_1 and ψ_2 are associated mainly with internal and end atoms, respectively; but, on adding up the contributions, each atom gets just the same share, one electron, and the charge is thus uniformly distributed. This is true for a large class of hydrocarbons though non-uniformities arise when hetero-atoms are introduced and when ionisation occurs; thus, for example, the removal of an electron from ψ_2 would give a net positive charge mainly on the *end* atoms. On the other hand, the electron density *between* the atoms is determined (p. 86) by products of adjacent AO coefficients. More precisely, $p_{1-2} = 2 \sum_{\substack{\text{occupied} \\ \text{MO's}}} c_1 c_2$ measures the π-bond density in link 1–2; it has the value 1 for ethylene (with $1\,\pi$ bond), but is fractional in other molecules. For butadiene, the π bond orders are about 0.45 for the central, and 0.89 for the outer bonds. These substantial differences in π-bonding in different regions of the molecule are reflected in the extent to which the underlying σ bonds are strengthened and shortened. It has in fact proved possible to interpret both bond lengths and bond properties in terms of bond orders.

Electronic structure of metals

Metals are generally distinguished from non-metals by (a) their excellent thermal and electrical conductivity and (b) their great mechanical strength and ductility. These properties are a direct result of the non-localised nature of the bonding in metals; the electrons are mobile, like the π electrons and, furthermore, in a true metal there are no underlying directed bonds.

Lorentz first suggested that a metal consists of an array of cations in a sea of free electrons, and Sommerfeld put the idea on a wave-mechanical basis, describing the electrons by standing waves. Fig. 56, which refers to the prototype of a one-dimensional crystal, shows that the standing wave description is not inappropriate even when the presence of the cations is explicitly recognised. But a more accurate picture shows more. The energies of the allowed 'standing waves', the Bloch orbitals, fall into characteristic *bands*, which cannot be elaborated upon here, one associated with each atomic level, whose widths and positions can be correlated with a range of non-structural (*e.g.* electric and magnetic) properties.

The true metals comprise the elements of Gps.IA, IB, IIA, and the transition elements, including lanthanides and actinides. With the exception of manganese and uranium they all have one of the three simple structures:

(i) Body-centred cubic (Fig. 58), *e.g.* Na, K, Mo, Fe;
(ii) Face-centred cubic (Fig. 59, 61), *e.g.* Cu, Ag, Au, Fe;
(iii) Close-packed hexagonal (Fig. 60, 61), *e.g.* Be, Mg, Zr.

The number of nearest neighbour atoms, *viz.* the crystal co-ordination number, is 8 in (i). A further 6 atoms, almost as close, makes 14 near neighbours. Obviously there are insufficient electrons to account for the

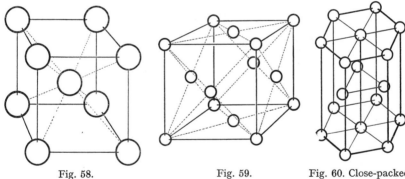

Fig. 58.
Body-centred cubic packing.

Fig. 59.
Face-centred cubic packing.

Fig. 60. Close-packed hexagonal packing.

binding in terms of normal electron-pair covalencies. For instance, the one valence electron of sodium cannot, in any conceivable way, provide 14 (or even 8) covalent bonds with its near neighbours. The necessary sharing, which results in 'partial' bonds, is strictly comparable with that which occurs in butadiene (4 electrons → 3 partial π bonds) or benzene (6 electrons → 6 partial π bonds); but the spreading out must be much more complete in a metal and the crystal bond orders must be relatively small.

It is largely because the formation of a close-packed metallic structure demands a fairly easy removal of electrons that the metals lie at the left hand side of the Periodic Table (p. 70). Such elements pool their valence electrons readily, having low ionisation potentials, and the large de-localisation energy then easily leads to a net binding. Proceeding to the right along every period, metallic properties become feebler and the tendency towards covalently-bonded structures increases. Carbon, for instance, does not allow its valence electrons to escape but readily shares them covalently with 4 neighbours. The open tetrahedral structure of diamond, with its strongly directed bonds (which make it brittle), is thus energetically preferred to a close-packed metallic structure. Here carbon completes its octet in the usual sense—a

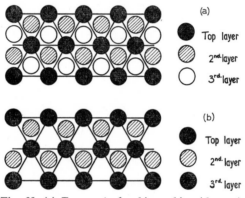

Fig. 61. (a) Face-centred cubic packing (shown in depth). (b) Hexagonal close-packing (shown in depth).

sense which entirely breaks down in the true metals—and in this context is said to satisfy the '$(8 - N)$ *rule*'. Every atom is bound covalently to $8 - N$ others, N being the number of its group in the Periodic Table.

Silicon, germanium and grey tin have diamond-like structures and, although the latter two are metallic to a considerable degree, their bonding is largely covalent, the localisation merely being less complete than in, say, diamond. Other structures are also possible. Graphite consists of well-separated layer planes in which every carbon has three neighbours (as in a giant polycyclic hydrocarbon), but the absence of a fourth covalent bond is compensated for by non-localised π bonding which makes graphite into a 'two-dimensional metal' (the conductivity being primarily along the single planes). Other elements conforming to the $(8 - N)$ rule are arsenic, antimony and bismuth $(N = 5)$ with three nearest neighbours, and selenium and tellurium $(N = 6)$ with only two. In the latter, the atoms are connected in spiral chains which are held together by much weaker forces. In iodine ($N = 7$) the essential units are simply diatomic molecules.

Thus a gradual breakdown of metallic properties is observed in passing along the various periods, together with a growing tendency to form covalently bonded units. Thermal and electrical conductivity diminish, density decreases, and the materials become hard but brittle. In the transition region are included the metals of Gps IIB and IIIB, where there is still a tendency to obey the $(8 - N)$ rule but their atoms lose electrons with a readiness approaching that of the true metals. Their atoms are sometimes said to be in an 'incompetely ionised' condition, and their structures are distorted forms fo the simple lattices.

Long-Range Bonds

Electrostatic bonds

A preliminary classification of the weak forces which hold together well-separated units such as the individual molecules in ice or napthalene has already been made (p. 82). The strongest of these are often termed 'electrostatic', signifying that the forces can be attributed to an interaction of the unmodified, static charge distributions of the separate systems. Examples are the *ion-dipole* bonds which occur in hydrates and ammoniates. These are usually weaker than ordinary covalent bonds and relatively easily break on heating. The binding force arises (Fig. 62) from the attraction between the

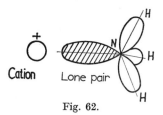

Cation   Lone pair

Fig. 62.

positive ion and the lone-pair electron density. The result differs from a dative bond in that appreciable mixing of the lone pair orbitals with those on the other atom is not required, overlap being small. The attraction arises mainly from a very asymmetrical charge distribution *within* the separate systems; this is an idealisation of the situation and some mixing (covalency) improves the description.

Similar forces account for the *hydrogen bond* between hydrogen, already bonded to one atom, and the lone pair on a strongly electronegative element such as fluorine, oxygen or nitrogen. Of these, the $H \cdots F$ bond is the strongest, with an energy about one tenth that of a σ bond and a length about twice as great. Such bonds are responsible for the open tetrahedral structure of ice, in which every hydrogen (with a net positive charge) attaches itself through the lone pair to a neighbouring oxygen atom. It is the persistence of this structure, in the liquid state, which makes the boiling point of water higher than that of other non-metallic hydrides. The boiling points of ammonia and hydrogen fluoride are high in relation to other hydrides of Gps.V and VII for the same reason. Similar $O \cdots H$ bonds occur in many polymers; thus, in non-polar solvents, they bind carboxylic acids into dimers (Fig. 63). And in *o*-hydroxy aromatic aldehydes and *o*-nitrophenols (Fig. 64) *intra*molecular $O \cdots H$ bonds prevent the characteristic O—H vibrations which are normally revealed in infra-red spectra and reduce the solubility of the compounds in water. The *m*- and *p*-isomers which give the normal O—H frequencies are much more soluble.

Electrostatic effects are undoubtedly of importance in molecular crystals, but, as heats of sublimation show, they are small and packing considerations must be put first. When electrostatic effects are weak, owing to high symmetry of the interacting systems, other forces must be sought.

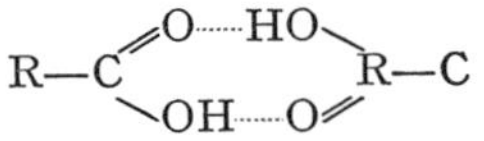

Fig. 63. Dimeric bonding in carboxylic acids.

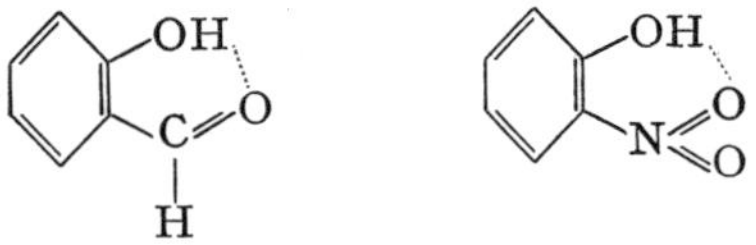

Fig. 64. Prevention of O—H vibration by $O \cdots H$ bonds.

Polarisation and dispersion forces

Electrostatic interactions between the atoms of an inert gas, which are very symmetrical, are exceedingly small. But weak long range forces do operate in both gases and liquids. To account for these *Van der Waals* forces, it is necessary to introduce a more refined treatment which recognises the disturbance of one charge density by another. Each electronic system can induce a weak dipole in the other, giving a *polarisation* force which depends on the polarisability of the system and falls off as the sixth power of the distance. At the same time a correlation of the electronic motions of the two systems provides further attractive force. London first suggested that the latter was like the force between rapidly varying electric dipoles. He called it a *dispersion force*. It is now known that dispersion forces operate over considerable distances and that they are strongest when (a) one system is in an excited state and (b) the systems are identical (the case of 'resonance' interaction). Van der Waals forces between atoms or small molecules are well accounted for in this way; those between large molecules are, as yet, but partly understood. Forces of this type always occur, over and above those of electrostatic origin, as a 'higher order' effect, and also play their part in determining the cohesive properties of molecular crystals and many other non-metallic solids. These forces are usually completely masked by those associated with true chemical valence and will not be considered further.

Chapter 6

Structure and Shape of Molecules

SOURCES OF EXPERIMENTAL EVIDENCE

The structure of solids and the shapes of individual molecules have been inferred from measurements of certain of their properties. The more important of the methods employed and the use made of the information derived from them are very briefly outlined below.

X-ray diffraction

Friedrich (1912), at the suggestion of von Laue, demonstrated that X-rays produce diffraction patterns when passed through crystals. W. L. Bragg (1912) determined the structures of NaCl, KCl and ZnS by directing a beam of monochromatic X-rays on a crystal of the respective compound. If the beam is deflected through an angle 2θ, the angles of incidence and reflection for a layer of atoms will be θ and the spacing d between the successive layers is given by

$$n\lambda = 2d \sin \theta,$$

in which λ is the wave length of the X-rays and n a small whole number.

Debye and Scherrer (1917) used the reflection of a monochromatic beam of X-rays falling on a powder of small crystals or crystal fragments. The random arrangement ensures that sufficient layers of atoms present suitable angles for all reflections to occur.

A single well-formed crystal (Schiebold, 1919) may be rocked in a narrow beam of monochromatic X-rays, and as successive planes pass through the orientation necessary for 'Bragg reflection' they are recorded as dark spots on a photographic film arranged cylindrically round the axis of rotation.

Measurement of the position and intensity of the lines on the X-ray photographs can be analysed to give the relative positions of atoms in a crystalline solid from which its structure may be deduced.

Electron diffraction

An electron, in a beam of electrons, exhibits wave properties (p. 42), the wave length being dependent on the exciting voltage. These wave properties are employed to measure bond lengths and bond angles in gas molecules. Electrons of about 5×10^4 volts ($\lambda \sim 0.05$ Å) are passed through the gas or vapour at low pressure. The atoms in the molecules scatter the electron beam in much the same way as they diffract a beam of X-rays.

Electron diffraction is applied to solids too, the principles being again similar to those for X-rays. That the electrons do not penetrate so deeply is in some ways an advantage because it enables the nature of the surface and the surface film on a solid to be ascertained. For this purpose a pencil of electrons almost parallel to the surface is used. However, neither X-rays nor electrons are diffracted sufficiently by hydrogen to enable the positions of its atoms to be ascertained with much certainty.

Neutron diffraction

The diffraction of X-rays and electrons is due to interaction with the orbital electrons of the atoms they encounter. The diffraction of neutrons (p. 5) springs from different causes.

(*i*) *Nuclear scattering* is brought about by interaction with protons or neutrons in the nucleus and depends upon (a) nuclear *size* (which increases only slowly with atomic weight) and (b) nuclear *structure* (a dependence which appears to vary arbitrarily from one element to the next). Thus the hydrogen atom scatters neutrons as well as the potassium and better than the cobalt. This is in marked contrast to X-rays where the scattering increases smoothly with the number of extra-nuclear electrons in the atom.

(*ii*) *Magnetic scattering* arises from interaction between the magnetic moment of the neutron and that of the atom or ion in question. Thus the Fe^{3+} ion, with its unpaired electrons, gives additional scattering superimposed upon the nuclear scattering. Magnetic scattering is used to investigate the magnetic properties of alloys.

Neutrons emerging from an atomic reactor have a range of energies. They are collimated and monochromated to give a narrow pencil of neutrons with an energy corresponding to a wave length of about 1 Å. After scattering by the specimen, usually a single crystal, the diffraction pattern is obtained by means of a counter, filled with $^{10}BF_3$, connected to a pen-recorder.

The diffraction of neutrons provides a way of locating hydrogen atoms in compounds and is used to complement X-ray study of crystals especially by locating and characterising water molecules in hydrates (Bacon, 1958).

Molecular spectra

When radiation from a hydrogen discharge tube, with a continuous range of wave lengths from about 5000 Å into the ultra-violet, is passed through a gas or liquid, energy is absorbed by the molecules with consequent changes in their rotational, vibrational and electronic states. Analysis of the resulting spectra enables the sizes of the vibrational and rotational quanta characteristic of the molecule to be calculated. The sizes of the vibrational quanta are determined by the stiffness of the molecule and those of the rotational quanta by its moment of inertia.

The accuracy with which small energy changes in molecules can be measured has been greatly enhanced by methods using the absorption of radio-waves. This microwave spectroscopy provides information about purely rotational transitions in heavy molecules, inaccessible to examination even in the infrared because of the very long wave lengths associated with them. The existence of 'umbrella' inversion in NH_3 was recognised by this means.

$$\begin{array}{ccc} H & & H \\ H-N & \rightleftharpoons & N-H \\ H & & H \end{array}$$

Raman spectra

When monochromatic light is passed through a gas or liquid some of it is scattered. A small fraction of the scattered light has a slightly different wave length because the incident radiation perturbs the molecule, inducing a vibrational or rotational change, and has its own frequency altered in the process. The Raman spectra (1928) of the scattered radiation supply the same kind of information as does absorption in the infra-red but have two advantages:

(i) the source frequency can be chosen to give an easily photographed spectrum;

(ii) homonuclear diatomic molecules which give no rotational lines in the infra-red region are often active in the Raman.

Ions in solution may be readily recognised by their Raman spectra. Thus all metal nitrates give an NO_3^- line which is also shown by nitric acid with maximum intensity in about a 7M solution. More concentrated nitric acid contains fewer NO_3^- ions and more HNO_3 molecules. Cd^{2+} ions in solution produce a Raman line. This disappears on the addition of excess bromide ion probably because $CdBr_4^{2-}$ is formed—a new line appears similar in energy increment to that of $SnBr_4$. The addition of $SnCl_4$ to $SnBr_4$, however, gives rise to new lines presumably due to such species as $SnClBr_3$ and $SnCl_2Br_2$. The chlorides of carbon and silicon do not behave in this way; evidently Sn-halogen bonds are more labile. $PFCl_2$ and $PFBr_2$ produce a new line on mixing, presumably due to the formation of $PFClBr$.

Dipole moments

When a non-conductor is placed between the two plates of a condenser a capacitance change is produced from which the dielectric constant of the medium can be calculated. The increase in capacitance is caused by polarisation of the molecules in the electric field and P_M, the molar polarisation, is given by

$$P_M = \frac{\varepsilon - 1}{\varepsilon + 2} \cdot \frac{M}{\varrho}$$

where ε is the dielectric constant, M the molecular weight and ϱ the density. P_M is the sum of P_μ, the orientation polarisation due to the alignment in the field of molecules with permanent dipoles, and P_D, the polarisation due to distortion of molecules by the field, the induced polarisation.

If P_M is plotted against $1/T$ straight lines are obtained (Fig. 65). P_D is temperature-independent because thermal collisions may disturb the direction of a molecule but not that of an induced dipole; on the other hand P_μ decreases with temperature because random collisions interfere with the *lining up* of permanent dipoles in the field.

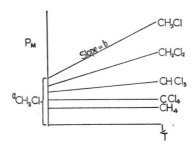

Fig. 65. Variation of molar polarisation with the reciprocal of absolute temperature.

The slope of the graph is thus a measure of the permanent dipole of the molecule. Debye (1912) showed that

$$b = \frac{4\pi N \mu^2}{9k}$$

Hence $\quad \mu = \sqrt{\dfrac{9kb}{4\pi N}}$

$$= 1.282 \times 10^{-20} \sqrt{b} \text{ esu}$$

$$= 0.01282 \sqrt{b} \text{ debye units } (10^{-18} \text{ esu}),$$

where μ is the dipole moment per molecule, k the Boltzmann constant, and N the Avogadro number.

Some values of μ (debye units) are given:

HCl	1.03	SO_2	1.61
HBr	0.78	CO_2	0
HI	0.38	BCl_3	0
H_2O	1.85	p-dichlorobenzene	0
NH_3	1.49	quinol	1.64

Dipole moments give information about the type of bond in a molecule.

(i) In HI the inter-atomic distance is 1.87 Å. As the electronic charge is 4.8×10^{-10} esu, the calculated moment of $\overset{+}{H}—\overset{-}{I}$ would be $(1.87 \times 10^{-8}) \times (4.8 \times 10^{-10})$ esu $= 9.0$ D. The actual moment is 0.38 D, which indicates that the bonding electrons are displaced only slightly towards the iodine and the bond is predominantly covalent.

(ii) The zero dipole moment of CO_2 must arise from the polarities of the two bonds cancelling exactly. This implies a linear molecule O=C=O. By the same token, H_2O and SO_2 must be angular. BCl_3 has zero moment because the molecule is planar with a Cl—B—Cl angle of 120°. NH_3, with its appreciable moment, must be a pyramidal molecule.

(iii) p-Dichlorobenzene has a zero moment and quinol an appreciable one. Evidently Cl atoms of the first are coplanar with the benzene ring but the OH groups of the second are not.

Paramagnetic susceptibilities

The number of electrons of unpaired spin in a molecule can usually be deduced from the paramagnetic moments (p. 78). This information may be useful in solving problems of valency, of choice between bond types, and of stereochemistry.

The Cu^+ ion, for instance, has a $3d^{10}$ structure. It is diamagnetic in all its compounds. The Cu^{2+} ion, however, has a $3d^9$ structure and its paramagnetic moment corresponds to the presence of one free electron. Thus the oxidation state of copper in one of its compounds can be found by measuring its paramagnetic susceptibility. Indeed the magnetic criterion of unpaired spin is so well established that, unless a compound is paramagnetic, the existence of an unpaired electron can be discounted.

A sample of powdered material, usually sealed in a glass tube, is suspended from a balance between the poles of a magnet. The lower end of the tube is in a strong field ($\sim 10,000$ gauss) and the upper in a negligible field (Gouy, 1889). The force exerted on the specimen is

$$\tfrac{1}{2} \varkappa H^2 A,$$

where $\varkappa$ is the volume susceptibility (p. 77), H the field strength in gauss, and A the cross-sectional area of the sample in cm². The force is measured by first counterpoising the sample without the magnetic field and adding weights (Δw) to restore the balance after the field has been applied. Then

$$\varkappa = \frac{2g\Delta w}{H^2 A}.$$

For strongly paramagnetic substances Δw may be several hundred mg when the cylindrical sample has a diameter of 5 to 10 mm, and an ordinary balance is sufficient. For measurements on weakly paramagnetic materials a micro-balance or electrodynamic balancing (Hilal and Fredericks, 1954) may be substituted.

An independent determination of the density ϱ of the solid is necessary for the calculation of the mass susceptibility χ (p. 77).

Nuclear magnetic resonance spectroscopy

Like an electron, an atomic nucleus possesses a spin; since the nucleus is not a single particle this is a resultant (*cf.* p. 61) and may or may not be zero. Many nuclei therefore have magnetic moments and exist in various quantum states in an applied magnetic field (*cf.* p. 54). As nuclear magnetic moments are $\sim$ 2000 times less than that of an electron, the separation, ΔE, of such states is very small. However, an applied field of several thousand gauss brings ν ($=\Delta E/h$) into the radio-frequency range. For the correct frequency, a sharp resonance occurs (Bloch and Purcell, 1946) in which spins are 'turned over' and radio-frequency energy is absorbed.

The field which determines the energy gap, ΔE, depends partly upon the molecular environment of a nucleus because orbital electrons produce magnetic effects which modify the applied field. Thus from the resonance absorption spectrum, it is possible to make inferences about this environment for nuclei with magnetic moments, such as those of ^{1}H and ^{19}F. There has been much interest in proton resonance and the method is being widely applied to solids, liquids and gases.

THEORETICAL INTERPRETATIONS

General principles

The forces holding atoms together in molecules and crystals have been interpreted (p. 81) in terms of the electron density. In recent years further theoretical principles have emerged; with them it has been possible to account for the shapes of molecules.

Although the forces on the nuclei depend on the charge density P (probability density for finding an electron at the given point), their equilibrium configuration is determined by the total energy of the system, and to understand the factors on which it depends, the *interaction* between different electrons must be examined. The interaction energy depends on the probability of two electrons being a given distance apart and accordingly on how their motions are *correlated*. Fortunately, this correlation is mainly associated with the exclusion principle (p. 59), which prevents electrons of like spin from occupying the same orbital or, more generally, the same region of space. If the various doubly occupied orbitals are chosen so as to be localised essentially in different parts of space, this correlation requirement is automatically met—for then electrons with the same spin are obviously always well separated. Thus, by working in terms of localised MO's, it is possible to get a picture not only of where an electron is *on the average* (the charge density) but also of where different electrons are *at the same instant*. The water molecule provides a good example. In the true molecular orbital approach, the electrons responsible for bonding would occupy orbitals extending over the whole molecule (Fig. 66 (a)): but in the earlier discussion of valency (p. 99) the electrons were supposed to occupy localised MO's

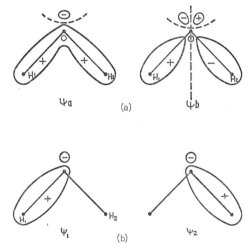

Fig. 66. (*a*) Molecular orbitals (each with two electrons) for the bonding electrons in H_2O (nodal surfaces indicated by broken lines).
   (*b*) Localised molecular orbitals (bond orbitals each with two electrons) for the bonding electrons in H_2O.

(Fig. 66 (b)). The two descriptions are, however, exactly equivalent, provided the two types of MO are related by

$$\psi_1 = \frac{1}{\sqrt{2}}\,(\psi_a + \psi_b) \quad \text{and} \quad \psi_2 = \frac{1}{\sqrt{2}}\,(\psi_a - \psi_b).$$

It is easily seen, for instance, that they give the same charge density contribution; for, when the orbitals are each doubly occupied, the density is

$$2\psi_1^2 + 2\psi_2^2 \;=\; (\psi_a^2 + 2\psi_a\psi_b + \psi_b^2) + (\psi_a^2 - 2\psi_a\psi_b + \psi_b^2) \;=\; 2\psi_a^2 + 2\psi_b^2.$$

But, by allocating the electrons to the localised MO's, we can describe, without mathematical analysis, the fact that two electrons with the same spin tend at any instant to occupy different regions of space. Different electron pairs have, in fact, an interaction energy which can be closely estimated by regarding each as a smeared-out charge.

The energy of interaction of different electron pairs plays an important role in determining the equilibrium shapes of molecules. Broadly speaking, its effect will be minimised when the different pairs (either lone pairs or bond pairs) are as far apart as possible. This idea is strongly supported by the observed spatial arrangement of the valencies of multicovalent atoms; it was, indeed, formulated on empirical grounds by Sidgwick and Powell in 1940.

Shapes of molecules and ions of non-transitional atoms

Beryllium has two valency electrons. It is in the sp state in its covalent compounds which have collinear σ bonds (Fig. 43, p. 100), the electron pairs of the two bonds being as far from each other as possible. This is the shape of the covalent halides of all metals with two electrons only in the valency shell, e.g. $HgCl_2$.

Boron, with three valency electrons, forms a planar trichloride, the boron being in an sp^2 valence state (Fig. 46, p.101). The electron pairs of the three bonds again are arranged at the greatest possible distances from one another. Tin in tin(II) chloride has also three pairs of electrons round the central atom but their disposition is no longer symmetrical since one of the valence states (roughly sp^2) holds a lone pair. The individual molecules observed in the vapour are therefore V-shaped (Fig. 67). The Cl–Sn–Cl angle is less than 120°, indicating that the lone pair repels the bonding pairs more strongly than they repel each other.

Four pairs of electrons tend to be arranged round a non-transitional atom in a tetrahedral configuration. This dictates the shapes of the methane, ammonia and water molecules (Fig. 68), already considered in some detail (p. 103). The bond angle in CH_4 is 109.5°, in NH_3 106.7° and in H_2O 104.5°, showing again the strong repulsion exerted by lone pairs on bonding pairs.

More than four electron pairs may be arranged about an atom only when

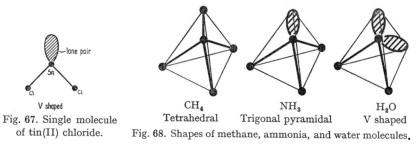

lone pair
Sn
Cl
Cl
V shaped

Fig. 67. Single molecule of tin(II) chloride.

CH_4
Tetrahedral
NH_3
Trigonal pyramidal
H_2O
V shaped

Fig. 68. Shapes of methane, ammonia, and water molecules.

d orbitals are used. As usual, it is convenient to work in terms of the orbitals d_{z^2}, $d_{x^2-y^2}$, d_{xy}, d_{yz}, d_{zx} (p. 52): the lobes of the first two are along the z

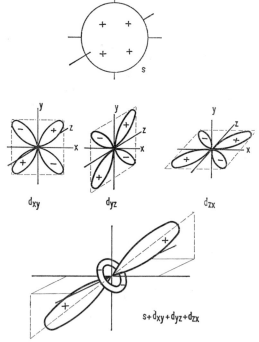

s
y
z
x
dxy
dyz
dzx
s+dxy+dyz+dzx

Fig. 69. Hybrid formed from s and d_ε orbitals.

axis and the x and y axes, respectively, and of the other three in the coordinate planes but falling between the axes. The two types are often referred to as d_γ (or e_g) and d_ε (or t_{2g}), respectively. It is the d_γ, s and p orbitals which can be mixed to give strongly directed hybrids; towards the corners of a trigonal bipyramid for sp³d (p. 105), of a square for sp²d (p. 106), and of an octahedron for sp³d² (p. 105). The d_ε orbitals give tetrahedral hybrids (more important in the transition elements), which are suitable for σ bonding when mixed with s (Fig. 69); when mixed with p, they commonly participate in π bonding (cf. Fig. 54, p. 106). As expected, five pairs tend to adopt the trigonal bipyramidal configuration and six pairs the octahedral.

The resulting shapes of molecules containing a central (non-transitional)

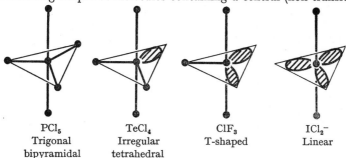

PCl₅	TeCl₄	ClF₃	ICl₂⁻
Trigonal bipyramidal	Irregular tetrahedral	T-shaped	Linear

Fig. 70. Shapes arising from the disposition of five electron pairs round a central atom. (In TeCl₄ and ClF₃ the two bonds are inclined from the vertical away from the lone pair(s).)

atom, about which there are five electron pairs, are shown in Fig. 70. In fact, all the covalent compounds of non-transitional elements with five pairs which have been investigated have the trigonal bipyramidal structure or one of these derived forms. Other shapes are possible but are ruled out if lone-pair–bond-pair repulsions are assumed to be stronger than bond-pair–bond-pair. Thus, in TeCl₄, lone-pair–bond-pair repulsion is minimised when the lone pair lies at about 120° to two of the bonds and about 90° to the other two. In the trigonal pyramid (Fig. 71) the lone pair would be close to

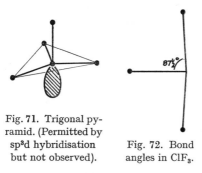

Fig. 71. Trigonal pyramid. (Permitted by sp³d hybridisation but not observed).

87½°

Fig. 72. Bond angles in ClF₃.

three (instead of two) bond pairs and electron repulsion energy would be higher; this alternative does not occur.

For similar reasons ClF_3 is T-shaped, not triangular. A triangular molecule involves six lone-pair–bond-pair angles of 90°, whereas a T-shaped molecule contains four lone-pair–bond-pair angles of 90° and two lone-pair–bond-pair angles of 120°. The latter is the more stable structure. The F—Cl—F angle is actually only 87.5° because of the strength of the lone-pair–bond-pair repulsions (Fig. 72).

The arrangement of six pairs of electrons about the atom of a non-transitional element is basically octahedral, but there again lone pairs tend to adopt positions in which their repulsive energy is a minimum (Fig. 73).

A most important principle to recognise is that the shapes of molecules and ions formed by non-transitional elements are determined mainly by the number of electron pairs round the central atom and by the repulsions between them. Lone-pair–lone-pair repulsion is strongest, lone-pair–bond-pair next and bond-pair–bond-pair weakest.

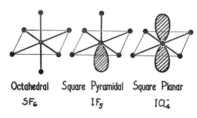

Octahedral   Square Pyramidal   Square Planar
SF_6 IF_5 ICl_4^-

Fig. 73. Shapes based on octahedral disposition of electron-pairs round a central atom.

Another factor affecting bond angles is the electronegativity of the central atom. Thus the bond angle in H_2O is 104.5° but in H_2S only 92.5°, corresponding to a fall in electronegativity from 3.5 in oxygen to 2.5 in sulphur. The bond pairs lie nearer to the O in H_2O than to the S in H_2S, so that in H_2O the bond-pair–bond-pair repulsion is greater and the effect of the lone pairs on the angle between the bonds less than in H_2S. If the bonding were truly ionic the configuration would become tetrahedral, possessing 4 equivalent lone pairs.

Molecules with π bonds

The description of π bonding already adopted (p. 94) apparently conflicts with the fact that electron pairs tend to stay apart, for the π pair is superimposed on the σ pair. But, as on p. 124, the same wave function can be built out of alternative orbitals which do lie in different regions. In, for instance, ethylene (Fig. 48, p. 102) we can choose

$$\psi_1 = \frac{1}{\sqrt{2}}(\psi_\sigma + \psi_\pi) \quad \text{and} \quad \psi_2 = \frac{1}{\sqrt{2}}(\psi_\sigma - \psi_\pi),$$

where ψ_σ and ψ_π are the σ bond and π bond MO's. The configurations $(\psi_1)^2(\psi_2)^2$ and $(\psi_\sigma)^2(\psi_\pi)^2$ both reproduce the same charge density, but the former also indicates the simultaneous dispositions of the two pairs. There is here striking resemblance to the *bent bond* picture of Bayer's *strain theory*; and indeed the bent bond orbitals, one lying above the molecular plane and one below, could have been approximated by overlapping tetrahedral hybrids.

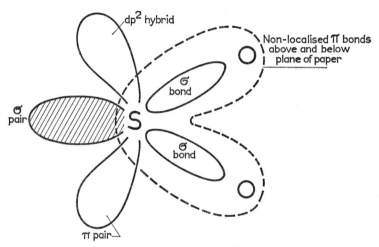

Fig. 74. Bonding in SO_2.

Nevertheless, it is simpler, and usually satisfactory, to employ the σ–π description, regarding the less strongly bound π electrons as of secondary importance in determining molecular shape. The basic configuration is settled by σ electron pairs; any remaining ambiguity is then resolved by π bond considerations. Thus in CO_2 the two single bonds formed by the central carbon adopt the linear configuration typical of bivalent metals, and the superimposed π bonding does not affect this shape. But in ethylene the pair of plane triangular CH_2 groups could rotate about the central bond were it not for the presence of π bonding. In SO_2 the sulphur may, in the first instance, be regarded as sp^2 hybridised, providing two single bonds and a lone pair with a second lone pair in the remaining 3p orbital; this gives the plane triangular form. If then pd² hybridisation is admitted, the 3p lone pair may be replaced by three π-type hybrids (Fig. 74) two of which

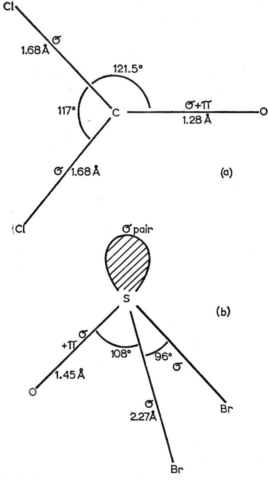

Fig. 75. (*a*) Plane triangular carbonyl chloride molecule. (*b*) Irregular pyramidal shape of thionyl bromide molecule.

overlap oxygen 2p orbitals, describing (dative) π bonds, while the third accommodates the original lone pair. Again, the π stabilisation does not affect the plane triangular form. Similarly, the plane triangular and irregular pyramidal forms of carbonyl chloride and thionyl bromide (Fig. 75) are associated with three and four electron pairs, respectively, and the π bonding is again relatively unimportant in determining the shapes of the molecules.

An examination of bond angles shows that π bonding may be assumed merely to increase the repelling power of the bond pair on which it is superimposed. This is natural since the π bond supplements the electron density of the underlying σ bond.

Transition elements. Complexes

The non-transitional elements are characterised by electron configurations of the type

$$[(\textit{filled shells})\ ns^y,\ np^z]$$

in which the number of valence electrons $y + z$, varies from 1 to 8 and hybridisation involves ns and np orbitals and, less commonly, nd. The metals with $y = 1$ or 2, $z = 0$, have small electronegativities and readily form ionic bonds. As z increases electrons are lost less easily, ionic character diminishes, and the atom holds near it up to 4 electron pairs; this number may be increased to 6 by d hybridisation and acceptance of electrons.

In the transition elements the electron configuration is

$$[(\textit{filled shells})\ (n - 1)d^x,\ ns^y]$$

in which $y = 1$ or 2 and x goes from 1 to 10. They resemble the Gp. I and Gp. II metals in having low electronegativity; but, owing to the incomplete d shell, the number of electrons available for bonding is potentially much larger. The $(n - 1)$d, ns, np and even the nd orbitals may lie so close together that promotion and hybridisation occur freely. The transition elements are accordingly distinguished by having a variable oxidation state and usually being highly ionic. Often, however, all the d orbitals are not free to participate in hybridisation; they may describe a stable sub-shell, not affected by bonding. The valence properties of a transition metal are thus controlled to some extent by the stability of incomplete d shells. This in turn is determined largely by the strength and symmetry of the electric field imposed by the attached atoms, ions or groups (known collectively as ligands) according to the *ligand field theory* (Bethe, 1929; Van Vleck, 1932).

In the simplest theory (Bethe) the electrons are allocated to atomic orbitals, from energy and electronegativity considerations, which may imply a limiting purely ionic model. Thus, the ion FeF_6^{3-}, which occurs in potassium fluoroferrate, would be regarded as Fe^{3+} surrounded octahedrally by 6 F⁻ ions. Covalent character can always be admitted later by allowing metal and ligand orbitals to mix, and the primary aim of the theory is to decide which metal orbitals are likely to take part in bonding.

In the free atom the d orbitals are degenerate (p. 51) and electrons occupy them as far as possible singly with parallel spins (Hund's rules, p. 63). The field produced by nearby ligands can, however, resolve this degeneracy. If, for example, six electron-rich groups are placed octahedrally (on the x, y, and z axes) about a central atom, an electron in a d_γ ($d_{x^2-y^2}$ or d_{z^2}) orbital will have a higher energy than one in a d_ε (d_{xy}, d_{xz} or d_{yz}) because it will spend more time close to the negative charges on the axes. Although the two d_γ orbitals differ in shape, it can be shown that they are equally affected by an octahedral perturbation, as also are the three d_ε orbitals. The sequence of the d orbital energies is given below for various arrangements of negative ligands:

d ORBITAL ENERGY LEVELS IN VARIOUS LIGAND FIELDS

	Octahedral	Square	Tetrahedral	Trigonal bipyramidal
Energy ↑	d_{z^2}, $d_{x^2-y^2}$ —	$d_{x^2-y^2}$ —	d_{xy}, d_{yz}, d_{xz} —	d_{z^2} —
		d_{xy} —		d_{xy} —
		d_{xz}, d_{yz} —		$d_{x^2-y^2}$ —
	d_{xy}, d_{yz}, d_{zx} —	d_{z^2}, —	d_{z^2}, $d_{x^2-y^2}$ —	d_{xz}. d_{yz} —

The order of energies in a square field varies considerably with the ligands: the $d_{x^2-y^2}$ always has the highest energy, but the order of the remaining orbitals depends markedly on the minor details of the model chosen. The order given is a typical one.

The splitting is substantial and the energies concerned may sometimes reach 40 to 50 kcal/mole. It is directly revealed in the strong absorption which is responsible for the brightly coloured salts of transition metals.

Consider now one of the simpler transition metals, titanium, whose ground state is $Ti(3d^2 4s^2)$. The molecule $TiCl_4$ would first be regarded as Ti^{4+} with four Cl^- ions attached tetrahedrally. The empty valence orbitals ($3d_\gamma$, $3d_\varepsilon$, 4s) would all be free to mix with ligand orbitals in setting up MO's to admit covalent character. The s and d_ε orbitals would be closest in energy (Fig. 76 (a)) and would mix freely; and d^3s hybridisation* in fact produces tetrahedral hybrids, of the type shown in Fig. 69, each of which overlaps an appropriately directed Cl^- lone pair to give (by donation) a doubly occupied, localised MO. Vanadium, with one more electron, also forms a tetrachloride; the bonding is similar but the natural place for the extra electron is now the low-lying d_γ orbital. Non-bonding electrons can therefore be accommodated in inner d orbitals—instead of having to go into antibonding MO's—and the ligand field theory shows which orbitals are available for this purpose.

* It is usual to arrange the orbitals in order of principal quantum number (p. 106). Here d^3s corresponds to $3d^3 4s^1$, whereas sd^3 would have implied $4s^1 4d^3$; the two types are often referred to as 'inner' and 'outer' hybrids.

Chromium, with a nuclear charge two higher than titanium, forms tetra-halides with *two* d_γ electrons. The number of extra electrons which can be accommodated in the low-lying d_γ orbitals is however limited, because such electrons exert a screening effect and thus weaken the bonds between the ligands and the central atom. Manganese does not form tetrahalides.

The number of non-bonding electrons which have to be accommodated in low-lying orbitals can be kept down by adding further strongly electroneg-ative ligands. The octahedral VF_6^- and TiF_6^{2-} ions are without non-bonding electrons in low-lying d orbitals (which are d_ε in the field created by the octa-hedrally-disposed negative ligands). The energy of the d_γ orbitals in this case lies near that of the 4s and 4p orbitals (Fig. 76b) and they are able to particip-ate in $d_\gamma{}^2sp^3$ hybridisation suitable for octahedral bonding. Manganese with a charge number of $+4$ does not occur in complexes of this type; thus in $MnCl_6^{2-}$, for example, which has three electrons accommodated in low-lying d_ε orbitals, none of these takes part in bonding.

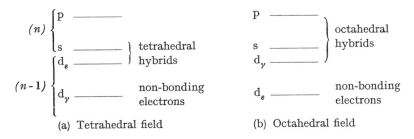

(a) Tetrahedral field   (b) Octahedral field

Fig. 76. Energies and functions of d orbitals in ligand fields. (The d orbitals are of the shell underlying that of the s and p orbitals.)

To summarise: when electron-rich ligands are symmetrically disposed about a transition element, the high-energy d orbitals are just the ones needed for covalent bonding while the low-energy d orbitals serve to drain off excess non-bonding electrons. It is worth noting that electron-deficient ligands never occur—because the order of the energy levels would be inverted and hybridisation inhibited.

The most interesting applications of ligand field theory have been made when there are several non-bonding electrons. Consider, for instance, an atom or ion with five d electrons in an octahedral ligand field. When the field is weak the electrons will, as in the free atom, occupy different orbitals singly (Fig. 77(a), (b)). But if the field is increased, the d_γ electrons will eventually fall into d_ε orbitals, the drop in orbital energy outweighing the increase in mutual repulsion of the electrons (Fig. 77(c)). The occupation and availability of the d orbitals is therefore determined by the field strength; and there will clearly be distinct strong-field and weak-field configurations for 4, 5, 6, and 7 d electrons. The Fe^{3+} ion provides a good example. The presence of five unpaired electrons in the ion $(FeF_6)^{3-}$ is revealed by magnetic measurements (p. 79) (moment $5.9\mu_B$, 5 parallel spins); and, since the ligands are F^- ions, the central ion must be Fe^{3+} with the weak-field configuration (Fig. 77(b)). The shell of five equally occupied d orbitals is completely symmetrical and evidently very stable. The F^- ions can each donate two electrons to a bond, when covalent character is admitted, but this requires the use of empty Fe orbitals; and sp^3d^2 octahedral hybridisation would require the use of d orbitals of the next shell (i.e. 4d).

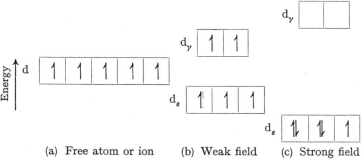

(a) Free atom or ion   (b) Weak field   (c) Strong field

Fig. 77. Effect of an octahedral ligand field on occupation of the d orbitals.

The same is true in $(FeCl_4)^-$, although the positions of d_γ and d_ε orbitals are reversed and, in admitting covalency, the appropriate hybrids would be $4s\,4p^3$ (tetrahedral). Such systems are often described as *spin-free, outer orbital* or *high spin*. In potassium hexacyanoferrate(III), however, $[Fe(CN)_6]^{3-}$ occurs, and the moment ($2.5\,\mu_B$) indicates only one free spin; evidently this is the strong-field case (Fig. 77(c)). The $3d_\gamma$ orbitals are thus made available for bonding, and d^2sp^3 hybrids overlap with, and partly accept, the carbon lone pairs of the CN^- groups, to produce six covalent bonds. Such systems are called *spin-paired, inner orbital*, or *low spin* complexes.

The magnitude of the splitting of the energy levels determines the type of the complex, and depends on the amount of electron density which the ligands put into the regions covered by the different d orbitals. It will be large if the lone pairs offered by the ligands occupy large and well directed orbitals, but smaller for those with more compact orbitals such as the electronegative halides. For a given cation, the splitting increases along the sequence:

I^-, Br^-, Cl^-, OH^-, F^-, H_2O, NH_3, CN^- (the *spectrochemical series*).

It is revealed in the shift towards the blue suffered by prominent absorption bands as one ligand is replaced by the next. The effect is increased when the central cation is replaced by the corresponding member of a higher transition series, and also by any π bonding which serves to reduce metal-ligand distances.

Shapes of complexes. Deviations from regularity

When all the orbitals of a degenerate group are equally occupied (*e.g.* d_γ^2, d_γ^4, d_ε^3, ... in octahedral or tetrahedral situations) the resultant non-bonding charge density has the same symmetry as the system of bonds and is without disturbing influence upon them. Thus, $(TiCl_6)^{2-}$ (d^0), $[Cr(NH_3)_6]^{3+}$ (d_ε^3), $[FeF_6]^{3-}$ $(d_\varepsilon^3 d_\gamma^2)$, and $[Zn(NH_3)_6]^{2+}$ $(d_\varepsilon^6 d_\gamma^4)$ all have perfect octahedral symmetry. But when the degenerate group orbitals are not equally occupied this is not so; $[Ti(H_2O)_6]^{3+}$ (d_ε^1), $[Fe(H_2O)_6]^{2+}$ $(d_\varepsilon^4 d_\gamma^2)$ and many other systems are slightly distorted. This distortion sometimes amounts to a radical change of symmetry, particularly with central ions possessing d^4 and d^9 elections.

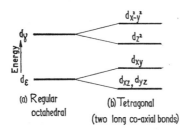

(a) Regular octahedral

(b) Tetragonal
(two long co-axial bonds)

Fig. 78. Effect of withdrawing the two ligands on the z axis; octahedral symmetry undergoing transition to tetragonal symmetry

The high-spin complex $[MnF_6]^{3-}$ is tetragonal, having four equal bonds in the plane square and two considerably longer axial ones. This effect is found whenever the electron configuration of the central ion contains unequally occupied degenerate orbitals, and was first predicted (theoretically) by Jahn and Teller (1937). The theory shows that the energy of, say, a $d_\varepsilon^3 d_\gamma^1$ ion in an octahedral field (*e.g.* Mn^{3+}) is reduced when the ligands on one of the axes are moved outwards and those on the others are moved symmetrically inwards. This results in a perfectly regular octahedral disposition of ligands changing spontaneously to one of tetragonal form. The change in energy levels as two ligands are withdrawn is shown in Fig. 78. Thus, in Mn^{III} in MnF_6 $^{3-}$ (weak field) only the $3d_{x^2-y^2}$ orbital would be available for bonding (the dsp^2 square system (p. 106), and the $4p_z$ or $4d_{z^2}$ orbital would have to be used in the longer axial bonds. In MnF_3, distorted MnF_3 octahedra are joined by sharing corners, and the lower symmetry of the structure, compared with other trifluorides of the first transition series, results from there being three different Mn–F bonds (2.09, 1.91 and 1.79 Å) within each octahedron (Hepworth, Jack and Nyholm, 1957). The magnetic moment of 4.9 Bohr magnetons implies that there are four unpaired electrons in the 3d shell of the manganese, three in the d_ε and the fourth possibly in the d_{z^2}. The empty $d_{x^2-y^2}$ points in the direction of four F^- ions and together with the 4s and two 4p orbitals form four hybrid dsp^2 bonds directed towards the corners of a square. The singly occupied $3d_\varepsilon$ orbitals offer no repulsion since they point between the fluoride ions, but the other singly occupied orbital, namely d_{z^2}, points along the axis to the remaining two Mn–F bonds and does exert repulsion, thus accounting for their abnormal length (2.09 Å). Neighbouring MnF_6 octahedra are oriented so that a fluorine atom, common to both, is at either 1.91 Å from each Mn or at 2.09 Å from one and 1.79 Å from the next, thus maintaining the close-packing of the distorted octahedra.

Theory predicts the same effect for any octahedrally co-ordinated crystal structure or co-ordination compound in which the central ion has four unpaired d electrons. This has been confirmed for CrF_2, in which the Cr^{2+} is isoelectronic with the Mn^{3+} ion (Jack and Maitland, 1957). The Cr–F distance is 2.43 Å along the z axis, but only 2.01 and 1.98 Å along the x and y axes. Clearly it is not possible always to assume spherically symmetrical ions of fixed radii, since the interionic distances depend on the geometry of the occupied orbitals and the direction of approach of the surrounding groups.

The same effect occurs in octahedral complexes containing Cu^{2+} ($d_\varepsilon^6 d_\gamma^3$), covalency again requiring the use of 4d orbitals. CuF_2 has a distorted rutile structure in which there are two F^- ions at 2.27 Å and four at 1.93 Å from the Cu^{2+} (Orgel and Dunitz, 1957). But when the metal ion has 5, 6, 7, 8, or 10 electrons, difluorides have essentially undistorted rutile lattices (Fig. 93).

Very often the ligands on the z axis are withdrawn altogether to give square complexes such as $[Cr(H_2O)_4]^{2+}$ ($d_\varepsilon^3 d_\gamma^1$); this is another example of a d^4 ion.

Equally filled degenerate orbitals are also present in the perfectly tetrahedral complexes: $[FeO_4]^{2-}$ (d_γ^2), $[FeCl_4]^-$ ($d_\gamma^2 d_\varepsilon^3$), $[CoCl_4]^{2-}$ ($d_\gamma^4 d_\varepsilon^3$), $[ZnCl_4]^{2-}$ and $[Zn(acac)_2]$ ($d_\gamma^4 d_\varepsilon^6$). Slightly distorted tetrahedra occur less frequently, probably, for example, in the vanadium tetrahalides, (d_γ^1). Usually there is a complete transition to the plane square form. A spin-free arrangement $d_\gamma^2 d_\varepsilon^2$ in a tetrahedral field would cause strong distorting forces; these are completely relieved in the square system, both degenerate pairs of orbitals being uniformly filled and $d_{x^2-y^2}$ being left free for dsp^2 hybridisation and covalent bonding.

A great variety of complexes exists (pp. 533–555), but the same general principles serve in the interpretation of their shapes and properties.

Factors influencing co-ordination number

In general, ligands which more readily share their electrons appear in complexes with smaller co-ordination numbers; Br^- and Cl^- ligands give 4 co-ordination with Co^{2+}, and H_2O and NH_3 give 6 co-ordination. The number also decreases with increasing electronegativity of the metal. These facts suggest that Pauling's 'postulate of neutrality'—that the net charge on any atom shall not differ greatly from zero (e.g. by not more than ± 1 electron)—is a useful criterion. Thus it takes six H_2O groups to donate 2 electrons to the Co^{2+} valence shell, but only four Cl^- ions which are clearly richer in electrons. And whereas Cu^+ and Ag^+ require 4 co-ordination to achieve approximate neutrality, the more electronegative Au^+ which can take a greater share of electrons from each bond, is often satisfied by 2 co-ordination.

Classical electrovalency and ligand field theory

The ligand field theory is essentially a development from the classical theory of 'electrovalency'. Both are concerned with a redistribution of charge whereby electrons are supplied to the more electronegative atoms at the expense of a metal. The theories differ in that the classical one described the result in terms of ions whereas it is now clear that the 'transfer' of electrons is merely a formal step. The electrons taken from the metal are best described by MO's which extend over both the electronegative and electropositive atoms, and these MO's, with their covalent character, return charge to the vicinity of the metal. Much of the older terminology is retained because, as a first step, the ionic model is invoked, after which the ligand theory suggests the orbitals available and the hybridisation appropriate. Thus, for example, an Fe^{III} compound (the superscript giving the classical electrovalency) is one in which for descriptive purposes we first remove three electrons to get Fe^{3+} and then re-allocate these electrons (and others from the ligands) to suitable bonding MO's. The metal then has a *formal charge number* $+3$, this being the number of electrons absorbed in bonding. Since the removal of electrons is intimately connected with oxidation (p. 181) the charge number of a metal in a compound is also referred to as its *oxidation number*.

Chapter 7

The Solid State

The properties of a solid depend not only on the number and kind of atoms composing it but also on their arrangement. The empirical formula reveals nothing of this, for AB_2 can exist in the solid
  (i) as separate molecules;
       (B—A—B in solid carbon dioxide),
 (ii) as an infinite layer (Fig. 79),
       (cadmium iodide, CdI_2, is like this, though the atoms are not quite co-planar);
(iii) in various three-dimensional structures (Fig. 80),
       (fluorite, CaF_2, has cubic crystals with one of these arrangements).

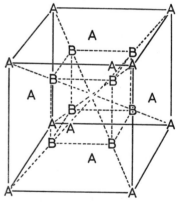

```
B   B   B   B
  B   B   B   B   B
A   A   A   A
  B   B   B   B
B   B   B   B
  A   A   A   A
B   B   B   B
  B   B   B   B   B
A   A   A   A
  B   B   B   B
B   B   B   B
```

Fig. 79. Infinite layer of formula AB_2.   Fig. 80. Cubic structure of formula AB_2.

In (i) every carbon atom is connected to two oxygen atoms, in (ii) every cadmium atom has six iodine atoms as nearest neighbours, and in (iii) every calcium atom has eight fluorine atoms as nearest neighbours. The chemical formula of a solid should therefore be considered in relation to its crystal structure. Even two solids, as similar in formulation as PCl_5 and PBr_5, differ structurally; the former consists of equal numbers of PCl_4^+ ions and PCl_6^- ions, the latter of PBr_4^+ and Br^- ions.

The unit cell

A crystalline solid consists of atoms (or ions) packed regularly in a three-dimensional arrangement. For any point in the pattern it is possible to find other points possessing exactly the same environment. Such points then define a regular *lattice:* one lattice point can be reached from another by taking a suitable number of primitive translations (steps) along each of three suitable directions. Clearly the whole pattern can be built up by translating a block of essentially different points lying in a certain *unit cell*. The nature of the solid is determined by the size, shape and content of its unit cell.

The size and shape of a unit cell is defined by the lengths (a, b, c) of three intersecting edges and the angles (α, β, γ) between them (Fig. 81).

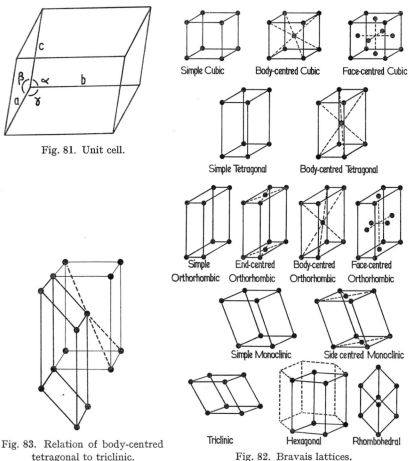

Fig. 81. Unit cell.

Simple Cubic   Body-centred Cubic   Face-centred Cubic

Simple Tetragonal   Body-centred Tetragonal

Simple Orthorhombic   End-centred Orthorhombic   Body-centred Orthorhombic   Face-centred Orthorhombic

Simple Monoclinic   Side centred Monoclinic

Triclinic   Hexagonal   Rhombohedral

Fig. 83. Relation of body-centred tetragonal to triclinic.

Fig. 82. Bravais lattices.

There are seven types of unit cell (see Table 14) and therefore seven *simple* or *primitive* lattices with one unit of pattern at each cell corner.

TABLE 14

THE SEVEN TYPES OF UNIT CELL

			Example
Cubic	$a = b = c$	$a = \beta = \gamma = 90°$	Rock salt
Tetragonal	$a = b \neq c$	$a = \beta = \gamma = 90°$	White tin
Orthorhombic	$a \neq b \neq c$	$a = \beta = \gamma = 90°$	Mercuric chloride
Monoclinic	$a \neq b \neq c$	$a = \gamma = 90° \; \beta \neq 90°$	Potassium chlorate
Triclinic	$a \neq b \neq c$	$a \neq \beta \neq \gamma \neq 90°$	Potassium dichromate
Hexagonal	$a \neq b \neq c$	$a = \beta = 90° \; \gamma = 120°$	Silica
Rhombohedral	$a = b = c$	$a = \beta = \gamma \neq 90°$	Calcite

Bravais lattices

If the *contents* of a unit cell have symmetry, containing a number of units of pattern (atoms, molecules), the number of distinct types of space lattice becomes *fourteen* (Fig. 82) (Bravais, 1848). And when other symmetry operations are recognised (*e.g.* rotation of the lattice) there are found to be 230 distinct varieties of crystal symmetry.

A compound lattice that contains body-, face-, or end-centred points can always be regarded as a *simple* lattice with a smaller unit cell. Thus, the body-centred tetragonal is a special case of the triclinic (Fig. 83). The centred lattices describe most readily the higher symmetry.

Cohesive forces in crystals

Although the sub-division of valency bonds into types is not rigid, four main types are distinguishable in solids. When all the bonds are of the same type the solid is *homodesmic*.

TABLE 15

SOME HOMODESMIC SOLIDS

Type of binding	Examples
(i) Ionic	Rock salt, fluorite
(ii) Homopolar	Diamond, zinc blende
(iii) Metallic	Copper, manganese
(iv) Van der Waals	Argon

Should the bonds be all of equal strength the solid is *isodesmic*, otherwise it is *anisodesmic*.

Heterodesmic solids contain more than one type of bond:

(i) Solid carbon dioxide has homopolar bonds in the individual molecules; but the molecules are held to one another by Van der Waals' forces.

(ii) Antimony consists of puckered sheets of covalently bound atoms with metallic binding holding the sheets together.

Ionic binding

Since the field due to an ion is spherically symmetrical, an ion attracts as many ions of opposite charge as can be grouped round it. Cations are usually smaller than anions. Only 6 Cl^- ions (1.81 Å) can be accommodated round a K^+ (1.33 Å) so that they all 'touch' the cation; very many more K^+ ions could be accommodated round the Cl^- ion. But electrical neutrality must be achieved, and as the system is stable only when the cation touches all the anions surrounding it, the co-ordination is 6 : 6. Any single K^+ has as its nearest neighbours 6 Cl^- ions arranged octahedrally; similarly any Cl^- has a corresponding arrangement of K^+ ions around it (Fig. 84).

The Cs^+ ion (1.69 Å) can accommodate about it 8 Cl^- ions and the co-ordination is 8:8 (Fig. 85).

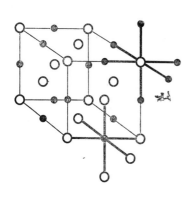

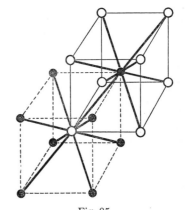

Fig. 84.	Fig. 85.
KCl lattice showing 6:6 co-ordination.	CsCl lattice, showing 8:8 co-ordination.

Radius ratios

The number of anions surrounding the cation, the *co-ordination number* of the cation, in the crystal depends on the ratio r_c/r_a, of the respective ionic radii. The limiting values of r_c/r_a for various co-ordination numbers are given in Table 16.

TABLE 16

CORRESPONDENCE BETWEEN r_c/r_a VALUES, CO-ORDINATION
NUMBER OF CATION, AND ARRANGEMENT

r_c/r_a	Co-ordination number of cation	Arrangement
1	12	Close packing
1 → 0.73	8	At cube corners
0.73 → 0.41	6	Octahedral
0.41 → 0.22	4	Tetrahedral

In anisodesmic crystals square, triangular and linear arrangements are possible:

0.73 → 0.41	4	Square
0.22 → 0.16	3	Triangular
0.16	2	Linear

The co-ordination numbers 5, 7, 9, 10 and 11 are excluded by geometry if the positive and negative charges are to balance one another.

In crystals of the compound AB_2 the co-ordination number of A is twice that of B and the structure is determined by the co-ordination number of the smaller ion. The *radius ratio rule* is clear-cut only with simple ions. Dimorphism is much commoner where complex ions are involved. Even the relatively simple CO_3^{2-} ion can co-ordinate in different ways without causing any change in the empirical formula of the compound; thus $CaCO_3$ exists as both calcite and aragonite. In general, the rule is most likely to break down where large, easily polarised anions are present.

Strength of ionic binding

As the energy required to separate a pair of ions is approximately proportional to

$$\frac{z_1 z_2}{r_c + r_a}$$

where z_1 and z_2 are the respective charges, the hardness (Table 17) and melting point (Table 18) of crystals with similarly charged ions should vary inversely as the inter-ionic distance. Where the inter-ionic distance is about the same, the relative hardness and melting point become dependent on the ionic charges (Table 19).

TABLE 17

$(r_c + r_a)$-VALUES AND HARDNESS OF SOME OXIDES

	MgO	CaO	SrO	BaO
$r_c + r_a$ (Å)	2.05	2.40	2.53	2.75
Hardness (Mohs' scale)	6.5	4.5	3.5	3.2

TABLE 18

$(r_c + r_a)$-VALUES AND MELTING POINTS OF THE SODIUM HALIDES

	NaF	NaCl	NaBr	NaI
$r_c + r_a$ (Å)	2.34	2.79	2.94	3.18
M.p. (°C)	988	801	740	660

TABLE 19

INFLUENCE OF IONIC CHARGE ON STRENGTH OF IONIC BINDING

	NaF	CaO
$r_c + r_a$ (Å)	2.34	2.40
$z_1 \times z_2$	1	4
Hardness (Mohs' scale)	3.2	4.5
M.p. (°C)	988	2570

Crystals with strong ionic bonds always have low coefficients of thermal expansion. Though the solids are non-conducting because the electrons are all firmly bound in atomic orbitals, conductance by migration of ions is possible in the fused state. Ionic bonds are often broken by media of high dielectric constant such as water ($\varepsilon = 78$). Binary simple salts, exemplified by NaCl, are generally more easily dissociated in aqueous solution than such compounds as MgO where the interionic attraction is large.

Certain principles are evident in the building up of ionic crystals. These, known as Pauling's rules, are useful even when the ionic picture is not strictly valid and considerable covalent character must be conceded:

(i) A co-ordinated polyhedron of anions is formed about each cation, the cation-anion distance being determined by the radius sum, and the co-ordination number by the radius ratio.

(ii) In a stable co-ordination structure, the total number of the valency bonds which reach an anion from all the neighbouring cations is equal to the charge of the anion.

(iii) The existence of edges, and particularly faces, common to two anion polyhedra decreases the stability of the structure.

(iv) Cations with a high charge number and a small co-ordination number tend not to share polyhedron elements with one another.

(v) The environments of all chemically similar anions in a structure tend to be similar.

These rules are particularly valuable in their application to more complicated structures.

Homopolar crystals

Unlike ionic structures where co-ordination numbers are determined by the radius ratio rule and the bonds are not directed, homopolar structures have directed bonds. An element in the Nth group of the Periodic Table can form $8-N$ bonds per atom and co-ordination numbers are small, usually four or less.

Few crystals are perfectly homopolar. Diamond is homopolar though not purely covalent (*cf.* H_2 where H^+—H^- and H^-—H^+ both contribute to the bond). In it the individual carbon atoms are held tetrahedrally to 4 others by bonds similar to those between the carbon atoms in aliphatic compounds; accordingly the crystal is a truly homopolar, homodesmic solid. Silicon and germanium are similar. Zinc blende, ZnS, has a like character, but the 4 bonds about the individial atoms are formed from 2 electrons derived from the zinc and 6 from the sulphur atoms. The valency electrons tend to be drawn towards the sulphur atoms, conferring some polarity on the bonds. This illustrates the fact that there is no sharp demarcation between homopolar and ionic crystals. Zinc blende would normally be considered covalently bonded—a low co-ordination number usually implies directed bonds—but in this, and indeed in many other instances, it is convenient to regard the structure formally as being composed of Zn^{2+} and S^{2-} ions, the latter distorted, or polarised, in the field of the former (p. 92). This is possible because in solids the exigencies of packing and electrical neutrality are determining factors. Of course, the greater the divergence from ionic character the greater is the disagreement with Pauling's first rule; bond lengths are shortened and co-ordination numbers reduced below those required by the radius rule.

Metals

The true metals comprise those of Gps. IA and IIA, the transitional elements and the coinage metals: they are designated by T (p. 113). Atoms of a T metal are closely packed and without directional bonds. The metals are relatively soft and malleable since the atoms glide easily over one another.

B sub-group metals are rather more covalent in character, those of Gps IIB and IIIB being nearer true metals than Se, Te, As, Sb and Bi. Zinc and cadmium, for example, have distorted, close-packed hexagonal arrangements in which the axial ratios are about 1.87 instead of the ideal 1.63 (Fig. 86). Aluminium and indium have approximately face-centred cubic lattices, and thallium has a close-packed hexagonal one. In Gp.VIB, white tin possesses a character between that of lead and silicon; its co-ordination number is 6. Grey tin has the diamond structure and a co-ordination number of 4. Lead is face-centred cubic and behaves as a true metal. The ions present in the solid may contain the $6s^2$ inert pairs, giving it the character of a Gp.2A metal.

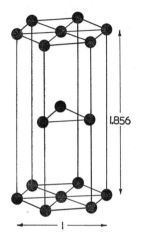

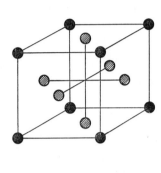

Fig. 86. Distorted h.c.p. structure of zinc.   Fig. 87. Alloy with Au:Cu ratio 1:3.

Substitutional alloys

These are obtained by starting with metal X and gradually replacing its atoms with those of Y. Two true metals yield a TT alloy. TB and BB alloys are also possible.

A typical TT combination is formed by silver and gold, both of which have a face-centred cubic lattice and atoms of very nearly the same size (Au, 1.339 Å; Ag, 1.342 Å). They give a continuous series of solid solutions with random distribution; an alloy of this type is possible when the radius ratio does not exceed 1.14 and the charge numbers are alike.

Copper has a radius of 1.176 Å. At a high temperature, gold forms a continuous solid solution with it. Rapid quenching retains this condition, but slow annealing allows the atoms to segregate. At a composition Au:Cu = 1:1, alternate sheets of gold and copper appear and the symmetry is converted from cubic to tetragonal. With Au:Cu = 1:3, the ordered form is cubic, Au being at the cube corners and Cu at the face centres (Fig. 87). The disordered form of this alloy is brittle; the ordered form is more malleable, more ductile, and a better conductor. At the *order-disorder transition temperature* the specific heat increases markedly, thermal energy being necessary to disorder the atoms and increase the entropy (p. 168).

An example of a TB alloy is found in the system silver-cadmium. Silver has a face-centred cubic structure, cadmium an elongated close-packed hexagonal one like zinc (p. 145). Five phases occur. The random α-phase contains less than 42% Cd. At about this composition a β-phase begins to be formed, and at 50% Cd the structure is ordered body-centred cubic. At 57% Cd a complicated γ-phase appears, and from 70–82% Cd a close-packed hexagonal ε-phase. Finally, at high Cd concentrations a η-phase is formed which is a solid solution of silver in cadmium in close-packed hexagonal arrangement. Many TB systems show a similar sequence of intermediate phases. In the zinc, aluminium and tin alloys of copper, β-, γ- and ε-phases appear at certain compositions (see Table 20).

TABLE 20

COMPOSITION AND PHASE OF SOME ALLOYS

β	γ	ε
$CuZn$	Cu_5Zn_8	$CuZn_3$
Cu_3Al	Cu_9Al_4	Cu_5Al_3
Cu_5Sn	$Cu_{31}Sn_8$	Cu_3Sn

Hume-Rothery (1926) pointed out that the appearance of a particular phase depended on the ratio of valency electrons to atoms (see Table 21). For a β-phase it is $\frac{3}{2}$.

TABLE 21

RATIO OF VALENCY ELECTRONS TO ATOMS FOR SOME ALLOYS

Cu (1) + Zn (2)	3/2
3Cu (1) + Al (3)	6/4
5Cu (1) + Sn (4)	9/6

For a γ-phase the ratio is 21/13 and for an ε-phase 7/4. The fractions are most easily remembered as β 21/14, γ 21/13 and ε 21/12. The phases themselves are sometimes referred to as *electron compounds*.

An alloy of a T metal with a B element of Gps. VB and VIB often has intermediate phases quite different from those of the constituent elements. They frequently have structures like NiAs (p. 149); examples are the arsenides, antimonides, bismuthides, sulphides, selenides and tellurides of many T metals. The binding is partly covalent and partly ionic.

Interstitial alloys

The hydrides, borides, carbides and nitrides of the transitional elements have metallic properties. Only atoms with small covalent radii are capable of occupying the interstices in relatively close-packed arrangements:

H	B	C	N
0.53	0.80	0.77	0.74 Å

These interstitial alloys are of great technical importance; all steels are interstitial alloys of carbon and iron.

When the radius ratio is less than 0.59 the alloy is 'normal' and the *metal—interstitial atom* arrangement is face-centred cubic, close-packed hexagonal or body-centred cubic. The 'complex' interstitial alloys have a radius ratio greater than 0.59 and are less stable. Carbon and nitrogen always occupy octahedral holes in interstitial alloys; hydrogen always occupies the smaller tetrahedral interstices. In face-centred cubic and close-packed hexagonal lattices there are as many octahedral holes as metal atoms and twice as many tetrahedral holes.

Austenite, an iron-carbon phase in steel, has a face-centred cubic arrangement of iron atoms and a maximum carbon content corresponding to the filling, quite at random, of one twelfth of the octahedral interstices. Rapid quenching of austenitic steel, which is stable at high temperature, causes the iron atom arrangement to change to body-centred, but the interstitial carbon atoms hold the metal atoms apart and allow them to assume a tetragonal, rather than a cubic, configuration. This supersaturated solid solution is martensite. Tempering precipitates the carbon as an ε-iron carbide with a close-packed hexagonal structure at low temperatures, but at higher temperatures cementite, Fe_3C, is produced. During these last transformations the iron positions alter only slightly, the changes being due to the diffusion and re-arrangement of the carbon atoms.

The nature of the valency forces in interstitial alloys has been variously explained. It is clear that such alloys are restricted to metals with incompletely filled d orbitals. Electrons may be donated by the interstitial atoms, leaving these as positive ions and resulting in binding of a metallic nature.

Clathrates

When quinol is crystallised from aqueous solution in the presence of argon at 40 atmospheres, the solid has the properties of quinol but contains argon which is set free when the quinol is melted or dissolved. The gas molecule is trapped inside a cage of hydrogen-bonded quinol molecules (Powell, 1948). Clathrates are formed by krypton, xenon and such gases as

HCl, HBr, SO_2 and CO_2 with quinol, the general formula being $[C_6H_4(OH)_2]_3X$, where X represents a molecule of the gas.

An ammoniacal solution of nickel cyanide produces a pale mauve clathrate when shaken vigorously with benzene. The formula is $Ni(CN)_2NH_3.C_6H_6$ and the structure as shown in Fig. 88.

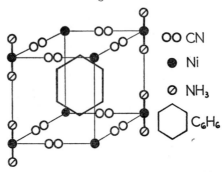

Fig. 88. Unit cell of benzene ammino-nickel cyanide clathrate.

AB structures

There are three principal types among isodesmic crystals of this empirical formula:

(i) 8:8 co-ordination as in caesium chloride (p. 141);
     e.g. CsBr, CsI, RbF, TlCl, TlBr, TlI, NH_4Cl, NH_4Br, AgLi, AlFe.

(ii) 6:6 co-ordination as in rock-salt (p. 141);
     e.g. Li, Na and K halides, NH_4I, RbCl, RbBr, RbI, Mg, Ca, Sr, Ba, Cd, Mn and Ni oxides, LaSb, CeBi.

(iii) 4:4 co-ordination as in zinc blende (Z) and wurtzite (W) (p. 149);
     e.g. (Z) AgI, AlSb, BeS, BeSe, CSi, CdSe, CuBr, HgS;
     (W) AgI, BeO, CdS, NH_4F, ZnO, MgTe.

Zinc forms a bipositive ion with an 18 electron structure and a moderately small radius (0.74 Å). The large S^{2-} ion (1.84 Å) is considerably polarised by it and the two forms of ZnS are predominantly homopolar, since both atoms can adopt sp^3 hybridisation and pool their valence electrons. Blende is cubic (Fig. 89), wurtzite hexagonal (Fig. 90), there being an average of 4 electrons per atom for bond formation as in diamond. Homopolar compounds of this type are formed by many pairs of elements whose valency electrons total 8. They are called *adamantine compounds* and have either a blende or wurtzite structure (see Table 22).

The *Grimm-Sommerfeld rule* states that if the sum of the atomic numbers is constant and the number of valency electrons is constant, the inter-atomic distances are constant.

TABLE 22

PROPERTIES OF ADAMANTINE COMPOUNDS

Formulae	Valency electrons	Atomic numbers	Inter-atomic distances
CuBr (Z)	$1 + 7 = 8$	$29 + 35 = 64$	2.46 Å
ZnSe (Z)	$2 + 6 = 8$	$30 + 34 = 64$	2.45 Å
GaAs (Z)	$3 + 5 = 8$	$31 + 33 = 64$	2.44 Å
GeGe (Z)	$4 + 4 = 8$	$32 + 32 = 64$	2.46 Å

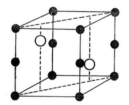

● Zn

○ S

Fig. 89. Cubic lattice of zinc blende.

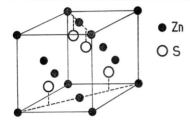

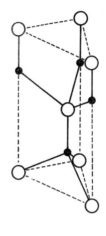

Fig. 91. Unit cell of nickel arsenide (hexagonal system).

Fig. 90. Hexagonal lattice of wurtzite.

The non-adamantine lattice of nickel arsenide, NiAs, is another common AB structure (Fig. 91); it is also displayed by FeS, FeSe, CoS, CoSe, CoTe, NiS, NiSe, NiTe, NiSb, MnSb, CoSb. Each metal atom is surrounded by a slightly distorted octahedron of six Gp. 5B or Gp. 6B atoms, which themselves form nearly regular tetrahedra without metal atoms, the structure being anisodesmic.

AB₂ structures

(i) The fluorite structure (p. 150) shows 8 : 4 co-ordination, every Ca^{2+} ion being surrounded by eight F^- ions arranged at the corners of a cube and every F^- by four Ca^{2+} arranged tetrahedrally. It is effectively the CsCl structure with the alternate diagonal pairs missing (Fig. 92). Other compounds with the fluorite lattice are SrF_2, BaF_2, $SrCl_2$, CdF_2, PbF_2, ThO_2, Mg_2Sn and Al_2Cu.

(ii) In rutile, a form of TiO_2, the co-ordination is $6:3$, every Ti being surrounded by six O atoms, arranged roughly octahedrally, and each O by three Ti atoms. The unit cell is tetragonal (Fig. 93). Other substances with this unit cell structure are ZnF_2, MnF_2, CoF_2, SnO_2, TeO_2, MnO_2.

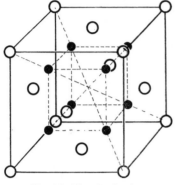

Fig. 92. Fluorite lattice.

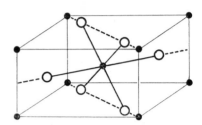

Fig. 93. Rutile structure.

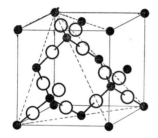

Fig. 94. β-Cristobalite, showing $4:2$ co-ordination (incomplete unit cell).

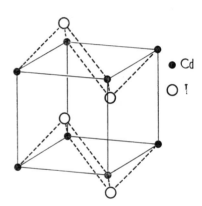

● Cd

○ I

Fig. 95.
The layer lattice of cadmium iodide.

(iii) Cristobalite, a form of SiO_2, shows $4:2$ co-ordination (Fig. 94).

(iv) Cadmium iodide, CdI_2, has a typical layer lattice; the unit cell is hexagonal (Fig. 95).

Unlike the truly ionic CdF_2 (fluorite structure), the iodide forms electrically neutral layers of large extent (Fig. 95). The force between the layers is small (Van der Waals) and the crystal easily cleaves into parallel sheets. Layer lattices are commonly formed by the iodides and bromides of bipositive metals and even by the chlorides of certain metals with very small cations. This results from polarisation of the anions. The same effect is exhibited by most hydroxides of the type $M(OH)_2$, but in these the two-dimensional, giant molecules are held together by the rather stronger forces between OH^- ions of adjacent layers—the so-called hydroxyl bonds.

Complex ions in crystals

Solids containing complex ions often have quite simple structures: for example K_2PtCl_6 consists of K^+ ions and octahedral $PtCl_6^{2-}$ ions in which the chlorine atoms are bound covalently to the platinum. The structure is that of fluorite with the complex ions occupying places in the cubic lattice corresponding to those of the Ca^{2+} ions, and the K^+ ions places corresponding to the F^- ions (Fig. 96).

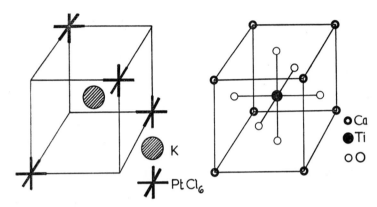

Fig. 96. Potassium chloroplatinate lattice.   Fig. 97. Perovskite structure.

Perovskites

Not all ternary compounds contain complex ions. Many possessing the empirical formula ABC_3 have the cubic perovskite $(CaTiO_3)$ structure (Fig. 97). Examples are $CaZrO_3$, $LaAlO_3$, and $KMgF_3$. The charges on the ions are not important provided the packing is close and the electrical neutrality is maintained. The larger cation occupies the Ca^{2+} position in all compounds of this structure:

$(1 + 5)^+ 6^-$	$(2 + 4)^+ 6^-$	$(3 + 3)^+ 6^-$	$(1 + 2)^+ 3^-$
Na W O$_3$	Ca Ti O$_3$	La Al O$_3$	K Mg F$_3$

Particularly interesting perovskite structures are the tungsten bronzes. The ideal composition is $NaWO_3$ (Fig. 98), the charge-type being $(1 + 5)^+ 6^-$, as shown above. However, the compound can be crystallised with varying deficiencies of Na^+, provided that, for every missing Na^+ ion, a 5-positive tungsten ion becomes 6-positive. These sodium deficient materials are known as *incomplete lattice* defect structures. When the deficiency is complete the limiting formula of WO_3 is reached.

Spinels

These are minerals of the empirical formula AB_2C_4. Examples are $MgAl_2O_4$, $FeAl_2O_4$, $CoAl_2O_4$, $MnAl_2O_4$ and Fe_3O_4. Normal spinels have a face-centred cubic array of anions with A^{2+} cations occupying one-eighth of the tetrahedral interstices (where an atom can be surrounded by four anions) and B^{3+} cations filling half the octahedral spaces between the anions. In Fe_3O_4 one-third of the iron is present as Fe^{2+}, the rest as Fe^{3+}.

In equipoint spinels $(TiMg_2O_4)$ half of the B^{2+} ions occupy tetrahedral holes in the array of O^{2-} ions; the other half, along with the A^{4+} ions, are randomly distributed in half the octahedral sites.

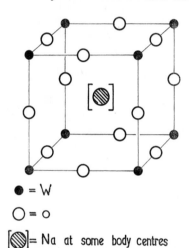

● = W

○ = O

⊘ = Na at some body centres

Fig. 98. Tungsten bronze structure.

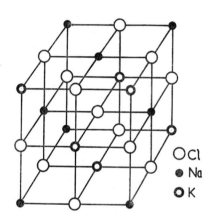

○ Cl

● Na

○ K

Fig. 99. Defect lattice in mixed crystal of sodium and potassium chlorides.

Defect structures

The sodium tungsten bronzes already described are examples of incomplete lattice defect structures. Iron(II) oxide is rather similar; it has a rock-salt structure but is always deficient in iron. Some Fe^{3+} ions are always present to maintain electrical neutrality. Fe_3O_4 has the spinel structure which has the same arrangement of O^{2-} ions as FeO. Fe_2O_3. has also the same arrangement; and oxidation of FeO to Fe_2O_3 consists of the replacement of Fe^{2+} ions by two thirds of their number of Fe^{3+} ions.

Solids in which different kinds of atoms occupy structurally equivalent sites have also defect structures. Thus mixed crystals, say of sodium and potassium chlorides (Fig. 99), are examples of defect lattices of this kind. Lithium titanate, Li_2TiO_3, has a rock-salt structure in which cation sites are occupied at random by Li^+ and Ti^{4+}. It forms a continuous series of solid solutions with magnesium oxide—Li^+ (0.78 Å), Ti^{4+} (0.68 Å) and Mg^{2+} (0.65 Å) are ions of about the same size. Substitutional alloys (p. 145) are other examples of this sort of defect structure.

Silver iodide exhibits an unusual property. In addition to a γ-(blende) form and a β-(wurtzite) form it has an α-form stable between 146° and 552° (the m.p.). In this the iodide ions are arranged in a body-centred cubic lattice but the Ag^+ ions form what may be called an interstitial fluid, being apparently free to move through the rigid network of I^- ions. The variation of conductance with temperature in silver iodide (Table 23) is particularly interesting.

TABLE 23

TEMPERATURE DEPENDENCE OF SP. CONDUCTANCE OF AgI (ohm^{-1} cm^{-1})

Temp. (°C)	143	146	540	560
Sp. conductance	0.00035	1.3	2.6	2.4

There is a very large increase in conductance at the transition point, 146°, and a slight decrease when the fusion temperature is exceeded. Evidently Ag^+ ions can move slightly more easily through the lattice of I^- ions than through the melt.

Silicates

In silica and the silicates oxygen atoms are arranged tetrahedrally round silicon atoms. These tetrahedra may be

(i) separate,
(ii) linked in chains or rings of 2, 3, 4 or 6 units,
(iii) linked in long single or double chains,
(iv) linked in sheets,
(v) joined in 3-dimensional frameworks.

The tetrahedra always share corners, never edges or faces (Pauling's rules p. 143).

Silicates usually contain other oxygen ions besides those forming the tetrahedra. These O^{2-} anions can be replaced by OH^- and F^- provided electrical neutrality is maintained by the replacement of cations by others of lower charge. Similarly cations are replaceable, without changing the structure of the silicate, by others of about equivalent size and the same charge, or by different numbers of other cations of different charge, for instance Ca^{2+} by $2Na^+$. The cation Al^{3+} is particularly important, since the ratio $r_{Al^{3+}}/r_{O^{2-}} \sim 0.43$ is close to the transition ratio from 4 co-ordination to

6 co-ordination. Aluminium thus fits into either a tetrahedral group, AlO_4^{5-}, or an octahedral one, AlO_6^{9-}. The AlO_4^{5-} group is roughly the same size as the SiO_4^{4-} tetrahedron and can replace it provided electrical neutrality is maintained by an adjustment of positive charge elsewhere in the structure.

In the orthosilicates, separate SiO_4^{4-} tetrahedra are linked only by cations. An example is olivine, Mg_2SiO_4, essentially a packing of SiO_4 tetrahedra and MgO_6 octahedra. The oxygen-silicon ratio higher than 4 found in some orthosilicates arises from oxygen atoms which are co-ordinated only to the metal atoms; thus, for instance, Al_2SiO_5 consists of Al_2O^{4+} ions and SiO_4^{4-} tetrahedra (Fig. 100).

Two SiO_4 tetrahedra may be linked by sharing one corner (Fig. 101), giving a separate Si_2O_7 unit. Thorveitite, $Sc_2Si_2O_7$, is an example.

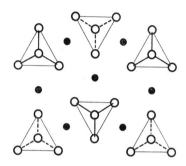

Fig. 100. Arrangement of Al_2O^{4+} ions and SiO_4^{4-} tetrahedra in Al_2SiO_5.

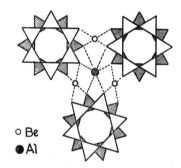

○ Be
● Al

Fig. 102. Structure of beryl, showing channels running through superimposed rings of SiO_4 tetrahedra.

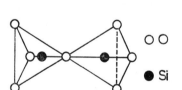

○ ○
● Si

Fig. 101. Two SiO_4 tetrahedra with one shared corner.

Fig. 103. Arrangement of SiO_4 tetrahedra in a pyroxene.

Closed rings of SiO_4 tetrahedra give an O:Si ratio of 3; found, for example, in beryl, $Be_3Al_2(Si_6O_{18})$. Each Be is co-ordinated by 4 oxygens from 4 different six-membered rings, and each Al by 6 oxygens from 6 different rings. Wide, empty channels pass through the structure (Fig. 102).

Pyroxenes are silicates in which the SiO_4 tetrahedra share two corners to form long chains. The O:Si ratio again is 3, and diopside, $CaMg(SiO_3)_2$, is an example (Fig. 103).

Amphiboles consist of double chains, exemplified by tremolite, $(F,OH)_2$ $Ca_2Mg_5Si_8O_{22}$. The additional OH^- and F^- anions cannot be linked to Si atoms; they are co-ordinated round the cations. Up to a quarter of the SiO_4 tetrahedra can be replaced by AlO_4^{5-}, electrical neutrality being maintained by replacing Mg^{2+} by Al^{3+}, or by adding Na^+ or Ca^{2+} cations (Fig. 104).

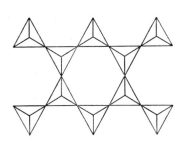

Fig. 104. Double-chain arrangement of SiO_4 tetrahedra in an amphibole.

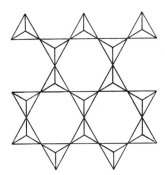

Fig. 105. Part of the sheet of SiO_4 tetrahedra in a mica.

Micas are made up of sheets of tetrahedra (Fig. 105), usually with AlO_4 tetrahedra replacing some of the SiO_4 units. In muscovite the sheet-composition is $(Si_3AlO_{10})^{5-}$, one quarter of the Si being replaced by Al. Two such sheets, with their tetrahedral vertices inwards, are linked by Al^{3+} ions whose octahedral co-ordination is completed by OH^- ions. The double sheets which have in consequence the composition $[Al_2AlSi_3O_{10}(OH)_2]^{-1}$ are stacked one upon another with sufficient K^+ ions between them to maintain electrical neutrality. The cleavage of the mica is due to weakness along these layers of K^+ ions. A wide variety of replacement is possible; thus the 'binding' aluminium may be replaced by magnesium and the 'sandwich' potassium by sodium. The structure of talc is somewhat similar, except that the sheets are electrically neutral. In clays, the sheets are held together by hydroxyl bonds.

Silica, in its various forms, is a three-dimensional framework of SiO_4 units which share all their corners. Cristobalite for instance has SiO_4 tetrahedra arranged as are the atoms in zinc blende; tridymite as are those in wurtzite.

The felspars have very open structures, shown (Fig. 106) for simplicity two-dimensionally. The cations are accommodated in holes running through the structure. Orthoclase, $KAlSi_3O_8$, has one quarter of the SiO_4 tetrahedra replaced by AlO_4 and to preserve neutrality requires one K^+ for every Al^{3+} present.

Zeolites have an even more open framework. They contain water molecules which can be removed without the framework collapsing. Because cations are easily exchanged, the materials have been used extensively as 'base exchangers' for water-softening (p. 568):

$$Na_3CaAl_5Si_5O_{20}.6H_2O + Ca^{2+} \rightleftarrows NaCa_2Al_5Si_5O_{20}.6H_2O + 2Na^+.$$

The solid reverts to the sodium form when treated with brine.

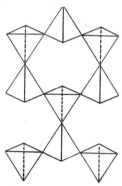

Fig. 106. Linking of SiO_4 tetrahedra in a felspar, showing very open structure.

Water of crystallisation

Salt hydrates hold water molecules as (i) co-ordinated water, (ii) anion water, (iii) lattice water, or (iv) zeolite water. The term water of constitution is a misnomer often applied to compounds wrongly formulated as $Fe_2O_3.H_2O$ and $MgO.H_2O$. These are the true hydroxides $FeO(OH)$ and $Mg(OH)_2$, and most of the class have a layer lattice consisting of sheets of OH^- and O^{2-} ions with cations between them.

Co-ordinated water. Many cations form complex ions with four or six molecules of water co-ordinated to the metal:

$$[Co(H_2O)_6]Cl_2, \qquad [Mg(H_2O)_6]Cl_2, \qquad [Be(H_2O)_4]SO_4$$

The metal ion has usually charge number $+2$ or $+3$ and, being small, has a high complexing power. Small ions such as Be^{2+} (0.31 Å) and Mg^{2+} (0.65 Å) give hydrated ions of much greater size. $Be(H_2O)_4^{2+}$ has about the same dimensions as the SO_4^{2-} ion and beryllium sulphate displays, in consequence, a caesium chloride structure. The magnesium compound $[Mg(H_2O)_6]Cl_2$ has a very slightly distorted fluorite lattice. The great majority of these aquo-complexes are of the 'spin-free' type (p. 134). Cations are frequently, but not always, hydrated to the same extent in solution as in the crystal.

Anion water. This is not common, but certainly occurs in $CuSO_4.5H_2O$ and probably in $ZnSO_4.7H_2O$. The former appears to have a hydrogen-bonded water molecule between the square $[Cu(H_2O)_4]^{2+}$ ion and the tetrahedral SO_4^{2-} ion (Fig. 107). On heating, the water of the complex ion is lost in two stages giving first $CuSO_4.3H_2O$ and then $CuSO_4.H_2O$; the anion water however remains tenaciously held up to 250°.

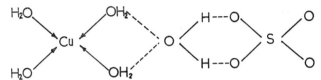

Fig. 107. Diagrammatic representation of $CuSO_4.5H_2O$.

The water molecule appears to behave in some crystals very much as it does in ice (p. 232), attaching itself to other molecules by approximately tetrahedrally disposed hydrogen bonds provided atoms of sufficiently high electronegativity are present (Fig. 108). It is attached to F or O atoms in various ways (Fig. 109); (b) shows the one employed in crystalline $CuSO_4.5H_2O$. In some instances the water molecule is attached directly to both anion and cation (Fig. 110).

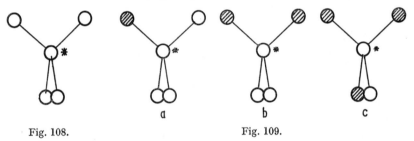

Fig. 108.   Fig. 109.

Fig. 108. Environment of a water molecule (*) in ice.
Fig. 109. Environment of water molecule (*) attached to oxygen atoms of anions and also to other water molecules.

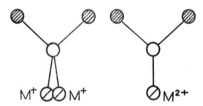

Fig. 110. Water molecules attached to both anions and cations.

Lattice water. In some crystals water molecules occupy definite lattice positions but are not associated directly with either anion or cation. In the alums six of the water molecules are co-ordinated round the 3+ cation and the other six are arranged at a much greater distance about the unipositive cation.

Zeolite water. This is the water found between the layers of a crystal lattice and in the interstices. It cannot be removed stepwise as can the water from $CuSO_4.5H_2O$. The lattice is only slightly affected by its removal.

Non-stoichiometric compounds

Iron(II) sulphide never has the precise composition FeS—the sulphur is always present in excess. This could be due either to the inclusion in the lattice of extra, interstitial S atoms or to the omission from it of some of the Fe atoms. The second explanation is correct (Hagg and Sucksdorff, 1933), the phenomeon being an example of lattice defect (p. 152). There are two types of lattice defect. In Schottky defects, found in iron(II) sulphide, 'holes' are left at random through the crystal because of migration of ions to the surface. In Frenkel defects, 'holes' are left at random by atoms which have moved to interstitial positions. Silver bromide has a perfect face-centred cubic arrangement of Br^- ions but the Ag^+ ions are partly in interstitial positions. The effect is even more marked in silver iodide (p. 153).

Non-stoichiometry in solids is a general phenomenon—indeed, stoichiometry is exceptional—and it has been shown thermodynamically that a condensed phase, even at equilibrium, is not of unique composition except at its singular points (m.p., etc.), and at a temperature near absolute zero. A typical Daltonide compound like sodium chloride when in equilibrium with sodium is deep blue, but when in equilibrium with chlorine is white. And, although the material remains homogeneous throughout these changes, the alteration in composition is great enough to be detected analytically.

Brewer (1961) has called attention to the problems which non-stoichiometry raises in the contexts of nomenclature, specification of properties, and prediction of chemical behaviour from thermodynamical data relating to one standard composition. As regards nomenclature, it is usual to designate a non-stoichiometrical phase by a formula; for instance, the NaCl phase region, the FeO phase region, or the UO_2 phase region. And this is to be taken as indicating compositions near the values implied by these formulae. Indeed, stoichiometric FeO does not exist in an equilibrium system, and an attempt to produce it results in disproportionation to iron and an oxide richer in oxygen. Properties in a non-stoichiometric phase may change remarkably; thus for a series of cerium sulphides for which the lattice constants and structure are the same, the colour varies from black to red. The first material is almost a metallic conductor, which can be heated rapidly without fracture, and which is a reducing agent. The second has the properties of a ceramic and readily fractures on rapid heating or cooling; it is an insulator and can act as an oxidising agent.

Non-stoichiometric solids are now extensively used in industry as transistor and maser materials and great developments in their use are to be expected. The manufacture of these remarkable phases frequently calls for inorganic substances of the highest purity and strictly controlled methods of production.

Crystal Growth
Natural and Induced Atomic Displacements

An increased precision in the location of atoms in the crystal lattice has shown that some irregularity in their position is very common. This in turn has led to an understanding of the way in which a crystal grows and of the changes brought about in a crystal lattice when it is bombarded by particles from without or suffers atomic disintegration within. It will be seen below that these may be matters of very practical concern.

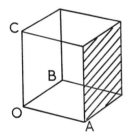
Fig. 111.
100 plane in cubic system.

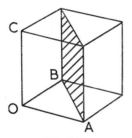
Fig. 112.
110 plane in cubic system.

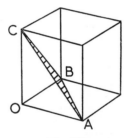
Fig. 113.
111 plane in cubic system.

Crystal growth through natural atomic displacements

First to recall the nomenclature used in naming the faces of, or planes within, crystals. This is done by *Miller indices* (1839) which are the reciprocals of the intercepts the plane makes with suitably chosen axes. The idea is most easily understood for the cubic system. The plane shaded in Fig. 111 is a 100 plane, the intercepts made on the OA, OB and OC axes by the plane being 1, ∞ and ∞ respectively so that the Miller indices are

$$\frac{1}{1}, \frac{1}{\infty}, \frac{1}{\infty} \text{ which are represented by 100.}$$

The plane shaded in Fig. 112 is a 110 plane, the intercepts on the OA, OB and OC axes being 1,1 and ∞; and that shaded in Fig. 113 is a 111 plane.

Crystal growth from vapour, as in sublimation, makes the simplest approach to the subject, and the principles involved apply to the more complicated situation in solutions. Consider the flat 001 surface of a cubic crystal in contact with its vapour and partly covered by an incomplete layer (Fig. 114).

When the vapour pressure is raised by an amount Δp above the vapour-solid equilibrium vapour pressure, the layer grows with a speed proportional to Δp until the surface is covered. But to start a new layer a two-dimensional nucleus must be formed (Fig. 115) for which the rate of nucleation has been found to be proportional to $e^{-A/\Delta p}$, A being a constant.

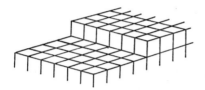 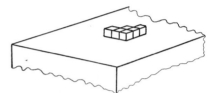

Fig. 114. 001 crystal surface partly covered with another layer.

Fig. 115. Nucleus for the start of a new layer.

Clearly the stepwise character of a 110, 101, 011 or 111 surface makes nucleation easy to occur, but these surfaces disappear in the course of their growth leaving 100, 010 and 001 surfaces only (Fig. 116).

For surfaces of low indices such as the 100, the rate of nucleation predicted by the $e^{-A/\Delta p}$ formula is smaller than the experimental rate by a factor of about $e^{3,600}$ for low values of Δp. But Volmer and Schultz (1931) found iodine crystals to grow at a measurable rate in iodine vapour when the vapour pressure was only 1.01 times the equilibrium vapour pressure. And Burton, Cabrera and Frank (1949) suggested that this great discrepancy between theory and practice could be understood if the growing crystal surface were assumed always to have random imperfections and, indeed, never to have been covered by an unbroken perfect layer.

Burgers (1939) had recognised that unit displacement of a *dislocation* need not be normal to the dislocation lines and could in an extreme case be parallel to it, giving rise to *screw dislocations* (Fig. 117).

When a screw dislocation terminates in the exposed face of a crystal, there is a permanently exposed 'cliff' of atoms; the addition of a further layer to the surface simply perpetuates the conditions and the need for two-dimensional nucleation disappears. The crystal grows up a series of spiral stairways.

At low supersaturations, crystals do not grow unless they contain dislocations, but these must not be too close to one another or growth is inhibited
because the surface then approaches a perfect form. Perfection is, of course,
impossible according to this theory, and is very unlikely to be realised in
practice. Frank's explanation of crystal growth is supported by study of the
markings present on crystal faces and by the great discrepancy between the
strength deduced theoretically for perfect crystals and the measured
strengths; imperfections often make actual crystals weaker by a factor of 100.

The growth of a crystal in solution probably proceeds similarly to the
growth in vapour but growth from supercooled melts needs further study.
In all instances a very high supersaturation (1.5 times) is normally needed
to initiate growth.

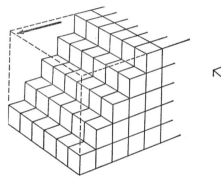

Fig. 116.
Growth of 001 surface from 101 plane.

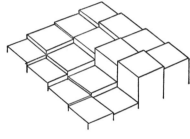

Fig. 117.
Screw dislocation in crystal.

Artificial displacement of atoms

It is convenient to designate as artificial the atomic displacements brought
about in a crystal by internal or external bombardment after its formation.
The displacement of an atom from its normal site creates a *vacancy* and an
interstitial atom, individually termed *point defects*. They are caused by
collision between the atom and another particle (electron, proton, neutron,
α-particle or recoil nucleus). An electron must have an energy of about
1MeV and an atom must receive 25eV for the impact to be effective. The
reception of less energy simply puts the atom into an excited state from
which it recovers by losing heat. The displacement of atoms has two results:
first, the crystal lattice is strained and distorted which may change its mechanical properties and even cause its disruption; secondly, energy is stored
in the structure and released when interstitial atoms return to vacancies.

The effect of the first result is marked in metals, that of the second in graphite. In both instances, a return of the interstitial atoms to vacancies, the interstitial-vacancy pair combination as it is termed, can be achieved by heating the material to the *annealing temperature*.

Damage by external radiation is well illustrated by copper which, on exposure to neutrons, develops point defects on its *dislocation lines*. These are thereby 'locked' so that there is not the normal extension along them under stress, but rather a sudden yielding when this reaches the critical value. Briefly, the metal loses ductility (Barnes and Redding, 1958). Other examples are provided by mild steel and uranium. The change from ductile to brittle in mild steel is at −30°, but the transition temperature can be raised by irradiation to +40°, making mechanical failure possible at ordinary atmospheric temperatures. Uranium crystals which are anisotropic grow more in the *c* axial direction than any other, with a consequent deterioration in the shape and strength of the fabricated metal.

Graphite is another anisotropic material and irradiation causes carbon atoms to vacate the layer planes and lodge between them. As a result the graphite grows in the *c* direction, just as it does when sandwich compounds (p. 299) are formed. In addition much energy is stored. When the irradiated graphite is raised to the annealing temperature interstitial-vacancy pair combination takes place; the potential energy is released as heat, and the damage repaired. Indeed, if the irradiation is carried out near the annealing temperature the damage is made good as it is sustained. This means that the graphite in nuclear reactors working at low temperatures accumulates more *Wigner energy* than its counterpart in reactors operated at higher temperatures. Hence a periodic annealing, or releasing of the energy, *Wigner release*, is necessary in the former, but may be unnecessary or infrequently required in the latter. The Windscale incident (1957) drew attention to the need to control the release of Wigner energy if dangerously high temperatures which will cause damage in the reactor and other troubles are to be avoided. The rate of energy release depends on the temperature; accordingly this must be under control at all stages of the operation.

The displacement of atoms just discussed is due to causes outside the affected crystal. But in the early days of radioactivity the destruction of radium salts by self-irradiation was recognised. Indeed the process occurs more or less in all minerals and compounds containing radioactive atoms. Recently D'Eye (1957) calculated that 2×10^{19} atoms in 1 mg of a polonium compound are knocked off their sites, mainly by recoil nuclei, in a day. As there are only about 10^{19} atoms in this weight of the compound, every atom suffered, on the average, one displacement a day. By X-ray powder photography, with the special precautions necessitated by the polonium activity

(p. 357), he was able to follow the progressive destruction of the crystal structure thus predicted. The films taken of the freshly made compound were good, when it had been kept a few days they were poor, and after it had been kept a few weeks they showed no lines. The destruction of the crystal structure by self-radiation had become complete and the material was amorphous.

Chapter 8

Chemical Thermodynamics

The nature of thermodynamics

The greater part of this book is concerned with the structure and properties of atoms and inorganic molecules. There are, however, certain general principles which govern the behaviour of matter in bulk. When the smallest systems considered are still large enough to contain vast numbers of atoms, they may often be regarded as pieces of homogeneous material with empirical bulk properties, density for example, which may be defined without reference to the idea of atoms and molecules. These principles and their application form the substance of *classical* thermodynamics; their detailed elucidation, in terms of atomic properties, is feasible, and is the aim of *statistical* thermodynamics, but is largely outside the scope of this book. Here the principles of classical thermodynamics are reviewed, and then only in so far as they are indispensible to a proper appreciation of chemical phenomena.

The systems to be considered are composed of various homogeneous parts, each of which is called a *phase* (*e.g.* water in a flask, or the gas above the water). The *content* of each phase is defined by giving the amounts of the smallest number of chemical substances, the *components*, which serve to describe the matter present. Thus, for instance, nitrogen containing water vapour is a two-component system; for although nitrogen, hydrogen and oxygen can be distinguished, the last two are always present in fixed proportions as H_2O. The description of the phase is made more complete by stating the pressure P under which it is kept. But this is still not sufficient, for its volume V depends on how hot it is. The *thermodynamic state* of the phase may be completely specified by the content and two other variables, P and V.

The concept of 'hotness' must be made precise. A system is in *equilibrium* if its thermodynamic state does not change with the time; this condition is preserved by keeping the system in a suitable container which isolates it from its surroundings and keeps its content and volume constant. When the equilibrium is not disturbed by changes occurring outside the container, the walls are said to be *thermally insulating*; otherwise they are *conducting*. Two systems, separated only by a conducting wall, are said to be in *thermal contact*; and the equilibrium they finally reach is called *thermal equilibrium*. Now it is found experimentally that any two systems in equilibrium with a third are in equilibrium with each other. This principle, sometimes called the Zeroth Law of Thermodynamics, implies that all systems in equilibrium with an arbitrary standard have a common property of being in thermal equilibrium with one another. They are said to be at the same *temperature*. In order to measure temperature numerically it is only necessary to adopt a standard system, called a *thermometer*, with some easily measurable characteristic which varies with hotness; for example, the volume of a given amount of gas at an agreed pressure. The value of the quantity selected, say x, is then used to define an *empirical temperature scale* $\theta = a + bx$, where the constants a and b are conveniently chosen so that, for instance, θ takes the values 0 and 100 units at two easily reproducible temperatures. When these are the freezing and boiling points of water, the temperature is measured in *centigrade degrees* and the fixed points are written $0°C$ and $100°C$. All systems in equilibrium with a thermometer reading, say $5°C$, then have the temperature $5°C$. Empirical scales are unsatisfactory because they depend on the behaviour of a particular substance whereas the concept of temperature does not. But an *absolute scale* can be found, with which all thermodynamic relationships assume a particularly simple form. It is realised practically by a thermometer in which x represents the volume of a fixed mass of gas at a sufficiently low pressure. More precisely, the *ratio* of two absolute temperatures is the same as that of the corresponding x's. A temperature on this scale is denoted by T and measured in degrees Kelvin (°K) and when the temperature difference between the freezing and boiling points of water is taken as $100°K$, then $T_{ice} = 273.15\ °K$.

Since the state of a system of fixed content is completely determined by the values of P and V, the temperature is unambiguously defined by them. Thus T is a function of P and V, written $T = T(P, V)$. Similarly, when P and T are known, it is implied that V has a unique related value, written $V = V(P, T)$. Such relationships embody an *equation of state* in which one variable is a function of the two *independent variables* or, since the latter specify the state, a *function of state*. Thus, for a gas, the equation of state is $PV = a + bP + cP^2$ ... where $a, b, c, ..$ depend only on the empirical temperature. In terms of absolute temperature a has the value RT, where R is the *gas constant* for the quantity of gas considered. When a gas behaves *ideally* the other terms on the right are negligibly small.

There are many important functions of state. Those of importance in chemistry determine the conditions of equilibrium in chemical systems and hence the equilibrium distribution of different reactants and products among the various phases.

Heat, energy

When the temperature of a system rises without any *mechanical* action taking place, it is said to accept heat from its surroundings. The same final state can, however, always be reached by doing *work* on the system; that is by putting mechanical *energy* into the system. It is therefore natural to describe heat as a form of energy. To render the definition more precise, consider a thermally insulated system on which work is done by, for example, compression or stirring. The changes which then occur are called *adiabatic*. It is found experimentally that the amount of work required to get the system adiabatically from one state to another is independent of how the change is brought about, depending only on the initial and final states themselves. If the work which must be done on a system to get it adiabatically from an agreed standard state to another state be denoted by U, then the work to be done to get the system adiabatically from state 1 to state 2 will be $w = (U_2 - U_1)$, irrespectively of how the change is brought about, U_1 and U_2 being the values of U in the two states. Thus U is a function of state, uniquely determined, just as is the volume, by the composition, temperature and pressure, once the standard state has been conventionally defined. U is called the *internal energy*. The increase in internal energy in a process is usually denoted by ΔU, and ΔU is clearly independent of the standard state. In an adiabatic change

$$\Delta U = w \quad \text{(the work done on the system).}$$

If, however, the system is not insulated from its surroundings, the change ΔU is not generally equal to w. If we write

$$\Delta U = w + q, \tag{1}$$

the quantity q is called the *heat* absorbed by the system from its surroundings and is most naturally measured in energy units such as Joules. When heat is defined in this way the principle of conservation of energy is evidently valid for systems undergoing both mechanical and *thermal* changes. The mechanical energy which disappears is converted into either internal (thermal) energy or heat. Historically, the unit of heat, the calorie, was defined as the quantity q necessary to produce a rise of temperature from $14.5°C$ to $15.5°C$ in 1 g of water without performing any work, w. Experiment shows that 1 calorie = 4.1858 International Joules. The unit most commonly employed in chemistry is the kilogram calorie (kcal) which is 10^3 cal.

The principles introduced so far apply to any kind of system. The facts that there is a function U which depends only on the state, not on how the state is reached, and that conservation of energy can be expressed quite generally, with a well-defined conversion factor between units of heat and mechanical energy, together comprise the *First Law of Thermodynamics*. Because of its generality, the conservation equation is immediately applicable to elaborate systems. Should the system consist of the contents of a bomb calorimeter, the heat absorbed during a chemical reaction can be directly measured. It is simply the heat necessary to restore the system to its initial temperature and, since no mechanical work is done when the volume is held constant, measures the increase in internal energy accompanying the chemical change at the particular temperature. Thus ΔU $(= q$, heat absorbed at constant volume) is an important characteristic of the chemical change. The First Law shows that it depends only upon reactants and products, at the given temperature, and not on what actually happens during the reaction.

Usually, reactions occur at constant pressure, frequently atmospheric but often higher, and changes of volume result; in consequence the heat absorbed is not equal to ΔU. For now $q = \Delta U - w = \Delta U + P\Delta V$, where V is the increase in volume of the system and P the constant pressure. The quantity $H = U + PV$, whose change at constant pressure is $\Delta H = \Delta U + P\Delta V$, is (like U) a function of state. It is called the *heat content*; and the heat absorbed in a chemical reaction, referred to a given pressure and temperature, is equal to the increase in heat content in the chemical change from reactants to products. ΔH is the *heat of reaction*. By convention ΔH denotes an increase, that is final value minus initial value, and the left-hand side of a chemical equation, the reactants, represents the initial state. When heat is absorbed, ΔH is positive and the reaction *endothermic*, conversely when heat is liberated ΔH is negative and the reaction *exothermic*. The heat actually evolved is thus $-\Delta H$. For a gas, U, PV, and hence H, are usually almost constant, and for a solid or liquid the compressibility is so high that V and U are scarcely affected by change of pressure; accordingly it is only necessary to state the temperature at which a heat of reaction is determined.

For the present purpose the most important heat of reaction refers to the formation of one mole of a chemical compound from its elements, in their most stable forms, at 25°C. This is the *standard heat of formation*, written ΔH_f°. In other instances the standard heat of reaction is denoted by ΔH_r°. Although relatively seldom directly measurable, it can be inferred from other reactions. If the heat content of one mole of a substance A is denoted by H_A and so on for B etc., the heat of reaction for

$$a\mathrm{A} + b\mathrm{B} + \ldots \rightarrow x\mathrm{X} + y\mathrm{Y} + \ldots$$

is $\qquad \Delta H = (xH_X + yH_Y + \ldots) - (aH_A + bH_B + \ldots).$

From a number of such relationships, the heat of reaction for a different process can be obtained. Thus, for the three reactions (all at 25°C)

$$CS_2(l) + 3O_2(g) \rightarrow CO_2(g) + 2SO_2(g) \quad \Delta H_r^\circ = -265.0 \text{ kcal,}$$
$$C(s) + O_2(g) \rightarrow CO_2(g) \quad \Delta H_f^\circ = -94.0 \text{ kcal,}$$
$$2S(s) + 2O_2(g) \rightarrow 2SO_2(g) \quad \Delta H_f^\circ = -140.4 \text{ kcal.}$$

Subtracting the first of these equations* from the sum of the other two:

$$C(s) + 2S(s) \rightarrow CS_2(l) \quad \Delta H_f^\circ = 30.6 \text{ kcal.}$$

Such considerations depend only on H being a function of state, that is on the First Law. They were first formulated on empirical grounds by Hess (1840). Since only differences of H occur, it is possible to adopt any convenient zero and to define a standard heat content, H°, for one mole of a substance. When H° is taken as zero for elements in their most stable states, at 25°C and 1 at., then H° for a compound is just ΔH_f°, its heat of formation from its elements under standard conditions.

Entropy

It was originally supposed (Thomson, Berthelot (1860) and others) that $-\Delta H$, the heat liberated in a reaction, measured the 'affinity' of the reactants. This view cannot be reconciled with the existence of endothermic reactions. The difficulty is, however, resolved by introducing further functions of state.

Thermodynamics deals with equilibrium states, but states can be changed only by disturbing an equilibrium. It is therefore theoretically useful to consider very gradual alteration of the variables (*e.g.* P, V) in which they are changed by infinitesimal steps so that the system passes through a continuous succession of equilibrium states. Changes of this kind, during which the system is always effectively in equilibrium, are termed *reversible*. The system can be guided through the same sequence of equilibrium states in reverse simply by changing the sign of every small increment. Such changes can be realised only approximately, but the ideal process forms a useful standard against which real processes can be discussed. Experiment shows that when a system is brought *reversibly* from one state to another, absorbing heat q at temperature θ in a typical infinitesimal step, the sum over all such steps, $\Sigma q/\theta$, is approximately independent of how the whole change is effected, *cf.* the work done in an *adiabatic* change. This approximation becomes remarkably good when θ is the temperature on a gas thermometer and suggests that by choosing the right scale there is an absolute temperature T for which the result becomes exact. Then $\Sigma q/T$, for any reversible change leading from one state to another, depends only on the initial and final states.

* Strictly, the associated heat-content equations (p. 167).

We say it measures the difference of *entropy* between them and write:

$$\Delta S = \Sigma\, q/T \quad \text{(reversible)}. \tag{2}$$

Provisionally T will be identified with the temperature on the *ideal* gas scale. By assuming the above property as a definition of the absolute scale, a crucial experiment can be devised (Joule and Thomson, 1862) which exactly verifies this conclusion. If a *standard entropy*, under chosen conditions, is denoted by S° then the entropy is generally

$$S = S^\circ + \Sigma\, q/T,$$

and may be calculated using any reversible path leading to the required state. Thus, to get the entropy of a system at (P, T) starting from a standard state (P°, T°) we simply raise the temperature slowly, noting that in any small step $q = C_P dT$, where C_P is the *heat capacity at constant pressure*, and find

$$S(P^\circ, T) = S(P^\circ, T^\circ) + \int_{T^\circ}^{T} \frac{C_P dT}{T}. \tag{3}$$

The integral is simply the area under a curve and is easily obtained from experimental data. Similarly it can be shown that

$$S(P, T^\circ) = S(P^\circ, T^\circ) - \int_{P^\circ}^{P} \alpha V dP, \tag{4}$$

where α is the coefficient of expansion. The entropy of any material relative to some standard state can be evaluated in this way. The fact that entropy is a function of state may be experimentally confirmed by, for instance, raising first T and then P to the final value and then repeating in the reverse order; the data used are very different but the end results identical. For a perfect gas C_P is a constant and

$$S(P^\circ, T) = S(P^\circ, T^\circ) + C_P \ln (T/T^\circ).$$

Also the fractional increase in volume per degree rise in temperature

$$\alpha = \frac{1}{V}\left(\frac{\partial V}{\partial T}\right)_P = \frac{1}{V}\frac{R}{P},$$

since $PV = RT$; and, changing the pressure,

$$S(P, T) = S(P^\circ, T) - R \ln (P/P^\circ).$$

Finally, therefore

$$S(P, T) = S(P^\circ, T^\circ) - R \ln (P/P^\circ) + C_P \ln (T/T^\circ), \tag{5}$$

and for a change from state 1 to state 2

$$\Delta S = -R \ln (P_2/P_1) + C_P \ln (T_2/T_1). \tag{6}$$

Although entropy was introduced from a consideration of idealised reversible changes, it is supremely important in considering real changes for the following reason. For any naturally occurring change, no matter how small, in a thermally insulated system

$$dS > 0, \tag{7}$$

the equality holding in the equilibrium case. This *Principle of Increase of Entropy* expresses most concisely the real content of the *Second Law of Thermodynamics*, though the law was deduced historically from the impossibility of certain thermal processes, such as flow of heat from a colder to a hotter body.

Two fundamental applications illustrate the use of the Second Law:

(i) Two systems in contact, thermally insulated from their surroundings and at temperatures T and T', may absorb infinitesimal amounts of heat, q and q', where $q + q' = 0$. The entropy principle, *cf.* (7), then requires

$$dS + dS' = \frac{q}{T} + \frac{-q}{T'} > 0.$$

The system at temperature T absorbs heat from the second (q positive) only when $T' > T$. In any natural process heat therefore flows from the hotter body to the colder. For no heat flow $T = T'$.

(ii) If the second system is the environment of the first and supplies it with heat q the entropy change of the environment is $-q/T$. This is calculated by considering reversible heating with $T' = T$. If now dS is imagined to arise from internal changes, for instance chemical reactions, as well as from heat intake,

$$dS + (-q/T) > 0 \qquad \text{or} \qquad TdS > q. \tag{8}$$

The quantities appearing now all refer to the system of interest. The Second Law in this form may now be combined with the First Law to give

$$TdS > dU + PdV. \tag{9}$$

This last result makes it possible to formulate criteria for equilibrium.

Equilibrium

In a thermally insulated system $q = 0$ in any change and therefore $TdS \geqslant 0$. This means the entropy increases spontaneously until a maximum is reached. In this state the equality $dS = 0$ will hold; the system will be in *equilibrium*, and small fluctuations will be reversible. This result may be stated otherwise by use of relationship (9). For a given entropy and volume ($dS = 0$, $dV = 0$), the internal energy will decrease until it is a minimum.

Other equilibrium conditions can be discussed in terms of other thermo-dynamic functions. The four most useful are*:

INTERNAL ENERGY	U
HELMHOLZ FREE ENERGY	$F = U - TS$
HEAT CONTENT	$H = U + PV$
GIBBS FREE ENERGY	$G = H - TS$

These are all *functions of state* of the system, just as U and S, but give equilibrium criteria appropriate to different situations:

	V constant	P constant
S constant	U is a minimum	H is a minimum
T constant	F is a minimum	G is a minimum

To justify the last statement, for example, we need only note

$$\mathrm{d}G = \mathrm{d}U + P\mathrm{d}V + V\mathrm{d}P - T\mathrm{d}S - S\mathrm{d}T$$
$$= (\mathrm{d}U + P\mathrm{d}V - T\mathrm{d}S) + V\mathrm{d}P - S\mathrm{d}T \leqslant V\mathrm{d}P - S\mathrm{d}T.$$

Thus G decreases spontaneously when $\mathrm{d}P = \mathrm{d}T = 0$ until equilibrium is reached.

It is now clear that Thomsen and Berthelot's conclusion would be valid only in somewhat artificial circumstances. If, for instance, besides the pressure, the entropy could be kept constant, then $\mathrm{d}H(= q) \leqslant 0$ and the reaction would proceed so long as it liberated heat, and made q negative. In practice, however, the conditions are determined by temperature and volume or by temperature and pressure, and internal changes of entropy do occur. Thus for given T and V a reaction may be initiated if it leads to a decrease of F; or for given T and P if it leads to a decrease of G. The latter conditions are more common and will be assumed unless otherwise stated. Since then $\mathrm{d}G = \mathrm{d}H - T\mathrm{d}S$, it is possible for an endothermic reaction ($\mathrm{d}H$ positive) to proceed spontaneously if it leads to a sufficient increase of entropy. On the other hand, a reaction which is energetically feasible ($\mathrm{d}H$ negative) may be prevented by a positive entropy term.

Free energy of a reaction

Suppose a moles of A, b moles of B, ... are completely converted into x moles of X, y moles of Y, ... in the reaction:

$$a\mathrm{A} + b\mathrm{B} + \ldots \rightarrow x\mathrm{X} + y\mathrm{Y} + \ldots$$

where $a, b, \ldots$ are the stoichiometric numbers. It is convenient to speak of this change as *one unit of reaction*.

---

* The symbols are those recommended by the International Union of Chemistry 1947). Some American textbooks still use F for the *Gibbs* free energy.

The total change in free energy, evaluated for standard conditions (25°C, 1 at. pressure), is the *standard free energy* of the reaction:

$$\Delta G_r^\circ = x G_X^\circ + y G_Y^\circ + \ldots - a G_A^\circ - b G_B^\circ - \ldots$$

where G_A° is the standard free energy of one mole of A etc. The decrease $-\Delta G_r^\circ$ provides a rough measure of the 'affinity' of the reactants but does not, in itself, determine whether the reaction will proceed to completion.

Since each G is a function of state, ΔG_r° for a given reaction may be obtained from values of ΔG_r° for other reactions, exactly as with heats of reaction. Again it is convenient to adopt a standard free energy for each species by suitable choice of arbitrary zero. This may be taken so that the free energies of the elements in their most stable states, at 25°C and 1 at. pressure, are zero. Then G° for a compound can be determined unambiguously; it is ΔG_f° for the reaction in which the compound is formed from its elements. As an example, consider:

(i) $C(s) + O_2(g) \rightarrow CO_2(g)$ $\Delta G_f^\circ = -94.5$ kcal,
(ii) $2H_2(g) + O_2(g) \rightarrow 2H_2O(l)$ $\Delta G_f^\circ = -113.4$ kcal,
(iii) $CH_4(g) + 2O_2(g) \rightarrow CO_2(g) + 2H_2O(l)$ $\Delta G_r^\circ = -195.6$ kcal.

Adding the free energy equations (i) and (ii) and subtracting (iii), gives for the reaction

$$C(s) + 2H_2(g) \rightarrow CH_4(g) \quad \Delta G_f^\circ = -12.3 \text{ kcal,}$$

hence $G_{CH_4}^\circ = -12.3$ kcal.

Similarly standard free energies of reaction can be written down immediately when the standard free energies of reactants and products are known. Thus, given $G_{C_3H_6}^\circ = 14.7$ kcal and $G_{C_3H_8}^\circ = -5.6$ kcal, the free energy of the reaction

$$C_3H_6(g) + H_2(g) \rightarrow C_3H_8(g)$$

is $\Delta G_r^\circ = (-5.6) - (14.7 + 0) = -20.3$ kcal.

Temperature dependence of ΔG and ΔH

It is important to be able to say how the standard heat and free energy of a reaction depend on the temperature. For ΔH we have

$$\frac{\partial(\Delta H)}{\partial T} = \frac{\partial}{\partial T}(x H_X + y H_Y + \ldots - a H_A - b H_B - \ldots)$$

$$= (x C_{PX} + y C_{PY} + \ldots - a C_{PA} - b C_{PB} - \ldots) = \Delta C_P, \text{ say,} \quad (10)$$

since $(\partial H/\partial T)_P$ is the heat capacity at constant pressure. This relation due to Kirchhoff can be integrated, to give $(\Delta H)_{T_2} - (\Delta H)_{T_1}$ as the area under a heat-capacity curve.

For ΔG, we have

$$(\partial G/\partial T)_P = -S = (G - H)/T \quad \text{or} \quad H = G - T(\partial G/\partial T)_P.$$

The differences are then related by

$$\Delta H = \Delta G - T \left(\frac{\partial \Delta G}{\partial T}\right)_P. \tag{11}$$

This is the *Gibbs-Helmholz relation* and may be written

$$\frac{\partial}{\partial T}\left(\frac{\Delta G}{T}\right) = \frac{-\Delta H}{T^2}. \tag{12}$$

The change in $(\Delta G_r^\circ/T)$ between two temperatures can therefore be obtained by numerical integration of heat of reaction data. The preceding equation is also useful to calculate heats of reaction in terms of free energies of reaction and their temperature variation.

Evaluation of free energies

When values of ΔG_r° are known for some reactions, others may be calculated as indicated above. There are three main methods of getting the necessary information:

(i) by direct calculation of $\Delta H - T\Delta S$, using calorimetric data;

(ii) by measurements on electrical cells, in which reactions proceed under controlled and essentially reversible conditions;

(iii) from the equilibrium constants of reactions.

Here the first two methods are considered.

(i) *Calorimetric Method.* For any reaction which proceeds to completion $-\Delta H$, the heat liberated at constant pressure, can be directly measured calorimetrically; other heats of reaction can then be inferred as shown on p. 168. It remains only to determine ΔS. Now S for any system may be obtained relative to an *arbitrary zero* by the numerical integration of heat capacity data (p. 169). But entropy changes in reactions, which are not directly measurable, will depend on the choice of zero for each substance. There is, however, a natural zero of entropy which allows the entropies of all pure crystalline solids in true thermodynamic equilibrium at $T = 0^\circ K$ to be regarded as zero. This result, which is one form of the *Third Law of Thermodynamics*, arises most naturally from statistical mechanics. It implies that ΔS for any chemical reaction tends to zero as T approaches zero and has been verified by extrapolation from low-temperature experiments. It is accordingly possible to obtain a completely consistent set of *Third-Law* entropies by considering the reversible absorption of heat as every substance is raised from absolute zero to its final state. Over most of the range (3) is applicable, a theoretical heat capacity curve being used to extrapolate to zero. During fusion and vaporisation there are further changes at fixed temperatures, *e.g.* (heat of fusion)/T. The entropies can also be calculated from statistical mechanics and there is generally complete agreement.

Because of the increase in entropy accompanying fusion and vaporisation, the standard molal entropies of gases are usually higher than those of liquids of similar molecular complexity, which are in turn higher than those of solids. As the figures show, the generalisation is approximate; nevertheless it is very useful.

TABLE 24

VALUES OF $S°$ (25°C, 1 ATMOSPHERE) CAL.DEG^{-1} MOLE^{-1}

Gases		Liquids		Solids	
CO_2	51.06	Br_2	36.70	NH_4Cl	22.60
CO	47.30	Hg	18.50	Mg	7.77
NH_3	46.03	H_2O	16.75	MgO	6.55
HCl	44.66			C (graphite)	1.36

In a reaction such as

$$MgO + C \rightarrow Mg + CO,$$

in which a gas is produced from solids, there is a large positive entropy change:

$$\Delta S = 47.30 + 7.77 - 6.55 - 1.36 = 47.56 \text{ cal. deg}^{-1} \text{ mole}^{-1}.$$

The temperature coefficient of ΔG is consequently negative and the affinity of the reaction increases with temperature.

In the reaction

$$NH_3 + HCl \rightarrow NH_4Cl,$$

in which two gases combine to form a solid, there is a large negative entropy change:

$$\Delta S = 22.60 - 46.03 - 44.66 = -68.09 \text{ cal. deg}^{-1} \text{ mole}^{-1}.$$

The temperature coefficient of ΔG is thus positive and the affinity of the reaction decreases with temperature.

(ii) *Cell Method.* When the poles of an electrical cell are connected by a wire, electrons flow and a chemical reaction proceeds. When the cell electromotive force is exactly balanced by a potentiometer, the current is reduced to zero and the reaction stops; but if the balance is not perfect, a very small current flows and the reaction proceeds exceedingly slowly and reversibly.

When the system can do electrical work (as well as work of expansion) it is easily seen that $dG \leqslant 0$ is replaced by $dG +$ electrical work done $\leqslant 0$. Under the reversible conditions the total decrease $-\Delta G$ during a process is

$$-\Delta G = \text{electrical work done.}$$

This is directly measurable. Consider, for example, the cell:

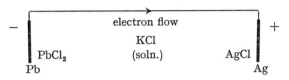

During normal operation, electrons flow through the external circuit from Pb to Ag, the negative and positive poles, and the following changes occur:

Negative pole	Positive pole
(i) $Pb + 2Cl^- \rightarrow PbCl_2 + 2e$,	(ii) $2AgCl + 2e \rightarrow 2Ag + 2Cl^-$.

The overall reaction is therefore

$$Pb + 2AgCl \rightarrow PbCl_2 + 2Ag,$$

since (i) provides the electrons for (ii) *via* the external circuit and (ii) replaces the chloride ions used in (i). Now each mole of electrons carries one *Faraday* $(1F = 96,500$ coulombs) of electricity and, when the potential drop between the terminals is E, the work done is FE. If z moles of electrons (p. 9) flow during one unit of reaction, it follows that $-\Delta G = zFE$; and if E is in volts this becomes, with sufficient accuracy, $-\Delta G = 23\,zE$ kcal. In the present reaction $E = 0.49$ volts at $25°C$, $z = 2$, the reactants and products are all solids and therefore in their standard states, so that $\Delta G = \Delta G_r^\circ$. Thus

$$\Delta G_r^\circ = -23 \times 2 \times 0.49 = -22.6 \text{ kcal.}$$

At the same time it is possible to obtain ΔH_r° and ΔS_r° by making one additional measurement, the temperature coefficient $(\partial E/\partial T)_P$. Since putting $\Delta G = -zFE$ in the Gibbs-Helmholz relation (11) gives immediately, for E in volts and T in °K,

$$\Delta H = -23\,z \left[E - T \left(\frac{\partial E}{\partial T} \right)_P \right] \text{kcal;} \qquad \Delta S = 23\,z \left(\frac{\partial E}{\partial T} \right)_P \text{kcal.} \qquad (13)$$

In the above reaction $(\partial E/\partial T)_P = -1.86 \times 10^4$ volt/°K; and therefore $\Delta H_r^\circ = -25.1$ kcal and $T\,\Delta S_r^\circ = 2.5$ kcal. The entropy term in the free energy is here quite small, even at room temperature, but this is not always so.

Chemical potential

A negative value of ΔG_r° does not indicate that a reaction proceeds to completion. Generally G depends on the concentrations of the various substances, possibly in a number of phases, and the reaction proceeds only so long as dG in the next infinitesimal step continues to be negative (Fig. 118). It is necessary, therefore, to know how G varies with the composition of the system throughout the whole course of a reaction in order to find when equilibrium will be reached.

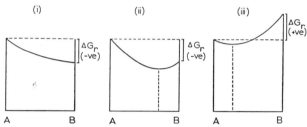

Fig. 118. Variation of Free Energy during reaction. A indicates reactants only, B products only.

(i) Proceeds virtually to completion.
(ii) Equilibrium reached before completion (ΔG −ve)
(iii) Equilibrium reached before completion (ΔG +ve).

First we must distinguish *intensive* and *extensive* properties. The temperature, pressure, density, ... of half of any homogeneous phase are the same as for the whole phase; but the volume, mass of each substance, internal energy, ... are half the values for the whole phase. Intensive properties can be defined at any point and have the same value throughout the phase, whereas the values of extensive properties are proportional to the *amount* of a phase. Clearly U, S, F, G are all extensive properties.

Consider a phase, with T and P given, containing n_A moles of A, n_B of B etc. For a system of fixed content (dn_A = dn_B = ... = 0) we know that d$U = T$d$S - P$dV for a small reversible change. If, however, a variation of content is permitted this must be replaced by

$$\mathrm{d}U = T\mathrm{d}S - P\mathrm{d}V + (\mu_A\,\mathrm{d}n_A + \mu_B\,\mathrm{d}n_B + \ldots)$$

where, for instance, $\mu_A = \partial U/\partial n_A$, the rate of change of U with n_A when all other variables are held constant. Now if the amounts of the various substances are increased in proportion to the amounts initially present, by taking d$n_A = \alpha n_A$, d$n_B = \alpha n_B$ etc., extensive quantities must all be increased by an amount $\alpha \times$ (original value). For example, $V \to V + \alpha V$ when $n_A \to n_A + \alpha n_A$ etc. But U will behave in this way only if $\mu_A, \mu_B, \ldots$ are fixed in value during any change which maintains the relative proportions of the various components. In other words, $\mu_A, \mu_B, \ldots$ must depend only on the ratios $n_A : n_B : n_C : \ldots$ which determine the composition of the phase, and are accordingly intensive properties. It is therefore possible to imagine a phase built up, the temperature, pressure and composition being kept constant, by the reversible addition of material so that T, P and the μ's keep constant values throughout. The final energy is then

$$U = TS - PV + (\mu_A n_A + \mu_B n_B + \ldots).$$

Therefore, since $G = U + PV - TS$,

$$G = \mu_A n_A + \mu_B n_B \ldots \tag{14}$$

The free energy of a phase is thus expressed in terms of the amounts of its various components and, through the μ's, in terms of its composition. $\mu_A, \mu_B, \ldots$ are called the *chemical potentials* of A, B, $\ldots$ in the phase, at the given temperature and pressure. They generally depend on composition, but sometimes this dependence is relatively simple. Thus for a mixture of ideal gases, U, S, F and G are all sums of terms, one for each gas regarded as though it alone were present. Thus $P = - (\partial F / \partial V)_S$ is a sum of *partial pressures* $(P_A, P_B, \ldots)$, in accord with Dalton's law, where $P_A V = n_A RT$ etc. Now the entropy of an ideal gas has already been found in the form [constant $-R \log P + C_P \log T$] and, since $G = H - TS$, then, for one mole at partial pressure P_A the dependence on pressure can be written

$$G_A(P_A, T) = G_A(P^\circ, T) + RT \ln P_A/P^\circ,$$

where P° is any convenient standard pressure. Also, since for a pure substance μ is just the free energy per mole,

$$\mu_A(P_A, T) = \mu_A(P^\circ, T) + RT \ln P_A/P^\circ,$$

and, for the mixture,

$$G = \Sigma n_A[\mu_A(P^\circ, T) + RT \ln P_A/P^\circ].$$

An extremely important property of the chemical potential is that it determines the equilibrium distribution of any species among a number of phases. For if dn_A mole of A leave phase 1 and enter phase 2, $dG = -\mu_A^{(1)} dn_A + \mu_A^{(2)} dn_A$ and, for equilibrium, $dG = 0$ and $\mu_A^{(1)} = \mu_A^{(2)}$. At equilibrium the chemical potential of any component is the same in every phase.

Chemical equilibrium

Consider now the general reaction

$$aA + bB + \ldots \rightarrow xX + yY + \ldots$$

in which complete conversion is not assumed. Let G be the free energy at any stage and consider the conversion of a further dn_A moles of A, dn_B of B etc. Since these amounts must be proportional to the stoichiometric numbers $a, b, \ldots$, the small increments may be written $dn_A = \alpha a$, $dn_B = \alpha b$, $\ldots$, $\alpha = 1$ corresponding to one unit of reaction in a system so large that the composition is virtually unchanged. Then in any natural change

$$dG = (\mu_X dn_X + \mu_Y dn_Y + \ldots - \mu_A dn_A - \mu_B dn_B - \ldots) < 0,$$

or

$$dG = \alpha(x\mu_X + y\mu_Y + \ldots - a\mu_A - b\mu_B - \ldots) < 0.$$

If, therefore, we know how the chemical potentials depend on the composition, the condition $dG = 0$ will determine the *equilibrium* composition. The quantity in brackets is ΔG, the free energy change per unit reaction (p. 171); it differs from ΔG_r because the reaction is not assumed to proceed to completion and ΔG depends, through the chemical potentials, on the instantaneous concentrations of all components (these being considered unchanged).

Recalling that for an ideal gas $\mu_A = \mu_A^\circ + RT \ln P_A/P^\circ$, where μ_A° is a standard free energy per mole of the pure component A at P° and T, it is useful to introduce a new quantity λ related to μ by $\mu = RT \log \lambda$. For then the ideal gas relationship, $\mu_A - \mu_A^\circ = RT \ln P_A/P^\circ$, becomes a special case of the general relationship $\mu_A - \mu_A^\circ = RT \ln \lambda_A/\lambda_A^\circ$. λ_A is called the *absolute activity* of the species A in the given phase, and $\lambda_A/\lambda_A^\circ$—its ratio to that of the pure species under given standard conditions—is the *relative activity*. In a mixture of ideal gases the activity is just the ratio (partial pressure/standard pressure). The equilibrium condition becomes, in terms of absolute activities,

$$\Delta G = RT \ln \left[\frac{(\lambda_X)^x (\lambda_Y)^y \ldots}{(\lambda_A)^a (\lambda_B)^b \ldots} \right] = 0, \quad \text{or} \quad \frac{(\lambda_X)^x (\lambda_Y)^y \ldots}{(\lambda_A)^a (\lambda_B)^b \ldots} = 1 \quad (16)$$

This is perfectly general: but in the ideal gas case $(\lambda_A/\lambda_A^\circ) = (P_A/P^\circ)$, and it becomes

$$\frac{(P_X/P^\circ)^x (P_Y/P^\circ)^y \ldots}{(P_A/P^\circ)^a (P_B/P^\circ)^b \ldots} = \frac{(\lambda_A^\circ)^a (\lambda_B^\circ)^b \ldots}{(\lambda_X^\circ)^x (\lambda_Y^\circ)^y \ldots} = K_p \quad (17)$$

which is the *equilibrium constant* for the reaction, depending only on the standard absolute activities of the pure substances involved.

Now

$$\Delta G_r^\circ = \mu_X^\circ n_X + \mu_Y^\circ n_Y + \ldots - \mu_A^\circ n_A - \mu_B^\circ n_B = RT \ln \frac{(\lambda_X^\circ)^x (\lambda_Y^\circ)^y \ldots}{(\lambda_A^\circ)^a (\lambda_B^\circ)^b \ldots} \quad (18)$$

where μ_A° etc. refer to pure substances in their standard states and are simply standard free energies per mole. This result used in (17) gives

$$-\Delta G_r^\circ = RT \ln K_p. \quad (19)$$

This is one of the most important equations in chemical thermodynamics: it shows that the equilibrium constant is determined entirely by the standard free energy change. At the same time it provides another experimental method of determining standard free energies.

The variation of free energy throughout the whole course of a reaction can now be determined. Putting the quotient

$$\frac{(P_X/P^\circ)^x \, (P_Y/P^\circ)^y \cdots}{(P_A/P^\circ)^a \, (P_B/P^\circ)^b \cdots} = Q_p, \text{ we see } \Delta G = RT \ln (Q_p/K_p) \cdots \quad (20)$$

So long as ΔG_r—the free energy change per unit of reaction—is negative, for any instantaneous values of the partial pressures, the reaction will proceed and equilibrium will occur when $Q_p = K_p$. This relationship defines the *reaction isotherm*. It is now clear why (*cf.* Fig. 118) a reaction whose standard free energy is positive may nevertheless proceed to some extent; for, with a high concentration of reactants, $\Delta G = RT \ln Q_p + \Delta G_r^\circ$ may initially be negative. Since $P_A = X_A P$, where X_A is the mole fraction of A, and P the total pressure, the partial pressures are easily related to the composition.

The equilibrium composition for any inital amounts of reactants and products is then readily determined. Reactions proceed effectively to completion when $-\Delta G_r^\circ$ is large. In the example above (p. 172) $-\Delta G_r^\circ = 20.3$ kcal and $K_p \sim 8 \times 10^{14}$; the reaction therefore proceeds until at least one of the reactants is very nearly used up (P_A or $P_B \simeq 0$).

In considering ideal gases we put the activity $a_A = \lambda_A/\lambda_A^\circ = (P_A/P^\circ)$. There was no need to do this. All the above relationships are valid for any kind of system if we replace P_A/P° etc. by the activities a_A etc., obtaining K_a and Q_a instead of K_p and Q_p. With non-ideal gases, solutions etc., it is convenient to have an analogue of the pressure, or partial pressure, so chosen that $\mu_A = \text{const.} + RT \ln P_A$ is replaced by $\mu_A = \text{const.} + RT \ln f_A$, though $f_A \to P_A$ at extreme dilution where the ideal form is appropriate. The term f_A, which may be regarded as an ideal pressure, corrected to allow for intermolecular attractions—a net 'escaping tendency'—is called the *fugacity*. Since then $\mu_A - \mu_A^\circ = RT \ln f_A/f_A^\circ$, the activity is a ratio of fugacities, $a_A = f_A/f_A^\circ$. Deviations from ideality in gas mixtures are negligible, except under extreme conditions, and with $P^\circ = 1$ at. the activity is numerically equal to the partial pressure in atmospheres. For liquid mixtures each component has the same chemical potential in the liquid as in the saturated vapour (p. 177) and $a_A = \lambda_A/\lambda_A^\circ = P_A/P_A^\circ$, where P_A and P_A° are vapour pressures of A over the mixture and the pure substance respectively, the vapour being regarded as ideal. Activities in solutions can therefore be determined from vapour pressure measurements. For most purposes the activities of pure liquids and solids may be taken as unity.

Temperature dependence of equilibrium

It is possible to change the extent to which a reaction proceeds by changing the temperature. Since $\Delta G_r^\circ/T = -R \ln K_p$, the temperature dependence of the equilibrium constant follows directly from the Gibbs-Helmholz equation (12)

$$\frac{d}{dT}(\ln K_p) = \frac{\Delta H_r^\circ}{RT^{\circ 2}} \tag{21}$$

This result, due to Van 't Hoff, may be integrated if the temperature variation of ΔH_r is known. Over a limited range ΔH_r is often nearly constant and then

$$\ln \frac{K_{p(T_2)}}{K_{p(T_1)}} = \frac{-\Delta H_r}{R}\left(\frac{1}{T_2} - \frac{1}{T_1}\right) \tag{22}$$

Thus for an exothermic reaction the equilibrium constant decreases with increasing temperature, the reverse being true of an endothermic reaction. This is one instance of *Le Chatelier's principle* (1885): *viz.* the equilibrium always changes in such a way as to oppose any change in conditions. Similarly an increase in pressure facilitates a reaction which leads to a decrease in volume, as may be seen by expressing partial pressure in K_p in terms of amounts of A, B etc.; and an increase in amounts of reactants makes the reaction proceed further by its effect on Q_p.

Oxidation-reduction processes

A great many chemical reactions can be broadly classified in terms of oxidation and reduction. Such reactions involve basically a transfer of electrons. Thus when sodium burns in chlorine the overall reaction can be regarded as the result of two processes:

$$\left.\begin{array}{l}2Na - 2e \to 2Na^+ \\ Cl_2 + 2e \ \to 2Cl^-\end{array}\right\} 2Na + Cl_2 \to 2Na^+ Cl^- \text{ (an ionic solid).}$$

The sodium loses an electron easily and is said to be oxidised by the chlorine; and the chlorine, which accepts an electron readily is an *oxidising agent*. By accepting an electron the chlorine is reduced and the sodium behaves towards the chlorine as a *reducing agent*. Normally the processes occur simultaneously, but in electrolysis they take place at different electrodes. One electrode puts electrons in, the other takes them out.

Generally speaking the metallic elements are reducing agents and the non-metallic elements, with the exception of the inert gases, oxidising agents. But the terms are relative. Two oxidising agents may compete for electrons as happens when fluorine is bubbled through molten sodium chloride with its ions Na^+ and Cl^-,

$$\left. \begin{array}{l} 2Cl^- - 2e \rightarrow Cl_2 \\ F_2 + 2e \rightarrow 2F^- \end{array} \right\} \quad F_2 + 2Cl^- \rightarrow 2F^- + Cl_2.$$

Here fluorine, the stronger oxidising agent, takes the electrons and oxidises the chlorine ion, which is just the reverse of the conversion of molecular chlorine to the ion by sodium. Now the ion acts as the reducing agent and is oxidised to the normal molecule. Cl and Cl^- are said to form an *oxidation–reduction couple*. The relative strengths of oxidising and reducing agents clearly depend on the free energy changes in the processes. These can be studied under controlled conditions in electric cells.

Although every electrode process is one of oxidation or reduction, it is convenient to recognise three main types of electrode:

(*i*) *The Cation Electrode* very readily liberates cations into the solution and is usually a metal, M. The reaction is $M \rightarrow M^{z+} + z\,e$; the electrons flow away through the external circuit and the cations migrate into solution, the metal being oxidised by the solution. But the direction of the reaction can be reversed by driving electrons in at the electrode (electrolysis), under these conditions the cations approach the electrode, the *cathode*, and are reduced to metal. One electrode of this kind is the *hydrogen electrode*, in which pure hydrogen passes over platinised platinum. Such a surface is thermodynamically equivalent to one of gaseous hydrogen, cations being produced according to $\frac{1}{2}H_2 \rightarrow H^+ + e$.

(*ii*) *The Anion Electrode* very readily liberates anions and is commonly a metal coated with one of its insoluble salts. Silver coated with silver chloride, for example, accepts electrons from the external circuit and produces anions which migrate into the solution, $AgCl + e \rightarrow Ag + Cl^-$. Silver ions, Ag^+, in the solid chloride are reduced, giving the metal. When the reaction is made to proceed in reverse, electrons are extracted from the electrode to give silver ions, $Ag - e \rightarrow Ag^+$. The silver ions combine with chloride ions from the solution to reform silver chloride on the surface of the electrode.

(*iii*) *The Oxidation–Reduction Electrode* is one in which the electrode itself is inert (*e.g.* pure platinum) and the solution contains ions of variable charge, say iron(II) and iron(III) ions. Supply of electrons then causes reduction of the higher ion to the lower, $Fe^{3+} + e \rightarrow Fe^{2+}$, and removal of electrons causes oxidation of the lower ion to the higher, $Fe^{2+} - e \rightarrow Fe^{3+}$.

The free energy changes which accompany the flow of electrons always depend on the chemical potentials of the ions taking part in the reactions and hence on the *ionic activities*. The nature of the electrolyte is irrelevant except in so far as it determines these activities. Each electrode in its ambient solution constitutes a *half-cell*. By putting two half-cells together, preventing mixing if the two solutions differ, a complete cell is formed, with a natural direction of operation determined by the free energy changes. It is customary to represent such an arrangement thus:

$$\text{Pt, H}_2 \mid \qquad \text{HCl(aq)} \qquad \mid \text{AgCl} \mid \text{Ag}$$

The phase boundaries are indicated by vertical lines, the solution here is common; the junction or 'bridge' used when the solutions are different is indicated by a double line. In this instance the reactions are

$$\tfrac{1}{2}\text{H}_2 \rightarrow \text{H}^+ + \text{e} \qquad \text{and} \qquad \text{AgCl} + \text{e} \rightarrow \text{Ag} + \text{Cl}^-,$$

or

$$\tfrac{1}{2}\text{H}_2(g) + \text{AgCl(s)} \rightarrow \text{Ag(s)} + \text{H}^+(aq) + \text{Cl}^-(aq) = \text{Ag(s)} + \text{HCl (aq)}.$$

The free energy change per Faraday is thus

$$\Delta G_r = \Delta G_r^\circ + RT \ln Q_a, \qquad Q_a = \frac{\{\text{HCl}\}\,\{\text{Ag}\}}{\{\text{H}_2\}^{\frac{1}{2}}\,\{\text{AgCl}\}}$$

where ΔG_r° refers to standard conditions and the braces, $\{\text{HCl}\}$ etc., indicate mean activities. At 25°C and 1 at. pressure, the solids and the gas are in their standard states, irrespective of the HCl concentration, and their activities are therefore both unity. Since $\Delta G_r = -FE$, where E is the cell electromotive force

$$E - E^\circ = -(RT/F) \ln \{\text{HCl}_{(aq)}\},$$

where E° is the electromotive force with standard concentration and $\{\text{HCl}_{(aq)}\}$ is the mean ionic activity of H^+ and Cl^- in solution, referred to this standard. For strong electrolytes at extreme dilution the activity would be measured by the molality (unity for a normal solution), but this is not true for real solutions and the concentration must be increased somewhat to achieve unit activity. E° is called the standard electrode potential of the AgCl,Ag electrode relative to the standard hydrogen, usually written E_h°.

Now consider any two half-cells, with electrode reactions 1 and 2, combined in turn with a hydrogen half-cell (reaction 0) thus:

Reaction 0	Reaction 1	$\Delta G_1 = \Delta G_0^\circ + \Delta G_1^\circ = -FE_1^\circ$
Reaction 0	Reaction 2	$\Delta G_2 = \Delta G_0^\circ + \Delta G_2^\circ = -FE_2^\circ$

Then the difference in standard free energies of the two processes is $\Delta G_2^\circ - \Delta G_1^\circ$, and this is seen to be $F(E_1^\circ - E_2^\circ)$. Standard free energies of reactions involving ions and electrons, into which many reactions may be conventionally separated, are therefore measured by their standard electrode potentials. Moreover, if reaction 1 is reversible, a third cell can be set up:

Reaction 1, reversed	Reaction 2	$\Delta G = \Delta G_2^\circ - \Delta G_1^\circ = F(E_1 - E_2).$

This cell will have a standard electromotive force E_{12}, say; and, since $\Delta G° = -FE_{12}°$, it follows that $E_{12}° = E_2° - E_1°$. The electromotive force of any cell may therefore be predicted when the standard electrode potentials of the constituent half cells are known.

The standard electrode potential for an oxidation–reduction process is often called the *standard redox potential* of the pair of ions involved. A table of redox potentials finds immediate application in inorganic chemistry.

TABLE 25

STANDARD REDOX POTENTIALS

System	$E(V)$	Electrode Reaction
Pt; Co^{3+}/Co^{2+}	$+1.84$	$Co^{3+} + e \rightarrow Co^{2+}$
Pt; Ce^{4+}/Ce^{3+}	$+1.61$	$Ce^{4+} + e \rightarrow Ce^{3+}$
Pt; Fe^{3+}/Fe^{2+}	$+0.77$	$Fe^{3+} + e \rightarrow Fe^{2+}$
Cu^{2+}/Cu	$+0.35$	$Cu^{2+} + 2e \rightarrow Cu$
Ag; $AgCl/Cl^-$	$+0.22$	$AgCl + e \rightarrow Ag + Cl^-$
Pt; Sn^{4+}/Sn^{2+}	$+0.15$	$Sn^{4+} + 2e \rightarrow Sn^{2+}$
Pt; H^+/H_2	0.00	$2H^+ + 2e \rightarrow H_2$
Pb^{2+}/Pb	-0.15	$Pb^{2+} + 2e \rightarrow Pb$
Fe^{2+}/Fe	-0.44	$Fe^{2+} + 2e \rightarrow Fe$
Zn^{2+}/Zn	-0.76	$Zn^{2+} + 2e \rightarrow Zn$
Na^+/Na	-2.71	$Na^+ + e \rightarrow Na$

Suppose, for instance, we wish to know what happens when a solution containing tin(II) and tin(IV) ions is mixed with one containing iron(II) and iron(III) ions. From Table 25,

$$Sn^{4+} + 2e = Sn^{2+} \qquad E° = 0.15 \text{ V}$$
$$Fe^{3+} + e = Fe^{2+} \qquad E° = 0.77 \text{ V}$$

The standard free energy of the reaction

$$Sn^{2+} + 2Fe^{3+} \rightarrow 2Fe^{2+} + Sn^{4+}$$

would thus be

$$\Delta G_r° = -2FE°, \quad \text{with} \quad E° = 0.62 \text{ V};$$

and allows us to write down immediately the equilibrium constant since $\Delta G_r° = -RT \ln K_a$. K_a is found to be $\sim 10^{21}$. Introducing activities (very roughly molalities),

$$\frac{\{Sn^{4+}\} \{Fe^{2+}\}^2}{\{Sn^{2+}\} \{Fe^{3+}\}^2} \sim 10^{21}.$$

Reduction of the iron(III) and oxidation of the tin(II) ions therefore proceeds virtually to completion, leaving in solution iron(II) and tin(IV) ions.

Quite generally, a couple of high potential will oxidise a couple of low potential. When the redox potentials are similar, the equilibrium constant is small and the oxidation may be incomplete; but, when one of the products separates through insolubility, its concentration in the denominator of the quotient Q_a will be almost zero, and the oxidation will continue.

Hydrogen ion concentration

Since the electromotive force of a cell depends on the activity of the ions of the electrolyte it is possible to determine activities potentiometrically, in particular that of the hydrogen ion which is a measure of acid strength. Strictly, however, the activity of a single ionic species is not measurable, for positive ions always exist in the presence of negative ions. Nevertheless, the mean activity of HCl which is measurable in a cell does conveniently indicate the mean activity of the ions which carry the current, and $-\log_{10}$ of this activity is the pH of the solution. The basic principle of potentiometric pH determination may be seen by considering a cell divided into two halves by a silver wall coated on both sides with silver chloride:

$$\text{Pt, H}_2 \left| \begin{array}{c} \text{HCl} \\ a \text{ unknown} \end{array} \right| \text{AgCl} \left| \text{Ag} \right| \text{AgCl} \left| \begin{array}{c} \text{HCl} \\ a = 1 \end{array} \right| \text{Pt, H}_2$$

The overall electromotive force of the cell between platinum electrodes is given by

$$E = -\frac{2RT}{F} \ln \text{ unknown } a_{H^+} = \frac{4.606\,RT}{F} \text{ pH.}$$

The hydrogen electrode has been largely superseded for routine pH measurement but the other devices depend on the same general principle.

Chapter 9

Chemical Kinetics

A chemical reaction hardly ever takes place as the stoichiometric equation appears to indicate. Both the equation and the free energy considerations (p. 171) are concerned only with the initial and final states of the system, although the overall reaction to which they refer may proceed by a series of related steps that cannot be investigated separately and are inferred from reaction-rate studies. The term *kinetics* implies the experimental and theoretical study of the way reactions take place and the rate at which they proceed. Here the subject is reviewed only very briefly, though it is of considerable importance in inorganic chemistry.

The study of reaction rates presents difficulties not encountered in investigations concerned only with the original and final states of a chemical system. The progress of a reaction can be followed by (a) physical methods such as the observation of changes in electrical conductance, colour, volume, ultra-violet absorption or optical activity, or the measurement of the gas evolved, (b) chemical methods leading to the determination of reactants and products, (c) radiochemical methods in which the transfer of radioactive material is observed.

Until recently little work has been done on the rates of ionic reactions in solution, principally because these are usually so fast as to make measurement difficult. Working with metal ions in non-aqueous solutions at very low temperatures, Bjerrum and Poulsen (1952) found, for example, that Ni^{2+} reacted at a rate which was measurable with dimethylglyoxime in methanol at $-75°$. Awtrey and Connick (1951) applied Hartridge and Roughton's dynamic flow method (1923) to the reaction between SO_3^{2-} and I_3^- in aqueous solution. Bell and Clunie (1952) have developed a thermal method for studying reactions occurring in a few seconds.

Order of a reaction

When substances react in the gaseous phase or in solution their concentrations fall and the reaction rate decreases. Experiment shows that the reaction rate is jointly proportional to various powers of the concentrations of the individual reactants. In the reaction

$$aA + bB \rightarrow \text{products}$$

this means $-\dfrac{d[A]}{dt} \left(= -\dfrac{b}{a}\dfrac{d[B]}{dt} \right) = k[A]^{n_A}[B]^{n_B},$

k being the specific reaction rate or velocity constant. The sum of the exponents $n_A + n_B$ is the *order* of the reaction.
Examples are:

(i) $2N_2O_5 \rightarrow 4NO_2 + O_2$ $-\dfrac{d[N_2O_5]}{dt} = k[N_2O_5]$ first order

(ii) $2NO_2 \rightarrow 2NO + O_2$ $-\dfrac{d[NO_2]}{dt} = k[NO_2]^2$ second order

(iii) $C_2H_4Br_2 + 2KI$
     $\rightarrow C_2H_4 + 2KBr + I_2$ $-\dfrac{d[KI]}{dt} = k[C_2H_4Br_2][KI]$ second order

(iv) $CH_3CHO \rightarrow CH_4 + CO$ $-\dfrac{d[CH_3CHO]}{dt} = k[CH_3CHO]^{3/2}$ 3/2 order

Zero order reactions also occur, the rate being independent of the measured concentrations of reactants. This often indicates an intermediate step that almost wholly determines the overall rate, in which an intermediary species is present in small and sensibly constant concentration.

Molecularity and reaction mechanism

The order of a reaction is derived from an empirical reaction rate equation; the *molecularity* refers to a molecular mechanism and hence to a theoretical model of a certain elementary step in a reaction. For example, it appears that in the reaction between iodine vapour and hydrogen there is a single elementary step involving the collision of *two* molecules (H_2 and I_2) and their emergence as two molecules of HI. This is accordingly a *bi*molecular reaction. The molecularity of an elementary reaction is defined as the smallest number of molecules which must coalesce prior to the formation of the products. The term does not apply to processes which consist of a succession of elementary steps, such as chemical reactions very often are. Thus, the oxidation of an iron(II) salt by a permanganate,

$$5Fe^{2+} + MnO_4^- + 8H_3O^+ \rightarrow 5Fe^{3+} + Mn^{2+} + 12H_2O,$$

does not proceed by the simultaneous meeting of fourteen ions of three specific types. Molecularity can be assigned only to the simple steps, though what the simple steps are is seldom obvious. When identified, they nearly always prove to be unimolecular or bimolecular, and the overall order and rate of reaction depends on their individual rates, often in a complicated way. Frequently, however, one of the steps is so much slower than the others that it alone largely determines the overall rate—it is the *rate-determining step*. In general, the order of a reaction which consists of, or is dominated by, a single rate-determining step is equal to the molecularity of that step. In other words a bimolecular reaction is of second order; but, since the mechanism may be uncertain, a second order reaction is not necessarily bimolecular. An example of a rate-determining step is provided by the reaction between H_2O_2 and the iodide ion:

$$H_2O_2 + 2H_3O^+ + 2I^- \rightarrow 4H_2O + I_2$$

is of second order, with

$$\frac{d[I_2]}{dt} = k[I^-]\,[H_2O_2].$$

It is believed to have three steps:

(a) $H_2O_2 + I^- \rightarrow H_2O + IO^-$ (slow)
(b) $IO^- + H_3O^+ \rightarrow HOI + H_2O$ (fast)
(c) $HOI + H_3O^+ + I^- \rightarrow 2H_2O + I_2$ (fast)

and that the rate is determined by the bimolecular mechanism (a).

For formal purposes it is convenient to distinguish six basic reaction types:
(i) Bond breaking: $Br_2 \rightarrow 2Br.$
(ii) Bond formation: $CH_3^{\cdot} + CH_3^{\cdot} \rightarrow C_2H_6.$
(iii) Electron transfer: $[Fe(CN)_6]^{3-} + e \rightleftharpoons [Fe(CN)_6]^{4-}.$
(iv) Proton transfer: $NH_4^+ + H_2O \rightarrow NH_3 + H_3O^+.$
(v) Atom or radical transfer: $CH_3^{\cdot} + CH_3 — C{=}O \rightarrow CH_4 + CH_3.C^{\cdot}{=}O.$
$$\underset{H}{|}$$

(vi) Partner exchange:
$$\begin{array}{cc} H{—}H & \quad H\ \ H \\ & \rightarrow \ \ |\ \ | \\ I{—}I & \quad I\ \ I \end{array}$$

However, this classification is not unambiguous and even the basic types are not necessarily simple. For instance, the ion exchange in aqueous solution, $Fe^{3+} + Fe^{2+} \rightarrow Fe^{2+} + Fe^{3+}$, which is formally an electron transfer, may actually proceed by ligand exchange:

$$(Fe^{III}—OH)^{2+}(aq) + Fe_2^+(aq) \rightarrow Fe_2^+(aq) + (Fe^{III}—OH)^{2+}(aq);$$

or even by *proton* transfer:

$$(Fe^{III}—OH)^{2+}(aq) + (Fe^{II}—OH_2)^{2+}(aq) \rightarrow (Fe^{II}—OH_2)^{2+}(aq) +$$
$$+ (Fe^{III}—OH)^{2+}(aq).$$

Determination of order

Since the overall order of a reaction is a guide to the molecularity of individual steps, a determination of the order is important in establishing probable reaction mechanisms. For simple reactions of first or second order, the rate equation may be integrated and the rate constant evaluated by fitting the theoretical expression to an experimental concentration–time curve. For more complicated reactions, this cannot be done; but the differential expression can still be used. Initially, before the concentration of the reactants has changed appreciably,

$$- \frac{d[A]}{dt} = [A]_0^{n_A}[B]_0^{n_B} \ldots$$

where $[A]_0$ etc. are initial concentrations of the reactants. From experiments with various initial concentrations, the exponents may then be inferred. Alternatively, the concentration of all but one of the reactants may be made large; in these circumstances the concentration of only one of the reactants changes appreciably during the reaction, the rate equations becomes integrable, and the order can be found from concentration–time curves as indicated above.

Temperature dependence of reaction rates

The first attempts to interpret the rate equation were made by Arrhenius. For an elementary gas reaction, $aA + bB \rightarrow xX + yY$, in which the order is equal to the molecularity,

$$- \frac{d[A]}{dt} = [A]^a[B]^b.$$

By regarding a *reversible* reaction as a pair of opposing elementary reactions, equilibrium is seen to result when $k_f[A]^a[B]^b = k_b[X]^x[Y]^y$ (using k_f and k_b to denote 'forward' and 'backward' velocity constants). Then the equilibrium constant (p. 179) is interpreted as a ratio of two velocity constants; and it is plausible, as Arrhenius pointed out, that the velocity constants themselves should depend on temperature according to the Van 't Hoff equation (p. 180). Putting

$$\frac{d[\ln k]}{dT} = \frac{E}{RT^2},$$

where E is a constant with dimensions of energy, then

$$k = A \, e^{-E/RT}.$$

This is indeed found to be true of many homogeneous reactions. The appropriate value of E is determined from a plot of $\ln k$ against $1/T$, which is linear with a slope $-E/R$.

Collision theories

Using simple kinetic theory, Arrhenius supposed that E was a critical energy (per mole) which the molecules must possess before they could react.

The idea is supported for reactions between ideal gases by Boltzmann's law, which shows that the fractional number of molecules with energy greater than a given value E is $e^{-E/RT}$. But the same inference clearly cannot be made for solutions. Now if the probability of a molecule having the necessary critical energy E is $e^{-E/RT}$ and the probability of collision is Z per unit time, then the probability of an *effective* collision is $Ze^{-E/RT}$ per unit time and this will be the fractional number of molecules reacting in unit time. In this simple *collision theory* it was customary to put

$$k = PZ\, e^{-E/RT}.$$

E is an *activation energy*, Z a *frequency factor*, and P a 'correction' or 'steric' factor, intended to allow for unfavourable orientation at the instant of collision. In fact P was chosen simply to get a good fit with experiment and is an unsatisfactory feature of the approach. Nevertheless, most homogeneous bimolecular reactions have rate constants which do conform quite closely to this equation.

The inadequacy of the simple Arrhenius theory becomes most apparent in simple decompositions with *first order* kinetics; for any collision theory implies a *bi*molecular mechanism which should result in *second order* kinetics. This difficulty was removed by Lindemann (1922) whose work marked the next advance in collision theory. He assumed simply that there is a time lag between the activation of a molecule, by absorption of energy from a collision, and its decomposition. This possibility depends on the existence of internal degrees of freedom, ignored in the 'hard sphere' model of elementary kinetic theory, in which energy gained through collision can be stored. The energy is exchanged among the various modes of vibration until, at some later time, either a particular bond is stretched to breaking point and decomposition occurs, or, on the other hand, the activated molecule loses its extra energy in another collision before the rupture takes place.

At low pressures, where collisions are infrequent and an activated molecule is almost sure to decompose before losing its energy, the reaction is

$$A + A \rightarrow A^* + A \qquad \text{Rate} \propto [A]^2.$$
$$\downarrow$$
$$\text{products}$$

But at higher pressures an equilibrium is possible, in which activated molecules disappear by collision as rapidly as they are formed, and the rate-determining step is the decomposition (*cf.* radioactive decay):

$$A^* \rightarrow \text{products} \qquad \text{Rate} \propto [A^*] \propto [A].$$

A simple decomposition, which is *initiated* by a bimolecular mechanism, may thus give an overall process which is either first or second order. The transition to second order at low pressures is observed in, for instance, the N_2O_5 decomposition.

Although the Lindemann theory is often satisfactory, it is incomplete since it does not fully recognise the relation between translational and internal energies. In many reactions the rate of activation by collision is not itself explicable unless it is assumed that activation can also occur by the transfer of *vibrational* energy from one molecule to another. This possibility was recognised by Hinshelwood and by Lewis and may be equivalent, in effect, to multiplying the frequency factor by 10^7 or more.

The whole basis of collision theories has recently been reinvestigated by Slater (1953), who has attempted a rigorous theoretical discussion of unimolecular reactions. But as yet there is no completely satisfactory collision theory of rate constants even for the simplest gas reactions; and there is no firm basis at all for any such discussion of reactions in the liquid phase.

The transition state theory

The postulation of a critical activation energy E in the collision theory is somewhat artificial. Theoretical consideration of a rearrangement such as

$$
\begin{array}{ccc}
\text{H \quad I} & \text{H----I} & \text{H—I} \\
| \quad | \;\rightarrow & \vdots \quad \vdots \;\rightarrow & \\
\text{H \quad I} & \text{H----I} & \text{H—I}
\end{array}
$$

shows that the total energy need never reach a sharp critical value corresponding to the breaking of two bonds prior to the reunion which leads to the products. The reorganisation is gradual, passing through a stage in which all atoms are partially bonded (*cf.* p. 112), and the energy changes continuously (Fig. 119).

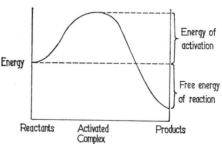

Fig. 119. Relation of energy of activation to energy of reaction.

In many bimolecular reactions the maximum occurs at about 30% of the dissociation energy required to break the original bonds (Hinshelwood, 1941). The essence of the *transition state theory* (Eyring, 1935) lies in the recognition of an actual *activated complex* corresponding roughly to the maximum of the energy curve—though it must be remembered there is no single curve, the energy varying with orientation and direction of approach. The activated complex is generally an idealised model of the result of a temporary union of the reacting molecules, and not necessarily a real complex with an appreciable lifetime. Nevertheless, transition state theory assumes not only that activated complexes occur but that they may be in approximate thermo-dynamic equilibrium with the reactants; the products then result from the *non*-equilibrium step in which the complex spontaneously decomposes:

$$\text{Reactants} \rightleftharpoons \text{Activated complex} \rightarrow \text{Products.}$$

With these assumptions, the specific rate can be related to the equilibrium constant for the first stage. In terms of the free energy, ΔG_a°, heat, ΔH_a°, and entropy, ΔS_a°, of *activation*:

$$k = (RT/Nh) \; e^{-\Delta G_a^\circ/RT} = (RT/Nh) \; e^{\Delta S_a^\circ/RT} \; e^{-\Delta H_a^\circ/RT}.$$

This resembles the result of simple collision theory, the ΔH_a° corresponding closely to E, and the entropy factor replacing the 'steric factor' P. Usually, in gases, ΔS_a° is negative (often large) because formation of the complex involves an association of molecules and a consequent reduction in the number of ways in which translational and rotational energy can be shared out, and hence a reduction in S (p. 168). In this way, the old steric factor, which commonly had empirical values as low as 10^{-6}, receives a much more plausible interpretation.

The entropy factor also suggests a reason for the rare occurrence of *ter*-molecular reactions (whose very existence is still open to doubt); for, although the number of collisions involving three molecules is significant, the resultant large entropy decrease would be most unfavourable to the existence of a three-molecule complex. Bimolecular reactions do occur in which the *presence* of a third body is known to be necessary, its purpose being to absorb excess energy which would otherwise lead to immediate disruption of the product. These reactions are bimolecular because the third body is not included in the activated complex. In them a large entropy decrease is not entailed and such reactions which depend on three-body collisions, for example $H + H \rightarrow H_2$, may nevertheless be rapid.

Although the transition state theory has advantages over collision theories in its generality, avoiding detailed consideration of kinetic mechanism by appeal to thermodynamic principles, it rests upon equally weak experimental foundations. However, its flexibility permits applications to reactions in the liquid phase where the gas kinetic model breaks down. In such applications the entropy factor is all-important and may range roughly from 10^{-8} to 10^{+8}.

Solutions, particularly ionic solutions, acids and bases, have also received much attention; but for these developments the reader is referred to books on physical chemistry.

Chain reactions

Many reactions which might appear to be bimolecular have very curious rate laws which arise from intermediate *chain reactions*. In such cases an 'initiation' leads to a quite small concentration of the intermediate which then continues to produce itself by a self-sustaining process. An example is the gas reaction,

$$H_2 + Cl_2 \rightarrow 2HCl,$$

whose kinetics can be accounted for by assuming:

Initiation: $Cl_2 \rightarrow 2Cl$ (induced by, for example, u.v. radiation).

Chain reaction: $\begin{cases} Cl + H_2 \rightarrow HCl + H, \\ H + Cl_2 \rightarrow HCl + Cl. \end{cases}$

The chain reaction sustains itself until it is terminated by direct combination of H and Cl, probably at the walls of the containing vessel. Such a reaction therefore tends to propagate itself without further encouragement until the reactants are exhausted. There are many examples of chain reactions in organic chemistry, where the active intermediate is often a free radical such as CH'_3. Sometimes these are undesirable (*e.g.* in the premature oxidation of hydrocarbons under pressure, which causes 'knocking' in internal combustion engines) and it is necessary to inhibit them by suitable additives which operate by terminating the chains.

Chain reactions proceed with explosive violence if the active intermediate produces itself in ever increasing quantities instead of merely regenerating itself, that is if *more than one* atom or molecule of intermediate appears for every molecule of the final product.

Catalysis

The feasibility of a reaction, in terms of equilibrium concentration of reactants and products, is indicated by the overall free energy change ΔG_r° (p. 176). But its speed is determined by ΔG_a°, for if this is too high the activated complex will not occur in appreciable concentration. A catalyst cannot affect ΔG_r; it operates by reducing ΔG_a (Fig. 120).

In *homogeneous catalysis* (one phase in solution for example) the catalyst is usually another molecule or ion which itself occurs in an activated complex with a reduced value of ΔG_a; and, when this decays to form the products, the catalyst re-emerges. Acid-base catalysis (p. 208) is of this type.

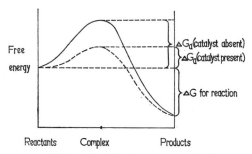

Fig. 120. Effect of catalyst on energy of activation.

In *heterogeneous catalysis* (surface catalysis) the reactants are commonly adsorbed on a suitable surface (*chemi*sorption usually being the more effective); and the activated complex, when attached in this way, may have a much lower activation energy than in the homogeneous phase.

Chapter 10

Acids and Bases

Early studies of acids and bases were restricted to aqueous solutions and were made with an inadequate understanding of the peculiarities of water. The compounds were defined as substances which dissociated in water, the acids to give free hydrogen ions and the bases free hydroxide ions (Arrhenius, Ostwald, 1887). This definition does not express present views about aqueous solutions and cannot be applied to solutions in other solvents. Thermodynamics shows that free H^+ ions cannot exist in appreciable concentration in water itself, and spectroscopy that the hydration of the proton is a strongly exothermic reaction. Accordingly the dissociation of an acid in water leads to H^+_{aq}, often represented by H_3O^+ and referred to as the hydroxonium ion:

$$H^+ + H_2O \rightarrow H_3O^+, \qquad -\Delta H \sim 290 \text{ kcal.}$$

The hydrogen ion in aqueous solutions is almost certainly associated with more than one water molecule (for the structure of water see p. 232). H_3O^+ exists in some ionic lattices, however, for instance in $H_3O^+ClO_4^-$ which is isomorphous with $NH_4^+ClO_4^-$.

On the other hand, an acid dissociates in anhydrous ethyl alcohol to give the cation $C_2H_5OH_2^+$, and in liquid ammonia to give the cation NH_4^+.

Bases behave similarly. Although sodium hydroxide is a strong base in water, it is less ionised in anhydrous alcohol than sodium ethoxide, C_2H_5ONa, the anion of which, $C_2H_5O^-$, also appears in solutions of amines in ethyl alcohol. In liquid ammonia, the anion present is NH_2^-. These liquids exemplify solvents in which the anion is not hydroxide.

Clearly acids and bases cannot be defined in terms of the ions H^+ and OH^-.

Lowry-Brönsted theory of acids and bases

Lowry and Brönsted (1923) independently defined an acid as a compound or ion with a tendency to lose a proton, and a base as a compound or ion with a tendency to gain a proton. The proton is likely to be associated with a solvent molecule but may be represented formally by H^+. An acid A by losing a proton becomes a base B. Base B will tend to regain the proton and revert to A. There will be an equilibrium:

$$A \rightleftharpoons B + H^+.$$

Thus for acetic acid:

$$CH_3COOH \rightleftharpoons CH_3COO^- + H^+.$$

The acetate ion is evidently a base. The acetic acid and the acetate ion are known as a *conjugate acid-base pair*. The term is applied generally to any two species related to each other as A is to B in the general equation.

The definition allows for the existence of three types of acid:

(i) *Molecular acids*, such as hydrochloric, sulphuric and acetic acids, which lose protons to give, as conjugate bases, the chloride, bisulphate and acetate ions respectively:

$$HCl \rightleftharpoons Cl^- + H^+,$$
$$H_2SO_4 \rightleftharpoons HSO_4^- + H^+,$$
$$CH_3COOH \rightleftharpoons CH_3COO^- + H^+.$$

(ii) *Anion acids*, such as the bisulphate HSO_4^- and bi-oxalate $C_2O_4H^-$ ions, which lose protons to give, as conjugate bases, the sulphate SO_4^{2-} and oxalate $C_2O_4^{2-}$ ions respectively:

$$HSO_4^- \rightleftharpoons SO_4^{2-} + H^+,$$
$$HC_2O_4^- \rightleftharpoons C_2O_4^{2-} + H^+.$$

(iii) *Cation acids*, such as the hydroxonium H_3O^+, ammonium NH_4^+, and the anilinium $C_6H_5NH_3^+$ ions, which lose protons to give water, ammonia and aniline, respectively, as conjugate bases:

$$H_3O^+ \rightleftharpoons H_2O + H^+,$$
$$NH_4^+ \rightleftharpoons NH_3 + H^+,$$
$$C_6H_5NH_3^+ \rightleftharpoons C_6H_5NH_2 + H^+.$$

Two types of base are possible:

(i) *Molecular bases*, such as ammonia and ethylamine:

$$CH_3NH_2 + H^+ \rightleftharpoons CH_3NH_3^+.$$

(ii) *Anion bases*, such as the hydroxide and acetate ions:

$$CH_3COO^- + H^+ \rightleftharpoons CH_3COOH.$$

The equilibrium $A \rightleftharpoons B + H^+$ is purely formal because of the non-existence of the proton in water and other solvents. When an acid loses its proton it does so to a base. The acid is thereby converted to its conjugate base and the base to its conjugate acid, as exemplified in the general and particular expressions:

$$A_1 + B_2 \rightleftharpoons B_1 + A_2,$$

$$\underset{acid}{CH_3COOH} + \underset{base}{H_2O} \rightleftharpoons \underset{base}{CH_3COO^-} + \underset{acid}{H_3O^+}.$$

The latter represents the transfer of a proton from an acetic acid molecule to a water molecule and the consequent formation of two ions. Written in the opposite sense,

$$CH_3COO^- + H_3O^+ \rightleftharpoons CH_3COOH + H_2O,$$

the equilibrium is seen to depend upon the transfer of a proton from a hydroxonium ion to an acetate ion; the process is responsible for the 'buffer action' (p. 197) of an acetate when an acid is added.

Acid-base equilibria in water

Reactions involving the transfer of a proton are known as *protolytic reactions*. The equilibrium constants of *protolyses* allow a comparison to be made of acid and base strengths. The conjugate pair, H_3O^+, H_2O, is used as a standard,

$$A + H_2O \rightleftharpoons B + H_3O^+,$$

and the equilibrium constant is the *acidity constant*, $K_a = \{B\}\ \{H_3O^+\}/\{A\}\{H_2O\}$. For dilute solutions $\{H_2O\}$ is independent of concentration and tends to unity, and the dissociation constant is $K_a \sim \{B\}\ \{H_3O^+\}/\{A\}$ in terms of activities. Equations of this type may be used to compare strengths of molecular, anion and cation acids. Thus for

$$CH_3COOH, \quad K_a = \{CH_3COO^-\}\ \{H_3O^+\}/\{CH_3COOH\};$$
$$HSO_4^-, \quad K_a = \{SO_4^{2-}\}\ \{H_3O^+\}/\{HSO_4^-\};$$
$$NH_4^+, \quad K_a = \{NH_3\}\ \{H_3O^+\}/\{NH_4^+\}.$$

The strengths of bases are inversely related to the strength of the conjugate acids, and it is necessary to use only one constant, expressing the strength of a base as the reciprocal of the strength of its conjugate acid. Thus for NH_3, $K_b = \{NH_4^+\}/\{NH_3\}\ \{H_3O^+\}$. Now if K_w is the acidity constant for H_2O, *i.e.* the equilibrium constant for

$$H_2O + H_2O \rightleftharpoons OH^- + H_3O^+,$$

$$K_w = \frac{\{OH^-\}\ \{H_3O^+\}}{\{H_2O\}^2} \sim \{OH^-\}\ \{H_3O^+\} \text{ (the autoprotolysis constant)}$$

and therefore

$$K_b = \frac{\{NH_4^+\}\{OH^-\}}{\{NH_3\}} \frac{1}{K_w} = \frac{K_b \text{ (classical)}}{K_w}$$

The exponent pK_a ($= -\log_{10}K_a$), cf. pH, is also a convenient measure of acid strength.

No acid species much stronger than H_3O^+ ($K_a = 55$ mole kg^{-1}) can appear in appreciable quantity in water. Hydrogen chloride which is stronger is almost entirely converted to H_3O^+ and Cl$^-$ and, similarly, H_2SO_4 to H_3O^+ and HSO_4^-. Since, however, K_a for HSO_4^- is 10^{-2} mole kg^{-1}, that anion can exist in appreciable concentrations in water.

On the same grounds, a base much stronger than OH$^-$ cannot exist in appreciable quantity because it is hydrolysed by water to its conjugate acid and OH$^-$:

$$H_2O + NH_2^- \rightleftharpoons NH_3 + OH^-.$$

The above are examples of *strong electrolytes* in water. A *weak electrolyte* in water is one with a neutral molecule which is not an electrolyte but which is partly changed into ions in aqueous solution.

TABLE 26

STRENGTHS OF SOME ACIDS

					K_a	pK_a.
Hydrochloric acid	HCl	$+ H_2O$	$\rightleftharpoons$ Cl$^-$	$+ H_3O^+$	$\sim 10^7$	-7
Iodic acid	HIO$_3$	$+ H_2O$	$\rightleftharpoons$ IO$_3^-$	$+ H_3O^+$	2.0×10^{-1}	0.7
Phosphoric acid	H$_3$PO$_4$	$+ H_2O$	$\rightleftharpoons$ H$_2$PO$_4^-$	$+ H_3O^+$	5.0×10^{-2}	1.3
Carbonic acid	H$_2$CO$_3$	$+ H_2O$	$\rightleftharpoons$ HCO$_3^-$	$+ H_3O^+$	4.5×10^{-7}	6.4
Hydrocyanic acid	HCN	$+ H_2O$	$\rightleftharpoons$ CN$^-$	$+ H_3O^+$	7.2×10^{-10}	9.1
Ammonium ion	NH$_4^+$	$+ H_2O$	$\rightleftharpoons$ NH$_3$	$+ H_3O^+$	5.6×10^{-10}	9.3
Bicarbonate ion	HCO$_3^-$	$+ H_2O$	$\rightleftharpoons$ CO$_3^{2-}$	$+ H_3O^+$	5.6×10^{-11}	10.3
Ethane	C$_2$H$_6$	$+ H_2O$	$\rightleftharpoons$ C$_2$H$_5^-$	$+ H_3O^+$	$\sim 10^{-34}$	34

Hydrolysis and buffer action

As the equilibrium

$$NH_4^+ + H_2O \rightleftharpoons NH_3 + H_3O^+$$

represents the hydrolysis of the ammonium salt of a strong acid, K_a for the ammonium ion is also the hydrolysis constant. The equation

$$CH_3COO^- + H_2O \rightleftharpoons CH_3COOH + OH^-$$

represents the hydrolysis of the acetate of a strong base. Here the hydrolysis constant, $K_h = \{CH_3COOH\}\{OH^-\}/\{CH_3COO^-\}$, is related to the dissociation of the acid by the expression $K_h = K_w/K_a$.

Hydroxonium ions added to a solution of acetate ions are largely converted into undissociated acetic acid molecules:

$$H_3O^+ + CH_3COO^- \rightleftharpoons CH_3COOH + H_2O.$$
$$\quad\quad base \quad\quad\quad\quad\quad acid$$

Since K_a for the acid $= \{base\}\ \{H_3O^+\}/\{acid\}$,
therefore $\{H_3O^+\} = K_a\ \{acid\}/\{base\}$,
and $pH = pK_a - \log_{10}\{acid\}/\{base\}$.

The ratio $\{acid\}/\{base\}$ is the *buffer ratio*. Because the buffer ratio is not altered by dilution, neither is the pH, except in strong solutions where the attraction between ions becomes sufficiently great to interfere with the simple equilibria. Small additions of acid and alkali alter the buffer ratio and pH very little. Buffering is obviously most efficient when $\{acid\} \sim \{base\}$, *i.e.* when $pH \sim pK_a$.

Thus a solution containing equimolar concentrations of acetic acid molecules and acetate ions has a pH given by

$$pH = pK_{acetic\ acid} - \log_{10}\frac{\{HAc\}}{\{Ac^-\}},$$
$$= 4.75 - \log 1.0 = 4.75.$$

When the acid concentration is 10 times that of the acetate ion,

$$pH = 4.75 - \log 10 = 3.75;$$

but when the acetate ion is 10 times more concentrated,

$$pH = 4.75 - \log 0.1 = 5.75.$$

Methods of studying acid-base equilibria in water

For an equilibrium such as

$$CH_3COOH + H_2O \rightleftharpoons CH_3COO^- + H_3O^+,$$

in which ions appear on one side of the equation only, the equilibrium constant is conveniently obtained from the electrical conductance. For equilibria such as

$$NH_4^+ + H_2O \rightleftharpoons NH_3 + H_3O^+,$$

where conductance changes are small, the concentration of H_3O^+ ions may be obtained from potential measurements. The concentration of hydroxonium and hydroxide can also be inferred from their respective catalytic effect in specific reactions. Sometimes the equilibrium may be investigated colorimetrically. The concentration of an uncharged species such as ammonia may, on occasion, be determined from partition coefficients with another phase, say chloroform (p. 572).

Acids and bases in non-aqueous protonic solvents

A protonic solvent is one which contains hydrogen in the molecule and which is thus capable of acting, under certain conditions, as a proton donor. The behaviour of a solute depends on whether the solvent (i) tends to gain or lose a proton, (ii) admits recombination of ions.

Water, being both a proton donor and a proton acceptor, is said to be *amphiprotic*. It has a considerable dipole moment and a very high dielectric constant so that solvation of the ions, together with the dielectric effect (p. 121), discourages their recombination. These characteristics are responsible for the simple form taken by the ionic theory before the study of non-aqueous solvents revealed the more complex relationship between concentration and degree of ionisation.

Amphiprotic solvents resembling water

Alcohols resemble water as solvents but have much smaller dielectric constants, 32 for methyl and 25 for ethyl alcohol against 78 for water. For equilibria such as

$$NH_4^+ + ROH \rightleftharpoons ROH_2^+ + NH_3,$$

where ions are involved on both sides, the dielectric effect is small; $\{NH_3\}\{EtOH_2^+\}/\{NH_4^+\}\{EtOH\}$ is only about six times greater than $\{NH_3\}\{H_3O^+\}/\{NH_4^+\}\{H_2O\}$, indicating that ethyl alcohol is a stronger base than water.

For equilibria such as

$$R.NH_2 + EtOH \rightleftharpoons EtO^- + R.NH_3^+,$$

where both ions are on one side, differences in dielectric constant cause the equilibrium constants to be much less than for aqueous solutions. Amines have dissociation constants in ethyl alcohol less by a factor of about 10^{-4} than in water; for fatty acids the figure is usually about 10^{-5}.

The electrical free energy of a pair of ions of charges $+e$ and $-e$ at a distance r in a medium of dielectric constant ε is given by $G = e^2/\varepsilon r$. The difference in value between the electrical free energy in water and that in ethyl alcohol as solvent is given by

$$\Delta G = \frac{e^2}{r}\left(\frac{1}{\varepsilon_1} - \frac{1}{\varepsilon_2}\right) \quad \text{(The Born equation)}$$

If $\varepsilon_1 = 78$, $\varepsilon_2 = 25$ and $r \sim 2 \times 10^{-8}$ cm, $\Delta G \sim -5600$ cal/mole. The ratio of the equilibrium constants is given by $e^{\frac{-\Delta G}{RT}} \sim 2 \times 10^4$. This is about the observed figure, suggesting the difference in behaviour to be due largely to differences in inter-ionic attraction.

Basic or protophilic solvents

Ammonia (b.p. $-33°$, ε 22) is, like water, an unsymmetrical molecule with a lone pair and a fairly high dipole moment. The autoprotolysis reaction is slight; $[NH_4^+][NH_2^-] \sim 10^{-22}$ at the boiling point ($-33°$). The protonic acid, NH_4^+, from ammonium salts in solution in ammonia, liberates hydrogen with such metals as calcium:

$$2NH_4^+ + Ca \rightarrow 2NH_3 + Ca^{2+} + H_2,$$

and decomposes salts of weaker acids:

$$4NH_4^+ + Mg_2Si \rightarrow 2Mg^{2+} + 4NH_3 + SiH_4.$$

Metallic amides, imides and nitrides behave as bases in the solvent. Thus potassamide turns phenolphthalein red and can be titrated conductometrically with an ammonium salt:

$$KNH_2 + NH_4Cl \rightleftharpoons KCl + 2NH_3.$$

Heavy metal amides, imides or nitrides are precipitated by potassamide:

$$\begin{align}
AgNO_3 + KNH_2 &\rightarrow AgNH_2 + KNO_3, \\
PbI_2 + 2KNH_2 &\rightarrow PbNH + 2KI + NH_3, \\
BiI_3 + 3KNH_2 &\rightarrow BiN + 3KI + 2NH_3.
\end{align}$$

These correspond with the precipitation, sometimes of the hydroxide:

$$CaCl_2 + 2KOH \rightarrow Ca(OH)_2 + 2KCl,$$

and sometimes of the oxide:

$$MgCl_2 + 2KOH \rightarrow MgO + 2KCl + H_2O,$$

by caustic potash in aqueous solution. Furthermore, zinc amide reacts with potassamide in liquid ammonia to give potassium ammonozincate;

$$Zn(NH_2)_2 + 2KNH_2 \rightleftharpoons K_2[Zn(NH_2)_4];$$

a reaction similar to that of zinc hydroxide and aqueous potash:

$$Zn(OH)_2 + 2KOH \rightleftharpoons K_2[Zn(OH)_4].$$

Ammonia, a strongly basic solvent and therefore a strong proton acceptor, encourages the dissociation of acids:

$$NH_3 + CH_3COOH \rightleftharpoons NH_4^+ + CH_3COO^-.$$

Acids of $pK_a \sim 5$ in water dissociate almost completely in liquid ammonia. The acids which dissociate extensively in water do not stand out so markedly in this respect in ammonia because the ionisation of acids weak in water, such as the carboxylic acids, is so much greater in the latter medium. The basic solvent is said to have a 'levelling' effect on the strength of the acids. However, as the acidic properties (proton donating power) of ammonia are very weak, strong bases dissociate in it only slightly and weak bases scarcely at all.

The solubilities of salts in liquid ammonia are markedly different from their solubilities in water. Ammonium salts are generally very soluble, as are nitrates and iodides, including silver iodide. Fluorides and chlorides have low solubilities. Ammonia is not, in general, a good solvent for highly ionic compounds, possibly largely because of its low dielectric constant. But it is a better solvent than water for non-polar compounds, and for those with highly polarisable anions such as iodides. Non-metals like iodine, sulphur, selenium and phosphorus show a moderate solubility.

The alkali metals dissolve in ammonia, without the evolution of hydrogen, giving blue, strongly conducting solutions. In dilute solutions the cation appears to be Na^+ (probably solvated) and the anion NH_3^- or $(NH_3)_n^-$, which also contributes the colour. Metals such as platinum and iron catalyse the reaction:

$$2Na + 2NH_3 \rightarrow 2NaNH_2 + H_2.$$

A solution of sodium in liquid ammonia furnishes a useful reducing agent, converting halides of the more noble metals to the element or an intermetallic compound:

$$Na + CuI \rightarrow NaI + Cu;$$
$$9Na + 4ZnI_2 \rightarrow 8NaI + NaZn_4.$$

Phosphine gives $NaPH_2$ and hydrogen. Compounds, formulated $NaNO$, KNO and $Ba(NO)_2$, are formed when nitric oxide is brought into ammonia solutions of the respective metal. These have structures different from the hyponitrites (p. 333).

Ammonolysis, the equivalent of hydrolysis in aqueous solution, is rather less extensive than the latter because of the slight autoprotolysis ($2NH_3 \rightarrow NH_4^+ + NH_2^-$) of ammonia itself:

$$HgCl_2 + 2NH_3 \rightleftharpoons HgNH_2Cl + NH_4Cl;$$
$$SbCl_3 + 4NH_3 \rightleftharpoons SbN + 3NH_4Cl.$$

Acidic or protogenic solvents

(i) Acetic acid has a strong levelling effect on the strength of bases, such as aliphatic amines and alkylanilines, which do not ionise greatly in water:

$$R.NH_2 + CH_3COOH \rightleftharpoons R.NH_3^+ + CH_3COO^-.$$

Inorganic acids which are strong acids in water ionise less readily in acetic acid, and differences between their strengths become more obvious in that medium; thus the dissociation constants of nitric, hydrochloric, sulphuric, hydrobromic and perchloric acids are spread in the ratios $1:9:30:160:400$. Because the dissociation of perchloric acid in acetic acid is considerable,

$$\underset{acid}{HClO_4} + \underset{base}{CH_3COOH} \rightleftharpoons \underset{acid}{CH_3COOH_2^+} + \underset{base}{ClO_4^-},$$

it may be used to titrate, potentiometrically, such compounds as amides and oximes which ionise fairly strongly as bases in the solvent.

(ii) As a solvent, formic acid might be expected to behave as does acetic acid; but, having a dielectric constant (62) almost 10 times greater (probably through hydrogen bonding in the liquid), it shows a particularly high autoprotolysis constant:

$$[H.COOH_2^+] [H.COO^-] = 10^{-6} \text{ at } 25°.$$

(iii) Sulphuric acid also displays a high degree of autoprotolysis:

$$[H_3SO_4^+] [HSO_4^-] = 2.4 \times 10^{-4} \text{ at } 25°$$

As, however, another dissociation,

$$2H_2SO_4 \rightleftharpoons H_3O^+ + HS_2O_7^-,$$

occurs to only a slightly less extent, the interpretation of conductance and e.m.f. measurements is difficult. The dielectric constant is not known, but it is probably high and interionic forces should be correspondingly small. The low volatility and the high viscosity are also consistent with a high dielectric constant.

Sulphuric acid is so strongly protogenic that most compounds of oxygen and nitrogen accept protons from it to some extent. Not only amines, but ethers and ketones, give twice the normal freezing point depression, suggesting that such reactions as

$$R_2O + H_2SO_4 \rightarrow R_2OH^+ + HSO_4^-,$$

go virtually to completion. Many carboxylic acids dissociate in sulphuric acid as bases:

$$R.COOH + H_2SO_4 \rightleftharpoons R.COOH_2^+ + HSO_4^-$$

And even perchloric acid ionises like a weak acid:

$$[H_3SO_4^+] [ClO_4^-]/[H_2SO_4] [HClO_4] \sim 10^{-4} \text{ at } 25°.$$

Certain substances undergo reactions more complicated than proton transfer.

With nitric acid, the nitronium ion is produced and is the active agent in aromatic nitration (Ingold, 1946):

$$HNO_3 + 2H_2SO_4 \rightleftharpoons NO_2^+ + H_3O^+ + 2HSO_4^-.$$

(d) Hydrofluoric acid has a surprisingly low conductance; but it has a very high dielectric constant (84), a high dipole moment (1.9 D) and a strong tendency to associate. For simplicity, it is treated here as a monobasic acid, rather than the dibasic acid, H_2F_2, which it really is. It is similar to sulphuric acid in its effects on acids and bases, the only acids showing measurable dissociation in it being perchloric and per-iodic acids. It dissolves water, ethers, ketones, aliphatic acids and even nitric acid, all of them functioning as bases:

$$H_2O \quad + HF \rightleftharpoons H_3O^+ \quad + F^-,$$
$$Et_2O \quad + HF \rightleftharpoons Et_2OH^+ + F^-,$$
$$HNO_3 + HF \rightleftharpoons H_2NO_3^+ + F^-.$$

Some non-metal fluorides dissolve to give acid solutions:

$$AsF_5 + 2HF \rightleftharpoons H_2F^+ + AsF_6^-.$$

Alkali metal chlorides, bromides, iodides and cyanides react to give the free acids:

$$NaCl + HF \rightarrow Na^+ + F^- + HCl \text{ (gas)}.$$

Many solutes react with the solvent, an example being sulphuric acid which produces fluorosulphuric acid;

$$H_2SO_4 + 2HF \rightarrow HSO_3F + H_3O^+ + F^-.$$

Mixtures of hydrogen fluoride and boron trifluoride are very powerful proton donors: the substances react as shown.

$$BF_3 + 2HF \rightleftharpoons H_2F^+ + BF_4^-.$$

In this mixture even aromatic hydrocarbons act as bases; for instance hexamethylbenzene is largely converted into $C_6H(Me)_6^+.BF_4^-$ and forms a strongly conducting solution.

Aprotic solvents

Hydrocarbons and their halogen derivatives have no tendency to gain or lose protons; they are inert and exhibit no levelling effect. The dielectric constants are very low (2 to 6) and the ions associate, making conductance measurements of no value for determining the extent of protolysis. Protolytic equilibria are also complicated by association of the uncharged molecules themselves; carboxylic acids, for example, exist as dimers in benzene. The same factors reduce greatly the solubilities of acids and bases in these solvents.

Comparison of acid strengths in various solvents

Because the dissociation of an acid depends in a complex way on the chemical properties, molecular dipole and dielectric constant of the solvent, attempts to define absolute acid strength independently of the solvent have been unavailing. Nevertheless, relative strengths are independent, within a power of 10, of the nature of the solvent provided the acids belong to the same charge type, whether molecular, anionic or cationic. The independence of the nature of the solvent shown by acids of the same chemical character is even more marked.

Acid strength and molecular structure

(i) Simple hydrides of Gps. V to VII show the approximate pK_a values given in Table 27.

TABLE 27

pK_a VALUES OF HYDRIDES OF GPS. V, VI, VII

Group V		Group VI		Group VII	
NH_3	23	H_2O	15	HF	4
		H_2S	7	HCl	-7
		H_2Se	4	HBr	-9
		H_2Te	3	HI	-11

The variations are regular and are associated with (a) the energy of dissociation of the hydrides to hydrogen atoms, (b) the electron affinity of the remaining atom or radical, (c) the energy of solvation of the remaining ion.

In the series NH_3, H_2O and HF, increasing electron affinity is the likeliest cause of increasing acid strength; but in the group HF to HI the determining factor is probably the decreasing dissociation energy.

(ii) Oxoacids of the general formula H_nXO_m fall into four fairly well-defined classes depending on the ratio of oxygen to hydrogen atoms in the molecule:

(a) Where $m = n$, as in HOCl, HOBr, H_3BO_3 and H_6TeO_6, the pK value for the first ionisation is between 7 and 11.

(b) Where $m = n + 1$, as in $HClO_2$, HNO_2, H_2SO_3 and H_3PO_4, the pK value is approximately 2.

(c) Where $m = n + 2$, as in HNO_3, $HClO_3$ and H_2SO_4, the pK value is between -1 and -3.

(d) Where $m = n + 3$, as in $HClO_4$ and HIO_4, the pK value is approximately -8.

Evidently telluric acid fits into this scheme as H_6TeO_6, not as $H_2TeO_4.2H_2O$. Phosphorous and hypophosphorous acids, with pK 2 and 1, respectively, behave as $HPO(OH)_2$ and $H_2PO(OH)$, in accordance with their known basicities. Increase in acid strength appears to be associated with the stabilisation of the anion which, in turn, depends on the bonding orbitals. These are stronger in HSO_4^- than in, say, OCl^- or $(HO)_2BO^-$.

(iii) Aliphatic acids have a pK of about 5. The substitution of hydrogen in alkyl groups by elements with high electronegativity (F, Cl) increases acid strength, particularly when more than one hydrogen atom is replaced, and when substitution is made at the carbon atom nearest the carboxylic group. In the dichloracetate ion, for example, stability is conferred through the chlorine increasing the electronegativity of the alkyl C and thereby lowering the energy of the whole ion by attracting away some of the negative charge conferred on the other C by the oxygen atoms.

Lewis acids

For an acid to be a proton donor, it must contain hydrogen. This led G. N. Lewis (1938) to develop a more general concept of an acid as an electron acceptor, the unshared electron pair of the base forming a covalent link with it. Thus described, boron trifluoride is an acid:

$$BF_3 + :NMe_3 \rightleftharpoons Me_3N \rightarrow BF_3,$$
$$BF_3 + OEt_2 \rightleftharpoons Et_2O \rightarrow BF_3.$$

The silver ion is also an acid:

$$Ag^+ + 2(:NH_3) \rightleftharpoons [H_3N \rightarrow Ag \leftarrow NH_3]^+.$$

And so, indeed, is any species with an outer electron structure capable of expansion. Most proton acids conform to the Lewis definition if the reaction between base and acid is considered to start with a hydrogen bond, XH...B. In this way an electron may be said to be accepted by the acid HX. Experimentally, Lewis classes as acids substances exhibiting the typical acidic properties: (a) catalytic action, (b) ability to neutralise bases, (c) effect on indicators, (d) displacement by a stronger acid.

Although boron trifluoride, sulphur trioxide and the like may be titrated against bases in inert solvents, there is no unequivocal instance of a Lewis acid causing catalysis in the absence of protons. Thus the concept is rather formal and has the weakness that it fails to lead, as does the Lowry-Brönsted theory, to a simple comparison of acid strengths. An importance of Lewis's definition lies in the attention it has drawn to electron-accepting species, whether they be called acids or not, for their behaviour is fundamental to reactions in non-protonic solvents.

The Lewis treatment of bases is not significantly different from that of Lowry and Brönsted.

Non-protonic solvents

(i) Dinitrogen tetroxide

This liquid (b.p. 21°) has a very low conductance and small dielectric constant (2.4). Its ionisation (Gray, 1957) is

$$N_2O_4 \rightleftharpoons NO^+ + NO_3^-.$$

There is no proton. The cation, NO^+, must be counted the acid, and the anion, NO_3^-, the base characteristic of the system. Zinc dissolves in liquid N_2O_4 evolving nitric oxide and forming $[NO^+]_2[Zn(NO_3)_4]^{2-}$. This compound is an acid in dinitrogen tetroxide and reacts with ethylammonium nitrate, a base in the solvent:

$$[NO^+]_2[Zn(NO_3)_4]^{2-} + 2EtNH_3^+NO_3^- \rightleftharpoons [EtNH_3^+]_2[Zn(NO_3)_4]^{2-} + 2N_2O_4$$

The liquid forms addition compounds with ethers, $N_2O_4.2Et_2O$ (m.p. $-75°$) with diethyl ether, and $N_2O_4O(C_2H_4)_2O$ (m.p. $+45°$) with dioxan, the latter having a high melting point possibly because the use of both oxygen atoms allows an indefinitely extended aggregation.

(ii) Bromine trifluoride

Bromine trifluoride, a pale yellow liquid (b.p. 128°), shows some conductance and is ionised:

$$2BrF_3 \rightleftharpoons BrF_2^+ + BrF_4^-.$$

Potassium and silver fluorides give strongly conducting solutions of tetrafluorobromites,

$$AgF + BrF_3 \rightleftharpoons AgBrF_4,$$

and antimony pentafluoride and tin(IV) fluoride form compounds which appear to be $BrF_2^+.SbF_6^-$ and $(BrF_2^+)_2SnF_6^{2-}$. The fluoroantimonate is a good conductor in bromine trifluoride and the reaction,

$$AgBrF_4 + BrF_2^+.SbF_6^- \rightleftharpoons AgSbF_6 + 2BrF_3,$$

has been followed conductometrically. Substances giving rise to BrF_2^+ ions are considered as acids in this solvent and those producing BrF_4^- ions as bases.

(iii) Sulphur dioxide

The liquid (b.p. $-10°$) which has a dielectric constant of 14 and a dipole moment of 1.61D, is a good solvent. There does not appear to be any self-ionisation of the type displayed by dinitrogen tetroxide (p. 329). Isotope exchange shows that sulphite sulphur exchanges with sulphur dioxide and that thionyl halide sulphur does not. SO_3 exchanges oxygen but not sulphur with solvent SO_2.

Jander (1938) found both sulphites and thionyl halides to dissolve in liquid SO_2 and increase the conductance. The latter probably form SOX^+ ions. Reactions, such as

$$SOCl_2 + Cs_2SO_3 \rightleftharpoons 2CsCl + 2SO_2,$$

have been followed conductometrically. Some inorganic salts form addition compounds corresponding to the hydrates and ammoniates; instances are $NaI.4SO_2$, $BaI_2.4SO_2$ and $KSCN.SO_2$. Of halides, the iodides are the most soluble.

Many amines give conducting solutions. Bateman, Hughes and Ingold (1944) conclude from molecular weight and conductance measurements that the ions R_3N^{2+} and SO_2^{2-} are present in the solution of a tertiary amine, but Jander considers the base $[(R_3N)_2SO]^{2+}SO_3^{2-}$ to be formed. Pyridine has been titrated conductometrically in the solvent with thionyl chloride, possibly by the reaction

$$[(C_5H_5N)_2SO]^{2+}SO_3^{2-} + SOCl_2 \rightleftharpoons [(C_5H_5N)_2SO]Cl_2 + 2SO_2.$$

Iodine is reduced to iodide by triethylamine, probably as indicated:

$$2[(Et_3N)_2SO]SO_3 + I_2 \rightleftharpoons [(Et_3N)_2SO]SO_4 + [(Et_3N)_2SO]I_2 + SO_2.$$

The oxidation is difficult to explain unless sulphite ions are assumed to be present.

(iv) Nitrosyl chloride

This liquid (b.p. $-6°$) has the comparatively high dielectric constant of 18.2 at the b.p. and a strong tendency to complex with metallic halides:

$$NOCl + FeCl_3 \rightarrow NOFeCl_4,$$
$$NOCl + AlCl_3 \rightarrow NOAlCl_4.$$

The first of these has been titrated conductometrically with tetramethyl ammonium chloride:

$$NO^+FeCl_4^- + Me_4N^+Cl^- \rightleftharpoons NOCl + Me_4N^+FeCl_4^-.$$

The idea that NO^+ is the acid and Cl^- the base in liquid nitrosyl chloride is supported by the observation that when the iron(III) complex, $NOFeCl_4$, is electrolysed, nitric oxide appears at the cathode and chlorine at the anode (Burg and McKenzie, 1952).

Acid-base catalysis

Iron reacts exceedingly slowly with pure water to give hydrogen because the concentration of hydroxonium ions is low. An acid strong enough to increase their concentration accelerates the reaction. Such an increase of positive ion concentration is typical of acid catalysis.

Friedel-Crafts catalysts are usually thought of as metal halides, such as $AlCl_3$, $FeCl_3$, $SnCl_4$ and $ZnCl_2$. If these halides are functioning as acids not differing fundamentally from proton-acids, the ordinary proton acids would be expected also to catalyse the Friedel-Crafts reaction. This, in fact, they do; toluene has been acylated (Simons, Randall and Archer, 1939) by carboxylic acids, with hydrogen fluoride as catalyst:

$$R.COOH + \langle \rangle CH_3 \xrightarrow{\ HF\ } R.CO.\langle \rangle CH_3 + H_2O.$$

The carboxylic acid dissolves in the hydrogen fluoride to produce a conducting solution,

$$R.COOH + HF \; \rightleftharpoons \; R.COOH_2{}^+ + F^-,$$
$$\text{base} \qquad\qquad\qquad \text{acid}$$

the acidity of the hydrogen fluoride being sufficient to cause the carboxylic acid to behave as a base. The resulting cation, on dissociation,

$$R.COOH_2{}^+ \; \rightleftharpoons \; R.\overset{+}{C}{=}O + H_2O,$$

produces an acyl carbonium ion which acylates the hydrocarbon by an electrophilic attack.

The halogenation of aromatic compounds has probably a mechanism similar to that of the Friedel-Crafts reaction, a Lewis acid acting as catalyst. For example:

$$Br_2 + FeBr_3 \; \rightleftharpoons \; Br^+ + FeBr_4{}^-,$$
$$\text{base} \quad \text{acid} \qquad\quad \text{acid} \quad\ \text{base}$$

$$Br^+ + C_6H_6 \; \rightleftharpoons \; C_6H_5Br + H^+,$$
$$\text{acid} \quad\ \text{base}$$

$$H^+ + FeBr_4{}^- \; \rightleftharpoons \; HBr + FeBr_3.$$
$$\text{acid} \qquad \text{base}$$

The function of an acid catalyst is to increase the concentration of the acid group immediately involved in the reaction by the familiar displacement of one acid by another.

Bases act as catalysts by accepting protons. Typical of base-catalysed reactions is the wide variety of aldol condensations, the catalysts being such bases as acetates, carbonates and amines.

$$CH_3CH=O + :B \rightleftharpoons CH_3-\overset{\overset{\displaystyle O}{\uparrow}}{\underset{\underset{\displaystyle H}{\downarrow}}{C}}\leftarrow B \rightleftharpoons [-CH_2-CH=O]^- + BH^+$$

acid   base

$$CH_3.CH=O + [-CH_2-CH=O]^- \rightleftharpoons [CH_3-\overset{\overset{\displaystyle O^-}{|}}{\underset{\underset{\displaystyle H}{|}}{C}}-CH_2-CH=O]$$

acid   base

$$[CH_3-\overset{\overset{\displaystyle O^-}{|}}{\underset{\underset{\displaystyle H}{|}}{C}}-CH_2-CH=O] + BH^+ \rightleftharpoons CH_3-\overset{\overset{\displaystyle OH}{|}}{\underset{\underset{\displaystyle H}{|}}{C}}-CH_2-CH=O + B.$$

base   acid

Here the weakly acidic acetaldehyde is converted into its conjugate base by the added base, and the anion formed reacts with a molecule of acetaldehyde which behaves as an acid, to produce a compound ion. This is finally converted to its conjugate acid (aldol) by the action of the conjugate acid of the original base.

The function of the basic catalyst is to increase the concentration of the basic group immediately involved in the reaction by the familiar displacement of one base by another.

Relation between acid-base and oxidation-reduction behaviour

In Lewis's terms, an acid accepts electrons with the formation of a covalent bond:

$$Cu^{2+} + 4NH_3 \rightarrow \begin{bmatrix} NH_3 & & NH_3 \\ & Cu & \\ NH_3 & & NH_3 \end{bmatrix}^{2+}$$

An oxidising agent accepts complete transfer of electrons:

$$Cu^{2+} + 2e \rightarrow Cu.$$

Thus the difference between acidity and oxidising character should be considered as one of degree; complete electron capture and electron sharing are just different aspect of electrophilic behaviour.

Similarly, a reducing agent transfers electrons completely:

$$Zn + Cu^{2+} \rightarrow Cu + Zn^{2+},$$

whereas a base donates electrons to form a covalent link:

$$NH_3 + H_3O^+ \rightarrow NH_4^+ + H_2O.$$

Both reducing action and basic behaviour are thus forms of electron donation.

Chapter 11

Hydrogen

Hydrogen has three isotopes. The atom of deuterium, ^2_1H, is about twice as heavy as that of the ordinary hydrogen; tritium, ^3_1H, three times. These large mass ratios are responsible for a difference in chemical properties between the isotopes of hydrogen far greater than that shown by those of any other element. However, so little deuterium and tritium are present in natural hydrogen (1.6×10^{-4} and 10^{-18} by weight respectively) that its properties are substantially those of ^1_1H.

With electron configuration $1s^1$, hydrogen nearly always forms covalent bonds; but positive and negative singly charged ions are recognised. Loss of the electron leaves the proton H^+, the ionisation potential being 13.6 eV. The proton exerts so strong a positive field that it is unable to exist alone in the presence of polarisable species. Thus the 'hydrogen ion' in water becomes H_3O^+, in ammonia NH_4^+, the proton being bonded by a lone pair (p. 103).

Addition of an electron yields the hydride anion, H^-, the electron affinity (energy drop) being 0.7 eV. The H^- ion is large (radius 1.45 Å) because of the mutual repulsion of the electrons which offsets the nuclear attraction. The relatively diffuse charge cloud of the ion is then very easily polarised. However, hydride ions do appear to exist in alkali metal hydrides. The H^- ion is an extremely strong base; the reaction

$$NaH + H_2O \rightarrow NaOH + H_2,$$

when represented

$$H^- + H_2O \rightarrow OH^- + H_2,$$

indicates that H^- is a stronger base than OH^- in aqueous solution. Similarly,

$$NaH + NH_3 \rightarrow NaNH_2 + H_2,$$

or

$$H^- + NH_3 \rightarrow NH_2^- + H_2,$$

shows H^- to be a stronger base than NH_2^- in liquid ammonia.

Ortho and para hydrogen

Two hydrogen atoms combine to form the very stable hydrogen molecule, $2H(1s^1) \rightarrow H_2(\sigma1s^2)$ with an energy drop of 102.5 kcal per mole. Heisenberg showed, however, that when nuclear spins are taken into account there are, in effect, two observable 'isomers'. These result from parallel coupling of the nuclear spins, with three possible quantum states; and antiparallel coupling, with only one (*cf.* p. 61). At room temperature, the different quantum states are about equally probable, but there are almost no spontaneous transitions between the different types. Ordinary hydrogen thus behaves as though it were a mixture of 3 vol. *ortho* hydrogen (spins parallel) and 1 vol. *para* hydrogen (spins anti-parallel). But, owing to symmetry, the allowed states of rotation of the molecule as a whole differ in the two instances, the lowest state being somewhat lower for the p- than for the o-form. Thus at very low temperatures, where the molecules tend to go into their lowest quantum states, the proportion of p-hydrogen should tend to 100%, when it would be in true thermodynamic equilibrium. However, transition from one nuclear spin state to another is so slow (the collision 'half-life' at room temperature is several years) that the 3:1 proportion persists in metastable equilibrium during cooling. These conclusions are confirmed by measurements of conductance and specific heat, which are distinctly greater for the p- than the o-form (in contrast with the b.p. and m.p. which are slightly less). True equilibrium at any temperature is achieved in the presence of a catalyst: (i) activated charcoal at low temperature, or a transition metal at room temperature; (ii) atomic hydrogen; (iii) a paramagnetic substance such as O_2 or NO. And it is also attained in the discharge tube or by heating to 800 °C or above. Thus, at 20 °K in the presence of active charcoal, 99.7% pure p-hydrogen results (Bonhoeffer and Harteck, 1929). On the other hand, concentration of o-hydrogen beyond 75% is impossible and its tabulated properties are those inferred from the mixture.

The mechanism of conversion, which is exothermal in the direction o → p, involves dissociation and recombination, during which the nuclear spins re-couple, parallel or anti-parallel, in equilibrium proportions. This occurs, for example, on collision (the high temperature mechanism); and probably in chemisorption (Eley and Rossington, 1957), when the atoms are separated by going into different lattice sites and subsequently recombine with nuclear spins oppositely coupled.

Knowledge of the two forms of molecular hydrogen has found recent industrial application. As stated, the change $o\text{-}H_2 \rightarrow p\text{-}H_2$ is exothermal, but so slow that it takes about a month for normal 25% p-liquid to be converted to 90% p-liquid. The energy released by the change is sufficient to evaporate 64% of the original liquid. Hence to keep liquid hydrogen without loss constant refrigeration is necessary. However a rapid and effective catalyst, a hydrous iron(III) oxide, has been developed which enables normal hydrogen to be converted to 99% p-hydrogen during liquefaction. The change greatly facilitates the storage of liquid by making it unnecessary to refrigate to prevent loss by boiling.

Deuterium also exists in ortho and para forms, but the ortho form is the more stable at low temperatures. The equilibrium mixture at elevated temperatures contains 33.3% of para deuterium.

The ortho forms of both hydrogen and deuterium have a small magnetic moment due to the nuclear spins of the two being of the same sense; the para forms have none. Nonetheless, hydrogen is essentially diamagnetic as it is without unpaired electrons, and the magnetic moment of a nucleus is very much less than that of an electron.

Strictly, hydrogen and deuterium are not unique, and nuclear spins should be recognised in discussing other molecules. But only with a low moment of inertia is the separation of rotational energy states large enough to give one form an appreciable preference, and then only at low temperatures. Ortho and para forms of F_2, Cl_2 and N_2 have been distinguished at very low temperatures; but generally the 'high temperature' mixture is the equilibrium form for all readily accessible temperatures and accordingly the nuclear spins may be disregarded.

Atomic hydrogen

The hydrogen molecule is dissociated into atoms by heat (Langmuir, 1912), radiation of specific wave length, and electric discharge at low pressure (Wood, 1920). Permanent recombination of the atoms does not occur on collision because the energy set free, 103 kcal per mole, causes immediate redissociation when converted into vibrational energy. A third body is necessary (p. 191) to absorb the excess of energy. Atomic hydrogen is a stronger reducing agent than H_2; unlike the latter it combines directly with Ge, Sn, As, Sb, Te (Pearson, Robinson and Stoddart, 1933):

$$As \quad + 3H \rightarrow AsH_3,$$
$$BaSO_4 + 8H \rightarrow BaS + 4H_2O.$$

It does not form a hydride with either lead or bismuth.

The lifetime of a hydrogen atom at room temperature, even at low pressures, is short on account of catalytic combination. Langmuir showed that a considerable proportion of the hydrogen passed through an arc between tungsten electrodes is split into atoms even with the gas at one atmosphere pressure. If this stream of partly atomised gas is directed on to a metal surface, the heat of combination is sufficient to produce a high temperature. This is the principle of the hydrogen torch, used in welding metals, which in action surrounds the weld with an atmosphere of the molecular gas and thus prevents surface oxidation. It is especially applicable to such metals as aluminium which are readily oxidised but which do not easily absorb hydrogen.

Deuterium

The existence of the isotope ^2_1H was shown spectroscopically in 1931 (Urey, Brickwedde and Murphy), and the preparation of nearly pure D_2O was achieved two years later (Lewis and Macdonald) by prolonged electrolysis of $0.5N$ NaOH with nickel electrodes. Three factors favour the liberation of H_2 at the cathode rather than D_2:

(i) H_2O is more readily reduced than D_2O: $H_2O + e \rightarrow OH^- + H$;

(ii) the activation energy for $H + H \rightarrow H_2$ is less than for $D + D \rightarrow D_2$;

(iii) HD exchanges with the H_2 of water: $HD + H_2O \rightarrow HDO + H_2$.

Differences in overvoltage (the potential arising from the non-reversible nature of the electrode processes) are probably not of major importance as the material of the cathode does not affect the separation factor.

The separation of D_2 from ordinary water is carried out in stages, involving a successive reduction of the original volume to about one seventh. As electrolysis proceeds the proportion of D_2 in the evolved gas rises. When it reaches 0.02%, the gas is burnt in oxygen and the H_2O/D_2O mixture added to the electrolyte of an earlier stage. Such an electrolytic separation has produced most of the considerable quantities of D_2O already in use for 'moderating' fast neutrons in heavy water atomic reactors.

Heavy water is also produced by the Spevack method which uses the exchange reaction:

$$D_2O \text{ (in ordinary water)} + H_2S \rightleftharpoons D_2S + H_2O \text{ (or DHS + DHO)}.$$

A temperature of 100° favours the forward reaction. The equilibrium mixture of sulphides is passed into water at 25°, when the reverse reaction is favoured. Continued cycles lead to a liquid containing $\sim 2\%$ D_2O which is concentrated to 90% by fractional distillation and to 99.8% by electrolysis.

The physical properties of D_2O differ slightly from those of H_2O (Table 28).

TABLE 28

PHYSICAL PROPERTIES OF H_2O AND D_2O

	B.p. (°C)	M.p. (°C)	S.g. (20 °C)
H_2O	100	0	0.998
D_2O	101.4	3.8	1.106

Its dielectric constant is about 2% below that of H_2O, making the liquid a slightly poorer ionising solvent; the autoprotolysis constant (p. 196) $[D_3O^+]$ $[OD^-]$, is 3×10^{-15} at 25°, and the solubilities of electrolytes are less than in water; for instance, the solubility of NaCl at 25° in H_2O is 35.9 g/100 g, in D_2O this figure is 30.9.

Deuterium gas is made by the electrolysis of D_2O containing some P_2O_5. The b.p., m.p., latent heats of fusion and evaporation, and heat of dissociation of D_2 are all higher than those of H_2 (Table 29).

TABLE 29

PHYSICAL PROPERTIES OF H_2 AND D_2

	B.p (°K)	M.p. (°K)	Latent heat of fusion (cal/mole)	Heat of dissociation (kcal/mole)
H_2	20.4	13.95	28	102.5
D_2	23.5	18.65	52	104.5

Deuterium compounds are exactly analogous to those of hydrogen, and are generally obtained from D_2O:

$$Mg_3N_2 + 6D_2O \rightarrow 3Mg(OD)_2 + 2ND_3;$$
$$CaC_2 + 2D_2O \rightarrow Ca(OD)_2 + C_2D_2;$$
$$SO_3 + D_2O \rightarrow D_2SO_4.$$

Deuterium is somewhat less reactive than hydrogen. Activation energies for reactions such as

$$D_2 + Br_2 \rightarrow 2DBr, \quad \text{and} \quad 3D_2 + N_2 \rightarrow 2ND_3$$

are greater than for those with H_2. In keeping with this, the adsorption of deuterium on an active surface is slower than that of hydrogen.

Exchange reactions

When H_2 and D_2 are mixed at a sufficient temperature exchange occurs:

$$H_2 + D_2 \rightarrow 2HD.$$

Many such exchange reactions are known; the one above is almost certainly an atomic reaction with a chain mechanism:

$$D + H_2 \rightarrow HD + H; \quad H + D_2 \rightarrow HD + D.$$

Exchange on catalytic surfaces is also common. Deuterium replaces hydrogen in water, ammonia, methane and other simple hydrides on metals such as platinum and nickel which are good catalysts for hydrogenation. The exchange of adsorbed deuterium with gaseous hydrogen on finely divided nickel is almost certainly an adsorption—desorption process (Schmit, 1957):

$$D_2 + 2 \text{ⓢ} \leftrightarrows 2D \text{ (adsorbed)}, \qquad H_2 + 2 \text{ⓢ} \leftrightarrows 2H \text{ (adsorbed)};$$
$$D \text{ (adsorbed)} + H \text{ (adsorbed)} \leftrightarrows HD \text{ gas} + 2 \text{ⓢ}.$$
$$\text{ⓢ represents an empty site.}$$

Heavy water exchanges deuterium with compounds containing labile hydrogens:

$$NH_4^+ \quad + D_2O \leftrightarrows NH_3D^+ \quad + HDO,$$
$$CH_3.NH_2 + D_2O \leftrightarrows CH_3NHD + HDO,$$
$$CH_3OH \quad + D_2O \leftrightarrows CH_3OD \quad + HDO.$$

The suggested mechanism of exchange between D_2O and the hexa-ammine-cobalt(III) ion is

$$Co(NH_3)_6^{3+} \quad\quad + D_2O \rightleftharpoons Co(NH_3)_5NH_2^{2+} \quad + HD_2O^+,$$
$$Co(NH_3)_5NH_2^{2+} + D_2O \rightleftharpoons [Co(NH_3)_5NH_2D^{3+} + OD^-,$$
$$H_2O^+ \quad\quad\quad + OD^- \rightleftharpoons HDO \quad\quad\quad + H_2O.$$

But the hydrogen atoms of alkyl groups do not exchange readily unless enol-keto tautomerism occurs:

$$
\begin{array}{c}
\text{OH} \\
|
\end{array}
$$
$$(CH_3)_2C{=}O \leftrightarrows CH_3.C{=}CH_2,$$

$$
\begin{array}{c}
\text{OH} \\
|
\end{array}
\qquad
\begin{array}{c}
\text{O} \\
|
\end{array}
$$
$$CH_3.C{=}CH_2 + D_2O \leftrightarrows [CH_3.C{=}CH_2]^- + HD_2^+O$$
$$\Updownarrow$$
$$CH_3.C - CH_2D + HDO.$$
$$
\begin{array}{c}
\| \\
\text{O}
\end{array}
$$

The rate of reaction in such an example is measured by removing some of the reaction product in the pure state, burning it to produce H_2O and HDO, and estimating the deuterium by density or with the mass spectrometer. Here deuterium is, in fact, being used as a non-radioactive tracer.

Tritium

Oliphant, Harteck and Rutherford (1934) made the heaviest isotope of hydrogen by bombarding deuterium compounds with deuterons:

$$^2_1D + ^2_1D \rightarrow ^3_1H + ^1_1H.$$

Certain nuclear reactions lead to tritium formation:

$$^{9}_{4}Be + ^{2}_{1}H \rightarrow 2^{4}_{2}He + ^{3}_{1}H;$$
$$^{6}_{3}Li + ^{1}_{0}n \rightarrow ^{4}_{2}He + ^{3}_{1}H.$$

The second of these has been extensively used in its production; the tritium is adsorbed by uranium metal and released by heating. The nuclide is a low-energy β-emitter (0.018 MeV) with a half-life of 12.5 years:

$$^{3}_{1}H \xrightarrow[\text{12.5 years}]{\beta^{-}} ^{3}_{2}He.$$

Tritium has proved a useful tracer, as the tritium content of a compound can be deduced from its β-activity. For the measurement of such low-energy radiation gas-counting is used (p. 31).

Industrial production and uses of hydrogen

Hydrogen is made principally by the Bosch process in which steam reacts with red hot coke to give water gas:

$$H_2O + C \rightarrow CO + H_2.$$

This is passed with more steam over an iron catalyst:

$$H_2O + H_2 + CO \rightarrow 2H_2 + CO_2.$$

The CO_2 is removed by dissolving in water under pressure, the residual CO by absorption in ammoniacal copper(I) formate, hydrogen of 99.9% purity being left. The gas is also made by electrolysis, a process which has gained in importance with the increasing demand for heavy water.

Vast quantities of hydrogen are produced in the petroleum industry in refining processes to increase octane number, typical reactions being the dehydrogenation of naphthalenes and paraffins to aromatic hydrocarbons:

$$C_6H_{12} \rightarrow C_6H_6 + 3H_2; \qquad C_6H_{14} \rightarrow C_6H_6 + 4H_2.$$

Industrial hydrogen is used mainly in catalytic hydrogenation processes:

(i) $N_2 \rightarrow NH_3$ (Haber process);
(ii) $CO \rightarrow CH_3OH$ (Methanol process);
(iii) Unsaturated vegetable oils $\rightarrow$ saturated fats (particularly for margarine).

Besides other synthetic purposes, it finds use in the removal of sulphur, nitrogen and oxygen from petroleum feed stocks by catalytically promoted reactions:

$$C_4H_4S + 4H_2 \rightarrow C_4H_{10} + H_2S; \qquad C_5H_5N + 5H_2 \rightarrow C_5H_{12} + NH_3;$$
$$C_6H_5OH + H_2 \rightarrow C_6H_6 + H_2O.$$

Chapter 12

The Hydrides

Hydrides are broadly of three types, saline, covalent and metallic. Saline hydrides are formed by the alkali metals (Gp. IA), the alkaline earths (Gp. IIA) and the lanthanides; they have ionic lattices, high melting points and, when fused, are electrolytes. Elements of the B Groups from IIIB to VIIB have covalent hydrides, most of them gaseous at room temperature. The metallic hydrides characteristic of some of the transition elements are in effect alloys and usually lack the stoichiometric composition of normal chemical compounds.

THE COVALENT HYDRIDES

Hydrides of boron

All the hydrides of boron, except B_9H_{15} recently isolated by Schaeffer, were discovered by Stock (1914–20). The starting material was the gaseous product of the reaction between magnesium boride and dilute hydrochloric acid. His remarkable success was due to a vacuum technique which he developed for handling compounds sensitive to oxygen and moisture, such as the hydrides of boron and silicon. Monomeric BH_3 was not found because there are insufficient electrons to stabilise the bonding in such a compound, as it is stabilised in the monomeric boron halides.

The higher hydrides belong to two series; diborane is related to the B_nH_{n+6} series in having BH_2 groups bridged to the rest of the molecule (Fig. 121).

BORON HYDRIDES

	B_2H_6			
B_nH_{n+4} series		B_5H_9	B_6H_{10}	$B_{10}H_{14}$
B_nH_{n+6} series	B_4H_{10}	B_5H_{11}	B_9H_{15}	

The yield of diborane by Stock's method is low; it was prepared later by Schlesinger and Burg (1931) by passing boron trichloride and hydrogen at low pressure through an electric discharge. Modern methods employ lithium hydride, lithium aluminium hydride or lithium borohydride.

(a) Boron trifluoride or trichloride is treated with lithium aluminium hydride in ether solution:

$$3LiAlH_4 + 4BF_3 \rightarrow 3LiF + 3AlF_3 + 2B_2H_6.$$

(b) A similar reaction occurs with lithium borohydride:

$$3LiBH_4 + 4BF_3.Et_2O \rightarrow 3LiBF_4 + 4Et_2O + 2B_2H_6.$$

(c) The best method of large scale preparation is to add the boron trifluoride-ether complex slowly to a suspension of lithium hydride in ether and gently reflux the mixture:

$$6LiH + 8Et_2O.BF_3 \rightarrow 6LiBF_4 + B_2H_6 + 8Et_2O.$$

Ethane, usually present as an impurity, is removed by passing the products into dimethyl ether at —80°, to form a solid complex, $B_2H_6.Me_2O$, from which the ethane may be pumped. The complex is decomposed by warming and the diborane purified by fractional distillation.

TABLE 30

MELTING AND BOILING POINTS OF THE BORANES

B_2H_6	B_4H_{10}	B_5H_9 Stable	B_5H_{11} Unstable	B_6H_{10}	$B_{10}H_{14}$
Diborane	Tetraborane	pentaborane	pentaborane	Hexaborane	Decaborane
M.p. —165°	—120°	—47°	—123°	—65°	100°
B.p. —92°	18°	48°	63°	V.p. 7.2 mm at 0°	213°

The higher volatile hydrides result from heating diborane alone or with hydrogen. Thus when passed through a tube at 115°, diborane is largely converted into the unstable pentaborane, B_5H_{11}. This, warmed with hydrogen at 100°, gives tetraborane with some diborane:

$$2B_5H_{11} + 2H_2 \rightarrow 2B_4H_{10} + B_2H_6.$$

When, however, diborane passes with hydrogen through a tube at 200–250° the stable pentaborane, B_5H_9, is obtained. Kinetic studies suggest the changes involve a radical mechanism with perhaps borine, BH_3, as an intermediate, though direct evidence of this entity is wanting.

When kept at room temperature diborane suffers about a ten percent decomposition per year. Tetraborane, unstable pentaborane and hexaborane decompose more rapidly, but stable pentaborane and decaborane, only very slowly below 150°. Diborane is rapidly attacked by cold water, yielding boric acid and hydrogen, but stable pentaborane is completely hydrolysed only after prolonged heating. All are oxidised by air but with varying ease, both pentaboranes spontaneously inflame but diborane does not usually ignite. Pyrolysis of the boron hydrides leads, in addition, to the formation of non-volatile compounds of variable composition $(BH_x)_n$. At 700°, the break-down of all these materials to boron and hydrogen is complete. All the boranes for which information is available prove to be endothermic compounds.

Considerable interest has centred on the structures of the boranes. They are all electron-deficient; that is they have too few valency electrons to permit every one of the adjacent atoms to be held together by electron-pair bonds. Diborane has been the most studied and much evidence has accumulated for a hydrogen-bridged structure (Fig. 121).

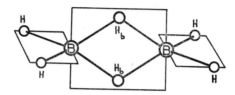

Fig. 121. Hydrogen-bridged structure of diborane.

The presence in the molecule of two kinds of boron-hydrogen bond is indicated both by its Raman spectrum and by the chemical evidence that four only of the hydrogen atoms are replaceable by methyl groups. Electron diffraction leads to B–H 1.19 Å, B–H_b 1.33 Å, B–B 1.77 Å, $\angle HBH$ 121.5° and $\angle H_b BH_b$ 100°. Raman and infrared spectra of the tetramethyl compound suggest an absence of terminal hydrogen atoms, and electron diffraction shows the four carbon atoms and two boron atoms to be coplanar.

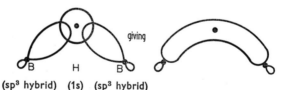

(sp³ hybrid) (1s) (sp³ hybrid)

Fig. 122. Contributions to molecular orbitals in diborane.

Although a double hydrogen bridge is certain, the precise nature of the bonds involved is still uncertain. Clearly they are abnormal and a recent suggestion is that they are formed by an overlap of the sp³ tetrahedral hybrids and hydrogen 1s orbitals. Each electron pair is then less localised than usual, extending over three centres (Fig. 122). This accounts for the symmetry and absence of free rotation between the boron atoms.

The higher boranes, also electron-deficient, clearly have hydrogen-bridge linkages. Structures, ascribed to them as the results of X-ray analysis, electron diffraction and microwave spectra, are available (Lipscomb, 1954).

The reactions of the boron hydrides, discussed by Lipscomb (1959), arise from (a) cleavage, to BH_3 or BH_2^+, (b) loss of H_2 or H^+, as an initial step. Release of the unstable borine seems to be the first stage in the reaction of B_2H_6 with amines, but with ammonia BH_2^+ appears to be the reacting species. In the higher boranes, the terminal hydrogen atoms are less negative than the bridging hydrogen atoms and may be removed as H^+ to leave a boron hydride anion. The loss of H_2 accounts for the familiar polymerisation of diborane, of which the first step appears to be established:

$$B_2H_6 \rightarrow 2BH_3 \qquad B_2H_6 + BH_3 \rightarrow B_3H_9$$

This is probably followed by the loss of hydrogen and the addition of a second BH_3:

$$B_3H_9 \rightarrow B_3H_7 + H_2 \qquad B_3H_7 + BH_3 \rightarrow B_4H_{10}$$

Although borine, BH_3, is not detectable in preparations of diborane, it is a possible intermediate in many reactions of the hydrides, where derivatives appear to be produced by borine acting as a Lewis acid (p. 205). The well-characterised white solid, m.p. 94°, borine trimethylamine, $Me_3N^+ . BH_3^-$, readily formed from NMe_3 and B_2H_6, in which the boron employs four sp^3 hybrid bonds, shows how the boron atoms in diborane achieve a more normal bonding when a base, here trimethylamine, supplies electrons—in this instance from the nitrogen lone pair which also occupies a roughly tetrahedral hybrid orbital. Similarly pyridine, when mixed with diborane at 0°, forms $C_5H_5N.BH_3$; dimethyl ether, a solid etherate, $(CH_3)_2O.BH_3$, which dissociates reversibly at $-70°$; and carbon monoxide, at 100° under 20 atmos. borine carbonyl, $OC.BH_3$, a compound stable below $-100°$. Again the electron-deficient boron uses the lone pair of electrons on the carbon to form the bond.

The reaction between ammonia and diborane depends upon the conditions. Excess of ammonia at low temperatures produces the salt-like diammoniate, $[(NH_3)_2BH_2]^+BH_4^-$, because with NH_3 there is an unsymmetrical cleavage $(BH_2^+ + BH_4^-)$ in contrast to the symmetrical one $(BH_3 + BH_3)$ resulting from reactions with amines. The monomer $BH_3.NH_3$ has indeed been made by the action of an ammonium halide on a borohydride:

$$NH_4X + MBH_4 \rightarrow BH_3.NH_3 + H_2 + MX.$$

At higher temperatures excess of ammonia gives boron nitride, BN. When, however, the proportions are two molecules of ammonia to one of diborane, the volatile cyclic borazole is produced in yields up to 45%.

The boron and nitrogen atoms are all in trigonal (sp²) valence state, the 2p lone pairs on the three nitrogens providing 6 π electrons as in benzene. The boron-nitrogen and carbon-carbon analogues are isoelectronic and compounds of this kind show certain similarities, but because the boron-nitrogen

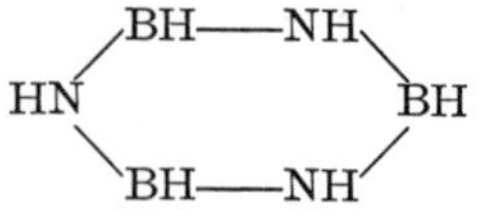

Fig. 123. Borazole.

bond is between atoms of different electronegativity and has an unsymmetrical charge cloud it is decidedly weaker. This is true even in borazole, although the bonds in it are non-localised. Consequently borazole is considerably more reactive than benzene, forming addition compounds with hydrogen halides, methanol, water and methyl iodide.

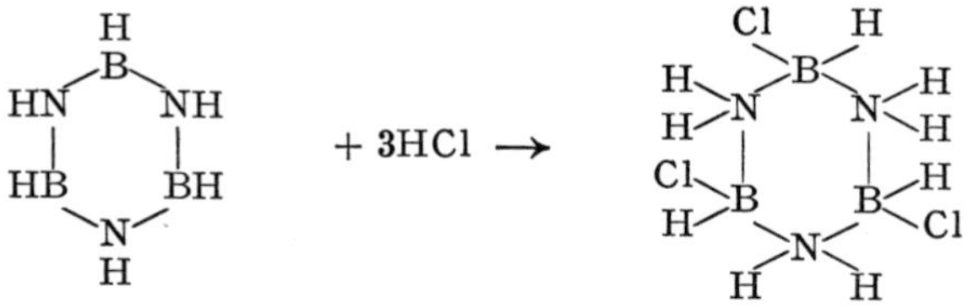

Fig. 124. Addition compound of borazole with HCl.

The hydrochloride loses hydrogen at 50° giving the symmetrical trichloroborazole:

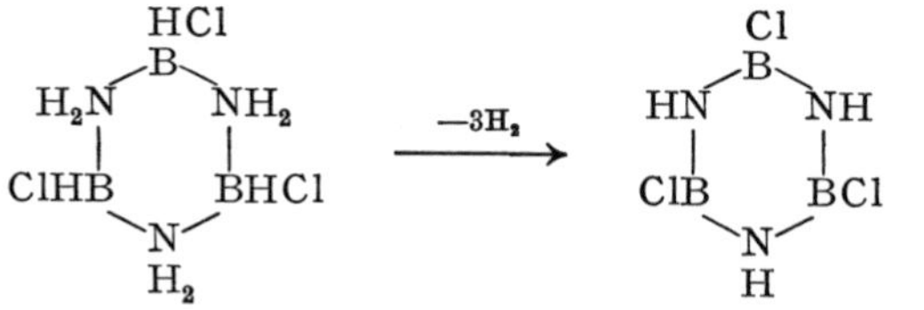

Fig. 125. Dehydrogenation of the hydrochloride of borazole.

Development from aminoboron chemistry led to phosphino- and arsinoboron compounds. Diborane and phosphine react at $-110°$ to give $B_2H_6.2PH_3$, much less stable than the diammoniate. Trimethylamine displaces phosphine from it quantitatively at $-40°$, suggesting the ionic structure $H_3P^+.BH_3^-$:

$$B_2H_6.2PH_3 + 2Me_3N \rightarrow 2PH_3 + 2Me_3N.BH_3.$$

At ordinary temperatures diborane and phosphine react slowly to form hydrogen and a non-volatile white polymer of the approximate composition $(H_2P.BH_2)_x$. It behaves similarly with arsine. Methyl substituted phosphine and arsine yield more stable compounds than the hydrides, some being recrystallisable from organic solvents even when they are exposed to air.

A number of oxygen and sulphur compounds are sufficiently powerful electron-pair donors to form borine adducts by reaction with diborane. Of these the unstable solid dimethyl ether borine, $Me_2O^+.BH_3^-$, used in the purification of diborane, is well known.

Borohydrides

Sodium borohydride results from the reaction

$$4NaH + B(OMe)_3 \rightarrow NaBH_4 + 3NaOMe$$

which proceeds rapidly at 250°, and is extracted from the products with isopropylamine. Lithium borohydride is best made by passing diborane into an ethereal solution of lithium hydride. These borohydrides are salt-like; the sodium compound has a face-centred cubic lattice of discrete Na^+ and tetrahedral BH_4^- ions, and the lithium compound is only a little less regular. They are involatile and unaffected by dry air. Lithium borohydride is particularly useful for making other borohydrides:

$$2LiBH_4 + BeBr_2 \rightarrow Be(BH_4)_2 + 2LiBr.$$

Beryllium, aluminium and some transition metals such as thorium differ from the alkali metals in forming volatile borohydrides which constitute the most volatile compounds of these elements. On pyrolysis they decompose giving hydrogen and non-volatile residues. Electron diffraction and infrared studies suggest they possess bridge structures.

Hydrides of aluminium, gallium and indium

When lithium hydride in limited amounts is added to ethereal aluminium chloride a white solid, $(AlH_3)_x$, separates slowly:

$$3LiH + AlCl_3 \rightarrow AlH_3 + 3LiCl.$$

Of unknown structure, it remains stable up to 100°, but beyond, decomposes into aluminium and hydrogen. It reacts with diborane to form aluminium borohydride.

Lithium hydride, added in larger amounts, produces the ether-soluble lithium aluminium hydride, a valuable, strong reducing agent:

$$4LiH + AlCl_3 \rightarrow LiAlH_4 + 3LiCl.$$

Not only aldehydes and ketones, but even carboxylic acids are reduced to alcohols by it; nitriles go to primary amines and metal halides to hydrides:

$$BCl_3 \rightarrow B_2H_6; \qquad SnCl_4 \rightarrow SnH_4; \qquad SiCl_4 \rightarrow SiH_4.$$

The behaviour of the trichloride of indium is interesting; at $-70°$ in ether, it is converted into indium aluminium hydride:

$$InCl_3 + 3LiAlH_4 \rightarrow 3LiCl + In(AlH_4)_3.$$

Whereas at room temperature a white, polymeric solid $(InH_3)_x$ separates.

The hydride of gallium is a liquid. When gallium trimethyl and hydrogen are subjected to an electric discharge, $Ga_2(Me)_4H_2$ may be isolated from the products. It reacts quantitatively with triethylamine:

$$3Ga_2(Me)_4H_2 + 4NEt_3 \rightarrow 4Ga(Me)_3.NEt_3 + Ga_2H_6.$$

Gallium hydride decomposes above $130°$ into its elements. Lithium gallium hydride has been prepared and has properties similar to lithium aluminium hydride.

Hydrides of carbon and silicon

No element forms such a variety of hydrides as carbon. In addition to the numerous known alkanes, C_nH_{2n+2}, structural isomerism predicts many more not yet isolated. For example, over thirty six million isomeric forms of $C_{25}H_{52}$ can be formulated. To these an even larger number of possible unsaturated hydrocarbons may be added.

Silicon, for reasons given below, presents a very different picture, the highest hydride having a chain of only six silicon atoms. The series corresponds to the simplest saturated hydrocarbons, the paraffins.

TABLE 31

MELTING AND BOILING POINTS OF THE SILANES

	SiH_4 Silane	Si_2H_6 Disilane	Si_3H_8 Trisilane	Si_4H_{10} n-Tetrasilane	Si_5H_{12} Pentasilane	Si_6H_{14} Hexasilane
M.p.	$-185°$	$-132°$	$-117°$	$-84°$	Isomers not yet separated	
B.p.	$-112°$	$-14°$	$53°$	$107°$	$> 100°$	$> 100°$

A mixture containing all the silanes is obtained when magnesium silicide is dropped into dilute hydrochloric acid in an enclosed, low-pressure system. Fairly pure monosilane itself is made in good yield by adding magnesium silicide to ammonium bromide in liquid ammonia, in which the ammonium salt behaves as a strong acid. The pure gas results from the action of lithium aluminium hydride on silicon tetrachloride:

$$LiAlH_4 + SiCl_4 \rightarrow LiCl + AlCl_3 + SiH_4.$$

The thermal stabilities of the silanes are much lower than those of the corresponding alkanes. The higher silanes decompose on heating to give lower silanes and solid unsaturated hydrides:

$$Si_5H_{12} \rightarrow Si_2H_6 + SiH_4 + \frac{2}{x}(SiH)_x.$$

Above 500°, decomposition to the elements is complete. The silanes are spontaneously inflammable and explosive in air; they are not hydrolysed at a pH of less than 7, but in water containing a trace of alkali hydrolysis is rapid and complete. They have strong reducing properties; permanganates are reduced to manganese dioxide, and mercury(II) to mercury(I) ions and mercury. Unlike the alkanes, the silanes enter into substitution reactions with halogen acids (other than hydrofluoric) on warming in the presence of the corresponding aluminium halide:

$$e.g. \quad SiH_4 + HCl \xrightarrow{\text{Al}_2\text{Cl}_6} SiH_3Cl + H_2.$$

Though bonds between silicon and other elements are usually stronger than the corresponding ones involving carbon, this is not true for the silicon-hydrogen bond (76.0 kcal/mole) which is weaker than the carbon-hydrogen bond (99.3 kcal/mole).

As the electronegativity of silicon (1.8) is less than that of carbon (2.5), the silyl radical SiH_3 should be a less powerful electron acceptor than the methyl group. This would be so but for the vacant d orbitals of the silicon atom which enable π-bonding to take place. Theory, supported by experimental evidence, indicates overlap between a vacant silicon d_π orbital and a p_π orbital on an atom of a Group 5, 6 or 7 element already attached to the silicon atom by a σ bond. The π bond is generally stronger the more electronegative the acceptor atom, but silicon attracts electrons more strongly than its recorded electronegativity would suggest. This kind of bonding cannot occur with carbon because its d orbitals (3d) are too high in energy to contribute appreciably. The fact also accounts nicely for the strength of the C—H bond and the weakness of the Si—H bond.

This point is illustrated by the silyl halides, whose properties are greatly affected by the presence of a silicon-silicon bond. The preparation of the chloride, bromide and iodide of monosilane is described above; the fluoride is made by the action of the chloride on antimony fluoride:

$$3SiH_3Cl + SbF_3 \rightarrow 3SiH_3F + SbCl_3.$$

The iodide is liquid at room temperature, the rest are gaseous. Surprisingly, only the bromide is spontaneously inflammable in air. The reaction of the fluoride with water is not recorded; the others are hydrolysed immediately to disilyl ether, a colourless gas:

$$2SiH_3X + H_2O \rightarrow (SiH_3)_2O + 2HX.$$

On the other hand, hydrolysis with aqueous alkalis is complete, producing hydrogen and silicates. Silyl iodide gives a Wurtz-type reaction with sodium, which affords a useful path to disilane:

$$2SiH_3I + 2Na \rightarrow Si_2H_6 + 2NaI.$$

Silyl chloride and ammonia give amines, the most stable being the liquid trisilylamine; this is spontaneously inflammable in air and vigorously decomposed by water into silica, ammonia and hydrogen. Silyl iodide may be converted into several other silyl compounds by means of a silver salt.

$$SiH_3I \rightarrow (SiH_3)_2Se \rightarrow SiH_3Br \rightarrow SiH_3Cl \rightarrow SiH_3.NC \rightarrow$$
$$SiH_3.NCS \rightarrow SiH_3.NCO \rightarrow (SiH_3)_2O \rightarrow SiH_3F.$$

The sequence implies that a compound may be converted into one coming later in the series by means of the appropriate silver salt, although all the changes have not been tested.

The disproportionation of silyl halides has theoretical interest:

$$2SiH_3X \rightarrow SiH_2X_2 + SiH_4.$$

It is most rapid with the fluoride and very slow with the iodide. Experiments suggest that the reactions proceed through the formation of intermediate complexes rather than radicals; the readiness with which they are formed must decrease with the electronegativity of the halogen. A silicon-halogen π bond possibly leads to the complexing.

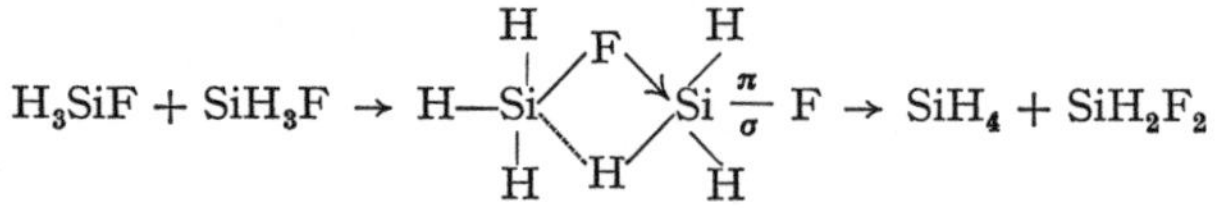

$$H_3SiF + SiH_3F \rightarrow H-Si \overset{H}{\underset{H}{\diagdown}} \overset{F}{\diagup} Si \overset{H}{\underset{H}{\diagup}} \frac{\pi}{\sigma} F \rightarrow SiH_4 + SiH_2F_2$$

Fig. 126. Disproportionation of silyl fluoride.

Hence the rate of disproportionation would be expected to fall from fluoride to iodide.

Disilanyl halides, such as $SiH_3.SiH_2Cl$, made by the action of the appropriate hydrogen halide in the presence of the aluminium halide on disilane, disproportionate much more easily than the silyl halides. This also is understandable in terms of a silicon-halogen π bond. According to the above mechanism, the formation of an *intermolecular* (between two molecules) π bond is made more difficult by the presence of an *intramolecular* (within a molecule) π bond already attached to the silicon atom.

$$H_3Si - Cl \rightarrow H_3Si \overset{\pi}{\underset{\sigma}{-}} Cl$$

But in $SiH_3.SiH_2Cl$ the silyl group is not directly attached to the chlorine atom and is, in consequence, less affected by an increase in negative charge caused by the intramolecular π bond, and can the more readily accept the intermolecular π bond:

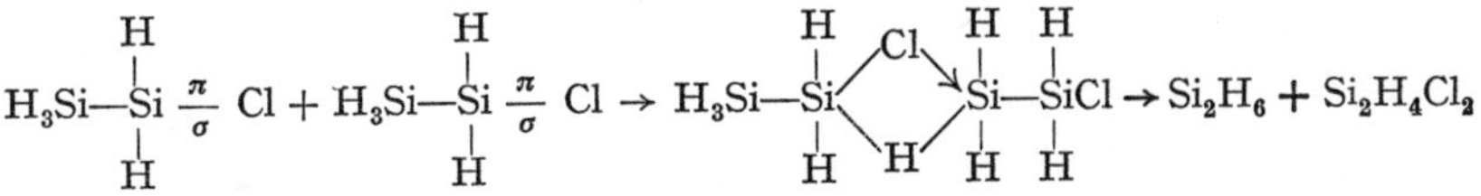

In general, silyl compounds present a contrast to their methyl analogues in that they more readily enter into reactions in which the respective group retains its identity. This is exemplified in the instantaneous conversion of the silyl halides by water into disilyl ether, and in their rapid reaction with silver salts. The principal causes of this reactivity are

(i) the ease with which the co-ordination number of the silicon atom rises from four to six;

(ii) the larger size, and consequently greater vulnerability to attack, of the silicon atom;

(iii) the appreciable polarity of the Si^+—H^- bond (almost absent in the C—H bond) which renders it more reactive towards nucleophilic reagents.

These three factors also favour the formation of complexes.

Hydrides of germanium and tin

Germanium hydrides are made in ways similar to those used for obtaining boranes and silanes. A mixture of mono-, di- and trigermanes results from the action of dilute hydrochloric acid on magnesium germanide. Monogermane alone is conveniently made by reducing germanium tetrachloride with ethereal lithium aluminium hydride. Germanes from di- to penta- have been made by circulating monogermane at 0.5 atm. pressure through an ozoniser electric discharge tube at -78° (Drake, 1961).

TABLE 32

MELTING AND BOILING POINTS OF THE GERMANES

		M.p.	B.p.
Monogermane	GeH_4	$-165°$	$-90°$
Digermane	Ge_2H_6	$-109°$	$29°$
Trigermane	Ge_3H_8	$-106°$	$110°$

The germanes decompose at lower temperatures than the silanes, but are less inflammable and much less easily hydrolysed; monogermane is not attacked even by 30% caustic soda. Halogenation may be effected as with the silanes. An amorphous, yellow polymer $(GeH_2)_x$ is obtained when calcium germanide, Ca_2Ge, is treated with acid. Between 120–220° it decomposes, the three volatile germanes being among the products.

Tin forms the gaseous hydride SnH_4. It is best made by reducing tin(IV) chloride with ethereal lithium aluminium hydride. Stannane decomposes, at room temperature, into tin and hydrogen, but it is not hydrolysed by 15% caustic soda. This hydride is formed by the action of atomic hydrogen on metallic tin.

There is considerable doubt about the existence of a lead hydride; certainly no trace of it appears when metallic lead is treated with atomic hydrogen.

Group VB hydrides

TABLE 33

MELTING AND BOILING POINTS OF GROUP VB HYDRIDES

		M.p.	*B.p.*
Ammonia	NH_3	−78°	−33°
Phosphine	PH_3	−132°	−87°
Arsine	AsH_3	−116°	−62°
Stibine	SbH_3	−88°	−17°
Hydrazine	N_2H_4	+2°	+113°
Phosphorus dihydride	P_2H_4	−99°	+52° (extrapolated)

(For hydrazoic acid see p. 340.)

The ammonia molecule has been shown by infrared and microwave studies to be pyramidal with the H—N—H angle $\sim 107°$. This is because the valency electrons round the nitrogen atom can be roughly described as using sp^3 hybrid orbitals, one containing two electrons (the lone pair) and the rest being singly occupied. Overlap of the latter with the 1s orbitals of the three hydrogen atoms should give three molecular orbitals (at the tetrahedral angle 109.5°) but, as Mellish (1954) and others have pointed out, the hybridisation is not strictly sp^3. The lone-pair orbital is more electron-repellant than the others, thus forcing the bonds together and reducing the angle between them to 107° (see p. 125).

Solid ammonia has an approximately face-centred cubic structure, the lone pair of electrons being involved in hydrogen bonding to three other molecules. There is thus no free inversion of the molecule in the solid, a conclusion supported by infrared spectroscopic evidence.

Ammonia, like water and hydrogen fluoride, is associated in the liquid state, as is evident from its melting point, boiling point, latent heats and surface tension considered in relation to those of phosphine and arsine. The association is due to hydrogen bonding which occurs in liquid ammonia but not in liquid phosphine and arsine.

Liquid ammonia has a significant dielectric constant (1.49 D) and is an ionising solvent. Through its lone pair, the molecule is a strong proton acceptor, and the liquid facilitates the extensive dissociation of weak acids (p. 200); thus acetic acid is almost as completely dissociated in liquid ammonia as a mineral acid is in water:

$$NH_3 + CH_3.COOH \rightleftharpoons NH_4^+ + CH_3.COO^-.$$

Hydrazine is still manufactured (Raschig, 1907) by oxidising aqueous ammonia in large excess with sodium hypochlorite:

$$NH_3 + NaOCl \rightleftharpoons NH_2Cl + NaOH,$$
$$2NH_3 + NH_2Cl \rightleftharpoons NH_2.NH_2 + NH_4Cl.$$

The reactants are mixed at a low temperature and rapidly heated to promote reaction of the chloramine with ammonia. Glue or gelatine is used to inhibit the secondary reaction:

$$N_2H_4 + 2NH_2Cl \rightarrow N_2 + 2NH_4Cl.$$

Commercially the hydrazine is recovered as the hydrate.

In the laboratory sulphuric acid and alcohol are added to the hot solution, from which crystals of hydrazine sulphate separate on cooling:

$$NH_2.NH_2 + H_2SO_4 \rightleftharpoons (NH_2.NH_3^+) HSO_4^-.$$

Distillation with concentrated caustic potash gives anhydrous hydrazine, b.p. 113.5°, which is thermally stable but is very reactive and burns in air.

It forms a monohydrate, $N_2H_4.H_2O$, and is a weak mono-acid base. Both it and its salts are strong reducing agents, converting iodates to iodides, iron(III) salts to iron(II) salts, and gold(III) salts to colloidal gold.

Hydrazine bears the same relation to ammonia as hydrogen peroxide to water. That the molecule is similar to hydrogen peroxide is shown by the Raman spectrum and high dipole moment (1.83 D) of the monomeric vapour. Like the hydroxyl groups in hydrogen peroxide, (p. 381) the NH_2-groups in hydrazine are without free rotation.

In the solid (m.p. 2°) the molecules, apparently hydrogen-bonded to one another, are arranged in zig-zag chains.

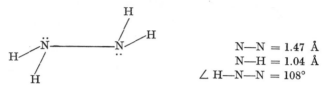

$$N—N = 1.47 \text{ Å}$$
$$N—H = 1.04 \text{ Å}$$
$$\angle \text{ H—N—N} = 108°$$

Fig. 127. Structure of hydrazine.

Anhydrous hydrazine burns spontaneously in dry oxygen and reacts readily with halogens:

$$2I_2 + N_2H_4 \rightarrow 4HI + N_2,$$

it sets free ammonia from ammonium chloride and decomposes when heated:

$$3N_2H_4 \rightarrow N_2 + 4NH_3.$$

It is a good solvent for sulphur, selenium, phosphorus, and arsenic. A weak base, it normally forms salts of the hydrazinium ion, $N_2H_5^+$, though salts of the $N_2H_6^{2+}$ ion are also known.

Aqueous solutions, like those of hydrogen peroxide, show both oxidising and reducing properties. In acids the redox potential is high (p. 183), and suggests that hydrazine should be a strong oxidising agent:

$$N_2H_5^+ + 3H^+ + 2e \rightleftharpoons 2NH_4^+ \qquad E° = + 1.24 \text{ V}.$$

The reaction is slow, however, with all but the strongest reducing agents such as Ti^{3+}. Hydrazine is easily oxidised in either acids or alkalis; the reactions are complicated, nitrogen being the commonest product:

$$N_2 + 5H^+ + 4e \rightarrow N_2H_5^+ \qquad E° = - 0.17 \text{ V};$$
$$N_2 + 4H_2O + 4e \rightarrow N_2H_4 + 4OH^- \qquad E° = - 1.15 \text{ V}.$$

The four-electron change necessary for the quantitative conversion to nitrogen occurs only within certain limits of pH, concentration and temperature. Chlorine, bromine, iodine and iodates bring about this reaction quantitatively at $\sim$ pH 7. Dissolved molecular oxygen oxidises aqueous hydrazine to nitrogen in a series of stages, so hydrazine is an effective deoxidant for boiler-water. Several metal ions, particularly copper, catalyse the reaction.

Interest in hydrazine has been stimulated by its use as a rocket fuel, for which it has the advantage that complete combustion to nitrogen and water yields a mixture of low average molecular weight. Liquid oxygen, very concentrated hydrogen peroxide or fuming nitric acid would be the best oxidising agents for the purpose.

Phosphine, like ammonia, is pyramidal with the H—P—H angle 93° (*cf.* NH$_3$, 107°). It is much less soluble and a much weaker base than ammonia, but a much stronger reducing agent. Phosphonium salts are decidedly less stable than those of ammonium. They dissociate as do ammonium salts on heating; PH$_4$Cl is stable at −75° and completely decomposed at ∼ −50°, the corresponding temperatures for PH$_4$Br and PH$_4$I being ∼ −50°, ∼ 0° and 0°, 62°, respectively. The same order is found for the ammonium salts, but with temperatures in the range 250–400°. The difference in behaviour is ascribable to the lower electronegativity of phosphorus (2.1 against 3.0) as also is the ready disruption of the phosphonium ion by water:

$$PH_4^+I^- + H_2O \rightarrow PH_3 + H_3O^+ + I^-.$$

Alkyl and aryl substituted phosphines are similar to the amines in structure but highly inflammable. The quarternary phosphonium bases are, like the corresponding nitrogen compounds, very strongly ionised.

The unstable, colourless, liquid diphosphine (m.p. −99°, b.p. 51.7°) is a minor by-product of the hydrolysis of phosphides (Ca$_3$P$_2$) which give mainly phosphine; it is separated from the latter by freezing. Unlike hydrazine it is without basic properties. But like hydrazine it is readily oxidised and is a strong reducing agent; it has the same structure. There the similarity ends because its lone pairs are quite ineffective, so that it is insoluble in water and without trace of basic character. It is photo- and heat-sensitive giving phosphine and phosphorus:

$$6P_2H_4 \rightarrow 8PH_3 + P_4$$

The latter adsorbs some of the phosphine to give a complex, (P$_2$H)$_x$, the yellow solid usually termed a hydride, which is odourless, insoluble in cold dilute hydrochloric acid, but decomposed by water giving hydrogen and a phosphorous acid.

Like phosphine, the trihydrides of arsenic and antimony are not formed by direct combination with molecular hydrogen. They are usually prepared by reducing arsenic or antimony compounds with atomic hydrogen produced at a zinc surface dissolving in dilute hydrochloric acid:

$$Zn + 2H^+ + 2Cl^- \rightarrow Zn^{2+} + 2H + 2Cl^-$$

They are strong reducing agents, without basic properties and easily decomposed by heat; the decomposition of arsine begins at 230°.

Phosphorus, arsenic and antimony are all readily attacked by atomic hydrogen to yield their respective trihydrides. There is evidence that a hydride of bismuth is not formed in this way.

Hydrides of Group VIB

The bond angles in water vapour, hydrogen sulphide and hydrogen selenide are respectively 104.5°, 92.3° and 90°. Roughly speaking the 'prepared' oxygen atom is well described as using tetrahedral hybrid sp^3 orbitals (p. 103), two doubly occupied and two singly, and the water molecule results from the overlap of each of the latter with an s orbital of hydrogen. Less hybridisation occurs in the other elements, decreasing with decreasing electronegativity (O, 3.5; S, 2.5; Se, 2.4), and the final form is determined by various factors. Oxygen probably adopts the symmetrical (tetrahedral) configuration because it is thus better able to 'draw in' the hydrogen electrons and approach the condition of two electrons in each hybrid.

Upon the singular properties of water all biochemistry, much of geochemistry and a great deal of general chemistry depends. Ice at —183° has a rigid arrangement of atoms in which oxygen is tetrahedrally co-ordinated by sp^3 orbitals with four hydrogens, two closely (1.00 Å) and two more remotely (1.76 Å). This leads to the very open Wurtzite structure (first suggested by Bernal and Fowler, 1933) with the oxygens 2.76 Å apart, and the hydrogens at points one third along this distance.

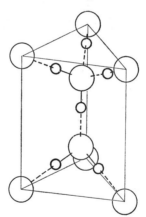

Fig. 128. Wurtzite-like structure of ice.

The hydrogen bonding in ice suffers a progressive break-down as the temperature rises and there is increasing freedom of movement of the H_2O units, but the structure remains sufficiently open for the density of melting ice at 0° to be less than that of water at 0°, when the liquid still retains some of the open character of the solid. As the liquid warms, the density is affected by (a) the breaking of hydrogen bonds leading to a closer packed structure, and (b) the thermal expansion. At 4° these just balance, and water is at its maximum density. Above 4° thermal expansion takes charge and the density continues to fall to the boiling point, but at 50° about half the hydrogen bonding still remains and even boiling water retains some.

Water is the most remarkable of all solvents (p. 93). It has one of the highest dielectric constants (78 at 25°), has a considerable dipole moment (1.85 D), and is amphoteric. As an ionising medium it acts, upon occasion, as either a donor or an acceptor of protons: it facilitates the dissociation of both bases and acids (p. 199):

$$H_2O + \underset{\text{crystal}}{Na_2O} \rightarrow 2\,Na^+ + 2\,OH^-,$$

$$H_2O + \underset{\text{gas}}{HCl} \rightarrow H_3O^+ + Cl^-.$$

Because water molecules are dipolar they cluster round both positive and negative ions; these hydrate sheaths greatly reduce the ionic attraction between the oppositely charged ions and hence their tendency to recombine.

The chemical versatility of water is further increased by its ability either to oxidise or reduce. For the equilibrium in pure water at 25°,

$$H^+ (10^{-7}\,M) + e \rightleftharpoons \tfrac{1}{2}H_2 \qquad\qquad E = -\,0.414\ V.$$

Water gives hydrogen with reducing agents possessing redox potentials (p. 183) more negative than this, but the process is very slow when the hydrogen overvoltage (p. 214) is high. Thus zinc ($E_h^\circ\ Zn^{2+}/Zn = -0.763$) is passive in pure water, though it sets free hydrogen from dilute acids where $E\ H^+/H$ is much nearer zero.

The reducing action of the water is summarised in the equation

$$\tfrac{1}{2}O_2 + 2H^+ (10^{-7}\,M) + 2e \rightleftharpoons H_2O \qquad E = +\,0.815\ V.$$

In consequence oxygen is liberated only by strong oxidising agents. The redox potential decreases as the OH^- ion concentration increases, and alkaline solutions are more easily oxidised than pure water.

By contrast, hydrogen sulphide is without hydrogen bonding; the solid is close-packed, and the liquid density has a normal temperature dependence. The gas burns in air, there being considerable decomposition within the flame which consequently deposits sulphur on a cold surface, and complete combustion at its outer edge. The catalysed oxidation by air on an iron(III) oxide surface can be made to release the whole of the sulphur:

$$H_2S + \tfrac{1}{2}O_2 \rightarrow H_2O + S.$$

In water it is a weak dibasic acid:

$$H_2O + H_2S \rightleftharpoons H_3O^+ + HS^- \qquad pK_a = 7.$$
$$H_2O + HS^- \rightleftharpoons H_3O^+ + S^{2-} \qquad pK_a = 15.$$

It acts also as a reducing agent with, generally, the liberation of sulphur, but in strong oxidising agents the sulphur may be converted into SO_2 or SO_3, or their derivatives:

$$S + 2H^+ + 2e \rightleftharpoons H_2S \qquad E^\circ = +0.141 \text{ V (in acid)}.$$
$$S + 2e \rightleftharpoons S^{2-} \qquad E^\circ = -0.508 \text{ V (in alkali)}.$$

Sulphur forms at least three liquid hydrides; hydrogen persulphide, H_2S_2, and the polysulphides H_2S_3 and H_2S_5. The first two are made by dissolving sulphur in aqueous sodium sulphide, pouring the solution of polysulphides, which certainly contains Na_2S_5, into concentrated hydrochloric acid at $-10°$, and fractionating the yellow oil which separates (Walton and Parsons, 1921):

$$x\,Na_2S + acid \rightarrow (NaCl + H_2S) + H_2S_2 + H_2S_3 + (S).$$

Pure anhydrous ammonium pentasulphide when treated with anhydrous formic acid gives H_2S_5 (Mills and Robinson, 1928). All the liquids readily decompose to H_2S and sulphur. They dissolve in solvents like benzene and chloroform. Their structures involve chains of sulphur atoms.

Hydrogen selenide, made by decomposing aluminium selenide with water, is much less thermally stable than its sulphur analogue:

$$Al_2Se_3 + 3\,H_2O \rightarrow 3\,H_2Se + Al_2O_3 \text{ (hydrated)}.$$

It is slowly oxidised to selenium by moist oxygen. The corresponding compound of tellurium decomposes rapidly at room temperature and is even more easily oxidised. Both have strong reducing properties; thus H_2Se gives free selenium in addition to the selenide when passed into a solution of a heavy metal cation. There are no hydrogen polyselenides or polytellurides, nor would these be expected in view of the weakness of the Se—Se and Te—Te bonds and of the bonds between these elements and hydrogen. The last point is exemplified by a marked decrease in the heats of formation of the simple hydrides in passing down Group VI. This decrease is also observed in the covalent hydrides of Groups IV, V and VII.

The last two compounds, like the hydrides of tin and antimony, are strongly endothermic, probably owing to the considerable heat of formation of the hydrogen molecule and the small electronegativity of the hydrogen atom.

TABLE 34

HEATS OF FORMATION OF HYDRIDES OF GROUP VI

(in kcal/mole)

	H_2O	H_2S	H_2Se	H_2Te
$-\Delta H_f^{\circ}$	68.3	4.8	-20.5	-36.9

The Group VI hydrides exhibit an appreciable increase in acid strength with increasing molecular weight, the pK_a (p. 197) values of aqueous solutions being approximately as given in Table 35.

TABLE 35

pK_a VALUES OF GROUP VI HYDRIDES

H_2O	H_2S	H_2Se	H_2Te
15	7	4	3

This is mainly due to a fall in dissociation energies; solvation energies and electron affinities increase in the reverse direction. There is no connection between acid strength and electronegativity for the dipole moments decrease from water to hydrogen telluride.

Hydrides of Group VIIB

TABLE 36

SOME PROPERTIES OF HYDRIDES OF GROUP VIIB

	HF	HCl	HBr	HI
B.p. (°C)	19.4	-85	-67	-35
$-\Delta H_f^{\circ}$ (kcal/mole)	65	22	12	-6
Bond energy (kcal/mole)	134	102	86	70
pK_a	4	-7	-9	-11

As in the two previous groups, the boiling point of the first member of Group VII is again notably high. Chlorine shows a considerable fall and thence the rise is very nearly proportional to molecular weight.

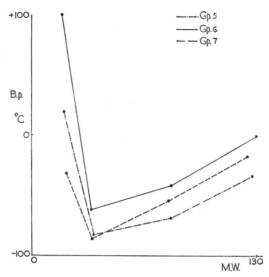

Fig. 129. Relation between boiling point and molecular weight in the volatile hydrides.

Hydrogen fluoride is very strongly hydrogen-bonded; its entropy of vaporisation at the boiling point is high (24.9 cal deg^{-1} per mole), but not as high as that of water (26.0 cal deg^{-1} per mole). Solid hydrogen fluoride probably consists of cyclic $(HF)_6$ molecules; some zig-zag chains (Fig. 130) are present in the liquid. The hydrogen bond with fluorine, though the strongest known, is considerably less than the 70 kcal typical of a σ covalent bond.

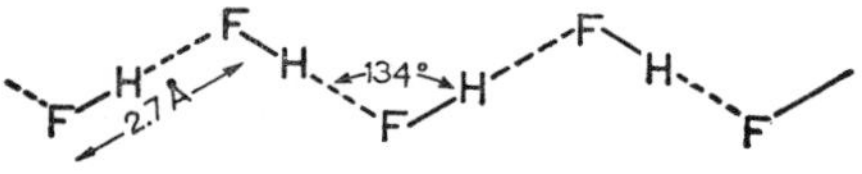

Fig. 130. Chain of hydrogen fluoride. 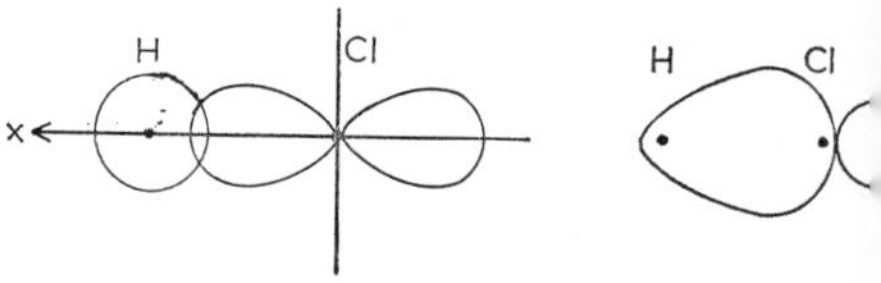   Fig. 131. Contributions to molecular p orbitals in HCl molecule.

The decrease in ionic character from hydrogen fluoride to hydrogen iodide is marked and due to increasing symmetry in the distribution of the bonding electrons. At first sight, the bond is a simple one, compounded of the 1s and the p_x atomic orbitals of hydrogen and halogen respectively.

$$\psi = a\psi(\text{H} : 1\text{s}) + b\psi(\text{Cl} : 3\text{p}_x)$$

In a molecular orbital of this kind, b/a always exceeds unity, but the ratio is much larger for fluorine than for iodine, indicating that the charge cloud 'leans' more heavily towards the halogen in the former case (Fig. 131).

It is now recognised that this simple picture is inadequate. Some sp hybridisation occurs on the halogen atom, one hybrid being engaged in the bond and the other pointing out behind the halogen and containing a lone pair; the lone pair plays a large part in determining the dipole moment (p. 96).

The disparity between the MO coefficients, a and b, indicates ionic character in every instance; the dipole moment of hydrogen chloride is 1.03 D. Infra-red absorption spectra indicate a bond length of 1.26 Å, so that, were the molecule completely ionic (*i.e.* H^+Cl^-), the value of μ would be $1.26 \times 4.80 = 6.05$ D. In fact, the bonding is mainly covalent in the free molecule. If the degree of polarity is measured by $1.03/6.05 = 0.169$, it could be said that the bond in HCl is about 83% covalent. On this basis hydrogen iodide would be 95% covalent, the corresponding polarity being 0.05.

Dissociation in polar solvents is due to the breaking of the hydrogen–halogen bond through the approach of a lone pair on the water molecule to a hydrogen atom in the hydrogen halide causing a retraction of the molecular orbital towards the halogen and thereby allowing the water molecule to capture the liberated proton.

$$H_2O + H\text{–}Cl \rightarrow H_2O \ldots H^+ Cl^-$$
$$\downarrow$$
$$H_3O^+ \qquad Cl^-$$

The necessary energy for the process is provided by the heat of formation of the hydroxonium ion. Thus the increase in acidity from hydrogen fluoride to hydrogen iodide arises almost entirely from the decreasing strength of the hydrogen-halogen bond.

The monohydrate formed by HCl at low temperatures has been shown by X-ray diffraction at $-35°$ to be $H_3O^+Cl^-$, every hydrogen atom being bonded by hydrogen bonds to the nearest chlorine atom. The hydrogen bonds OH...Cl are 2.95 Å.

THE SALINE HYDRIDES

These are crystalline compounds made by heating the metal in hydrogen; calcium, for instance, reacts at 150°. Those of the alkali metals, XH, have the sodium chloride type lattice (p. 141); those of the Gp. IIA metals are less regular. All have stoichiometric compositions and the crystals are ionic, being somewhat denser than the metal from which they are made owing to the strong polar bonds in the ionic lattice.

Those stable in the fused state (LiH), or dissolved in a suitable melt (CaH_2), yield hydrogen at the anode on electrolysis in accordance with Faraday's laws.

The hydrides of lithium, calcium and strontium are the most stable of this class; others undergo thermal decomposition above 400°. All are oxidised by air and some ignite spontaneously at room temperature; all react vigorously with water:

$$H^- + H_2O \rightarrow H_2 + OH^-.$$

Lithium, alone of the Group IA hydrides, has a heat of formation comparable with those of the Group IIA compounds.

TABLE 37

HEATS OF FORMATION OF THE SALINE HYDRIDES
(kcal/mole hydrogen)

LiH	NaH	KH	RbH	CsH	CaH_2	SrH_2	BaH_2
21.6	13.9	14.1	13.5	13.0	45.1	42.3	40.9

It is doubtful whether the hydrides of the lanthanides are truly ionic. The heats of formation of some are high, that of the cerium compound $CeH_{2.8}$ being 42.3 kcal/mole. Most of them resemble the metallic hydrides in being non-stoichiometric. But as regards composition much may depend on mode of preparation since a titanium hydride, precisely TiH_2, has recently been made from the carefully purified elements.

A similar uptake of hydrogen occurs in the actinide series; uranium absorbs it rapidly at 250° to give a black powder UH_3, which decomposes at 450°, leaving the metal as a highly reactive powder. This hydride has a cubic lattice. It is a strong reducing agent, converting silver nitrate, copper sulphate and mercury(II) chloride to the respective metals. Its specific gravity is about 11, compared with 18.7 for uranium itself.

THE METALLIC HYDRIDES

Reversible adsorption or occlusion of hydrogen by metals is common, particularly in those belonging to the transition series. Palladium is the most striking example; during electrolysis a cathode of the metal absorbs about 800 times its volume of hydrogen. The hydrogen thus taken up can usually be removed by heating in a vacuum but traces are often tenaciously retained. Iron, palladium and platinum are permeable to hydrogen at high temperatures. The properties of the metallic hydrides are not very different from those of the parent metals. Their formulae are not stoichiometric.

$$TiH_{1.73}, \quad VH_{0.6}, \quad CeH_{2.8}, \quad PrH_{2.7}.$$

The metal lattices are expanded but otherwise little distorted; the densities are below those of the parent metal. Many are interstitial compounds but with lanthanide and actinide hydrides the high heats of formation suggest that the bonding is to a certain degree ionic.

Palladium hydride has a long history. Gillespie and Hall (1926) obtained pressure-composition curves which suggest the formation of two solid solutions; one at 250°, stoichiometrically Pd_2H, a second at 180° with a composition approaching $PdH_{0.6}$. Metallic palladium is face-centred cubic, and the absorption of hydrogen increases the lattice parameter from 3.883 Å to 3.894 Å without a change of phase, but further absorption so strains the metallic lattice as to cause a sudden increase to 4.018 Å with the appearance of a β-phase.

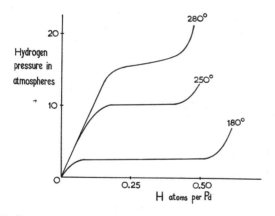

Fig. 132. Pressure–composition curves for hydrogen–palladium system.

Iron behaves similarly; there is a sudden increase in the uptake of hydrogen at about 900°, just the transition temperature of the α–γ phase change, followed by an equally sudden release of hydrogen at about 1400°, the γ–δ transition temperature. Both the α and δ phases are body-centred cubic. The γ phase is face-centred; so presumably there is greater interstitial space in that phase.

HYDRIDES OF INDETERMINATE STRUCTURE

Cobalt, iron and nickel yield black precipitates when hydrogen is passed through suspensions of their respective anhydrous dichlorides mixed with phenyl magnesium bromide in dry ether:

$$NiCl_2 + 2C_6H_5.MgBr \rightarrow Ni(C_6H_5)_2 + MgBr_2 + MgCl_2,$$
$$Ni(C_6H_5)_2 + 2H_2 \rightarrow 2C_6H_6 + NiH_2.$$

They have compositions corresponding to FeH_2, CoH_2 and NiH_2 and their structures are unknown. Copper hydride, $\sim CuH$, has been made recently by mixing lithium aluminium hydride, dissolved in pyridine and ether, with copper(I) iodide in pyridine:

$$CuI + LiAlH_4 \rightarrow LiI + AlH_3 + CuH.$$

The blood-red solution formed yields a bright red, crystalline solid when more ether is added. This is stable below 50° and decomposes rapidly above 100°. It is a copper(I) hydride, $CuH_{0.96}$, stoichiometrically deficient in hydrogen, and does not resemble the saline hydrides, having a low heat of formation ($-\Delta H_f = 5.1$ kcal/mole).

Rather similar hydrides of zinc, cadmium, beryllium and magnesium have been made by reducing their dialkyls with lithium aluminium hydride dissolved in ether:

$$Zn(CH_3)_2 + 2LiAlH_4 \rightarrow ZnH_2 + 2LiAlH_3.CH_3.$$

They are white solids of unknown structure. The beryllium compound, BeH_2, which decomposes into the elements at 120°, is the most thermally stable. Very recently magnesium hydride has been prepared by direct union. Hydrogen under moderate pressure is needed as the synthesis is sufficiently rapid only at temperatures for which the dissociation pressure is also appreciable. The product is more stable in air and much less easily hydrolysed than that obtained from magnesium diethyl. The heats of formation of beryllium and magnesium hydrides are not known, but the low thermal stabilities suggest them to be less exothermic than calcium hydride. In view of the high ionisation potentials and the small ionic radii of Mg^{2+} and Be^{2+}, their hydrides are probably not ionic as is CaH_2 but more likely highly polymerised, covalent compounds linked by hydrogen bridges, as are the units in aluminium hydride.

Chapter 13

The Inert Gases

GROUP O

The inert gases, helium, neon, argon, krypton, xenon and radon, the first five isolated by Ramsay and his associates (1894–98), constitute Group O of the Periodic Table. All are monatomic and, with the exception of He, have electronic configurations completed by a closed subshell of three doubly-occupied p orbitals. The resulting ^1S ground state is without tendency to covalent bonding and the formation of a diatomic molecule, because the two atoms possess between them sufficient electrons to fill both the bonding and anti-bonding molecular orbitals (p. 85). Although He_2^+, with only one electron in the σ^* 1s orbital, does occur in the discharge tube. Moreover, the first ionisation potentials of closed shell structures are very large (p. 64) and ionic bonding is thereby ruled out.

TABLE 38

	He	Ne	Ar	Kr	Xe	Rn
Electron configuration	$1s^2$	$2s^22p^6$	$3s^23p^6$	$4s^24p^6$	$5s^25p^6$	$6s^26p^6$
Atomic number	2	10	18	36	54	86
Ionisation potential (eV)	24.5	21.5	15.7	13.9	12.1	10.7

Ions with the inert gas configuration are easily formed from the alkali metals, and those of the halogens are also stable. The ionisation potential for

$$Na\ (1s^2\ 2s^22p^6\ 3s^1)\ \rightarrow\ Na^+\ (1s^2\ 2s^22p^6) + e$$

is small, 5.1 eV; and the electron affinity for

$$Cl\ (1s^2\ 2s^22p^6\ 3s^23p^5) + e\ \rightarrow\ Cl^-\ (1s^2\ 2s^22p^6\ 3s^23p^6)$$

is positive. Accordingly both atoms, and all similar pairs, readily achieve the inert gas electronic configuration. The presence of such ions in solution is strongly favoured by electrostatic interaction with solvent molecules, although this is offset to some extent by the $T\Delta S$ term (which arises from the local ordering of solvent molecules) in the free energy change.

Interaction between inert gas atoms is slight, the Van der Waals forces being due entirely to dispersion interaction (p. 116). Liquefaction is therefore difficult; the elements have much lower b.p. than compounds of about the same molecular weight with less symmetrical electron distributions and correspondingly larger electrostatic and polarisation interactions.

TABLE 39

	Mass	B.p. (°K)		Mass	B.p. (°K)
He	4	4.2	H_2	2	20
Ne	20	27	CH_4	16	92

The liquefaction of helium by a controlled expansion process necessitates preliminary cooling because its Joule-Thomson coefficient is negative (spontaneous expansion heats the gas) down to an 'inversion temperature' of 40 °K. All the gases have C_p/C_v ratios very close to 5/3, the theoretical value for an ideal monatomic gas. The elements are liquid over very small temperature ranges. Helium can be solidified only under pressure; under 26 atmospheres it solidifies at 0.9 °K.

TABLE 40

	He	Ne	Ar	Kr	Xe	Rn
M.p. (°K)		24	84	116	161	202
B.p. (°K)	4.2	27	87	121	164	211
Atomic radius (Å)	1.2	1.6	1.9	2.0	2.2	—

When helium is cooled to 2.18 °K at 1 atmosphere (the λ-point), a remarkable liquid, helium II, is obtained. It has:
  (i) very high heat conductance—600 times that of copper at room temperature;
  (ii) very low viscosity—about one thousandth that of hydrogen gas;
  (iii) ability to flow up the surface of the container.
The liquid is produced only from $^4_2$He, not from $^3_2$He.

Helium

The α-particles set free in radioactive disintegration take up electrons to form helium atoms. The gas is therefore associated with minerals containing α-emitters; pitchblende ($^{238}_{92}$U) and monazite ($^{232}_{90}$Th) are examples. Helium-3, though a stable nuclide, comprises only $1.4 \times 10^{-3}\%$ of natural helium; it is a product of the radioactivity of tritium, itself a result of the action of cosmic rays on deuterium (p. 216):

$$^3_1H \xrightarrow[12.5\ y.]{\beta} {}^3_2He\ \text{(stable)}.$$

If a helium isotope of mass 5 should exist, it must have a very short life indeed. Incidentally, there is no other nuclide of this mass and there is no mass number, other than 5, which is not represented by at least one nuclide. Helium-6 is a β-emitter of short half-life.

$$\ce{^6_2He} \xrightarrow[\text{0.8 sec}]{\beta} \ce{^6_3Li}\,(\text{stable}).$$

Helium is much less common on earth than on larger planets or stars (p. 29). Its high velocity, and the large mean free path available, enable it to escape readily from the upper atmosphere, where it is relatively abundant, because the gravitational field is not very strong. The element is now extracted principally from natural gas (up to 8% He) in the south of the U.S.A., the other gases, mainly hydrocarbons, being separated by liquefaction. Attempts are being made to obtain it from the atmosphere by making use of its ability to diffuse through heated, thin-walled silica capillaries.

The non-radioactive inert gases are all present in the atmosphere. The volume percentages are: argon 0.93 %, neon 1.8×10^{-3} %, helium 5×10^{-4} %, krypton 1.1×10^{-4} %, xenon 8×10^{-6} %.

Separation from air

Liquid air is, to a first approximation, a ternary mixture of nitrogen (b.p. 77 °K), argon (87 °K) and oxygen (90 °K). In its fractional distillation there is a point on the column where the mid-boiling fraction reaches a maximum concentration, and from which a side-cut gives a liquid containing mainly oxygen and argon. This is fractionated separately and the oxygen is returned to the column. The crude argon, with up to 20% oxygen, is mixed with hydrogen and sparked; the unused hydrogen is oxidised by hot CuO.

Neon is not condensed; it accumulates on the nitrogen side and has to be withdrawn. The nitrogen in the extracted gas is removed, first by low-temperature liquefaction and, finally, by charcoal adsorption. Krypton and xenon remain dissolved in the liquid oxygen; they can be separated by selective low-temperature adsorption.

Uses

Helium, formerly much used for airships, is now employed, like argon, to provide an inert gaseous shield during the welding of Mg, Al, Ti and stainless steel. It probably has a great future in gas-cooled atomic reactors as a material for transferring heat, since it is inert and does not become active. An oxygen-helium mixture is used in the treatment of asthma as it diffuses more rapidly than air through constricted lung passages. A similar mixture is supplied to deep-sea divers because helium, being less soluble than nitrogen, does not cause caisson sickness or 'bends' by bubbling out of the blood when the pressure is released. Helium is a suitable gas for low temperature gas thermometry, both because of its low boiling point and near-ideal behaviour.

Argon has been used since about 1920 in gas-filled electric bulbs to reduce the rate of evaporation from the tungsten filament, and also more recently in thermionic tubes (thyratons) and fluorescent lamps. Krypton replaces argon in high-efficiency filament lamps, such as miners' cap lamps. Xenon is employed in some electronic flash tubes for high-speed photography. The first four members of the group, particularly neon but krypton increasingly, are important gases for coloured signs.

Compounds of helium formed in discharge tubes

The question of compound formation by Gp. O elements has frequently arisen. The passage of a discharge through low-pressure hydrogen-helium mixtures gives spectra which appear to be due to HeH^+ and HeH_2^+ ions. Manley (1927) reported $HgHe_{10}$ as being made in a glow discharge. Several transition metals when used as electrodes in a discharge tube take up the gases. Of the products, the most thoroughly studied, Pt_3He, certainly has an X-ray diffraction pattern different from that of Pt. It is a material probably similar in character to an interstitial hydride.

Chemical properties

The only way in which the inert gases could form compounds would be by the donation of electron pairs. Several attempts have accordingly been made to obtain evidence of reaction with strong Lewis acids. Booth and Willson (1935) made a thermal analysis of the system argon-boron trifluoride between -127 and $-133\,°C$ at pressures up to 40 atmospheres. They reported the existence of compounds $Ar(BF_3)_x$ where $x = 1, 2, 3, 6, 8$ and 12, but Wiberg and Karbe (1948) failed to confirm this.

Hydrates and deuterates have, however, been made by compressing the inert gases with water and D_2O. Those formed by the heavier elements are the most stable and contain six H_2O or D_2O molecules to one inert gas atom, as in $Xe.6H_2O$ where the xenon atom is evidently polarised by the strong dipole. This thesis is supported by the increase in water-solubility down Gp. O:

TABLE 41

	He	Ne	Ar	Kr	Xe	Rn
Absorption coefficient in water at 20 °C	0.0097	0.014	0.05	0.11	0.24	0.51

Nikitin (1940) made a compound of xenon with phenol, $Xe(C_6H_5OH)_2$, isomorphous with $H_2S(C_6H_5OH)_2$.

Quinol forms clathrates (p. 148) with argon, krypton and xenon when crystallised from benzene or water under considerable pressure of the inert gas (Powell, 1950). The inert gas atoms are caged inside groups of quinol molecules joined together by hydrogen bonds. The argon clathrate contains about 9% argon by weight, corresponding to about three quinol molecules per argon atom. The molecular ratios are nearly the same for krypton and xenon as for the clathrates holding other molecules of about their size such as CO, CO_2 and SO_2.

Radon

Element 86 has three principal isotopes, all α-emitters of short half life, derived from $^{238}_{92}U$, $^{232}_{90}Th$ and $^{235}_{92}U$, respectively.

$^{222}_{86}Rn$ (Radon) $\xrightarrow[\text{3.8 days}]{\alpha}$ $^{218}_{84}Po$ (Radium A; α, 3 min).

$^{220}_{86}Rn$ (Thoron) $\xrightarrow[\text{54.5 sec.}]{\alpha}$ $^{216}_{84}Po$ (Thorium A; α, 1.5×10^{-1} sec).

$^{219}_{86}Rn$ (Actinon) $\xrightarrow[\text{3.9 sec.}]{\alpha}$ $^{215}_{84}Po$ (Actinium A; α, 1.8×10^{-3} sec).

Chapter 14

The Alkali Metals

GROUP IA

These elements all have a singly occupied s orbital outside a closed shell of inert gas structure. Owing to the screening of the nucleus by the closed shell, the valence electron is very weakly bound. The elements therefore exist as metals, in which the valence electrons are 'pooled' (p. 112), and, in combination with electronegative elements, tend to form ionic solids. Only the unipositive or M^+ ion occurs.

TABLE 42

SOME PROPERTIES OF THE ALKALI METALS

	Li	Na	K	Rb	Cs	Fr
Atomic number	3	11	19	37	55	87
Electron configuration	$1s^2 2s^1$	$2s^2 2p^6 3s^1$	$3s^2 3p^6 4s^1$	$4s^2 4p^6 5s^1$	$5s^2 5p^6 6s^1$	$6s^2 6p^6 7s^1$
Atomic radius (Å)	1.33	1.57	2.03	2.16	2.35	—
Ionic radius, M^+ (Å)	0.78	0.98	1.33	1.48	1.69	—

The ionisation potentials decrease down the sub-group. But lithium, with the highest ionisation potential, has a relatively low electrode potential owing to the high heat of hydration of the ion, which, in turn, is due to its small size and less effectively screened nuclear charge. As a result, lithium in contact with water is as strong a reducing agent as caesium, but when dry it is less easily oxidised than any other metal of the sub-group.

TABLE 43

IONISATION AND ELECTRODE POTENTIALS OF THE ALKALI METALS

	Li	Na	K	Rb	Cs
Ionisation potential I (eV)	5.39	5.14	4.34	4.18	3.90
Electrode potential E_h° M^+/M (V)	−3.02	−2.71	−2.92	−2.99	−3.02

Elements: preparation and properties

TABLE 44

SOME PROPERTIES OF THE ALKALI METALS

	Li	Na	K	Rb	Cs
Density (g/cc)	0.53	0.97	0.86	1.53	1.90
Atomic volume	12.9	23.7	45.5	56.1	69.8
M.p. (°C)	180	98	63.5	39	28.5
B.p. (°C)	1336	883	759	700	670

Sodium (2.63%) and potassium (2.40%) are high in abundance among the elements in the earth's crust; their amounts in sea water are respectively 1.14% and 0.04%. Sodium and its compounds are chiefly derived from sodium chloride; the principal source of potassium is carnallite, $KMgCl_3.6H_2O$. The other elements of the family are much less common. Lithium (0.0065%), mainly in aluminosilicates such as petalite, $(Li, Na)AlSi_4O_{10}$, and spodumene, $LiAl(SiO_3)_2$, has an abundance less than rubidium (0.031%) and about ten time greater than caesium. Francium occurs naturally only in minute amounts and, of its four known isotopes—all radioactive—the longest lived is ^{223}Fr (half-life 21 min). Its progenitor is actinium-227, and the nuclide is itself a β-emitter:

$$^{227}_{89}Ac \longrightarrow {}^{223}_{87}Fr + {}^{4}_{2}He;$$

$$^{223}_{87}Fr \xrightarrow{\text{21 min}} {}^{223}_{88}Ra + \beta^-.$$

It is co-precipitated with rubidium and caesium perchlorates or chloro-platinates.

Both potassium and rubidium have natural active isotopes. Potassium-40 is a feeble β-emitter with a half-life of 1.3×10^9 years; it makes up about 0.012% of the natural element. Of the two natural isotopes of rubidium, one, ^{87}Rb, which accounts for nearly 28%, is a weak β-emitter, half-life 6×10^{10} years.

Separation of the isotopes of lithium

Lithium occurs as $^{6}_{3}Li$ (7.3%) and $^{7}_{3}Li$ (92.7%) with one isotope nearly 17% greater in mass than the other, and a difference in chemical behaviour has been detected. Lewis and MacDonald (1936), by allowing drops of lithium amalgam to fall through a methanol solution of lithium chloride, showed that an equilibrium is established:

$^{7}_{3}Li$ (in amalgam) $+ {}^{6}_{3}Li^+$ (in methanol) $\rightleftharpoons {}^{6}_{3}Li$ (in amalgam) $+ {}^{7}_{3}Li^+$ (in methanol).

Evidently ^6Li possesses a slightly higher electrode potential; and, by repeating the process, they increased the proportion of ^6Li in the amalgam to 16.4%.

Taylor and Urey (1937) found $^6Li^+$ ions to be preferentially adsorbed by a zeolite in its sodium form. With a column of nearly one hundred feet and aqueous lithium chloride the first runnings were depleted in $^6Li^+$, and elution with sodium chloride gave a solution containing 10.2% of $^6Li^+$. The preferential adsorption of an ion higher in a group appears to be exceptional, for Taylor and Urey found K^+ more readily adsorbed than Na^+.

The metals

Reduction of the cations is difficult and the only practicable methods of preparing the metals are electrolytic; and, currently, electrolyses of the fused chlorides are employed. In most compounds the elements appear as an extremely ionic type, nevertheless covalent diatomic molecules exist in vapour of the metals though the proportion is small, not more than 1% even in lithium vapour, for the dissociation energies are low, Li–Li 27.2, Na–Na 17.5, K–K 11.8, Rb–Rb 11.3, Cs–Cs 10.4 kcal. The σ bonds in the molecules are covalencies formed by the overlap of s orbitals. Although the overlap is considerable, the resultant charge cloud is diffuse, owing to an efficient screening of the nuclear attraction, and does not give rise to strong bonding.

The metals are highly active, increasingly so with atomic number. Lithium, with its high ionisation potential, reacts rather slowly with water and with liquid bromine, and not at all with oxygen below 100°. But with non-metals possessing small anions, the metal is more active and forms compounds more stable than those of any of the other metals. Its hydride, carbide and nitride may all be made by direct combination, whereas sodium gives only hydride in this way. The combination of two elements, both with small ions, confers a high lattice energy on the crystal, and these reactions of lithium are highly exothermic. A remarkable property of metallic lithium, undoubtedly related to the size and reactivity of its ion, is its ability to attack glass; the other alkali metals can be manipulated in glass vessels, but molten lithium rapidly cuts a way through.

The metals are employed in a variety of alloys. Lithium generally hardens and strengthens, but also causes embrittlement; from 0.05 to 0.1% is used in Al, Zn and Mg alloys. Sodium is an important additive to lead; such an alloy is the basis of the manufacture of lead tetraethyl, and another, containing 0.6% Na, 0.6% Ca and 0.05% Li, is a bearing metal. Ternary alloys of caesium with aluminium and either barium or strontium are used in photoelectric cells. Liquid sodium or sodium-potassium alloy is employed to transfer heat from the core of certain atomic reactors, e.g. Dounreay fast breeder.

Halides

All the alkali metal halides except the chloride, bromide and iodide of caesium form cubic crystals with the rock salt lattice and show a co-ordination number of 6. The exceptions are also cubic, but have the caesium chloride structure (Fig. 133) characterised by a co-ordination number of 8. The radius ratio for CsCl, $Cs^+/Cl^- = 0.93$, allows 8 co-ordination, but is so near the ratio for 6 co-ordination that caesium chloride is dimorphous, changing, at 445°, from the caesium chloride to the rock salt structure. The crystalline halides are generally markedly ionic, though, as expected, lithium iodide is somewhat covalent, for iodide is the largest and most easily polarised simple anion and lithium, the smallest alkali metal cation, possesses the strongest polarising power.

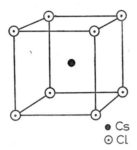

• Cs
⊙ Cl

Fig. 133. Caesium chloride structure.

Lithium iodide forms a solid complex with ammonia, $Li(NH_3)_4I$, but the related hydrate, alcoholate and amine complexes are less stable. These complexes presumably involve ion-dipole bonds (p. 115), the nitrogen lone pairs surrounding the Li^+; some covalent character (dative bonding) is also permissible if s and p orbitals on the Li are invoked. The chloride, bromide and iodide of lithium are much more soluble in alcohol and ether than those of the other alkali metals, but this is not always a reliable indication of covalent character. The property is employed in separating lithium from sodium.

Lithium chloride is particularly deliquescent and forms hydrates:

$$LiCl.3H_2O \xrightarrow[-15.0°]{} LiCl.2H_2O \xrightarrow[125°]{} LiCl.H_2O \xrightarrow[198°]{} LiCl.$$

Reference has already been made to the high lattice energies of crystalline compounds containing small ions; lithium fluoride is such a compound, and its high heat of formation and low solubility are not unexpected.

Many polyhalides of alkali metals are known, the most important being the tri-iodides and the very stable mixed halides of the type $MICl_4$. Lithium and sodium do not form tri-iodides. The potassium compound exists as a monohydrate stable below 25°, but dehydration is accompanied by loss of iodine. The rubidium and caesium compounds are anhydrous and crystalline. The stronger positive fields round the lithium and sodium ions curtail the spread of negative charge from the iodide ion to an iodine molecule.

$$I^- + I_2 \longrightarrow (I—I—I)^-.$$

Rubidium and caesium also form tribromides, and mixed trihalides, particularly of the $MICl_2$ type, are known; in these the $(Cl—I—Cl)^-$ ion is linear. The compounds KIBrCl and CsIBrF have also been isolated. All the alkali metals form stable orange-red polyhalides of the type $MICl_4$, containing a square complex ion (p. 127).

Potassium, rubidium and caesium form sparingly soluble chloroplatinates that can be readily separated from the soluble lithium and sodium compounds:

	K_2PtCl_6	Rb_2PtCl_6	Cs_2PtCl_6
Solubility at 20° (g/100 g)	1.12	0.141	0.07

Oxides

The metals burn in oxygen to yield (i) lithium monoxide, (ii) sodium peroxide and (iii) potassium, rubidium and caesium superoxides (p. 384). Successive additions of oxygen give the oxide (O^{2-}), peroxide (O_2^{2-}) and superoxide (O_2^-) anions:

$$M \rightarrow M_2O \rightarrow MO—OM \rightarrow MO_2.$$

The lithium ion, because so small, has a much stronger positive field round it than the sodium ion, the relative strengths being inversely proportional to the squares of the ionic radii:

	Li^+	Na^+	K^+	Rb^+	Cs^+
$1/r^2$	1.64	1.04	0.57	0.46	0.35

A strong positive field near one oxygen anion restricts the spread of negative charge towards another oxygen atom, making the formation of higher oxides difficult. Thus lithium peroxide is only readily made by precipitation from alcoholic lithium hydroxide with hydrogen peroxide:

$$2LiOH + 2H_2O_2 + H_2O \rightarrow Li_2O_2.H_2O_2.3H_2O.$$

The precipitate when dried over phosphorus pentoxide in a vacuum becomes the white, anhydrous peroxide which reverts to the monoxide on heating. The positive field round the sodium ion is too weak to prevent the conversion of the O^{2-} anion into a peroxide ion, but is strong enough to limit further oxidation.

The weaker field round a larger unipositive ion allows the formation of the superoxide ion O_2^- to take place.

The superoxides have the tetragonal lattice of calcium carbide, in which the anion has an unpaired electron, its structure (*cf.* the oxygen molecule p. 95) being $KK\ (z\sigma)^2(y\sigma)^2(x\sigma)^2(w\pi)^4(v\pi)^3$. It confers paramagnetism on the compounds, the only ones, among those of Gp. IA, known to be paramagnetic.

The normal oxides of the alkali metals, other than lithium, are usually made by reducing the nitrate or nitrite with the metal itself:

$$2NaNO_3 + 10Na \rightarrow 6Na_2O + N_2.$$

Lithium oxide dissolves quietly in water; the others more energetically. Lithium hydroxide monohydrate crystallises from the solution. Structurally every lithium ion is surrounded tetrahedrally by two hydroxide ions and two water molecules. Every tetrahedral group has an edge and two corners to produce double chains held laterally by hydrogen bonds (shown by broken lines) between the hydroxide ions and the water molecules. Every water molecule has four near neighbours, two lithium ions of the same chain and two hydroxide ions, one from each of two other chains (Fig. 134).

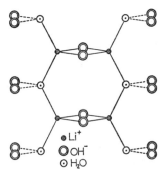

Fig. 134. Structure of $LiOH.H_2O$.

Phase rule studies show that both sodium and potassium hydroxide form several hydrates, but their structures are unknown.

Sulphides

All the alkali metals form hydrosulphides MHS, monosulphides M_2S, and a series of polysulphides M_2S_x, where x has values from 2 to 6. The hydrosulphides are prepared by saturating an aqueous or aqueous alcoholic solution of the appropriate hydroxide with hydrogen sulphide, and may be crystallised as hydrates therefrom, *e.g.* $NaHS.3H_2O$ and $KHS.\frac{1}{2}H_2O$. These may be dehydrated or even fused without serious decomposition.

The monosulphide and polysulphides are formed by burning the metals in sulphur vapour, by the action of sulphur on the metals dissolved in liquid ammonia, and by the action of the molten metals on sulphur dissolved in toluene. Hydrates or alcoholates and, in some cases, the anhydrous compounds may be prepared by dissolving sulphur in hot solutions of the hydrosulphides or monosulphides. Potassium, rubidium and caesium give all the sulphides where $x = 1$, 2, 3, 4, 5, or 6; sodium only up to the pentasulphide, and lithium only those for which $x = 1$, 2 and 4 (Pearson and Robinson, 1931). All the metals form two polysulphides of relatively outstanding stability; one is invariably the disulphide, and the other tetrasulphide in the case of lithium or sodium, and pentasulphide in the case of potassium, rubidium or caesium. The amount of water of crystallisation and the solubility decrease with increase in atomic number of the metal, the gradation being most marked between sodium and potassium.

That the metals of highest atomic number should form compounds with the larger numbers of sulphur atoms is in accordance with their behaviour towards oxygen, where the superoxides of rubidium and caesium are the most stable. The polysulphides consist of zig-zag chains of sulphur atoms with the metal atoms situated terminally.

Oxoacid salts

Lithium carbonate decomposes on heating in a stream of hydrogen at 800°:

$$Li_2CO_3 \rightarrow Li_2O + CO_2.$$

The strong polarising action of the small cation on the large complex anion, CO_3^{2-}, may initiate the reaction. Lithium oxide has the antifluorite structure and the reaction proceeds because (i) the highly polarisable carbonate ion readily loses an oxygen ion and (ii) the gain in lattice energy resulting from the substitution of a smaller oxide ion for the larger carbonate ion enables the centres of charge to approach more closely.

Lithium carbonate is so sparingly soluble as to be precipitated from solutions of lithium salts by sodium carbonate. It dissolves in water containing carbon dioxide but there is no direct evidence that a bicarbonate is formed. The bicarbonates of the other alkali metals may all be obtained in solid form. Those of rubidium and caesium are more soluble and thermally stable than the sodium and potassium salts.

Lithium nitrate decomposes on heating in a similar way to calcium nitrate:

$$4LiNO_3 \rightarrow 2Li_2O + 2N_2O_4 + O_2.$$

The other alkali metal nitrates yield the nitrites and oxygen. Only the lithium and sodium salts are deliquescent.

Lithium orthophosphate, Li_3PO_4, is precipitated when sodium phosphate is added to an alkaline solution of a lithium salt. Phosphates of the other metals are soluble.

The sulphates of potassium, rubidium and caesium are isomorphous and anhydrous. The solubility of sodium sulphate depends upon the composition of the solid phase. It increases rapidly with temperature up to 32.38°, and within this range crystallisation gives the decahydrate. Above 32.38° the solubility falls slightly with temperature and the anhydrous salt separates as fine crystals. Lithium sulphate crystallises as the monohydrate, $Li_2SO_4.H_2O$.

Complex compounds

Though the sizes and electronic configurations of the alkali-metal cations are not conducive to co-ordination with ligands, chelating groups do impose some acceptor properties on them. Thus when sodium hydroxide is added to salicylaldehyde the salt produced takes up a further molecule of salicyl-aldehyde to form a compound which is covalent.

A similar result is sometimes achieved by hydration. The anhydrous sodium derivative of acetylacetone is salt-like but the dihydrate shows covalency, being soluble in non-polar solvents like toluene.

Potassium, rubidium and caesium form both 4- and 6-covalent compounds with salicylaldehyde; a 6-covalent one is shown.

Increasing atomic number influences the stability of these covalent compounds because it is accompanied by (i) increased ease of ionisation which weakens the tendency to accept electrons, (ii) increased size of the atom which raises the maximum co-ordination number.

These factors accord well with the stability of the 4-covalent compounds of sodium and of the 6-covalent compounds of rubidium (Brewer, 1931).

Similarities between lithium and magnesium

A feature of the first period of the Periodic Table is the similarity the individual elements show to the element a group higher in the second period, *diagonal similarities* as they are often termed:

$$Li \quad Be \quad B \quad C$$
$$Na \quad Mg \quad Al \quad Si$$

In general the polarising powers of cations increase across a period because of the increasing charge, but diminish down a group because of the increasing ionic radius (*cf.* Fajans' rules, p. 90). When both movements are made one effect, in part at least, compensates for the other and there may be no marked change in properties. The similarity between lithium and magnesium is exemplified by:

  (i) the formation of the normal oxides on burning;

  (ii) the instability of the carbonates and nitrates;

 (iii) the formation of the carbides and nitrides by direct combination;

 (iv) the insolubility of the carbonates and phosphates;

  (v) the strong hydration of the ions;

 (vi) the solubility of salts such as chlorides in organic solvents;

 vii) the high solubility of the alkyls in organic solvents.

Chapter 15

Beryllium, Magnesium
and the Alkaline Earth Metals

GROUP IIA

The trend of properties throughout this group is similar to that in Gp. IA, but the greater nuclear charges make the atoms smaller. The bipositive ions of the alkaline earth metals are much smaller than the unipositive ions of the alkali metals, and the extreme smallness of Be^{2+} makes that element even more exceptional than lithium in Gp. IA. On the older electrovalent picture, beryllium would be said to form incompletely ionic bonds because of the very high 'polarising power of Be^{2+}'. It would now be said that the promotion $Be[1s^2\,2s^2] \rightarrow Be[1s^2\,2s^1\,2p^1]$ occurs easily, giving rise (*e.g.* through sp hybridisation) to two largely covalent bonds. Provided electron-rich ligands are available the number of valencies can be increased to four by donation (*e.g.* using sp^3 hybrids). In these circumstances it is usual to associate the valence electrons formally with the more electronegative groups, the metal being shown as M^{2+}, thus recognising the availability of the s and p orbitals for introduction of covalent character (pp. 99 and 134).

TABLE 45

SOME PROPERTIES OF GROUP IIA ELEMENTS

	Be	*Mg*	*Ca*	*Sr*	*Ba*	*Ra*
Electronic configuration	$1s^2\,2s^2$	$2p^6\,3s^2$	$3p^6\,4s^2$	$4p^6\,5s^2$	$5p^6\,6s^2$	$6p^6\,7s^2$
Atomic number	4	12	20	38	56	88
Atomic radius (Å)	0.89	1.36	1.74	1.91	1.98	—
Ionic radius M^{2+} (Å)	0.31	0.65	0.99	1.13	1.35	—

The first ionisation potentials decrease considerably from beryllium to calcium. Despite the second ionisation potentials often being large, the few compounds with unipositive ions such as CaCl, CaF and CaI (Wöhler and Rodewald, 1904) revert easily to dihalides.

Beryllium has a standard electrode potential less negative than magnesium; the anomalous behaviour of lithium in this respect is not repeated by beryllium, even though Be^{2+} hydrates strongly. But, unlike K^+, Rb^+ and Cs^+, all these bipositive cations are hydrated.

TABLE 46

IONISATION AND ELECTRODE POTENTIALS OF GROUP IIA ELEMENTS

	Be	Mg	Ca	Sr	Ba	Ra
I 1 (eV)	9.32	7.64	6.11	5.69	5.21	5.27
2 (eV)	18.21	15.03	11.87	10.98	9.95	10.1
$E°_h$ M^{2+}/M (V)	−1.70	−2.34	−2.87	−2.89	−2.90	—

The smaller atomic diameters lead to higher densities, much higher m.p. and b.p., and greater hardness than are shown by the Gp. IA elements. Beryllium has a particularly high melting point.

TABLE 47

SOME PROPERTIES OF GROUP IIA ELEMENTS

	Be	Mg	Ca	Sr	Ba	Ra
Density (g/cc)	1.86	1.75	1.55	2.6	3.6	5.0
Atomic volume	4.85	14.00	26.1	34.0	38.3	45.2
M.p. (°C)	1280	651	851	800	850	960
B.p. (°C)	1500	1107	1437	1366	1537	1140

Beryllium (6×10^{-4} % of lithosphere) has its only commercial source in beryl, $Be_3Al_2Si_6O_{18}$. This when fused and quenched in water becomes soluble in concentrated H_2SO_4, giving a solution containing the sulphates of beryllium, aluminium and the alkali metals. The addition of $(NH_4)_2SO_4$ allows the aluminium to be removed as the sparingly soluble ammonium alum. The $BeSO_4$ is then crystallised from the solution and converted to BeO (Fig. 135).

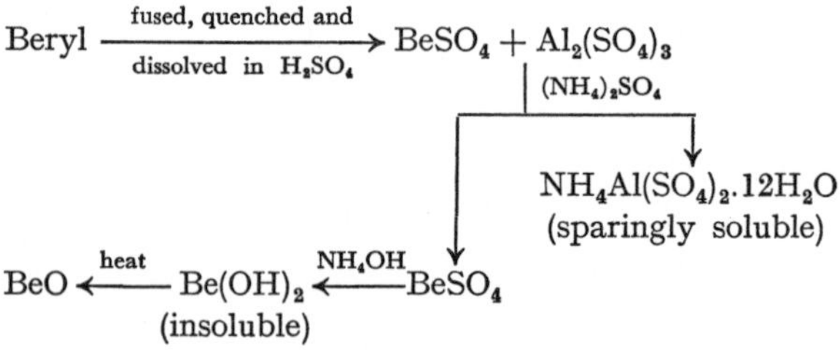

Fig. 135. Beryl as a source of BeO.

Other beryllium compounds and the metal are obtainable from the hydroxide (Fig. 136).

An alternative route to $Be(OH)_2$ is to heat compacts of beryl powder and Na_2SiF_6 at 750°. From the sinter sodium fluoroberyllate, Na_2BeF_4, is extracted with water, most of the Al and Si remaining in insoluble compounds, Crude $Be(OH)_2$ is precipitated by raising the pH. This is purified by converting it to Na_2BeO_2 with NaOH, filtering and throwing down the $Be(OH)_2$ by hydrolysis which follows on dilution and boiling.

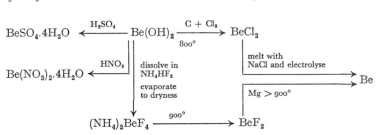

Fig. 136. Formation of beryllium and some of its compounds from $Be(OH)_2$.

The metal is purified by melting in a vacuum and cast under argon. Of h.c.p. structure, it has a high tensile strength, but is brittle even in the purest form yet obtained. Its mechanical properties are greatly improved by sintering it as a compressed powder (1150 °C). Its transparency to X-rays makes Be a useful window material, and its high m.p. and low neutron cross-section render it a possible canning metal for reactor fuel elements, especially as it remains protected by an oxide film up to at least 600 °C. Increasingly, it is being used in alloys; beryllium copper, containing 2–2.25% Be and 0.25–0.5% Ni, is particularly hard and has a high elasticity. BeO has ceramic properties likely to be of use in atomic reactors.

Magnesium (1.93% of earth's crust) occurs in magnesite, $MgCO_3$, dolomite, $MgCa(CO_3)_2$, kieserite, $MgSO_4.H_2O$, carnallite, $KMgCl_3.6H_2O$, and many silicates. The chlorophyll of green plants is a magnesium compound. The metal is being extracted on an increasing scale from sea water, from which $Mg(OH)_2$ is precipitated by treatment with a suspension of calcined dolomite and separated from all the other salts which are soluble (Fig. 137). Magnesium chloride is also obtained from carnallite, from which it separates as a solid phase when the mineral is fused.

The metal, like beryllium, has a h.c.p. structure and is used in light alloys, particularly with aluminium, but also with Zn, Mn, Sn, Zr and Ce. Mg is a good reducing agent; turnings are heated with UF_4 in graphite-lined, closed, steel reactors to produce billets of uranium metal.

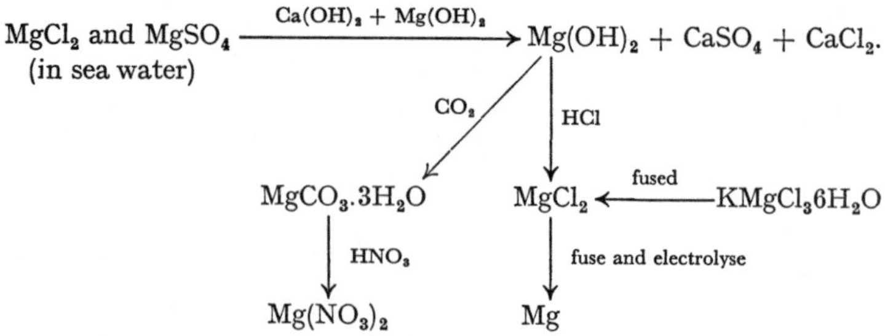

MgCl$_2$ and MgSO$_4$ $\xrightarrow{\text{Ca(OH)}_2 + \text{Mg(OH)}_2}$ Mg(OH)$_2$ + CaSO$_4$ + CaCl$_2$.
(in sea water)

$\swarrow$ CO$_2$ $\downarrow$ HCl

MgCO$_3$.3H$_2$O   MgCl$_2$ $\xleftarrow{\text{fused}}$ KMgCl$_3$6H$_2$O

$\downarrow$ HNO$_3$ $\downarrow$ fuse and electrolyse

Mg(NO$_3$)$_2$ Mg

Fig. 137. Manufacture of magnesium metal from a sea water source.

Calcium (3.4% of lithosphere) occurs as carbonate in the minerals aragonite and calcite and the rocks limestone, chalk and marble, and as sulphate in anhydrite, CaSO$_4$, and gypsum, CaSO$_4$.2H$_2$O. All are plentiful and widely distributed. The metal, which has both h.c.p. and c.c.p. forms, is made (Fig. 138) by electrolysing the fused chloride, CaCl$_2$, a by-product of the Solvay process.

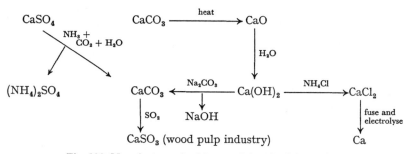

Fig. 138. Manufacture of calcium metal and calcium sulphite.

The high free energies of formation of CaO and CaF$_2$ make calcium a powerful reducing agent. It has been used in the preparation of a number of metals which have oxides particularly resistant to reduction (*e.g.* chromium from Cr$_2$O$_3$).

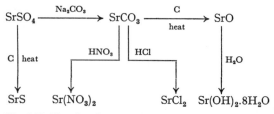

Fig. 139. The chemistry of some strontium compounds.

Strontium (0.02% of lithosphere) occurs as strontianite, $SrCO_3$, and celestite, $SrSO_4$. The metal which has the c.c.p. structure is without economic importance except in pyrotechnics. The radioactive strontium-90 is long-lived and, being easily assimilated and incorporated in bone, is a dangerous product of uranium fission.

Barium (0.04% of lithosphere) occurs widely in veins as barytes, $BaSO_4$, which is sometimes converted to witherite, $BaCO_3$, by atmospheric agency. The reactions used in the production of barium compounds from sulphate and carbonate are shown in Fig. 140.

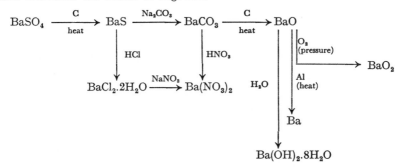

Fig. 140. Manufacture of barium and some of its compounds from barytes.

Radium is obtained from pitchblende, U_3O_8, in which it is formed by the disintegration of ^{238}U (p. 15), the equilibrium ratio being 3.4×10^{-7}. The sulphate is co-precipitated with $BaSO_4$ when $BaCl_2$ is added to a sulphuric acid extract of the ore. After boiling with NaOH to remove lead, the sulphates are converted to carbonates by sodium carbonate fusion and dissolved in HCl to the chlorides. Fractional crystallisation of these removes much of the barium; the final separation is effected by the same means after conversion to bromides.

Chemical properties of the metals

The metals combine directly, at an appropriate temperature, with all the halogens, oxygen, sulphur and nitrogen. Ca, Sr and Ba also combine directly with hydrogen.

$$M + X_2 \rightarrow MX_2 \qquad 2M + S_2 \rightarrow 2MS$$
$$2M + O_2 \rightarrow 2MO \qquad 3M + N_2 \rightarrow M_3N_2$$

Ca, Sr and Ba decompose cold water,

$$M + 2 H_2O \rightarrow M(OH)_2 + H_2,$$

but Mg does so only when amalgamation prevents the formation of a protective layer of oxide. Mg burns in steam but Be fails to react at red heat.

Except for Be, which is rendered passive by nitric acid, the metals dissolve readily in dilute mineral acids. Unlike the other four metals, Be, like Al, is soluble in caustic alkalis.

Halides

Unlike the Gp. IA halides, some of these are only feebly ionic, particularly those of beryllium. BeF_2 appears to be one of very few metal fluorides which are not completely ionised in solution. The solid often occurs in a glassy modification of random structure rather than crystals. It is hygroscopic and very soluble in water, the very great solvation energy of Be^{2+} outweighing the effect of a high lattice energy. The complex tetrafluoroberyllate ion, BeF_4^{2-}, is stable in solution as well as in crystals; its compounds resemble sulphates in structure and solubility. Several compounds are known of the type $M_2^I M^{II}(BeF_4)_2 6H_2O$, analogous with schönite, $K_2Mg(SO_4)_2 6H_2O$.

The fluorides of magnesium and the alkaline earth metals are sparingly soluble; MgF_2 and KF form K_2MgF_4, but the MgF_4^{2-} ion does not exist in solution. Magnesium forms many double salts but few true complexes.

Beryllium chloride is without dipole moment, its molecule being linear, corresponding to Be in the sp valence state. In the fused state (440°), $BeCl_2$ is one of the few halides with an electrical conductance intermediate between that of a characteristically ionic halide (NaCl) and a covalent one (CCl_4). The compound is soluble in organic solvents and, like $AlCl_3$, catalyses the Friedel-Crafts reaction; it thus behaves as a Lewis acid (p. 205). Aldehydes, ketones and ethers co-ordinate readily to anhydrous $BeCl_2$, $BeBr_2$ and BeI_2.

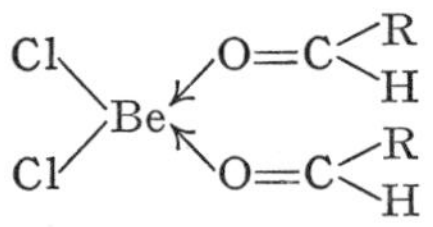

These complexes involve the use of sp^3 hybrid orbitals giving a tetrahedral disposition of the four bonds about the Be atom:

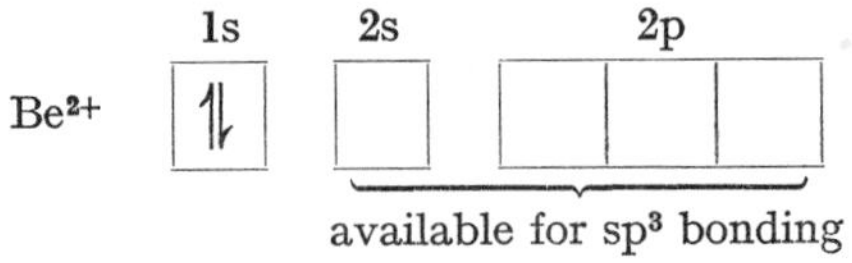

$BeCl_2$ forms many double salts such as Na_2BeCl_4, but the $BeCl_4^{2-}$ ion does not exist in solution as does BeF_4^{2-}.

Beryllium chloride has a hydrate $BeCl_2.4H_2O$ and an unusually stable tetra-ammine $Be(NH_3)_4Cl_2$. The formation of 4-co-ordinate complexes by Be^{2+} is very common; nearly all its inorganic salts have tetrahydrates containing the ion $[Be(H_2O)_4]^{2+}$. The ionic mobility in water is low, the solutions have high viscosities and abnormal osmotic pressures. The large ions of the group, such as Ba^{2+}, do not form co-ordinate links with water molecules, the solvation forces being of ion-dipole type (p. 115).

Magnesium chloride forms complexes with ethers, aldehydes and ketones similar to those of $BeCl_2$. It has several hydrates. A strong aqueous solution of $MgCl_2$ dissolves MgO giving a compound $MgCl_2.3Mg(OH)_2.8H_2O$; and Coates and Glockling (1953) suggest the structure:

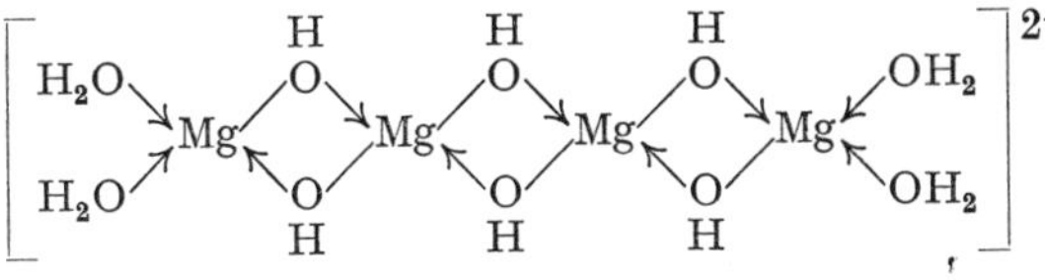

for the ion. Most aqueous beryllium salts dissolve $Be(OH)_2$. The 'beryllated' ions were believed to be $[Be\,(OBe)_x\,(H_2O)_{4-x}]^{2+}$ (Sidgwick and Lewis, 1926), but their form may be similar to that suggested for the magnesium complex.

$MgBr_2$ and $MgCl_2$ are soluble in many organic solvents and the halides (other than the fluorides) of even strontium and barium are moderately soluble in alcohol, resembling lithium in this respect.

Oxides

All the normal oxides have the sodium chloride structure, except BeO which has a wurtzite lattice (4:4 co-ordination). The heats of formation are very large (135–150 kcal/mole). BeO is unreactive to water; even the large heat of hydration of Be^{2+} is evidently insufficient to overcome the stabilising effect of the high lattice energy. MgO reacts with water only when prepared at a low temperature, but the alkaline earth oxides slake readily:

$$CaO + H_2O \rightarrow Ca(OH)_2.$$

The hydroxides increase in solubility with molecular weight. SrO and BaO are converted to peroxides when heated with oxygen under pressure.

$$2BaO + O_2 \rightleftharpoons 2BaO_2.$$

The stability of the $[-O-O-]^{2-}$ ion is evidently due to the low polarising power of these cations compared with those earlier in the group. Hydrates of the form $MO_2.8H_2O$ are formed by Ca, Sr and Ba when H_2O_2 is added to cold saturated solutions of the hydroxides; dehydration is possible without decomposition. All three anhydrous peroxides contain $[-O-O-]^{2-}$ ions in the tetragonal calcium carbide lattice. They are the only simple compounds in this group which exhibit paramagnetism.

Sulphides

Beryllium burns in sulphur vapour forming BeS. This cannot be made in the wet way, though, like BeO, it is unreactive to water. Magnesium sulphide, similarly made, hydrolyses rapidly:

$$2MgS + 2H_2O \rightarrow Mg(OH)_2 + Mg(SH)_2.$$

The hydrosulphide is soluble and the reversible reaction

$$Mg(SH)_2 + 2H_2O \underset{\text{low temperature}}{\overset{\text{high temperature}}{\rightleftharpoons}} Mg(OH)_2 + 2H_2S$$

provides a means of purifying hydrogen sulphide. The sulphides of Ca, Sr and Ba are made by reducing the sulphates with carbon. They hydrolyse in the same way as MgS.

The structures of the sulphides, selenides and tellurides of the Gp. IIA metals illustrate the effect of the cation/anion size ratio on co-ordination number (Table 48).

TABLE 48

STRUCTURES AND CO-ORDINATION OF SULPHIDES ETC.

OF GROUP IIA ELEMENTS

	Be	*Mg*	*Ca*	*Sr*	*Ba*
Sulphide	B	R	R	R	R
Selenide	B & W	R	R	R	R
Telluride	W	B	R	R	R

Structures: B = zinc blende.   W = wurtzite.   R = rocksalt.
Co-ordination: 4:4   4:4   6:6

Polysulphides. Studies on barium sulphide—sulphur mixtures indicate the existence of BaS_2 and BaS_3, both unstable at their respective m.p. When sulphur is added to boiling aqueous $Ba(SH)_2$ it dissolves, and orange red crystals of $BaS_4.H_2O$ together with a little yellow $BaS_3.3H_2O$ separate on cooling. No individual polysulphide of the other members of the group has been made.

Complexes

Not already mentioned are the chelate oxo-complexes of beryllium.

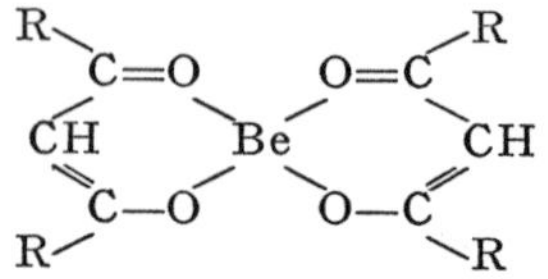

There is also an interesting series of basic beryllium complexes with the carboxylic acids which are covalent compounds of remarkable stability. Basic beryllium acetate, $Be_4O(OOC.CH_3)_6$ melts at 283°, boils at 330° without decomposition and dissolves in $CHCl_3$ as the monomer; it lacks ionic properties. Its structure has a central O atom surrounded tetrahedrally by four Be atoms, and with six $CH_3.C{<}^O_O$ groups spanning the edges of the tetrahedron.

Magnesium compounds hydrate readily, and anhydrous magnesium halides form addition compounds with aldehydes, ketones and ethers, which are structurally similar to those of Be. Otherwise its complexes are few and unstable.

Calcium, strontium and barium form some poorly characterised β-diketone complexes and rather unstable ammines; tendency to covalence, even as indicated by hydration of the ions, has decreased with cation size. The determination of magnesium and calcium with sodium ethylenediamine tetra-acetate, E.D.T.A., probably involves the formation of a chelate complex whose stability is enhanced by the presence of 5-membered rings.

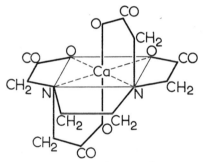

Calcium E.D.T.A. complex

Oxoacid salts

The carbonates exhibit the increase in stability with molecular weight expected to accompany increase in cationic size. Addition of a soluble carbonate to a solution of a beryllium salt gives hydroxide carbonates of indeterminate composition. Magnesium salts, similarly treated, yield the carbonates $Mg(OH)_2(MgCO_3)_4xH_2O$, where $x = 4$ or 5 depending on the temperature of precipitation. Passage of CO_2 gas into the suspension gives a solution, probably not hydrogen carbonate; this deposits $MgCO_3.3H_2O$ on warming to 50°. The same rhombic hydrate is obtained from solutions of $MgSO_4$ and sodium hydrogen carbonate when they stand. Na_2CO_3

precipitates the anhydrous carbonates of Ca, Sr and Ba from solution. Their thermal stability is indicated by their dissociation pressures at 800°: $CaCO_3$ 168 mm, $SrCO_3$ 0.70 mm, $BaCO_3$ 0.03 mm. A figure for $MgCO_3$ is not available but its thermal stability is certainly less than that of $CaCO_3$. The trend is similar to that in the Gp. IA carbonates, and for similar reasons (p. 252).

Carbonates of bipositive cations crystallise in hexagonal form when their radii lie between 0.78 and 1.00 Å, and in rhombic form when between $\sim$ 1.00 and 1.43 Å. The radius of Ca^{2+} being 0.99 Å, both a hexagonal (calcite) and a rhombic (aragonite) form occur.

Beryllium chloride dissolved in an ethyl acetate–dinitrogen tetroxide mixture gives straw-coloured crystals of $Be(NO_3)_2.2N_2O_4$. These decompose on heating in a vacuum, first to the involatile anhydrous nitrate, $Be(NO_3)_2$ then to the volatile oxide nitrate, $Be_4O(NO_3)_6$ (Addison and Walker, 1961), The structure of this closely resembles that of the well known oxide acetate, $Be_4O(CH_3CO_2)_6$ (Bragg and Morgan, 1923), in which an oxygen atom is at the centre of a tetrahedron of beryllium atoms, and the acetate groups form six chelate rings along the edges of the tetrahedron, of which one is shown:

In $Be_4O(NO_3)_6$, the nitrate groups form the bridges between the beryllium atoms:

Beryllium oxide nitrate (basic beryllium nitrate)

Like the oxide acetate and similar compounds, the oxide nitrate is volatile;

it differs from them in being insoluble in non-polar liquids such as CCl_4 and C_6H_6.

The hydration and solubilities of the sulphates are of interest. In the $BeSO_4$-H_2SO_4-H_2O system $BeSO_4.4H_2O$ is the stable crystalline form below $89.0°$ and $BeSO_4.2H_2O$ above; there is no evidence of a monohydrate. $MgSO_4$ has many hydrates: Robson (1927) found 1, $1\frac{1}{4}$, $1\frac{1}{2}$, 4, 5, 6 and 7 H_2O, the last displays both rhombic (Epsom salt) and monoclinic habit. $BeSO_4$ and $MgSO_4$ are freely soluble in water. $CaSO_4$ has a low solubility and gypsum, $CaSO_4.2H_2O$, is readily dehydrated:

$$CaSO_4.2H_2O \xrightarrow{120-130°} CaSO_4.\tfrac{1}{2}H_2O \xrightarrow{140-200°} CaSO_4.$$

The easy cleavage of gypsum crystals arises from its layer lattice structure; the Ca^{2+} and SO_4^{2-} together make up the individual layers which are linked by hydrogen bonds between the water molecules and oxygen atoms of the sulphate ions. Every water molecule has as its nearest neighbours one Ca^{2+} and two oxygen atoms. By contrast strontium and barium sulphates are anhydrous and very sparingly soluble: $CaSO_4$ 2.0 g/l, $SrSO_4$ 0.1 g/l, $BaSO_4$ 0.0024 g/l at 15°.

Similarities between beryllium and aluminium

Though considerably larger than Be^{2+}, the greater charge of the Al^{3+} ion renders its polarising power of the same order; for the ions the charge/(radius)^2 is Al^{3+} 12.0 and Be^{2+} 19.2. The similarities between the two metals led earlier workers to believe beryllium to be in Group III. Its low atomic heat supported this idea, and not until 1871 did Mendeleev correctly place the element in Group II—an early triumph for the periodic classification. The diagonal similarity (see p. 254) remains:

(i) The standard electrode potentials of the metals are of the same order $(Be^{2+}/Be - 1.70$ V; $Al^{3+}/Al - 1.67$ V).

(ii) Both metals are rendered passive by nitric acid.

(iii) Both dissolve in caustic alkalis with hydrogen evolution.

(iv) The halides are similar in their solubilities in organic solvents and their behaviour as Lewis acids.

(v) Beryllium carbide, Be_2C, and aluminium carbide, Al_4C_3, both yield methane on hydrolysis:

$$Be_2C + 4H_2O \rightarrow 2Be(OH)_2 + CH_4,$$
$$Al_4C_3 + 12H_2O \rightarrow 4Al(OH)_3 + 3CH_4.$$

Chapter 16

Boron and Aluminium

The first two elements of Gp.III, although they have the configuration $ns^2\,np^1$, are effectively tervalent since promotion to $ns^1\,np^2$ occurs very readily. They form cations with an inert-gas structure much less readily than the elements of Gp.II which precede them, and their bonding is predominantly covalent. The covalent and M^{3+} ionic radii are given in Table 49.

TABLE 49

SOME PROPERTIES OF BORON AND ALUMINIUM

	B	Al
Electron configuration	$2s^2\,2p^1$	$3s^2\,3p^1$
Atomic number	5	13
Atomic radius (Å)	0.80	1.25
Ionic radius M^{3+} (Å)	0.20	0.50

Like the atoms of Gp. II, boron and aluminium are electron-deficient since an octet (p. 100) is not normally present. There are only three electron pairs in the valence shell, instead of the four characteristic of Gps.IV to VII, and electron-pair repulsions are, accordingly, smaller than usual, so the atoms tend to be electron 'acceptors'. Simple molecules with an incomplete octet around the metal invariably contain sp^2 hybrid bonds lying in a plane with the electron pairs as far apart as possible (p. 125). But the tendency to complete an octet is shown by the existence of tetrahedral compounds, such as BH_3CO, in which sp^3 hybridisation may be invoked, the fourth hybrid sharing the carbon lone pair which it overlaps. Such compounds could, very artificially, be formulated as complexes containing the B^{3+} ion (the approach of ligand field theory, p. 134) but there is no doubt that the use of electron-pair bonds gives a more realistic description. At the same time, the ionic formulation is useful in discussing more elaborate complexes and forms a convenient bridge with classical chemistry provided it is understood that the bonding is largely covalent.

Though the first ionisation potential of boron and aluminium is fairly low, the second is high, the p electron being removed much more easily than one of the s pair. In spite of the large total ionisation potentials, the standard redox potentials for M^{3+}/M are negative because of the high heats of hydration.

TABLE 50

IONISATION AND ELECTRODE POTENTIALS OF BORON AND ALUMINIUM

	B	Al
Ionisation potential I 1 (eV)	8.30	5.95
,, ,, 2 ,,	25.15	18.82
,, ,, 3 ,,	37.92	28.44
E_h° M^{3+}/M (V)	−0.73	−1.67

The elements: preparation and properties

The densities and atomic volumes are normal for the places occupied in the Periodic Table. Boron's extremely high m.p. indicates very strong binding forces; the structure of several crystalline forms of pure boron have been clearly established. Crystals of the purest material are very hard, 9–10 on Mohs' scale. The specific conductance increases about 100 times between 20° and 600°. Aluminium has a low m.p. compared with neighbouring elements; its face-centred cubic lattice is characteristic of a true metal; it is soft, and its conductance is high.

TABLE 51

SOME PROPERTIES OF BORON AND ALUMINIUM

	B	Al
Density (g/cc)	2.4	2.7
Atomic volume	4.4	10.0
M.p. (°C)	2300	660
B.p. (°C)	2550	2500

Boron ($5 \times 10^{-3}\%$ of the lithosphere) probably owes its scarcity to the readiness with which it suffers transmutation. It occurs principally as borates in hot springs and lakes in volcanic regions: the minerals are borax, $Na_2B_4O_7.10H_2O$, kernite, $Na_2B_4O_7.4H_2O$, and colemanite, $Ca_2B_6O_{11}.5H_2O$. An amorphous form of the element can be made by reducing the oxide with magnesium:

$$Na_2B_4O_7 \xrightarrow[\text{to aqueous solution}]{HCl} H_3BO_3 \xrightarrow{\text{heat}} B_2O_3 \xrightarrow[\text{Mg}]{\text{heat with}} B.$$

The brown product always contains some boron suboxide in solid solution. It is used in the manufacture of impact-resistant steels and, because of its high neutron cross-section, of alloys for reactor control rods. Alumino-thermic reduction of B_2O_3 yields crystalline material once thought to be pure boron but now known to contain the aluminium borides, AlB_{12} and AlB_2. Black crystalline boron has been made by reducing BBr_3 vapour with hydrogen on a tantalum filament at 1300°. Probably because of the larger particle size and more nearly perfect lattice, this solid is much less reactive than amorphous boron. Electrolysis of KBF_4 also yields boron of high purity.

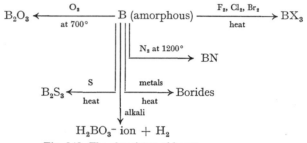

Fig. 141. The chemistry of boron.

Aluminium (7.45% of the lithosphere) is widely distributed in igneous rocks, but the only workable ore is bauxite (p. 272). A solution of sodium aluminate results when bauxite is digested under pressure with caustic soda; Fe_2O_3 and some other impurities may be removed by allowing them to settle. The clear solution resulting is stirred, at 25–50°, with a little crystalline $Al_2O_3.3H_2O$, when much of the aluminium is thrown down as the trihydrate of alumina. This, on heating to 1200°, becomes $\alpha\text{-}Al_2O_3$; it is dissolved in a fused mixture of cryolite, Na_3AlF_6, with a little fluorspar and electrolysed for the technical production of the metal.

The metal appears unreactive because of the rapid formation, in air, of a tenacious oxide layer. Though its standard electrode potential is -1.67 V, it does not dissolve in water and, even with dilute HCl, reacts slowly until the oxide layer has been removed, after which the reaction is rapid. Amalgam-ation dislodges the oxide layer, causes the metal to oxidise rapidly in air, and makes it a good reducing agent even in neutral solution. The metal reacts in a similar way to boron with oxygen, sulphur, nitrogen and the halogens. The very great heat of formation of alumina enables aluminium to be used for the reduction of metal oxides such as MnO_2 and Cr_2O_3, the *thermit process*:

$$2Al + 1\tfrac{1}{2} O_2 \rightarrow Al_2O_3, \qquad \Delta H = -404 \text{ kcal};$$
$$2Cr + 1\tfrac{1}{2} O_2 \rightarrow Cr_2O_3, \qquad \Delta H = -273 \text{ kcal};$$
$$\text{thus } 2Al + Cr_2O_3 \rightarrow Al_2O_3 + 2Cr, \qquad \Delta H = -131 \text{ kcal}.$$

Aluminium dissolves readily in caustic alkali solutions:

$$2Al + 2OH^- + 2H_2O \rightarrow 2AlO_2^- + 3H_2.$$

Nitric acid renders the metal passive.

Aluminium furnishes light, strong alloys: Al-Si alloys ($\sim$ 12% Si) can be cast; Duralumin (4% Cu, 0.5% Mn and 0.5 Mg) and Y-alloy (4% Cu, 2% Ni and 1% Mg) can be both wrought and cast.

Halides

Boron and aluminium give trihalides. BF_3 is most conveniently made by heating B_2O_3 with concentrated H_2SO_4 and a fluoride. It reacts with aluminium chloride and bromide to produce involatile AlF_3 and volatile BCl_3. The volatility of the boron halides decreases with molecular weight.

TABLE 52

MELTING AND BOILING POINTS OF BORON AND ALUMINIUM HALIDES

	B		Al	
	M.p.	B.p.	M.p.	B.p.
Fluoride	$-127°$	$-101°$	†	1291° (subl.)
Chloride	$-107°$	12°	192°*	180° (subl.)
Bromide	$-46°$	91°	97°	255°
Iodide	43°	210°	180°	381°

† Unknown.   * Material in a sealed tube.

The boron compounds are covalent and monomeric in the vapour phase, as is BCl_3 in benzene solution. By contrast, AlF_3 is an ionic, crystalline solid of high m.p.; but the more volatile chloride and bromide exist as dimers, both in the vapour phase and in non-polar solvents, in which the halogen atoms are tetrahedrally arranged about each aluminium atom (Fig. 142). The

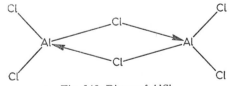

Fig. 142. Dimer of $AlCl_3$.

arrows indicate donations of chlorine lone pairs, imagined to be in tetrahedral hybrids, to bonds formed with vacant sp^3 hybrids on the Al atoms. This results in a 'bridge' structure, typically formed by electron-deficient atoms.

Hydrides with this type of bridge bonding are specially important and are discussed elsewhere (p. 220).

In co-ordinating solvents such as ether, however, Al_2Cl_6 gives place to a tetrahedral, mononuclear molecule:

$$R_2O + AlCl_3 \longrightarrow R_2O \rightarrow AlCl_3.$$

Electron diffraction shows that the boron trihalides are planar molecules with the angle X—B—X 120°; the bonds are somewhat shorter than the normal single bonds, there being fewer bond-pair repulsions.

Hydrolysis of the chloride, bromide and iodide of boron is rapid and complete. The reaction presumably begins with the donation of an oxygen lone pair to the boron:

$$H_2O + BCl_3 \longrightarrow H_2O \rightarrow BCl_3 \longrightarrow HO \rightarrow BCl_2 + HCl$$
$$\downarrow 2H_2O$$
$$B(OH)_3 + 2HCl$$

The trifluoride, however, forms 1:1 and 1:2 adducts with water:

$$BF_3 \xrightarrow{H_2O} H^+ \begin{bmatrix} F{\searrow}B{\swarrow}F \\ F{\nearrow}{}{\nwarrow}OH \end{bmatrix}^- \xrightarrow{H_2O} H_3O^+ \begin{bmatrix} F{\searrow}B{\swarrow}F \\ F{\nearrow}{}{\nwarrow}OH \end{bmatrix}^-,$$

the latter being stable enough to be distilled without decomposition.

The relative acceptor strengths of BF_3, BCl_3 and BBr_3 have been found by measuring the heats of formation and dipole moments of such compounds as their 1:1 adducts with pyridine. The results, together with those from infrared studies, indicate that the electron-acceptor power increases in the order

$$BF_3 \ll BCl_3 < BBr_3.$$

This is opposite to the order suggested by the relative electronegativities of the halogens; the inductive effect is evidently outweighed by another—a tendency for electrons from the smaller halogen atoms to be partly back-donated to the boron, to give some double-bond character to the B-X bonds and to reduce the electron deficiency on the boron.

The fact that BF_3 forms a wider range of complexes than the other trihalides is probably due to a greater difficulty of heterolysis with the B—F bond than with the B—Cl and B—Br bonds. Thus molecules of the alcohols, aldehydes and ketones, which form addition compounds with BF_3, break the boron-halogen bonds in the other halides:

$$2\ ROH + BF_3 \longrightarrow ROH^+_2\ [BF_3OR]^-$$
$$3\ ROH + BCl_3 \longrightarrow B(OR)_3 + 3\ HCl.$$

The tendency of donor groups containing O, N, S and P to co-ordinate with BF_3 makes the compound an extremely useful catalyst in organic chemistry.

Boric acid dissolves in 50% HF to give tetrafluoroboric acid:

$$H_3BO_3 + 4HF \longrightarrow HBF_4 + 3H_2O,$$

but the compound has not been isolated in the pure state. The BF_4^- ion in crystalline fluoroborates is shown, by X-ray analysis, to be tetrahedral, KBF_4 being isomorphous with $KClO_4$. Tetrafluoroborates also resemble perchlorates in solubility. Other tetrahalogenoborates have been made recently, $C_5H_5NHBCl_4$ and $C_5H_5NHBBr_4$ by Lappert (1957) and the corresponding iodo-complexes by Waddington (1960).

Anhydrous $AlCl_3$ resembles BF_3 in its acidity and catalytic power (p. 208). Anhydrous AlF_3 is insoluble in water, though soluble stable hydrates may be prepared; the other halides dissolve with considerable hydrolysis. Their solutions in organic solvents have low conductance.

Unstable oxide halides of both boron and aluminium are known. When B_2O_3 and BF_3 are heated together a cyclic compound is formed:

AlOCl and AlOBr result from heating compounds of the trihalides with ether:

$$Et_2O \rightarrow AlCl_3 \longrightarrow AlOCl + 2EtCl.$$

A liquid subchloride of boron, B_2Cl_4, with the structure

is made by passing BCl_3 vapour at 1–2 mm through a glow discharge between mercury electrodes. The compound is reduced by $LiBH_4$ (p. 223) to diborane. It decomposes slowly at room temperature to B and BCl_3, and reacts with BBr_3 to give B_2Br_4 and BCl_3. The compound B_2I_4 is made by the same method as B_2Cl_4. Gaseous B_2F_4 is produced by fluorinating B_2Cl_4 with SbF_3.

B_4Cl_4 and B_8Cl_8 are formed by the spontaneous decomposition of B_2Cl_4; they have interesting structures. B_4Cl_4 has a tetrahedron of boron atoms surrounded by four chlorine atoms, each bound to one boron. B_8Cl_8 has a dodecahedron of boron atoms with a chlorine atom bound to every one of them.

Oxides

A glassy form of B_2O_3 results from dehydrating H_3BO_3 at red heat:

$$H_3BO_3 \xrightarrow[-H_2O]{100°} HBO_2 \xrightarrow[-H_2O]{red\ heat} B_2O_3.$$

A crystalline form (p. 274), m.p. 450°, appears after dehydrating HBO_2 by keeping it under reduced pressure and slowly raising the temperature to 400° over a period of some weeks. Boric oxide, though more acidic than Al_2O_3, is amphoteric; it combines with metal oxides to give metaborates as in the borax-bead test:

$$CuO + B_2O_3 \longrightarrow Cu(BO_2)_2,$$

and with P_2O_5 to give a phosphate:

$$B_2O_3 + P_2O_5 \longrightarrow 2\ BPO_4.$$

This is slightly soluble when freshly prepared, but crystallises and becomes insoluble on heating, when it is stable enough to be sublimed (1450°). In the crystal lattice both the boron and phosphorus atoms are surrounded, tetrahedrally, by oxygen atoms. There is also an arsenate, $BAsO_4$.

An oxide with the empirical formula BO is obtained by heating sub-boric acid, $B_2(OH)_4$, which is made from B_2Cl_4 by the action of water vapour. The white solid turns brown on prolonged heating. It exists mainly as B_2O_2 in the vapour, and is probably more highly polymeric in the solid.

Alumina, Al_2O_3, just as boric oxide, may be prepared by dehydrating one of the hydrous oxides. These exist in four well defined forms: the monohydrate $AlO(OH)$, as boehmite (γ-monohydrate) and diaspore (α-monohydrate), and the trihydrate $Al(OH)_3$, as gibbsite (γ-trihydrate) and bayerite (α-trihydrate). Of these, all but bayerite occur naturally in bauxite. On dehydration diaspore passes directly to corundum (α-alumina); the others yield a series of anhydrous aluminas, e.g. γ-alumina, which pass into α-alumina only at higher temperatures (about 850°C). α-Al_2O_3 has a well-defined, close-packed O^{2-} structure with Al^{3+} in the tetrahedral holes, whereas γ-Al_2O_3 has a distorted, badly organised, microcrystalline structure of the spinel type. In consequence, α-Al_2O_3 is dense, hard, and resistant to chemical attack and can be brought into solution only after fusion with a flux such as $KHSO_4$, whereas γ-Al_2O_3 is less dense, is soft, and has a high surface area, so that it is relatively soluble in aqueous alkalis and acids and an excellent and selective absorbent used in dehydration, decolorisation and chromatography. Ruby, sapphire, amethyst and emerald are impure α-alumina. Artificial forms are made by fusing finely powdered alumina with a trace of the colouring oxide (Cr_2O_3 for ruby) in an oxyhydrogen flame.

Aluminium hydroxide acts primarily as a base, but it also ionises weakly as an acid ($pK_a = 12.2$). The osmotic properties of sodium aluminate solutions are identical with those of NaOH; both must have the same number of ions. Dissociations such as

$$Na_3AlO_3 \rightleftharpoons 3\,Na^+ + AlO_3{}^{3-},$$
$$n\,NaAlO_2 \rightleftharpoons n\,Na^+ + (AlO_2)_n{}^{n-}\text{ micelle,}$$

are ruled out. Furthermore, conductance and pH measurements indicate that hydrolysis to NaOH and colloidal alumina is slight. Sodium aluminate appears to ionise as a 1 : 1 electrolyte:

$$NaAl(OH)_4(H_2O)_2 \rightleftharpoons Na^+ + [Al(OH)_4(H_2O)_2]^-.$$

The high viscosity can be explained by the linking of hydrated aluminate ions (Fig. 143) with each other and with water molecules by hydrogen bonding (Scott, 1955).

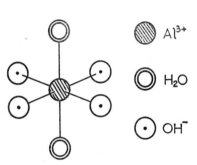

Al^{3+}

H$_2$O

OH$^-$

Fig. 143. Aluminate ion present in sodium aluminate.

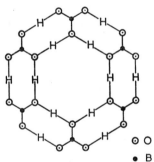

○ O
● B

Fig. 144. Hydrogen-bonded structure of boric acid. (The H atoms are not, of course, equidistant from the B atoms.)

Boric acid and the borates

Phase studies of the system B_2O_3–H_2O show that HBO_2 and H_3BO_3 are the only stable boric acids, though salts of greater complexity exist such as $Na_2B_4O_7$, $Ca_2B_6O_{11}$ and $NaCaB_5O_9$. The flaky crystals of orthoboric acid have a layer structure of triangular BO_3 groups joined by hydrogen bonds (Fig. 144). The compound is volatile in steam. It is a very weak acid:

$$H_2O + H_3BO_3 \rightleftharpoons H_3O^+ + H_2BO_3{}^- \qquad pK_a = 9.2.$$

Crystal analysis of borates shows they bear some similarity to the silicates (p. 153), the unit being the triangular BO_3 in place of the tetrahedral SiO_4.

The rather uncommon orthoborates, *e.g.* $Mg_3(BO_3)_2$, contain discrete BO_3^{3-} ions. The pyroborates such as $Co_2B_2O_5$ contain ions of the form:

$$\left[\begin{array}{c} O \\ O \end{array} \!\!\! B—O—B \!\!\! \begin{array}{c} O \\ O \end{array} \right]^{4-}$$

Of the borates much the most common are the metaborates; these have chain and ring forms. Sodium metaborate, correctly formulated $Na_3B_3O_6$, contains the six-membered ring ions:

$$\left[\begin{array}{c} O{\diagdown}_B{\diagup}^O{\diagdown}_B{\diagup}^O \\ \quad | \qquad \qquad | \\ O{\diagdown}_B{\diagup}O \\ \quad | \\ O \end{array} \right]^{3-}$$

Calcium metaborate, typical of the bipositive metal borates, has negatively charged chains:

$$\begin{array}{c} O^- \qquad\qquad O^- \\ | \qquad\qquad\quad | \\ O{\diagdown}_B{\diagup}^{O-B}{\diagdown}_O{\diagup}^{B}{\diagdown}_O{\diagup}^{B}{\diagdown}_O{\diagup}^{B}{\diagdown}O \\ | \qquad\qquad | \qquad\qquad | \\ O_- \qquad\qquad O_- \qquad\qquad O_- \end{array}$$

held together by Ca^{2+} ions between them. B_2O_3 itself, in its crystalline form (p. 272), displays two-dimensional sheets:

$$\begin{array}{c} | \qquad\qquad | \\ B \qquad\qquad B \\ O{\diagdown}_B{\diagup}^{O}{\diagdown}{\diagup}^{O}{\diagdown}_B{\diagup}^{O}{\diagdown}{\diagup}^{O}{\diagdown}_B{\diagup}O \\ | \qquad\qquad | \qquad\qquad | \\ O \qquad\qquad O \qquad\qquad O \\ | \qquad\qquad | \qquad\qquad | \\ O{\diagup}^B{\diagdown}_O{\diagdown}_B{\diagup}^O{\diagdown}_B{\diagup}^O{\diagdown}_B{\diagdown}O \\ | \qquad\qquad | \end{array}$$

Nitrogen compounds

White, insoluble, refractory boron nitride, BN, is simply made by fusing together B_2O_3 and NH_4Cl, by strongly heating compounds such as borazole (p. 222) and $BF_3.NH_3$, and by burning boron in nitrogen. It has a graphite-like structure (Brager, 1937) in which the bonding within the layers is by sp^2 hybrids of both B and N, the remaining electrons being in delocalised

π orbitals above and below the plane. The separation of the layers is consider-able and the bonding is essentially of the Van der Waals type (p. 116).

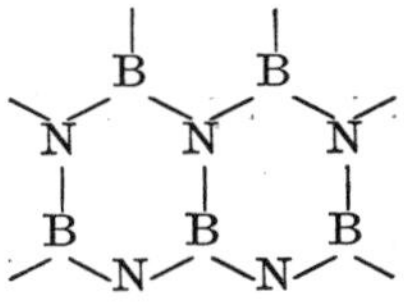

Pease (1950) found the structure to differ from that of graphite in having the hexagons directly under one another (B under N). Boron nitride is very stable and unreactive. It is, however, decomposed by steam at red heat:

$$BN + 3H_2O \longrightarrow NH_3 + H_3BO_3,$$

and by fluorine and HF at lower temperatures:

$$2BN + 3F_2 \longrightarrow 2BF_3 + N_2$$
$$BN + 4HF \longrightarrow NH_4BF_4.$$

Bridgman (1957), using pressures of about 70,000 atmospheres, has converted boron nitride at 3000° into the adamantine form (p. 148), borazon, claimed to be harder than diamond.

Aluminium combines directly with nitrogen on heating to give AlN with a wurtzite structure. It is much more reactive than BN, being hydrolysed by cold water:

$$AlN + 3H_2O \longrightarrow NH_3 + Al(OH)_3.$$

Complexes

Boron's strong tendency to 4 covalence is shown in its complexes. The BF_4^- ion, like the isoelectronic BeF_4^{2-} ion and CF_4 molecule, is tetrahedral. The borohydride ion is also tetrahedral, the boron atom again being in the sp^3 valence state. Complex oxo-anions containing 4-covalent boron are formed by the borate ion with some cis-diols:
Catechol,

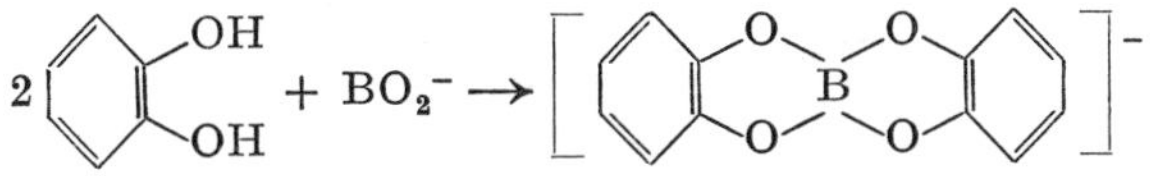

Mannitol,

$$C_6H_8(OH)_6 + BO_2^- \longrightarrow C_6H_8(OH)_4BO_4^-,$$

an ion in which boron has the environment

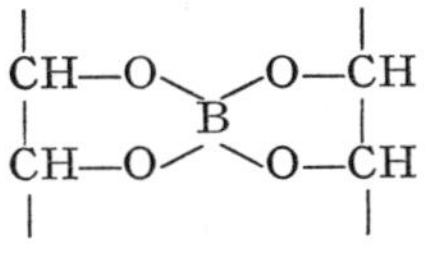

The ion does not combine with a proton since the boron is already exerting its maximum covalence of four, but it does bind H_3O^+ electrostatically. Boric acid can be titrated against NaOH in the presence of mannitol or glycerol for this reason.

BF_3 and BCl_3 differ in their reactions with β-diketones in benzene solution:

$$
BF_3 + \underset{R}{\overset{R}{\underset{\displaystyle \diagdown C=O}{\overset{\displaystyle \diagup C=O}{CH_2}}}} \longrightarrow \underset{R}{\overset{R}{\underset{\displaystyle \diagdown C=O}{\overset{\displaystyle \diagup C-O}{CH}}}}\overset{\diagup F}{\underset{\diagdown F}{B}} \;+\; HF
$$

$$
BCl_3 + 2\,CH_2 \longrightarrow \left[\;\text{complex}\;\right]^+ \; Cl^- \;+\; 2HCl
$$

This complex is a positive boronium ion. Another example of a boronium compound is the $[(C_6H_5)_2B\,(\text{dipyridyl})]^+ClO_4^-$ made by Davidson and French (1959).

Aluminium forms fluoro-, chloro- and bromo-complexes, containing tetrahedral AlX_4^- ions and, in the case of fluorine, AlF_6^{3-} octahedra. In the cubic cell of cryolite, Na_3AlF_6, the corners and centre are occupied by distorted AlF_6^{3-} octahedra, and the Na^+ ions are arranged as in Fig. 145. In

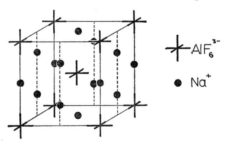

Fig. 145. Structure of Na_3AlF_6.

$TlAlF_5$, infinite chain ions $(AlF_5)_n^{n-}$ are formed by the sharing of corners of AlF_6^- octahedra (Fig. 146), whereas in $NaAlF_4$, the planar $(AlF_4)^{2-}$ ions are formed by sharing corners with four other octahedra (Fig. 147).

The oxo-complexes of aluminium are mainly 6 co-ordinate and octahedral. They may be described in terms of sp^3d^2 hybridisation (p. 105), the 3d orbitals being energetically only slightly higher than the 3p. No such orbitals are available in boron and octahedral complexes do not occur. This is true of the β-diketone complexes and the trioxalato-aluminates such as

$$K_3 \left[Al \begin{pmatrix} COO \\ \vdots \\ COO \end{pmatrix}_3 \right].$$

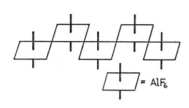

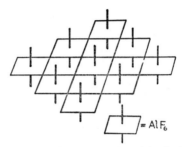

Fig. 146. Infinite chain ions in TlAlF₅.

Fig. 147. Infinite planar ions joined at corners in NaAlF₄.

Borides

Metal borides can be made by direct combination of the elements in a vacuum at a high temperature ($\sim 2000°$), by reduction of a metal oxide with B_4C and carbon,

$$2 \, TiO_2 + B_4C + 3 \, C \longrightarrow 2 \, TiB_2 + 4 \, CO,$$

or by electrolysis of a fused borate (Andrieux, 1949). In the last method, the liberated metal reduces borate to boron and combination then occurs. The borides are hard, have high m.p. and are good conductors; they resemble the interstitial carbides and nitrides (p. 147). They are usually fairly stable and resistant to attack but basic oxidising agents such as Na_2O_2 decompose them on heating. The structures, like those of intermetallic compounds, are determined more by the requirements of the metal and boron lattices than by valency relationships.

Kiessling (1951) suggests that metal borides have arrangements based on: (i) isolated boron atoms (M_2B), (ii) zig-zag chains (MB), (iii) double chains (M_3B_4), (iv) hexagonal layers (MB_2), (v) three dimensional frameworks (MB_6). FeB (Fig. 148) is an example of (ii). The Fe atoms are at the corners of trigonal prisms and the B atoms at their centres. The borons are covalently bound in zig-zag chains. AlB_2 is an example of (iv). The borons are joined in hexagons to form infinite layers with the aluminiums in layers between them (Fig. 149). CaB_6, SrB_6, BaB_6, and several isomorphous borides of the lanthanides have cubic CsCl-type structures with an octahedron of borons occupying the centre of the unit cell (Fig. 150).

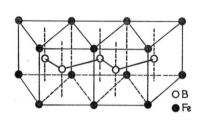

Fig. 148. Structure of FeB.

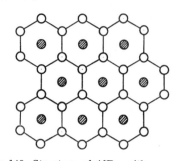

Fig. 149. Structure of AlB_2, with separate layers of aluminium atoms and boron atoms.

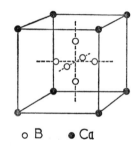

o B • Ca

Fig. 150. Cubic structure of CaB_6.

Alums

Potash alum, $KAl(SO_4)_2 12H_2O$, contains K^+, Al^{3+} and tetrahedral SO_4^{2-} ions. Six of the water molecules are octahedrally co-ordinated to the Al^{3+} and six are used to link these $[Al(H_2O)_6^{3+}]$ ions to neighbouring sulphate ions. It is thus a lattice compound rather than a complex. Unipositive ions smaller than K^+ do not form very stable alums. The M^{3+} radius must be small; the large lanthanide M^{3+} ions do not form alums.

Oxo-compounds of aluminium

Al^{3+} (0.50 Å) is near enough in size to Si^{4+} (0.43 Å) to replace it in the SiO_4 tetrahedra of silicate structures (p. 153). The deficiency of positive charge is made up by incorporating positive ions (p. 155). Such compounds as $AlPO_4$ and $AlAsO_4$ have quartz structures, made possible because the deficiency of positive charge in the AlO_4 tetrahedron is balanced by the excess in the adjacent PO_4 tetrahedron. The corresponding compounds of boron, BPO_4 and $BAsO_4$, have distorted cristobalite structures.

Compounds of unipositive aluminium

When the vapour of either $AlCl_3$ or $AlBr_3$ is passed over Al metal at 1000° under reduced pressure, the aluminium evaporates quickly and can be condensed in a state of high purity, apparently because of the reversible reaction:

$$2\,Al + AlX_3 \rightleftharpoons 3\,AlX \quad (X = Cl, Br).$$

The procedure has been proposed as a method of purifying aluminium (Gross, 1946). In AlX, the Al may be regarded as in an sp valence state with a lone pair on the side remote from the X. The electron deficiency would then encourage slight sharing of two halogen lone pairs to give two weak π bonds. In this situation the aluminium would be described as formally unipositive.

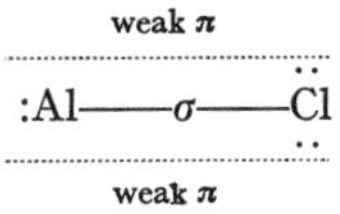

Supporting this picture, band spectra show the strength of the bond in AlCl to be greater than the strengths of the Al—Cl bonds in $AlCl_3$.

Evaporation of Al_2O occurs when Al_2O_3 and Al are heated together under reduced pressure at a very high temperature. (Brewer and Searcy, 1951). A similar observation has been made when Be is heated in contact with BeO; some volatile suboxide is again formed.

Chapter 17

Gallium, Indium and Thallium

GROUP IIIB

Gallium, indium and thallium all have the $ns^2 np^1$ configuration and ^2P ground state, met with in boron and aluminium. The most common ion is M^{3+} and both the atomic and ionic radii increase somewhat with increasing atomic number.

TABLE 53

SOME PROPERTIES OF GROUP IIIB ELEMENTS

	Ga	In	Tl
Electron configuration	$4s^2 4p^1$	$5s^2 5p^1$	$6s^2 6p^1$
Atomic number	31	49	81
Atomic radius (Å)	1.25	1.50	1.55
Ionic radius, M^{3+} (Å)	0.62	0.81	0.95

The ionisation potentials do not differ greatly from those of aluminium but owing to the reduced 'polarising power' of the larger M^{3+} ions (p. 92) the heats of hydration become smaller and the standard electrode potentials less negative.

TABLE 54

IONISATION AND ELECTRODE POTENTIALS OF GROUP IIIB ELEMENTS

	Ga	In	Tl
Ionisation potential I 1 (eV)	6.0	5.8	6.1
,, ,, 2 ,,	20.4	18.8	20.3
,, ,, 3 ,,	30.6	27.9	29.7
E_h° (M^{3+}/M) (V)	−0.52	−0.34	0.72
E_h° (M^+/M) ,,		−0.25	−0.34

The chemistry of the elements departs from that of aluminium largely because of this decreasing tendency for co-ordination involving M^{3+}. Thus, indium is unipositive in InCl (the $5s^2$ shell persisting) although, as the redox potential data indicate, this disproportionates in water to give the trichloride. The trichloride would be regarded, to take the extreme view, as M^{3+} co-ordinated with three Cl^- ions; but in fact there would be considerable covalent character, which could be described by invoking sp³ hybrid orbitals and allowing a partial return of the valence electrons to the metal (p. 137). The 6s² shell of thallium is even more stable, a Tl⁺ ion (radius 1.44 Å) being recognised in the well-characterised thallium(I) salts. But the description of thallium(III) compounds in terms of a Tl³⁺ ion would usually be quite artificial, the bonding being essentially covalent.

Preparation and properties of the elements

The metals themselves have remarkable melting points and boiling points. The extreme example, gallium, is liquid at ordinary pressure over a range of two thousand degrees and has been employed for high-temperature (1000°) thermometry, in a quartz envelope. It has a strong tendency to super-fusion and will remain liquid at room temperature for a considerable period.

TABLE 55

SOME PROPERTIES OF GROUP IIIB ELEMENTS

	Ga	In	Tl
Density (g/cc)	5.93	7.29	11.85
Atomic volume	11.76	15.74	17.25
Melting point	29.8°	156°	449°
Boiling point	2070°	2100°	1390°

Gallium ($10^{-4}\%$ of the earth's crust) is present in zinc blende, which may contain up to 0.5%, and in certain (*e.g.* British) coal ash. The metal, which is deposited by electrolysis from alkaline solutions of its salts, is silvery-white, hard and brittle. The orthorhombic crystal has a complex lattice. The co-ordination is strictly one-fold, a given gallium atom having one atom situated at 2.43 Å and six others at distances varying from 2.70 to 2.79 Å. This co-ordination is denoted by $1 + \bar{6}$; the notation applies only if the six atoms are separated from the reference atom by a distance not greater than 1.2 times that of the nearest one. The metal is stable in dry air and does not decompose water. It dissolves in caustic alkalis and in mineral acids, other than nitric which renders it passive. Its chemistry (Fig. 151) is, in fact, very similar to that of aluminium.

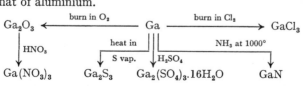

Fig. 151. The chemistry of gallium.

Indium (10^{-5}% of the earth's crust) is also present in zinc blende, but rarely above 0.1%. It can be precipitated from solution by zinc and purified electrolytically. Its tetragonal unit cell is a very slightly distorted version of the f.c.c. of a true metal (Fig. 152). The metal is soft. It differs from aluminium and gallium in its insolubility in boiling caustic alkalis; otherwise its reactions are similar.

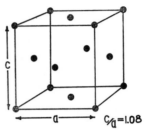

Fig. 152. Structure of indium.

Thallium (10^{-5}% of earth's crust) is recovered principally from the flue dust of pyrites burners. The soft, grey metal, which has a hexagonal close-packed structure, is rather more reactive than gallium and indium because of the ease with which it forms a unipositive ion. It oxidises in moist air, decomposes steam at red heat and dissolves readily to form thallium(I) compounds in dilute mineral acids other than HCl, because of the insolubility of TlCl.

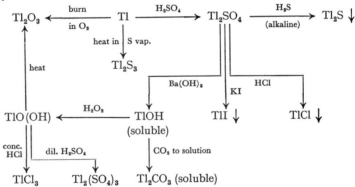

Fig. 153. The chemistry of thallium.

Halides

The trifluorides are ionic solids of high m.p. and low solubility similar to AlF_3. The other trihalides are soluble, though strongly hydrolysed, and largely covalent when anhydrous. The trichloride of Ga is a white solid, m.p. 78°. The vapour at 500° is largely Ga_2Cl_6; the liquid, on the evidence of its Raman spectrum, appears to be dimeric also. $GaCl_2$ can be made by heating $GaCl_3$ with the metal. On heating to a higher temperature $GaCl_2$ disproportionates:

$$3\,GaCl_2 \;\rightleftharpoons\; 2\,GaCl_3 + Ga.$$

The iodide responds rather differently:

$$2\,GaI_2 \;\rightleftharpoons\; GaI_3 + GaI.$$

Although the empirical formula $GaCl_2$ indicates bipositive gallium, the material is not paramagnetic, as it would be with a $GaCl_2$ unit containing an odd electron; like that of $GaBr_2$, its structure is ionic, containing the $[GaCl_4]^-$ anion (which is well known) and the Ga^+ cation. The monochlorides of both gallium and indium have been made (Gastinger, 1955) by heating the metals in argon containing 1% Cl_2. $InCl_3$ has a much higher m.p. (586°) than the other trichlorides of the group. There is no evidence of dimerisation and the fused material is a fairly good conductor. The bromide, too, is far more ionic in character than those of Ga and Tl. $InCl_2$ is obtained by heating the metal in gaseous HCl.

Thallium(III) chloride is most conveniently made as $TlCl_3.4H_2O$ by passing Cl_2 into a suspension of TlCl and evaporating at 60°. The anhydrous compound melts at 60–70°; further heating converts it to TlCl. It resembles BCl_3 in giving stable addition compounds with NH_3 and Et_2O and in not forming a dimer. Material of the composition TlI_3, made by treating TlI with iodine (Sharpe, 1952), is not thallium(III) iodide but a polyiodide containing Tl^+, isomorphous with RbI_3 and CsI_3. On heating it decomposes in two stages:

$$TlI_3 \;\rightarrow\; Tl_3I_4 \;\rightarrow\; TlI.$$

Thallium(I) chloride, bromide and iodide are made by precipitation from a thallium(I) sulphate solution. TlCl resembles AgCl in solubility, structure and sensitivity to light but is insoluble in ammonia; the Tl^+ ion is evidently too large to form ammonia complexes. TlF is yellow and resembles AgF in colour, structure and solubility.

Halogen complexes are formed by the three metals. The fluorogallates have the octahedral $[GaF_6]^{3-}$ ion but the solids are hydrates and differ in structure from cryolite. Chlorogallates contain the tetrahedral $[GaCl_4]^-$ complex but indium gives hydrated 6-co-ordinate complexes, $M_3^I[InCl_6]H_2O$. Thallium has four types of chlorocomplexes:

$$M^I[TlCl_4]xH_2O, \quad M_2^I[TlCl_5]xH_2O, \quad M_3^I[TlCl_6]xH_2O, \quad M_3^I[Tl_2Cl_9]xH_2O.$$

The $[Tl_2Cl_9]^{3-}$ ion is composed of two octahedra sharing three corners

Fig. 154). Bromocomplexes are generally similar to the chlorocomplexes. Iodocomplexes are known for thallium but not for the others.

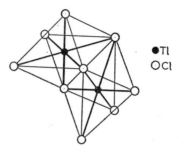

●Tl
○Cl

Fig. 154. Structure of the $Tl_2Cl_9^{3-}$ ion.

The luminescence of solutions of thallium(I) chloride with alkali metal chlorides is due to the $[TlCl_2]^-$ ion (Hu and Scott, 1955).

Oxides

The oxides, M_2O_3, can all be made by heating the metals in oxygen. The heats of formation, though high, are much lower than that of Al_2O_3, and the oxides are easily reduced.

TABLE 56

HEATS OF FORMATION OF Al_2O_3, Ga_2O_3 AND In_2O_3

	Al_2O_3	Ga_2O_3	In_2O_3
$-\Delta H_f$	404	258	223 kcal

Black Ga_2O can be made by heating Ga_2O_3 with Ga to 500° in a vacuum. Black, easily fusible Tl_2O results on heating TlOH to 100° in the absence of air. Thallium(I) hydroxide, made by adding baryta water to thallium(I) sulphate solution and evaporating, is a yellow crystalline solid which dissolves to give an alkaline solution. The addition of H_2O_2 to this precipitates brown thallium(III) oxide hydroxide, TlO(OH). The hydroxides of gallium and indium are amphoteric and very similar to $Al(OH)_3$. Ga also forms an oxide hydroxide, GaO(OH).

Other complexes

The most stable oxo-complexes are chelate compounds. Gallium and indium form tris-β-diketone complexes, soluble in alcohol and benzene, and structurally similar to those of aluminium (Fig. 155). Gallium and thallium form trioxalato compounds like the oxalato-aluminates: $M_3^I[Ga(C_2O_4)_3]H_2O$. All the metals form tris-complexes with oxine (Fig. 156).

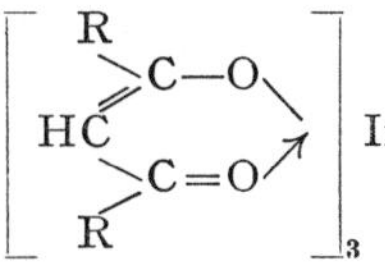

Fig. 155.
Tris-β-diketone complex of indium.

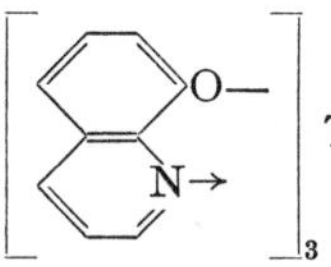

Fig. 156.
Tris-complex of thallium with oxine.

Other compounds

The sulphides M_2S_3 are all made by direct combination of the elements. But GaS is also known and has an unusual layer lattice containing Ga_2^{4+} ions (Hahn and Frank, 1955). The nitride GaN, unreactive to water and acids, is made by heating gallium in ammonia at 1000°; the corresponding indium compound is best made by heating $(NH_4)_3InF_6$. Both have the wurtzite lattice.

Gallium resembles aluminium in not forming a carbonate, but a basic carbonate of indium can be precipitated from solution. Gallium sulphate, $Ga_2(SO_4)_3.16H_2O$, and indium sulphate, $In_2(SO_4)_3$, both form alums but $Tl_2(SO_4)_3.7H_2O$, formed by dissolving Tl_2O_3 in dilute sulphuric acid, does not. The Tl^{3+} ion (radius 0.95 Å) is evidently too large for the lattice, resembling those of the lanthanides in this respect.

Bridge bonds (p. 220), of the kind formed by boron (the first member of Gp.III), are also formed by both aluminium and gallium, though less frequently. An example is

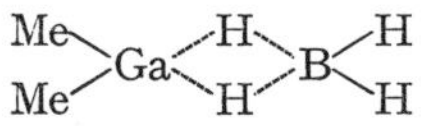

$$\text{Me} \diagdown \quad \diagup \text{H} \diagdown \quad \diagup \text{H}$$
$$\qquad \text{Ga} \qquad \text{B}$$
$$\text{Me} \diagup \quad \diagdown \text{H} \diagup \quad \diagdown \text{H}$$

Thallium(I) salts

The single charge and large size of the Tl^+ ion endows its salts with many properties reminiscent of the alkali metals. For instance, alkaline TlOH absorbs CO_2 to form a solution of Tl_2CO_3, which hydrolyses similarly to K_2CO_3. The hydroxide is evidently a strong base. The sulphate, Tl_2SO_4, the orthophosphates, Tl_3PO_4, Tl_2HPO_4 and TlH_2PO_4, the chlorate and the perchlorate are all isomorphous with the corresponding potassium salts (K^+ radius $= 1.33$ Å, Tl^+ radius $= 1.44$ Å). The sulphate gives an alum $TlAl(SO_4)_2.12H_2O$. It forms a continuous series of solid solutions with $(NH_4)_2SO_4$ and K_2SO_4 and a double salt with $CuSO_4$ which is isomorphous with $(NH_4)_2SO_4.CuSO_4.6H_2O$.

In its halides and sulphide, unipositive thallium bears some resemblence to silver (Ag^+ radius $= 1.26$ Å); Tl_2S is precipitated by H_2S only from slightly alkaline solutions. The variable charge number of thallium, according as its $6s^2$ shell is disturbed or not, is largely responsible for the diversity of its properties.

Chapter 18

Carbon and Silicon

The electronic structure of the carbon atom gives the element a remarkable diversity of chemical properties. The four valence electrons occupy the configuration $2s^2 2p^2$ in the ^3P ground state but promotion and hybridisation (p. 97) occurs very freely and accounts for the characteristic valency of four which is never exceeded. Silicon differs in that 3d orbitals are accessible, giving a greater variety and an increased number of valencies (p. 104). It can thus exhibit a covalency greater than 4, as in the SiF_6^{2-} ion.

TABLE 57

SOME PROPERTIES OF CARBON AND SILICON

	C	Si
Atomic number	6	14
Electron configuration	$2s^2 2p^2$	$3s^2 3p^2$
Atomic radius (Å)	0.77	1.17
Ionic radius M^{4+} (Å)	—	0.39

The radius of the carbon atom is small, and of the C^{4+} ion remarkably small. The element forms covalent bonds except with metals of insignificant electronegativity; thus, for instance, $NaCH_3$ ionises to Na^+ and CH_3^-. Even with the most strongly electronegative element, fluorine, carbon forms bonds which are predominantly covalent.

The ionisation potentials (Table 58) indicate that silicon is capable of forming positive ions more easily than carbon, but it too forms mainly covalent compounds.

TABLE 58

IONISATION POTENTIALS OF CARBON AND SILICON

	$1st$	$2nd$	$3rd$	$4th$
Carbon (eV)	11.3	24.4	47.9	64.5
Silicon (eV)	8.15	16.3	33.5	45.1

Bond strengths in carbon and silicon compounds

A striking feature of the chemistry of carbon is the ease with which its atoms combine with one another. The strength of the C—C single bond is exceptionally high for a homopolar bond. But the Si—Si single bond is much weaker than that between silicon and either chlorine or oxygen, elements which are so much more electronegative than silicon.

TABLE 59

BOND ENERGIES (kcal) OF CARBON AND SILICON

Carbon		Silicon	
C—C	85	Si—Si	53
C—Cl	81	Si—Cl	91
C—O	86	Si—O	108
C—H	99	Si—H	76

The C—H bond is particularly strong and this accounts for the great stability of saturated hydrocarbons and the enormous number of compounds with carbon-hydrogen bonds. Only short chains of Si atoms occur and the links between them are readily broken. There are not many hydrides and they are very reactive.

The elements

Elementary carbon occurs in two forms. In diamond the C atoms are arranged tetrahedrally and equidistant (Fig. 157), C—C = 1.54 Å. They are bound covalently by electron pairs occupying localised MO's formed by an overlapping of the sp³ hybrids. This structure confers great hardness on the crystal but permits of four well-defined cleavages.

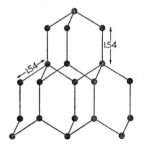

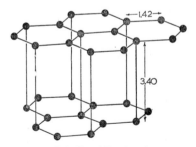

Fig. 157. Diamond structure.   Fig. 158. Graphite structure.

Silicon also has the diamond structure, the interatomic distance being 2.34 Å.

In graphite the layers of carbon atoms form a regular hexagonal network with a C—C bond length of 1.42 Å, the different layers being 3.40 Å apart (Fig. 158). Every carbon atom is bound to three others in the layer by covalent bonds which could be described by localised molecular orbitals, built up by overlapping sp^2 hybrids, holding two electrons in each. The electrons in the unhybridised p orbitals form a mobile system of metallic type (p. 114). In single crystals the material is soft, one layer of atoms sliding easily over another. Carbon has particularly high m.p. and b.p.

TABLE 60

SOME PROPERTIES OF CARBON AND SILICON

	C		Si
	Diamond	Graphite	
Density (g/cc)	3.52	2.25	2.49
Atomic volume	3.4	5.3	11.4
Melting point (°C)		3500	1420
Boiling point (°C)		4200	2300

Carbon (0.08% of the earth's crust) occurs in the elementary form, in solid, liquid and gaseous hydrocarbons, and in mineral carbonates such as limestone, magnesite and dolomite. The atmosphere contains 0.03% of CO_2 by volume, from which source a great variety of compounds of biological generation are derived.

Clear diamonds, occasionally in coloured form, are used as gems because the high index of refraction (~ 2.42) enhances internal reflexion and brilliance in the cut stone. Diamond powder, much now manufactured industrially, is an abrasive for arming grinding and cutting wheels; larger opaque, natural diamonds are mounted in tools for cutting metal and rock.

Graphite, of which the natural supply is limited, is manufactured in various ways depending upon the purpose for which it is intended. Finely divided material, pure and soft for lubrication, is produced in the Acheson process. In this, powdered coke is heated for about a day to temperatures reaching $\sim 2500°$, by letting it serve as the resistance in an electric furnace. The conversion to graphite is probably catalysed by the presence of a little silicon derived from the coke or the furnace walls.

Massive graphite required for electrodes and other refractory purposes is made by mixing powdered coke (see p. 289 for varieties) with pitch, moulding, pressing or extruding the plastic material to shape, heating to $\sim 1250°$ to drive off volatiles, and finally graphitising at $\sim 2500°$ by making the pieces resistance elements in an electric furnace. The purity depends on the raw materials used and the precautions taken; it must be high when the products are intended for electrodes or building into atomic reactors. The graphite blocks for the latter purpose are formed by an extrusion process which orients the crystallites and renders the finished material anisotropic (for irradiation damage and Wigner energy see p. 162). Graphite is singular in being the only known material whose mechanical properties improve with rising temperature; accordingly it is used for dies and plungers in the high temperature ($>$ 1500°) hot pressing of powders of metals such as beryllium and of refractory 'hard metals' such as TiC.

Other artificial carbons are:

(i) Charcoal, made by carburising wood, cellulose or sugar. The ash depends on the starting material and can be very low.

(ii) Coke, made by carburising coal, can vary widely in composition and mechanical properties; that made by carburising residues from the distillation of pitch and natural oil is a more uniform product.

(iii) Gas carbon, found in the upper part of retorts used for gas manufacture.

(iv) Animal charcoal, made by charring treated bones, consists of finely divided carbon supported on calcium phosphate. It is used as a decoloriser.

(v) Carbon black, made by burning natural gas in a deficiency of air and collecting the soot on cooled metal plates, is low in ash, but contains tars and liquid and gaseous hydrocarbons. It has a large surface area and is used as a catalyst and filler in rubber manufacture.

These carbons are usually described as amorphous but most of them show some crystallinity, the more so the higher the temperature of preparation.

Diamond does not ignite in oxygen below $\sim$ 800° and is only slowly attacked by sulphur vapour at 1000°. Graphite reacts a little more readily, igniting in oxygen at 690°. Both burn with a bright, flameless glow to the dioxide. The structure of diamond renders it chemically unreactive but that of graphite allows penetration between the layer planes of carbon atoms. Thus, though not attacked by dilute acids, it is converted to graphite oxide (p. 298) by a mixture of concentrated H_2SO_4 and HNO_3 to which a little $KClO_3$ has been added.

Silicon (25.7% of the earth's crust) though only about half as plentiful as oxygen is the second most abundant element. It occurs extensively in many forms of SiO_2, silicates and aluminosilicates. The element, hard, grey and crystalline, is made commercially by heating silica with carbon or CaC_2 in an electric furnace. It can be purified by zone refining (p. 309) until the impurity content is less than 10^{-7} %, when it may be employed in semiconductor devices such as transistors. Silicon dissolves, generally with the formation of a silicide, in most metals, exceptions being Bi, Pb and Tl. It is used as a deoxidiser and an alloying constituent in steel making, and in massive quantities in the manufacture of acid-resistant iron. For these purposes the silicon is usually added as ferrosilicon prepared by the electrochemical reduction of SiO_2 and Fe_2O_3 with carbon.

Silicon is chemically more reactive than carbon. It burns in oxygen at 400°, the reaction being strongly exothermic:

$$Si + O_2 \rightarrow SiO_2, \qquad \Delta H = -191 \text{ kcal};$$
$$C + O_2 \rightarrow CO_2, \qquad \Delta H = -94 \text{ kcal.}$$

It combines directly with all the halogens at temperatures ranging from 300° upwards, with sulphur vapour at 600°, with nitrogen at 1300° and with carbon at 2000°. Though acid resistant (excepting HF) it is attacked by hot alkalis:

$$Si + 2NaOH + H_2O \rightarrow Na_2SiO_3 + 2H_2,$$

and by steam at red heat:

$$Si + 2H_2O \rightarrow SiO_2 + 2H_2.$$

Halides

The halides of carbon are very numerous because of the tendency of carbon atoms to form chains. A limited number of halides containing Si chains have been made, one with every halogen in compounds of the formula Si_2X_6, additional chlorides up to Si_6Cl_{14} and bromides up to Si_3Br_8.

Of the simple tetrahalides, CF_4 and SiF_4 are gases; CCl_4, $SiCl_4$ and $SiBr_4$ liquids; CBr_4, CI_4 and SiI_4 solids. CCl_4 is made on a large scale by passing Cl_2 into CS_2 in the presence of a little iodine:

$$CS_2 + 3Cl_2 \rightarrow S_2Cl_2 + CCl_4.$$
$$\text{(b.p. 138°)} \quad \text{(b.p. 76.7°)}$$

SiF_4 is conveniently made by treating a mixture of fluorite and silica with concentrated H_2SO_4:

$$2CaF_2 + 2H_2SO_4 + SiO_2 \rightarrow 2CaSO_4 + SiF_4 + 2H_2O.$$

The water is retained by the sulphuric acid, and the SiF_4 is freed from HF by passing it over dry NaF. The other silicon tetrahalides are generally made by direct combination with the halogen. Mixed tetrahalides such as SiF_3Cl and $SiCl_2Br_2$ have also been obtained (Schumb, 1942).

The fluorides of carbon are interesting. Fluorine enters graphite at 200° to form the interstitial compound $(CF)_n$. At higher temperatures the elements give a mixture of CF_4, C_2F_4, C_2F_6 and C_3F_8. Fluorocarbons are made by passing hydrocarbons over cobalt(III) fluoride at 150–200° or chlorocompounds over SbF_3 (Swarts' Reaction). Under these conditions CCl_4 gives a mixture of CCl_3F, CCl_2F_2, $CClF_3$ and CF_4. The mixed fluorochlorocarbons, known as freons, are useful refrigerants, being volatile, non-toxic and non-corrosive. Higher boiling fluorocarbons form important lubricants.

The fluorocarbons are inert. Their derivatives are often very different in properties from those of the corresponding hydrocarbons because of the high electronegativity of fluorine. Thus $(CF_3)_3N$ is not basic; the attraction of electrons by the fluorine atoms prevents the nitrogen acting as a donor.

Carbon halides resist hydrolysis because only s and p orbitals are available for bond formation. This ensures a maximum covalency of four and precludes the donation of electrons by the oxygen atom in a water molecule to a carbon atom. But silicon compounds do hydrolyse, since the unoccupied silicon 3d orbitals lie not far above the 3s and 3p.

$$SiX_4 + 2H_2O \rightarrow SiO_2 + 4HX.$$

But with the fluoride, the HF formed reacts with the tetrafluoride:

$$2SiF_4 + 4H_2O \rightarrow SiO_2 + 2H_3O^+ + SiF_6^{2-} + 2HF.$$

The octahedral SiF_6^{2-} ion is the only halogeno-complex of silicon; the bonding involves sp^3d^2 hybrids and accordingly carbon forms no such compound. Fluorosilicic acid, H_2SiF_6, known only in solution, is a strong acid, of which the heavy metal salts are soluble, and those of Na, K, Ba and the lanthanides sparingly soluble.

Silicon resembles Ge, Sn and Pb in forming a dichloride. The relation between pressure and temperature in the $Si/SiCl_4$ system shows an equilibrium to exist:

$$Si + SiCl_4 \rightleftharpoons 2SiCl_2.$$

But the dichloride is present in appreciable quantities only above 1100°.

Carbon forms oxohalides: COF_2 and $COCl_2$ are colourless gases made by union of carbon monoxide and the halogen. The molecules are planar, a form which suggests sp^2 hybridisation. In $COCl_2$ the small angle of 112° between the C—Cl bonds is due to a strong repulsion exerted on each by the spin-paired electrons of the C—O bond. Carbonyl bromide, $COBr_2$, is a colourless liquid best made by dropping concentrated H_2SO_4 on to CBr_4:

$$CBr_4 + H_2SO_4 \rightarrow 2HBr + SO_3 + COBr_2.$$

All three compounds are easily hydrolysed:

$$COX_2 + H_2O \rightarrow 2HX + CO_2.$$

Silicon oxohalides of structure,

$$
\left[
\begin{array}{ccc}
 & X & X \\
 & | & | \\
X & -Si-O-Si- & X \\
 & | & | \\
 & X & X
\end{array}
\right]_n
$$

can be obtained either by treating SiO_2 with a mixture of oxygen and chlorine or bromine, or by partially hydrolysing the silicon tetrahalide with moist ether. The fluoride Si_2OF_6 is made by fluorinating the corresponding chloride:

$$Si_2OCl_6 \xrightarrow[\text{SbCl}_5]{\text{SbF}_3} Si_2OF_6.$$

Oxides

Carbon suboxide, C_3O_2, is a gas formed when malonic acid, or one of its esters, is heated with P_2O_5. When dry, it is fairly stable at room temperature but polymerises readily on warming; the liquid (b.p. 6°) so produced further polymerises to a dark red, water-soluble solid. C_3O_2 behaves as the anhydride of malonic acid:

$$C_3O_2 + 2H_2O \longrightarrow CH_2\begin{array}{l}\diagup COOH \\ \diagdown COOH\end{array}$$

$$C_3O_2 + 2NH_3 \longrightarrow CH_2\begin{array}{l}\diagup CONH_2 \\ \diagdown CONH_2\end{array}$$

A mixture with oxygen explodes when sparked. The molecule is linear, but the structure

$$O=C=C=C=O$$

is an over-simplification; the bonds are all somewhat shorter than normal double bonds, the carbon-carbon distance being 1.28 Å (*cf.* 1.33 Å) and the carbon-oxygen 1.19 Å (*cf.* 1.22 Å). There are two π-bond systems (*cf.* N_2 triple bond, p. 94) but these are non-localised, and contribute only *fractional* π bonds (p. 112).

Carbon monoxide, CO, though made by the dehydration of formic acid, is too insoluble to be considered as the acid anhydride. The gas is produced in large quantities by the reaction between carbon and CO_2 at high temperatures:

$$CO_2 + C \rightleftharpoons 2CO.$$

In the presence of carbon the CO/CO_2 ratio increases with temperature, significantly favouring CO production above 800°. The gas is an effective reducing agent below this temperature:

$$Fe_2O_3, \; MnO_2 \; \text{etc.} \longrightarrow \text{Metals,}$$
$$H_2O \longrightarrow \text{Hydrogen.}$$

It reacts with chlorine and bromine in sunlight, and with molten sulphur and heated selenium in the dark:

$$CO + Br_2 \rightarrow COBr_2,$$
$$CO + S \;\; \rightarrow COS,$$
$$CO + Se \rightarrow COSe.$$

Several transition metals give carbonyls (p. 301) and some of their salts and complexes also combine with carbon monoxide:

$$CO + K_3Fe(CN)_6 \rightarrow K_3Fe(CN)_5CO,$$
$$CO + PtCl_2 \rightarrow PtCl_2CO.$$

The reaction of hydrogen with CO forms the basis of an industrial process for making methanol carried out at high pressure over a mixed copper-zinc catalyst. Though CO is insoluble in, and unreactive with, water at ordinary pressures, formic acid is produced at very high pressures. Under similar conditions CO and aqueous NaOH combine to give sodium formate.

The CO molecule is isoelectronic with N_2 and its MO's are formally the same:

$$C \, (1s^2 \, 2s^2 \, 2p^2) + O \, (1s^2 \, 2s^2 \, 2p^4) \rightarrow CO \, (KK(z\sigma)^2 \, (y\sigma)^2 \, (x\sigma)^2 \, (w\pi)^4).$$

However the CO^+ ion has a shorter carbon–oxygen bond than the neutral molecule, indicating that the highest occupied orbital is non-bonding, whereas the N_2^+ ion has a longer nitrogen–nitrogen bond than the neutral molecule. It is likely that the oxygen 2s electrons form a lone pair $(z\sigma)$ and that one carbon sp hybrid holds a second lone pair $(y\sigma)$. The bonding orbital $x\sigma$ would then be formed by overlap of a carbon sp hybrid and an oxygen p orbital. Lateral overlap of the remaining (singly occupied) 2p orbitals results in two π-type MO's, leaning somewhat towards the oxygen. The p orbitals are drawn

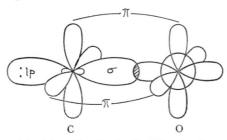

Fig. 159. π-Bonding in the CO molecule.

so that their orientation is clear; they are actually much thicker and overlap as indicated in Fig. 159. Ionisation is probably from the carbon lone pair and not from a π-bond orbital. The dipole moment of the π electrons is strongly offset by the carbon lone pair; this lone pair is also responsible for the co-ordinating power displayed in the carbonyls.

Silicon monoxide is believed to be formed by the reduction of SiO_2 by Si at a high temperature:

$$Si + SiO_2 \rightarrow 2\,SiO.$$

Its existence at room temperature has been questioned by Geller and Thurmond (1955) who consider the X-ray diffraction pattern, formerly attributed to SiO, to arise from a mixture of β cristobalite and β silicon carbide; the carbon being derived from the reaction vessel.

Carbon dioxide is the most stable oxide of carbon at room temperature. Industrially it is recovered from flue gases and lime kilns, SO_2 and H_2S being removed from the gases by scrubbing with aqueous $KMnO_4$ and Na_2CO_3. Carbon dioxide dissolves in water giving, at N.T.P., a 0.04 molar solution in which the carbonic acid is only slightly ionised:

$$H_2O + CO_2 \rightleftharpoons H_2CO_3 \xrightleftharpoons{H_2O} H_3O^+ + HCO_3^-, \quad pK_a = 6.5.$$

The equilibrium moves to the left as the temperature is raised and the gas may be completely expelled from the water. The pH of a saturated solution of the gas at 1 atmosphere is 3.7. Commercially the gas is solidified as dry ice, added to oxygen as a respiratory stimulant, and to flavoured water for carbonated drinks.

The molecule is linear with carbon–oxygen distances of 1.15 Å, which is considerably shorter than that calculated for a double bond (1.22 Å). Two π-bond systems are expected, in perpendicular planes, but each would extend over all centres (cf. carbon suboxide) contributing slightly more than half a π bond in each link.

In contrast to the discrete molecules of carbon dioxide, silicon dioxide forms condensed, three-dimensional systems of indefinite extension which are high-melting solids. Silica has three forms, quartz, tridymite and cristobalite, each of which has a low-temperature (α) and a high-temperature (β) modification.

$$
\begin{array}{ccc}
\alpha\text{-quartz} & \alpha\text{-tridymite} & \alpha\text{-cristobalite} \\
\updownarrow 573° & \updownarrow 140° & \updownarrow 240° \\
\beta\text{-quartz} \underset{870°}{\xrightleftharpoons} & \beta\text{-tridymite} \underset{1470°}{\xrightleftharpoons} & \beta\text{-cristobalite}
\end{array}
$$

In cristobalite the Si atoms are arranged as are the C atoms in diamond, except that they have O atoms midway between them. In quartz and tridymite the regular structure is replaced by a screw-like arrangement of the atoms. Transitions between the forms take place slowly, and all three are found in nature. The transitions between their respective α and β modifications are rapid.

Silica melts at 1710°. Even when slowly cooled the molten material sets to a vitreous, non-crystalline solid. Its plastic range allows masses to be forged and hollow ware to be blown; its low coefficient of expansion renders it immune to thermal shock; its transparency especially to u.v. makes it suitable for lenses and prisms. Specially pure synthetic silica is now made for laboratory ware used in preparing the pure materials required by the electrical industry (*e.g.* transistors), and for optical parts calling for minimum absorption.

Silica gel is a hard, granular, translucent material containing about 4% H_2O. It results from the removal of salts and water from the continuous gel formed by acidifying the solution of an alkali-metal silicate, and has a large surface area. Silica gel is employed as a drying agent, as a catalyst in the hydrolysis of aryl halides to phenols, and as a support for other catalysts, as for example the V_2O_5 used in the oxidation of naphthalene to phthalic acid or SO_2 to SO_3. A silica-alumina gel with 10 to 13% of Al_2O_3 is made by co-gelation of silicate and aluminate solutions with acid and is a catalyst for the cracking of petroleum.

The monosilicic acid, $Si(OH)_4$, is probably the only species to be found in neutral solutions. However, the isothermal dehydration of silicic acid, prepared by the action of damp air on SiS_2, indicates an acid $H_8Si_4O_{12}$ to which Schwartz (1954) assigns the structure:

$$
\begin{array}{c}
\text{HO} \diagdown \diagup \text{OH} \\
\text{Si} \\
\text{HO} \diagdown \quad \diagup\text{O} \diagup \diagdown \text{O} \diagdown \quad \diagup \text{OH} \\
\text{Si} \qquad\qquad \text{Si} \\
\text{HO} \diagup \diagdown \text{O} \diagdown \quad \diagup \text{O} \diagup \diagdown \text{OH} \\
\text{Si} \\
\text{HO} \diagup \diagdown \text{OH}
\end{array}
$$

Further dehydration by dioxan or SO_2Cl_2 provides less definite evidence for other silicic acids.

Other silicon-oxygen compounds

When silicochloroform is hydrolysed with steam at 450°, a compound $[(HSiO)_2O]_n$, with strong reducing properties is formed. Its structure resembles that of mica, having large sheets of connected hexagons with Si atoms at the corners and O atoms midway along the sides (Fig. 160). When heated to 507°, the compound is converted to Si_2O_3 with a loss of the hydrogen which presumably had provided hydrogen bonds between the sheets;

bonds which are now replaced by Si—Si interplanal links (Wiberg and Simmler, 1956).

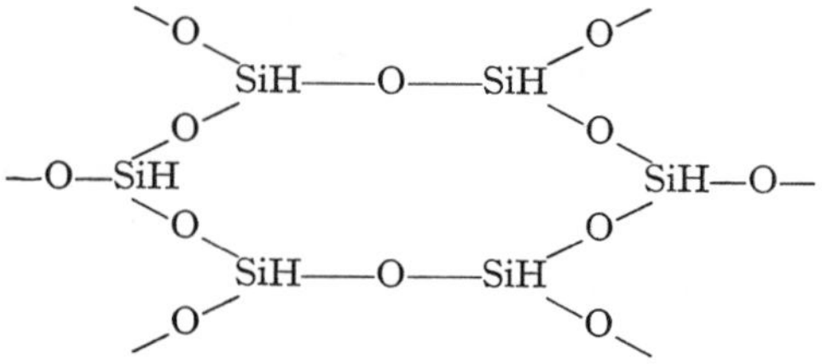

Fig. 160. Structure of $[(HSiO)_2O]_n$.

Siloxene, a similar compound in the form of a flaky, white solid, is made by the action of HCl gas and ethyl alcohol on $CaSi_2$. It is spontaneously inflammable in air and a strong reducing agent. The H atoms can be replaced partly or wholly by halogens:

$$(Si_2H_2O)_n \xrightarrow{Br_2} (Si_2Br_2O)_n \begin{array}{c} \xrightarrow{H_2O} [Si_2(OH)_2O]_n \\ \xrightarrow{NH_3} [Si_2(NH_2)_2O]_n \end{array}$$

Siloxene

Silicones

Hydrolysis of the alkyl and aryl substituted silicon halides produces silicones (Kipping, 1937). The halogen derivatives themselves are made by passing an alkyl or aryl halide over a copper-silicon alloy at about 300°. Hurd and Rochow (1945) found evidence for the mechanism:

$$2Cu + CH_3Cl \longrightarrow CuCl + CuCH_3,$$
$$Si + CuCl \longrightarrow Cu + SiCl \text{ (active intermediate)},$$
$$SiCl + CuCH_3 \longrightarrow CH_3SiCl + Cu.$$

And so on till the four valencies of silicon are saturated. Hydrolysis of $(CH_3)_3SiCl$ gives a disiloxane:

$$(CH_3)_3SiCl + H_2O \longrightarrow (CH_3)_3SiOH \text{ (trimethyl silanol)} + HCl$$
$$\downarrow \text{condensation}$$
$$(CH_3)_3Si—O—Si(CH_3)_3.$$

$(CH_3)_2SiCl_2$ gives a chain compound:

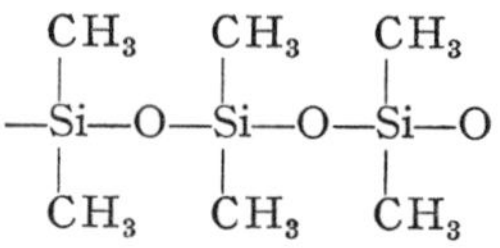

$$\begin{array}{ccc} CH_3 & CH_3 & CH_3 \\ | & | & | \\ —Si—O—Si—O—Si—O \\ | & | & | \\ CH_3 & CH_3 & CH_3 \end{array}$$

CH_3SiCl_3 gives a cross-linked chain system:

$$
\begin{array}{ccccccc}
\mid & & & & & & \mid \\
O & & CH_3 & & CH_3 & & O \\
\mid & & \mid & & \mid & & \mid \\
-Si-O- & Si-O- & Si-O- & Si- \\
\mid & & \mid & & \mid & & \mid \\
CH_3 & & O & & O & & CH_3 \\
CH_3 & & \mid & & \mid & & CH_3 \\
\mid & & \mid & & \mid & & \mid \\
-Si-O- & Si-O- & Si-O- & Si- \\
\mid & & \mid & & \mid & & \mid \\
O & & CH_3 & & CH_3 & & O
\end{array}
$$

The extent of the cross-linking and the nature of the alkyl or aryl substituent determines the nature of the polymers. They range from oily liquids to rubbery solids. All are water-repellant, thermally and electrically insulating and chemically inert. These properties render them widely useful in industry; they appear as lubricants, antifoams, low temperature hydraulic fluids, and in cosmetics.

Though the copper silicide method is preferred for the production of methyl-substituted compounds, a Grignard-type synthesis is commonly used for other alkyl and aryl substituted substances:

$$Mg + \text{dry ether} + RCl \longrightarrow RMgCl$$
$$\downarrow SiCl_4$$
$$RSiCl_3, \quad R_2SiCl_2, \quad R_3SiCl.$$

Sulphides

Carbon disulphide, CS_2, is a volatile liquid (b.p. 46°), highly refractive, insoluble in water but soluble in ethyl alcohol and ether. It is made by the action of sulphur vapour on electrically heated coke. Its main uses are as a solvent and in the manufacture of CCl_4 (p. 290), thiocarbanilide and viscose rayon:

$$\text{Cellulose} + NaOH + CS_2 \rightarrow S=C{\overset{\textstyle O-(Cel)}{\underset{\textstyle SNa}{}}} \qquad (Cel = \text{cellulose residue}).$$

The cellulose xanthate is converted into rayon on acidification. Thiocarbanilide, $S=C:(NH.C_6H_5)_2$, results when CS_2 is passed into boiling aniline. It is used in the manufacture of dyes and pharmaceuticals, and in the vulcanisation of rubber.

A brown polymer, $(CS)_n$, is formed when CS_2 is exposed to light and a subsulphide, C_3S_2, when an arc is struck beneath it. If the arc is between a graphite cathode and a selenium or tellurium anode then the liquids CSSe or CSTe are formed.

Silicon disulphide forms fibrous crystalline macromolecules with a structure intermediate between that of CO_2, with its individual molecules, and the three-dimensional SiO_2. In it the sulphur atoms are arranged tetrahedrally round the Si atoms (Zintl and Loosen, 1935):

$$\begin{array}{c} S \diagdown \quad\;\; S \quad\quad\quad\quad\quad S \\ \quad\; Si \quad Si \diagdown S \diagup Si \\ S \diagup \quad\;\; S \quad\quad S \quad\quad S \end{array}$$

Though solid SiO cannot be obtained from SiO_2 (p. 294), the monosulphide, SiS, can be made by heating SiS_2 with silicon (Schumb and Bernard, 1955):

$$SiS_2 + Si \longrightarrow 2SiS.$$

Nitrides*

Cyanogen, C_2N_2, is evolved on heating mercuric cyanide with mercuric chloride:

$$Hg(CN)_2 + HgCl_2 \rightarrow Hg_2Cl_2 + C_2N_2.$$

The colourless, very poisonous, gas (b.p. —21°) reacts with alkaline solutions to give a mixture of cyanide and cyanate:

$$C_2N_2 + 2OH^- \rightarrow CN^- + CNO^- + H_2O.$$

The molecule is linear and without dipole moment, the intermolecular distances being C—N, 1.16 Å and C—C, 1.37 Å. Since the lengths are 1.15 Å for the C≡N bond and 1.54 Å for the C—C single bond, it suggests that the π bonds of the C≡N groups are sufficiently delocalised to reduce the electron density between carbon and nitrogen and increase it between carbon and carbon.

Silicon nitride, Si_3N_4, is a refractory material made by direct combination of the elements above 1300°. Another method is to allow the hydrides or halides of silicon to react with ammonia and to heat the amino- and imino-silanes produced. These give the polymer $[Si(NH)_2]_n$ which yields Si_3N_4.

Graphite compounds

Fredenhagen (1929) observed that graphite absorbed liquid potassium; and at the same time swelled in a direction perpendicular to the cleavage. When the excess potassium was evaporated, there remained a copper-coloured material with the composition KC_8 which was converted, on further heating, to KC_{24}. X-ray examination showed KC_8 to have potassium atoms

* For a general account of the pseudohalogens see p. 420.

inserted between every layer of carbon atoms, and KC_{24} to have them between alternate layers only. The diamagnetism of the original graphite is absent from KC_8 which is, in fact, a better conductor than solid potassium (McDonnel, Pink and Ubbelohde, 1951). Equilibrium pressure measurements have disclosed the entity KC_{24} (Herold, 1951). 'Sandwich' compounds MC_8 and MC_{24} (where M represents Rb or Cs) have also been made, their stability increasing with the size of the metal atom. The bonding in these compounds is essentially ionic.

Graphite also swells when heated for a period in a solution of $KClO_3$ in HNO_3, with the formation of graphite oxide (Brodie, 1850), the normal interplanar distance of 3.4 Å in graphite being increased. The material absorbs water so that the interplanar distance is $\sim$ 6 Å when it is dried over P_2O_5, $\sim$ 9 Å in air, and $\sim$ 11 Å in water. A rapid method of preparation is to heat graphite with an anhydrous mixture of H_2SO_4, $NaNO_3$ and $KMnO_4$ at below 45° for less than 45 min. Thus prepared, the 'dry' oxide is said to have the composition $C_7O_4H_2$, whatever the graphite used. The C:O ratio has been variously reported over the years, but always as less than 2:1. Preparations have varied from yellow to dark brown. The oxide is unstable, decomposing at $\sim$ 200° to CO_2, CO and carbon.

The constitution and structure of graphite oxide has been much investigated (Hofmann, 1934–57; Ruess, 1946). Finality has not been reached, but it is probable that the planar aromatic rings of the graphite (p. 287) are puckered and partly broken to allow both C—OH and C=O bonds to be formed. Although the oxide shows some acidic character (C—OH → C—O⁻ + H⁺) the bonding of the interplanar species, in contrast to that in the alkali-metal compounds, is predominantly covalent.

'Graphitic salts' can also be made. For instance sulphuric acid in the presence of strong oxidising agents forms the compound $C_{24}HSO_4 \cdot 2H_2SO_4$. Phosphoric, selenic and perchloric acids behave somewhat similarly. Lamellar compounds are also formed by CrO_2Cl_2 and CrO_2F_2 (Croft and Thomas, 1951); the product of reaction between graphite and fluorine at 200°, $(CF)_n$, is of the same type, with an inter-sheet distance of 8.17 Å.

Carbides

The carbides can be divided into four groups: (1) salt-like, (2) interstitial, (3) iron-type, and (4) covalent.

(1) *Salt-like carbides*

Members of this class can usually be made by heating the metal, its oxide or hydride with carbon, CO or a hydrocarbon. The salt-like carbides are easily hydrolysed by water and are classified according to the aliphatic hydrocarbon they give.

(a) The acetylides, such as CaC_2, CrC_2, BaC_2 and MgC_2, made by heating the oxide and carbon have tetragonal crystals containing M^{2+} and C_2^{2-} ions arranged as are the Na^+ and Cl^- in rock salt but with the axis parallel to the C—C bonds lengthened ($c/a \sim 1.2$). The compounds Cu_2C_2, Ag_2C_2 and Au_2C_2 are precipitated from aqueous solution, the first by passing acetylene into ammoniacal copper(I) chloride, and the last by passing acetylene into gold(I) thiosulphate. They are formally acetylides, but are not hydrolysed by water.

(b) The methanides, such as Al_4C_3 and Be_2C, yield methane on hydrolysis. Both are made by combination of the elements at about 1500°, and are much harder materials than the acetylides.

(c) Magnesium carbide, Mg_2C_3, which is formed when MgC_2 is heated, and is believed to contain C_3^{2-} ions, yields allylene on hydrolysis:

$$Mg_2C_3 + 4H_2O \rightarrow 2Mg(OH)_2 + CH_3.C{\equiv}CH.$$

(d) Thorium and the lanthanides form carbides, MC_2, when their oxides are heated with carbon in an electric furnace. They have been reported as giving a mixture of acetylene, olefines and hydrogen on hydrolysis. But later work suggests that pure ThC_2 yields only acetylene.

(2) *Interstitial carbides*

These are made by the direct union of metal and carbon or the reduction of the oxide with carbon at about 2000°. They are very high melting (particularly TaC, m.p. 3900°), good electrical conductors, very hard but brittle, and inert chemically except under oxidising conditions. Cemented carbides, based on WC, are used as hard facings for tools and dies, the metallic binder (Co) which gives increased strength permits fabrication by sintering at 1200°, and additions of TiC and TaC serve to vary the properties. Self-bonded carbides are made by hot pressing at 2000°.

(3) *Carbides of the iron type*

These metals have an atomic radius below 1.3 Å. Iron (1.16 Å), chromium (1.17 Å) and manganese (1.17 Å) form carbides with properties intermediate between the salt-like and the interstitial. Structurally Fe_3C, Mn_3C and Ni_3C have C atoms inside the trigonal prisms formed by the metal atoms. They are easily decomposed by acids and water. In Cr_3C_2 the carbon atoms form chains in the solid.

(4) *Covalent carbides*

Most of these are gases or volatile liquids, some with little thermal stability, (CH_4, CS_2, CCl_4); but the carbides of silicon and boron are thermally stable, hard, chemically-inert solids. SiC exists in three forms related to one another as are diamond, zinc blende and wurtzite. It is made by reducing SiO_2 with carbon in an electric furnace. B_4C, also made by reducing the oxide with carbon, has a complicated structure in which icosahedra of 12 boron atoms alternate with C_3 chains.

Silicon carbide, widely employed as an abrasive (carborundum), is finding increasing use as a refractory. It has a better thermal conductivity at high temperatures than any other ceramic and is very resistant to abrasion and corrosion especially when bonded with silicon nitride. Hot-pressed, self-bonded SiC may be suitable as a container for the fuel elements in high-temperature gas-cooled reactors and also for the structural parts of the reactors. Boron carbide, which is even harder than silicon carbide, is now readily available commercially because of its value as a radiation shield, and is being increasingly used as an abrasive.

Metal carbonyls

Many of the transition metals of Gps VI, VII and VIII form volatile, diamagnetic carbonyls in which the charge number of the metal atom is zero.

V	VI	VII	$VIIIa$	$VIIIb$	$VIIIc$
$V(CO)_6$	$Cr(CO)_6$	$Mn_2(CO)_{10}$	$Fe(CO)_5$	$Co_2(CO)_8$	$Ni(CO)_4$
			$Fe_2(CO)_9$		
			$Fe_3(CO)_{12}$	$Co_4(CO)_{12}$	
	$Mo(CO)_6$		$Ru(CO)_5$	$Rh_2(CO)_8$	
			$Ru_2(CO)_9$		
			$Ru_3(CO)_{12}$		
	$W(CO)_6$	$Re_2(CO)_{10}$	$Os(CO)_5$	$Ir_2(CO)_8$	
			$Os_2(CO)_9$		

Palladium and platinum have no simple carbonyls.

(Compounds with the empirical formulae M^ICO and $M^{II}(CO)_2$ formed by alkali and alkaline earth metals, are not true carbonyls.)

Preparation

(1) Nickel when freshly reduced combines with CO at room temperature and ordinary pressures:

$$Ni + 4CO \rightleftharpoons Ni(CO)_4.$$

Retention of the carbonyl by adsorption on the metal surface with consequent fall in yield is largely avoided by passing the CO over the metal, freezing out the carbonyl, and recycling the stripped gas.

Finely divided iron reacts less easily, 200° and 100 atmospheres pressure being necessary:

$$Fe + 5CO \rightarrow Fe(CO)_5.$$

The carbonyls of tungsten and molybdenum are made similarly, both sulphur and sulphides catalysing the reactions.

(2) An ethereal solution of a Grignard reagent reacts readily with CO in the presence of anhydrous chromium(III) chloride (Job, 1927). One of the products is the ether-soluble $Cr(CO)_6$. If the $CrCl_3$ is replaced by $MoCl_5$ or WCl_6 the hexacarbonyl of molybdenum or tungsten is formed.

(3) Carbonyls can sometimes be made by passing CO into solutions or suspensions of other compounds of the metal. Suspensions of $Ni(CN)_2$ and NiS in aqueous alkali give $Ni(CO)_4$. The complex cyanide $K_2Ni(CN)_3$ reacts with CO to form an addition compound which is decomposed by acid to give $Ni(CO)_4$.

(4) Carbonyls of some of the metals near osmium in the Periodic Table can be made by the reaction of CO under pressure with some of their compounds:

$$RuI_3 \xrightarrow[\text{room temperature}]{CO} Ru(CO)_2I_2 \xrightarrow[\text{at high pressure}]{\text{over Ag or Cu}} Ru(CO)_5;$$

$$OsO_4 \xrightarrow[\text{at 100° and 50 atmospheres}]{CO} Os(CO)_5 \text{ and } CO_2;$$

$$Re_2S_7 \xrightarrow[\text{at 250° and 200 atmospheres}]{CO} Re_2(CO)_{10}.$$

(5) Certain of the more complex carbonyls result from heating or irradiating simpler ones:

$$2Fe(CO)_5 \xrightarrow[\text{irradiation}]{\text{ultra-violet}} Fe_2(CO)_9 + CO;$$

$$2Fe_2(CO)_9 \xrightarrow{\text{heat}} Fe_3(CO)_{12} + Fe(CO)_5 + CO.$$

(6) Vanadium carbonyl is made by the action of CO on ditoluenevanadium (O). The first Gp.V metal carbonyl to be obtained (Pruett and Wyman, 1960), it is dark green, stable up to 60°, and readily reduced to the $[V(CO)_6]^-$ anion. The paramagnetic moment indicates one unpaired electron, and an X-ray examination of the solid shows the carbonyl groups to be arranged octahedrally. It is almost certainly monomeric, $V(CO)_6$.

Physical properties

Simple carbonyls of the $M(CO)_n$ type are generally colourless, though $Fe(CO)_5$ is yellow. The hexacarbonyls formed by Gp VI metals are colourless solids, the rest liquids. The binuclear carbonyls with more than one metal atom per molecule are usually coloured solids, though the monoclinic crystals of $Re_2(CO)_{10}$ are colourless.

Derivative compounds

(*i*) *Carbonyl hydrides.* $Fe(CO)_5$ dissolves in alcoholic KOH and when the solution is acidified in the absence of air, the very unstable carbonyl hydride $Fe(CO)_4H_2$ is produced (Hieber and Leutert, 1931):

$$Fe(CO)_5 + 2\ OH^- \rightarrow Fe(CO)_4H_2 + CO_3^{2-}.$$

It is a pale yellow liquid with strong reducing properties. The reaction of $Co_2(CO)_8$ with alkali is more complex but one of the products is $Co(CO)_4H$, also unstable and strongly reducing.

In solution these carbonyl hydrides act as very weak monobasic acids. The iron and cobalt carbonyl hydrides are isoelectronic with $Ni(CO)_4$ and have the same tetrahedral structure:

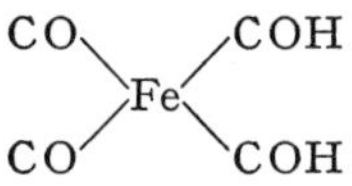

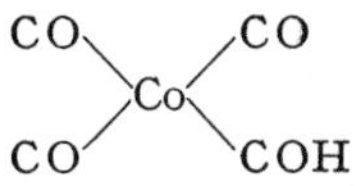

Thus $Fe(CO)_4H_2$ forms the salts $Ca[Fe(CO)_4H]_2$ and $Mg[Fe(CO)_4H]_2$. With mercury(II) salts, however, $Fe(CO)_4H_2$ gives a precipitate of a stable, yellow, polymeric substance $[Fe(CO)_4Hg]_n$ which is also made when $Fe(CO)_5$ is substituted for the carbonyl hydride:

$$Fe(CO)_5 + HgSO_4 + H_2O \rightarrow H_2SO_4 + CO_2 + Fe(CO)_4Hg.$$

These are essentially covalent compounds. But $Co(CO)_4H$ also reacts with Na, K and Ca in liquid ammonia to give the salts $NaCo(CO)_4$, $KCo(CO)_4$ and $Ca[Co(CO)_4]_2$ in the anions of which cobalt is uninegative (p. 494). Solutions of $Co(CO)_4H$ react with both cadmium and mercury(II) salts to produce monomeric substances, $[Co(CO)_4]_2Cd$ and $[Co(CO)_4]_2Hg$, soluble in organic solvents, and having a molecule of the kind shown:

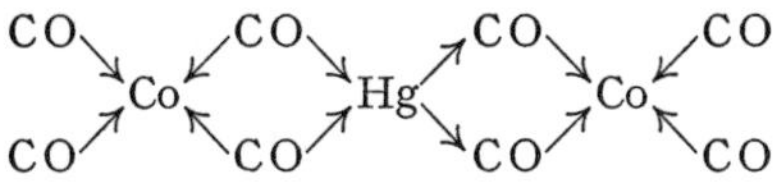

(*ii*) *Carbonyl halides.* $Fe(CO)_5$ forms unstable addition compounds with the halogens:

$$Fe(CO)_5 + X_2 \rightarrow Fe(CO)_5X_2.$$

These lose carbon monoxide to give more stable substances of the formula $Fe(CO)_4X_2$. The iodide can even be sublimed in a vacuum without decomposition. Reduction of the iodide by hydrogen produces $Fe(CO)_2I_2$ which can also be made by the reaction between $Fe(CO)_5$ and I_2 in boiling benzene.

Though $Ni(CO)_4$ and $Co_2(CO)_8$ are decomposed by halogens, there are carbonyl halides of ruthenium, rhodium, rhenium, osmium and iridium (Hieber, 1943). There are also carbonyl halides of elements which do not form a simple carbonyl; examples are $[Pd(CO)Cl_2]n$, $[Pt(CO)X_2]n$ and $Cu(CO)X$ ($X = Cl$, Br or I).

(*iii*) *Amine-substituted carbonyls.* Strong electron donors such as pyridine and ethylenediamine replace the CO groups by amine groups. Thus $Fe(CO)_5$ gives such compounds as $Fe(CO)_3(NH_3)_2$, $Fe_2(CO)_4(pyr)_3$ and $Fe_2(CO)_5(en)_2$.

(*iv*) *Nitrosyl carbonyls.* When CO is passed into a suspension of $Co(CN)_2$ in aqueous potassium hydroxide at 0°, a solution of $KCo(CO)_4$ results. Passing NO into this solution produces $Co(CO)_3NO$, a volatile liquid with physical properties very similar to $Ni(CO)_4$. Dry nitric oxide reacts with $Fe_3(CO)_{12}$ to give a mixture of $Fe(CO)_2(NO)_2$ and $Fe(CO)_5$. A comparison of these monomeric nitrosyl carbonyls with $Ni(CO)_4$ illustrates the idea of effective atomic number (Sidgwick, 1927).

Structure

In simple carbonyls of the $M(CO)_n$ type, the M—C—O bonds are linear. The carbon-oxygen distances are but slightly greater than the 1.13 Å observed in CO itself and the carbon-metal distances somewhat less than the usual single bond. The donor power of the lone pair on the carbon atom in CO is evidently slight, for CO forms only very weak complexes with a few Lewis acids. With transition metal ions, however, electrons accepted by d orbitals are favourably placed to take part in bonding with the vacant antibonding π orbitals of the CO molecule. This explains the partial double-bond character of the metal–carbon and the weakness of the carbon–oxygen bond. In these carbonyls the metals invariably have even atomic numbers and the lone pairs of the ligands would, if completely donated, give the metal the configuration of the next higher inert gas. Complete donation does not actually happen, but such considerations correctly indicate the number of ligands:

Simple carbonyl	Electrons from CO's	Z (metal)	Effective atomic numbers	Inert gas for comparison	Z
$Ni(CO)_4$	8	28	36	Kr	36
$Fe(CO)_5$	10	26	36	Kr	36
$Cr(CO)_6$	12	24	36	Kr	36
$Mo(CO)_6$	12	42	54	Xe	54

This suggests that simple carbonyls are invariably spin-paired complexes (p. 134). These metals have even atomic numbers, those with Z odd do not form simple carbonyls. In the carbonyl nitrosyls and carbonyl hydrides which are mononuclear, a metal atom with an odd atomic number can similarly complete its d shell. Thus in $Co(CO)_3NO$ and $Co(CO)_4H$, the —NO group and —COH group can be considered to contribute the single electron necessary to complete the 3d shell of the metal atom. The three CO molecules and the isoelectronic NO or COH are co-ordinated tetrahedrally, as are the four CO molecules in $Ni(CO)_4$.

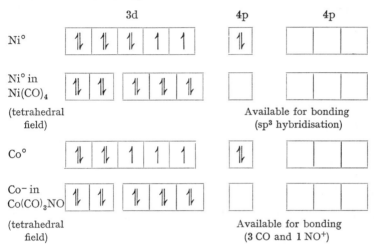

Also isoelectronic with $Ni(CO)_4$ are $Fe(CO)_4H_2$ and $Fe(CO)_2(NO)_2$ which have bonds of about the same length.

$Fe(CO)_5$ itself has the trigonal bipyramidal structure associated with dsp^3 hybridisation, the Fe having five orbitals available:

The hexacarbonyls of Cr, Mo and W have the octahedral structure consistent with d^2sp^3 hybridisation:

The binuclear and polynuclear carbonyls have metal–metal bonds and bridges formed by $>C=O$ groups:

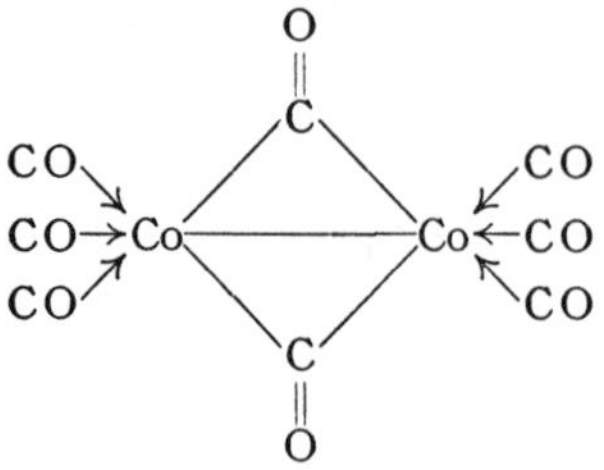

(a) $Co_2(CO)_8$

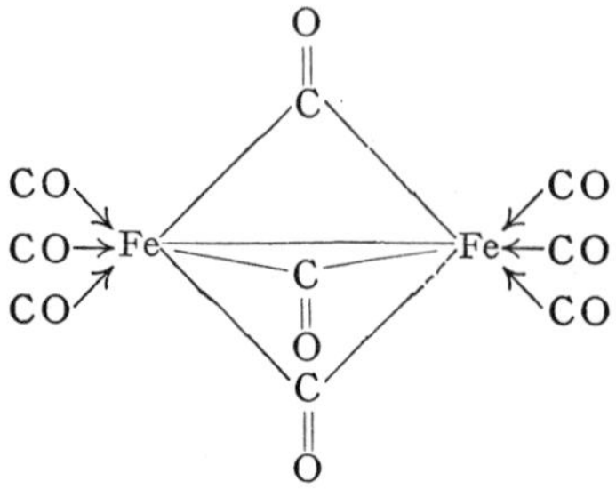

(b) $Fe_2(CO)_9$

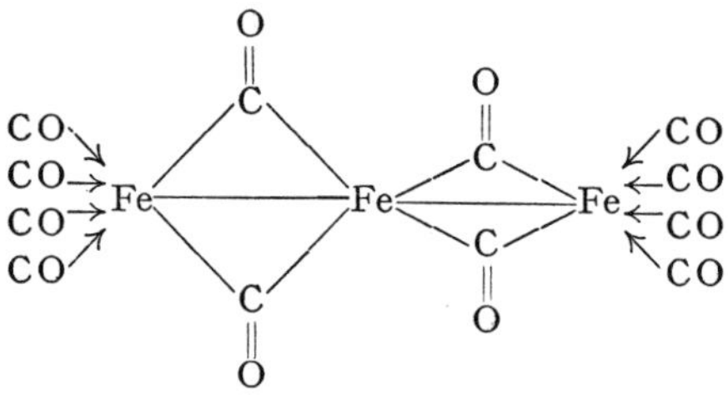

(c) $Fe_3(CO)_{12}$

By comparison the structure of $Mn_2(CO)_{10}$ is simple; there are no bridging groups:

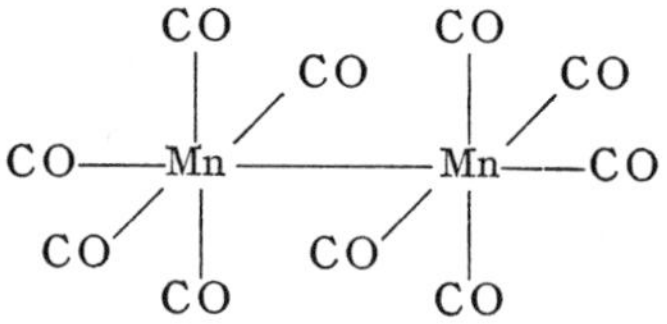

Chapter 19

Germanium, Tin and Lead

GROUP IVB

The atoms of the Gp.IVB elements resemble carbon and silicon in having the ns^2np^2 electron configuration and ^3P ground state, and in forming the tetrahedral bonds associated with sp³ hybridisation. But there is an increasing tendency to form instead an 'inert-pair' ion; and, in its most stable salts, lead preserves an ns^2 'core', appearing as Pb^{2+}. Since the atoms have fairly low electronegativities, the bonds in many of their compounds are fairly strongly ionic. The usual practice is to regard the metals formally as ions, with charge number +4 or (for Pb) +2, and to assign ionic radii (as distinct from the atomic or 'metallic' radii) on this basis.

TABLE 61

SOME PROPERTIES OF GROUP IVB ELEMENTS

	Ge	Sn	Pb
Atomic number	32	50	82
Electron configuration	$4s^2\,4p^2$	$5s^2\,5p^2$	$6s^2\,6p^2$
Atomic radius (Å)	1.22	1.41	1.54
Ionic radius, M^{2+} (Å)			1.32
Ionic radius, M^{4+} (Å)	0.53	0.71	0.84

Pb^{2+} is recognisable in PbS, which has the typical rock salt structure, and in the solid PbF_2 (m.p. 818°); but Sn^{2+} is not an apt description of tin in its bivalent compounds, these being predominantly covalent. The ionisation potentials and M^{2+}/M electrode potentials are shown in Table 62.

TABLE 62

IONISATION AND ELECTRODE POTENTIALS OF GROUP IVB ELEMENTS

	Ge	Sn	Pb
Ionisation potential I 1 (eV)	8.13	7.32	7.41
,, ,, 2 (eV)	15.86	14.5	14.96
E_h° M^{2+}/M (V)		−0.136	−0.146

The first ionisation potentials of Sn and Pb may be contrasted with those of Cd (8.99) and Hg (10.43), atoms with comparable radii (~ 1.48) but with the closed shell structure ns^2. Their similar electrode potentials indicate similar free energies (and hence, roughly, heats) of hydration of the M^{2+} ions. The electrode potentials for M^{4+}/M^{2+} are, however, very different:

$$E_h^{\circ}Pb^{4+}/Pb^{2+} = 1.5 \text{ V}. \qquad E_h^{\circ}Sn^{4+}/Sn^{2+} = 0.15 \text{ V}.$$

Consequently, lead(IV) compounds in acid solution are much stronger oxidising agents than tin(IV) compounds.

Properties of the elements

The elements themselves show a marked transition from non-metallic to metallic character. Germanium has a diamond-type lattice and a m.p. intermediate between the high values of carbon and silicon and the low ones of tin and lead. Tin exists in three solid forms:

$$
\text{grey } (\alpha) \text{ tin} \underset{}{\overset{13.2\,^{\circ}\text{C}}{\rightleftharpoons}} \text{ white } (\beta) \text{ tin} \underset{}{\overset{161\,^{\circ}\text{C}}{\rightleftharpoons}} \text{ brittle tin}
$$
(diamond-type   (body-centred)   (rhombic)
lattice)   tetragonal)

Lead, however, has only the characteristically metallic c.c.p. form. Tin and lead resemble gallium and indium in their long ranges of liquidity.

TABLE 63

SOME PROPERTIES OF GROUP IVB ELEMENTS

	Ge	Sn	Pb
Density (g/cc)	5.36	5.77 (α)	
		7.29 (β)	11.34
Atomic volume	13.55	16.23 (β)	18.27
M.p. (°C)	959	232	327
B.p. (°C)	2700	2360	1755

Germanium has remarkable electrical properties. In the purest form it has a specific resistance, at room temperature, of about 50 ohm/cm. But, on raising the temperature, increasing numbers of electrons are excited and pass from a filled energy band (p. 111), over a narrow energy gap, into an empty 'conduction band' and the resistance falls. The metal is an 'intrinsic semiconductor'. It also forms 'impurity' semiconductors. One part per million of a Gp. III or Gp. V metal can reduce the specific resistance by a factor of 50 or more. Antimony, for instance, with 5 valence electrons, is incorporated in the lattice with 4 co-ordination and *donates* an electron to the conduction band, providing *negative* current carriers: it produces an 'N type' semiconductor. A Gp. III impurity such as Al produces a 'P type' semiconductor, the more electronegative atoms *accepting* electrons from the filled band and leaving 'holes' which behave as *positive* carriers.

Preparation of the elements

In Britain, germanium is recovered principally from flue dusts and coal ashes. The only ore used commercially is germanite, (Cu,Ge,Fe,Zn,Ga) (S,As), containing about 6% Ge. When these substances are strongly heated with HCl the chloride, $GeGl_4$, distils off. It is hydrolysed to GeO_2, which is reduced by H_2, C, or a mixture of C and KCN under a molten salt flux. The element is silvery-white, hard and brittle.

Very pure germanium is made by the method of zone refining, usually achieved by slowly traversing a rod of solid with a molten zone by means of radio-frequency heating. Impurities are concentrated in a short section at one end of the bar, which is discarded. The success of the process depends on the difference between the solid and liquid solubilities of one element in another at the point of solidification.

Tin 4×10^{-3}% of the earth's crust) is remarkable for its numerous stable isotopes, of which there are ten, ranging in mass from 112 to 124 (p. 13). The only important ore is cassiterite, SnO_2. When the ore is roasted, sulphur and arsenic are oxidised to SO_2 and As_2O_3 respectively; the latter sublimes into cooled chambers and forms an important source of arsenic. The SnO_2 is reduced with carbon in a blast or reverberatory furnace and the metal is tapped off. Its principal use is in the manufacture of tinplate, but the alloys with copper (bronzes), with lead (solders) and with lead and antimony (type metals) are important. The metal, ordinarily in its tetragonal form, is silvery, with a slight blue tinge, soft and malleable. Grey tin, stable below 13.2°, has a diamond-like structure and is brittle. The change from white to grey is slow above $-50°$ unless some grey tin is present to catalyse the change.

Lead (2×10^{-4}% of the earth's crust) occurs principally as galena, PbS, and cerussite, $PbCO_3$. The metal is obtained by ore-hearth smelting:

$$2PbS + 3O_2 \rightarrow 2PbO + 2SO_2,$$
$$[PbS + 2O_2 \rightarrow PbSO_4],$$
$$PbS + 2PbO \rightarrow 3Pb + SO_2,$$
$$[PbS + 2PbSO_4 \rightarrow Pb + 2PbO + 3SO_2];$$

or by an oxidising roast:

$$2PbS + 3O_2 \rightarrow 2PbO + 2SO_2,$$

followed by blast furnace smelting:

$$PbO + CO \rightarrow CO_2 + Pb.$$

A new method of extraction is by the electrolysis of PbS dissolved in molten $PbCl_2$; Pb and S are liberated at cathode and anode respectively.

The pure metal is very soft; the hardness is increased by the presence of

Sb and Cu. Its resistance to atmospheric corrosion and to attack by acids leads to employment in chemical plant, for pipes and cable sheathing. The presence of 0.050—0.065% of tellurium improves the properties desirable for these purposes, such as grain-size, hardness, tensile strength and corrosion resistance. Alloyed with a little Sb, it is used in large quantities for the electrode grids in lead-acid storage batteries.

Silver occurs in lead ores and appears in metal from the smelter; its removal and recovery is usually worthwhile. Parkes' process is based on the low solubility of Zn in molten Pb and the very high distribution coefficient for silver between the zinc and lead layers. After stirring zinc into the molten lead, the Zn-Ag alloy which floats to the top is skimmed off and treated for the recovery of silver.

Reactions of the metals

The principal reactions of Ge and Sn are shown in Fig. 161.

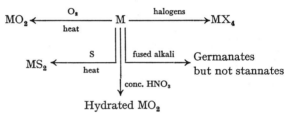

Fig. 161. The chemistry of Ge and Sn (M).

Owing to its reluctance to form the Pb^{4+} ion, or, more realistically, to allow its 2s electrons to participate in sp^3 hybridisation, lead reacts rather differently (Fig. 162).

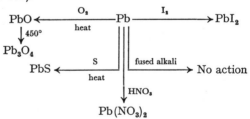

Fig. 162. The chemistry of Pb.

The elements are rather unreactive towards acids. Germanium is not attacked by HCl or HF. Both Ge and Sn are oxidised by concentrated HNO_3 to the hydrated dioxides:

$$3M + 4HNO_3 \rightarrow 3MO_2 + 4NO + 2H_2O,$$

but lead is dissolved, forming the nitrate:

$$3Pb + 8HNO_3 \rightarrow 3Pb(NO_3)_2 + 4H_2O + 2NO.$$

The high hydrogen overvoltage at tin is responsible for the metal's lack of reactivity towards cold dilute acids. On heating, concentrated HCl and H_2SO_4 both react, however:

$$Sn + 2HCl \rightarrow SnCl_2 + H_2,$$
$$Sn + 2H_2SO_4 \rightarrow SnSO_4 + SO_2 + 2H_2O.$$

Their action on lead is limited by the low solubilities of $PbCl_2$ and $PbSO_4$, but on heating both acids dissolve the metal; some H_2 is obtained, as well as SO_2, from concentrated H_2SO_4.

Halides

The physical properties of the tetrahalides, except SnF_4 and PbF_4, correspond to those of the covalent halides of carbon and silicon. GeF_4 is a gas similar to SiF_4, the tetrachlorides of the three elements and the bromides of germanium and tin are liquids, and GeI_4 and SnI_4 solids of low m.p. However, SnF_4 sublimes at 705° and PbF_4 melts at 600°, both being more ionic in character.

The tetrahalides of Ge and Sn are usually made by the action of the halogen on the heated element; the fluorides are conveniently obtained by the reactions:

$$GeO_2 + 4HF \rightarrow GeF_4 + 2H_2O,$$
$$SnCl_4 + 4HF \rightarrow SnF_4 + 4HCl.$$

PbF_4 and $PbCl_4$ result from oxidising the dihalide with the corresponding halogen. Bromine, but not iodine, is just sufficiently strongly electron accepting to withdraw electrons from the $6s^2$ shell of Pb^{2+} and unstable $PbBr_4$ occurs. PbF_4 and $PbCl_4$ are themselves unstable and dissociate on warming:

$$PbX_4 \rightarrow PbX_2 + X_2.$$

The tetrafluoride is consequently a good fluorinating agent.

The tetrahalides are hydrolysed irreversibly by water, complexes often being produced. Thus $SnCl_4$, hydrolysed in the presence of cineol, produces a salt of the ion $[SnCl_3(OH)_3]^{2-}$, indicating that hydrolysis is initiated by the co-ordination of water molecules to the metal atom:

$$SnCl_4 + 2H_2O \rightarrow SnCl_4(H_2O)_2 \leftrightharpoons H_2[SnCl_4(OH)_2] \leftrightharpoons H[SnCl_3(OH)_2] + HCl.$$
$$H[SnCl_3(OH)_2] + H_2O \leftrightharpoons H_2[SnCl_3(OH)_3].$$

A crystalline hydrate, $SnCl_4.5H_2O$, is obtained when a limited amount of water is added to tin(IV) chloride. The ionic character of this solid, as compared with $SnCl_4$, is probably due to the presence of the complex ion $[Sn(H_2O)_4]^{4+}$.

GeF_4 hydrolyses similarly to SiF_4 (p. 290):

$$3GeF_4 + 2H_2O \rightarrow 2H_2GeF_6 + GeO_2.$$

Octahedral complex ions, MX_6^{2-}, are generally very stable; GeF_6^{2-}, like SiF_6^{2-}, is particularly so. Ammonium hexachloroplumbate(IV) is precipitated when NH_4Cl is added to the solution produced by passing Cl_2 into a suspension of $PbCl_2$ in HCl:

$$PbCl_2 + Cl_2 \quad \rightarrow PbCl_4,$$
$$PbCl_4 + 2NH_4Cl \rightarrow (NH_4)_2PbCl_6.$$

The dihalides are more ionic in character. Those of germanium are colourless-to-yellow solids made by heating the tetrahalide with the metal:

$$GeX_4 + Ge \rightarrow 2GeX_2.$$

At higher temperatures this reaction is reversed. The germanium dihalides are all strong reducing agents. The solids possibly have bridged structures:

$GeCl_2$ reacts with HCl gas at 40° to give the colourless fuming liquid, $GeHCl_3$ germanochloroform.

The dihalides of tin and lead are monomeric in the vapour; the molecules are angular (p. 125). In $PbBr_2$ the Br–Pb–Br angle is 86°. These anhydrous compounds cannot strictly be considered ionic, but tetratin(II) hydroxide dichloride, $Sn_4(OH)_6Cl_2$, the only definite compound crystallising from aqueous solutions, is the salt $[Sn_3(OH)_4]^{2+}[Sn(OH)_2Cl_2]^{2-}$ (Donaldson, Moser and Simpson, 1961). The lead dihalides are all sparingly soluble in cold water and can be precipitated:

$$Pb(NO_3)_2 + 2HF \rightarrow PbF_2 + 2HNO_3.$$

Yellow PbI_2 dissolves in hot water to give a colourless solution containing hydrated Pb^{2+} ions. Complex halides such as $KSnCl_3$, K_2SnCl_4, K_2PbCl_4 and $NH_4Pb_2Cl_5$ can be made from tin(II) and lead(II) chlorides. The formulae of the alkali metal fluoroplumbates (II) depend on the ionic radius of the Gp. I metal (Schmitz-Dumont and Bergerhoff, 1956). Potassium fluoride gives K_4PbF_6 with PbF_2, but RbF and CsF give the perovskite-type compounds $MPbF_3$. Potassium and rubidium also form non-stoichiometric compounds $M_nPb_{1-n}F_{2-n}$ where $n = 0.2$ to 0.3. These have an anti-αAgI structure (p. 153) with additional F^- ions.

When $GeCl_4$ is passed with an inert carrier gas through a tube at $1000°$ and then over a cold surface, brown $(GeCl)_x$ separates (Schwarz and Baronetzky, 1954). The substance is insoluble in most solvents. Alkalis attack it:

$$2GeCl + 6KOH \rightarrow 2K_2GeO_3 + 2KCl + 3H_2.$$

Heating to $500°$ causes disproportionation:

$$4GeCl \rightarrow 3Ge + GeCl_4.$$

Moulton and Miller (1956) found that the disproportionation of $GeCl_2$ is by way of this polymeric substance.

Oxides

GeO_2 and SnO_2 are the ultimate oxidation products of the metals. PbO_2 is made by the oxidation of Pb^{2+} in alkaline solution. All three dioxides exist as structures of the rutile type (p. 150) but GeO_2 has also a quartz-like structure stable above $1033°$. Though freshly precipitated germanium dioxide was formerly referred to as germanic acid there is no X-ray evidence for a definite hydrate (Brauer and Renner, 1955). However, GeO_2 reacts with basic oxides to form germanates, usually isomorphous with the silicates. Sodium metagermanate, Na_2GeO_3, is soluble in water. Tetraethyl germanate, $Ge(OEt)_4$, b.p. $185°$, made by refluxing $GeCl_4$ with NaOEt in alcohol, is converted into a gel of hydrated GeO_2 on the addition of water to the alcoholic solution. Removal of the alcohol under reduced pressure leaves a hard material with adsorbent characteristics similar to silica gel.

The alkali metal stannates and plumbates form trihydrates containing octahedral anions —$Sn(OH)_6{}^{2-}$. These are isomorphous with one another and with the platinates. The dioxides dissolve in acids only in the presence of F^- and Cl^- ions.

X-ray examination of the products of the thermal decomposition of PbO_2 discloses two intermediate, non-stoichiometric phases between PbO_2 and Pb_3O_4. The α-phase is close to Pb_7O_{11} and the β-phase to Pb_2O_3 (Butler and Copp, 1956).

Red lead itself, Pb_3O_4, consists of chains of PbO_6 octahedra sharing opposite edges linked by Pb atoms each co-ordinated to three oxygens (Fig. 163).

The monoxides, though amphoteric, are only weakly so on the acidic side, particularly SnO and PbO. Black GeO can be made by heating in an inert atmosphere the yellow precipitate obtained when NaOH is added to a $GeCl_2$ solution. Gastinger (1935) obtained it by oxidising Ge metal with CO_2 at $800°$:

$$Ge + CO_2 \rightarrow GeO + CO.$$

Black crystalline SnO and yellow PbO are both tetragonal with layer lattices in which the metal atom is bonded to four oxygens in a square on one side of it. The adjacent layers are held together by metal-metal bonds (Fig. 196, p. 376).

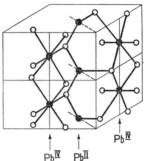

Fig. 163. Structure of Pb_3O_4.

Sulphides

GeS_2 and SnS_2, unlike SiS_2, are not hydrolysed by water. GeS_2 is made by direct combination of the elements, but the reaction between Sn and S goes as far as SnS_2 only in the presence of NH_4Cl. GeS_2 has a quartz-like structure, SnS_2 a layer lattice of the cadmium iodide type. The compounds are precipitated in a somewhat impure condition by adding H_2S to acidified germanate and stannate solutions. The precipitates redissolve in alkali sulphide solutions to give thiogermanates and thiostannates: $Na_2SnS_3.8H_2O$ and $Na_4SnS_4.18H_2O$ have been isolated but a thiogermanate has not been obtained from solution.

Black GeS is formed by reducing GeS_2 in hydrogen at 500°. SnS is obtained as a grey solid by heating the metal with sulphur at 900°, or as a brown precipitate when H_2S is passed into a tin (II) salt solution. It does not dissolve in alkali sulphides; but in polysulphides, such as yellow ammonium sulphide, it gives solutions of thiostannates from which the higher sulphide is precipitated on acidification.

The structure of PbS is of particular interest as the compound crystallises with the typically ionic NaCl lattice in marked contrast to the layer lattice of PbO. It may well be the least ionic compound to do so.

Nitrogen compounds

When germanium tetraiodide is treated with NH_3 the compound $Ge(NH)_2$ is obtained (cf. $NCNH_2$). Heating to 150° converts this to germanam, the germanium analogue of silicam and cyanimide:

$$2Ge(NH)_2 \rightarrow (GeN)_2NH + NH_3.$$

Further heating yields the nitride Ge_3N_4. Germanium di-iodide reacts with liquid ammonia to give the imide Ge : NH.

Tin(IV) iodide reacts with potassamide to give potassium ammonostannate and not an amide or imide,

$$SnI_4 + 6KNH_2 \rightarrow K_2Sn(NH_2)_6 + 4KI,$$

and metallic tin reacts with KNH_2 in liquid NH_3 to give $KSn(NH_2)_3$, easily oxidised in the presence of excess KNH_2 to the ammonostannate above. Lead iodide reacts with potassamide in liquid ammonia to give an imide:

$$PbI_2 + 2KNH_2 \rightarrow PbNH + 2KI + NH_3.$$

Oxoacid salts

The only Gp.IVB oxo-salts of importance are those of lead. Most of the lead(II) salts are sparingly soluble. The solubilities of $PbSO_4$, $PbCrO_4$ and PbC_2O_4 resemble those of the corresponding barium salts; the Pb^{2+} ion (1.32 Å) and the Ba^{2+} ion (1.29 Å) are similar in size. Lead acetate $Pb(CH_3COO)_2.3H_2O$ is easily soluble in water; the salt ionises very slightly, however.

Lead tetra-acetate, the only stable lead(IV) oxoacid salt, is deposited in white needles on cooling solutions of Pb_3O_4 in hot acetic acid (PbO_2 is insoluble). It is used as an organic oxidising agent:

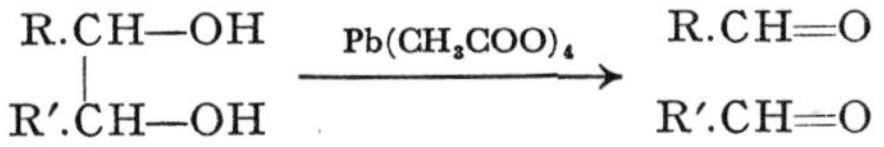

$$\begin{array}{cc}
\text{R.CH—OH} & \\
\underset{\displaystyle R'.CH—OH}{|} & \xrightarrow{Pb(CH_3COO)_4} \quad \begin{array}{c} R.CH=O \\ R'.CH=O \end{array}
\end{array}$$

and is also employed as a methylating agent:

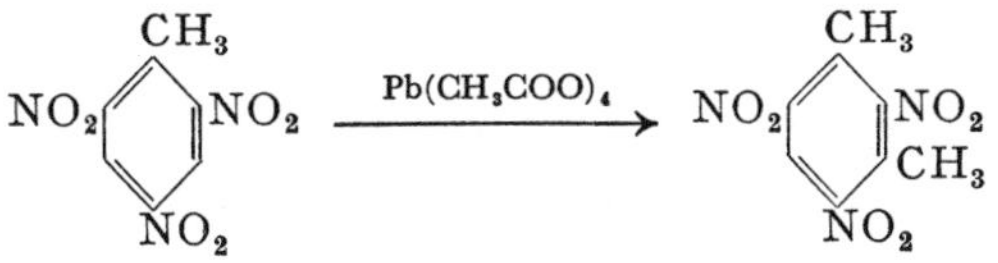

This is probably a free-radical reaction in which the CH_3 radical, derived from the pyrolysis of the tetra-acetate, takes part:

$$Pb(CH_3COO)_4 \rightarrow CH_3. + CH_3COO. + CO_2 + Pb(CH_3COO)_2.$$

Lead tetraethyl

This became one of the more commercially important lead compounds when its value as an 'antiknock' additive to lower grade petrols was recognised. On pyrolysis in the explosion it produces ethyl radicals which break oxidation chain reactions (p. 192); these are initiated by compression before ignition by the spark in the cylinder of an internal combustion engine. The compound is made by the action of ethyl chloride vapour on sodium-lead alloy:

$$4NaPb + 4EtCl \rightarrow PbEt_4 + 3Pb + 4NaCl.$$

Polyanionic compounds of lead

Lead dissolves in liquid ammonia solutions of sodium giving a highly coloured liquid. The formation of polyplumbides has been demonstrated by electrometrically titrating a solution of sodium in ammonia with one of lead iodide in ammonia; the compounds formed are Na_4Pb_7 and Na_4Pb_9. The electrolysis of such a solution releases Na at the cathode and Pb at the anode. Evaporation gives $[Na(NH_3)_x]_4Pb_9$ which loses NH_3 to leave pyrophoric Na_4Pb_9. These compounds seem to possess a character between that of a true valency compound and an intermediate phase (Zintl, 1929).

Chapter 20

Nitrogen and Phosphorus

These elements, with five valence electrons, form bonds which are almost exclusively covalent in character. For this reason, it is not generally profitable to invoke an ionic description, however formal, and the definition of an ionic radius is usually of little value. An exception might be made in certain phosphorus complexes where an empirical P^{5+} radius may be defined and used in the usual way.

TABLE 64

SOME PROPERTIES OF NITROGEN AND PHOSPHORUS

	N	P
Atomic number	7	15
Electron configuration	$2s^2\,2p^3$	$3s^2\,3p^3$
Atomic radius (Å)	0.74	1.10
Ionic radius, M^{5+} (Å)		0.34

The chief differences between nitrogen and phosphorus arise from the availability of d orbitals in the shell with principal quantum number 3. This gives phosphorus valence properties not shared by nitrogen; for example, a capacity for 6 co-ordination associated with octahedral hybridisation (p. 105).

In the ground state, both atoms have three singly occupied p orbitals. With this configuration, which gives a ^4S state, is associated a spherically symmetrical distribution of electrons and a high ionisation potential. Since the compounds are essentially covalent, however, ionisation potentials are less important than electronegativities.

TABLE 65

IONISATION POTENTIAL AND ELECTRONEGATIVITY
OF NITROGEN AND PHOSPHORUS

	N	P
Ionisation potential (eV)	14.48	10.9
Electronegativity (Pauling scale)	3.0	2.1

Owing to the readiness with which both atoms form covalent bonds, the simple ions do not exist in solution; but compounds like NH_3 are proton acceptors, and complex ions such as NH_4^+ are therefore common.

The chemistry of nitrogen and phosphorus is dominated by a tendency of the atoms to complete their octets, an end which may be achieved in a considerable number of ways. The electron configuration of the nitrogen molecule may be described in molecular orbital terms as

$$N_2 [KK\ (z\sigma)^2(y\sigma)^2(x\sigma)^2(w\pi)^4]$$

where it is evident (p. 94) that the σ bond results from occupation of $x\sigma$, which may be roughly a $\sigma 2p$ orbital, while $(w\pi)^4$ represents two filled $\pi 2p$ orbitals and describes two π bonds. The result is a triple bond, of length 1.09 Å, giving a heat of dissociation of 225 kcal per mole ($cf.$ H_2, 103 and O_2, 117). The character of this bond is largely responsible for the inert nature of the gas and the low thermal stabilities of the oxides (see Table 66). It is now thought likely that the σ bond in N_2 is better described by invoking sp

TABLE 66

HEATS OF FORMATION OF OXIDES OF NITROGEN (KCAL/MOLE)

N_2O	-17	NO_2	-2
NO	-21.5	N_2O_5	$+5$
		($cf.$ P_4O_{10}	$+365$)

hybridisation; in this case $(z\sigma)^2$ and $(y\sigma)^2$ are replaced by the lone pairs (one on each nitrogen) which point away from the bond ($cf.$ p. 96). It then becomes more obvious that there are four electron pairs (lone pairs or bond pairs) in the vicinity of each nitrogen atom. The tendency to form compact electron pairs becomes more marked in compounds where the hybridisation is dictated by molecular geometry; as, for example, in tetrahedral NH_4^+ (p. 102). Examples of the principal types and of the situations in which they are appropriate are given in Table 67.

Bond angles in NH_3, NMe_3 and NF_3 decrease as the electronegativity of the atom or group attached to the nitrogen increases (p. 128). In such angular species as NOCl and NO_2^-, the bond angles, here of 116° and 115°, are consistent with strong lone-pair–bond-pair repulsion. The bond angles in the series NO_2^+, NO_2, NO_2^- are interesting:

$$\left[\underset{180°}{O-N-O} \right]^+ \qquad \left[\underset{132°}{O-\overset{\cdot}{N}} \diagdown O \right]^0 \qquad \left[\underset{115°}{O-\overset{\cdot\cdot}{N}} \diagdown O \right]^-$$

TABLE 67

HYBRIDISATION OF NITROGEN ATOM

Hybrid	Bonding pairs	Lone pairs	Molecular shape	Examples
sp³	4σ	0	Tetrahedral	NH_4^+, NEt_4^+, Me_3N—O
	3σ	1	Pyramidal	$:NH_3$, $:NMe_3$, $:NF_3$
sp²	3σ 1π	0	Triangular	Cl—N⟨^O_O $\overline{O}$—N⟨^O_O
	2σ 1π	1	Angular	$_{Cl}$>N̈—O $_{\overline{O}}$>N̈—O
sp	2σ 2π	0	Linear	O—N̟⁺—O

The nitronium ion, being without non-bonding electrons, is linear, the others are angular; the repulsion exerted by the bonding pairs in NO_2 is less than that exerted by the non-bonding pair in NO_2^-.

In the gas phase, phosphorus, unlike nitrogen, exists as a tetrahedral molecule P_4 (Fig.164). The σ bonds, in spite of their being 'bent', are apparently preferred to the π bonds of a nitrogen-like configuration. The dissociation energy of the phosphorus molecule is small and the element accordingly much more reactive than nitrogen.

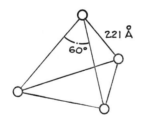

Fig. 164. Structure of P_4 molecule.

Phosphorus, like nitrogen, can complete an octet of four tetrahedrally arranged electron pairs either by forming three covalent bonds, which thus have pyramidal arrangement, or by forming tetra-co-ordinated complexes such as PH_4^+, akin to NH_4^+. But because 3d orbitals are available in phosphorus all the valency electrons can be used to form five bonds with trigonal-bipyramidal arrangement. Octahedral complexes also occur in anions such as PCl_6^- (Table 68).

The bond angle in PH_3, ~ 94°, is much less than in NH_3, ~ 107°; the nitrogen, with its much greater electronegativity, forms stronger and shorter

TABLE 68

HYBRIDISATION OF PHOSPHORUS ATOM

Hybrid	Bonding pairs	Lone pairs	Molecular shape	Examples	
sp^3	4σ	0	Tetrahedral	PH_4^+,	PCl_4^+
	3σ	1	Trigonal pyramidal	PCl_3,	P_4O_6
	4σ 1π	0	Tetrahedral	$POCl_3$,	PO_4^{3-}
sp^3d	5σ	0	Trigonal bipyramidal	PCl_5,	PF_5
sp^3d^2	6σ	0	Octahedral	PCl_6^-	

bonds with the hydrogen, whereby the repulsive effect of the lone pair is less than in the phosphorus compound.

In molecules of the type POX_3, the angle X–P–X is always less than the tetrahedral angle (POF_3, 102.5° and $POCl_3$, 103.5°) because the double bond repels the single bonds more than the single bonds repel each other (p. 127).

The elements: preparation and properties

Nitrogen, the principal gas of the atmosphere, is separated from liquid air by fractional distillation. The gas is finding increasing use as an inert furnace-atmosphere. Chemical separation from the air by means of the producer-gas reaction provides nitrogen for ammonia and cyanamide manufacture.

Nitrogen, in common with oxygen and hydrogen, gives a characteristic colour in the low-pressure electrical discharge. When the discharge is switched off there is no 'afterglow' in hydrogen, it is exceedingly brief in oxygen, but persists for several seconds in nitrogen. It seems reasonably certain that the discharge produces nitrogen atoms in the ground state and that the 'afterglow' accompanies a pre-association of atoms into unstable molecules from which they pass into stable molecules.

$$N_2 \xrightarrow{\text{discharge}} 2N \rightarrow \text{pre-associated molecules} \rightarrow \text{stable molecules}$$

The process giving rise to the afterglow is of second order with respect to nitrogen atoms and first order with respect to nitrogen molecules, suggesting an overall reaction,

$$N + N + N_2 \rightarrow N_2 + N_2,$$

involving a three-body collison (p. 191). The process is not simple, because the nitrogen atom, having three unpaired electrons, can form a variety of nitrogen molecules, one of which is the pre-associated molecule. This may reach a stable form by one of three routes, giving rise to emission of energy belonging to three band systems.

The behaviour of active nitrogen at the temperature of liquid helium suggests that the solid contains atoms which, on reacting, emit a bright green glow accompanied by blue flashes on the surface of the vessel. The chemical reactions of active nitrogen are also consistent with the presence of atoms; thus hydrocarbons yield chiefly HCN, presumably by an attack on the C atoms rather than the abstraction of hydrogen, since neither NH_3 nor $NH_2.NH_2$ has been detected (Jennings and Linnett, 1958).

The chemically inert character of nitrogen is largely due to the high bonding energy of the molecule. Combination occurs with both oxygen and hydrogen under suitable conditions; both reactions have been extensively studied and used commercially:

$$N_2 + O_2 \rightarrow 2NO, \qquad N_2 + 3H_2 \rightarrow 2NH_3.$$

Of the metals, only lithium combines at moderate temperatures, $6Li + N_2 \rightarrow 2Li_3N$; the Gp.IIA metals at about red heat, $3Ca + N_2 \rightarrow Ca_3N_2$; and boron and aluminium at bright red heat, $B + N \rightarrow BN$.

Silicon and some elements of higher groups (p. 298) react at temperatures above 1200°. The nitrides of the Gp.I metals other than lithium cannot be made by direct combination (p. 248).

Active nitrogen is much more chemically reactive, forming a nitride with mercury in the cold, and combining directly with phosphorus, iodine, sulphur and arsenic. It has no action on molecular oxygen or hydrogen but it decomposes nitric oxide into its elements:

$$2N + 2NO \rightarrow 2N_2 + O_2.$$

TABLE 69

SOME PROPERTIES OF NITROGEN AND PHOSPHORUS

	Nitrogen	*Phosphorus (white)*
Density (g/cc)	1.027 (solid at $-210°$)	1.83
Atomic volume	13.65	16.96
Melting point (°C)	-210	44
Boiling point (°C)	-196	287

Phosphorus (0.11% of the lithosphere) is found mainly in minerals based on calcium phosphate, collophanite, the monohydrate, $Ca_3(PO_4)_2.H_2O$, and apatite, $Ca_5F(PO_4)_3$. About 90% of the phosphate rock mined is converted into fertilisers, the rest is used for making elementary phosphorus, phosphorus compounds and such alloys as phosphor bronze. For fertilisers rock phosphate is finely ground and treated with sufficient concentrated sulphuric acid to convert it to the soluble dihydrogen phosphate:

$$Ca_3(PO_4)_2 + 2 H_2SO_4 \rightarrow Ca(H_2PO_4)_2 + 2 CaSO_4.$$

Phosphorus is extracted from the mineral by heating with sand and coke, generally electrically, and condensing the vapour to give the white variety of the element:

$$Ca_3(PO_4)_2 + 3 SiO_2 \rightarrow 3 CaSiO_3 + P_2O_5$$
$$P_2O_5 + 5 C \rightarrow 2 P + 5 CO.$$

White phosphorus when pure melts to a colourless liquid which crystallises in the cubic system; the solid contains individual P_4 tetrahedra held together by Van der Waals forces. It can be changed to a hexagonal form by high pressure, the transition temperature being $-77°$. The black allotrope, similar to graphite in appearance and conductance, was formerly made only at very high pressures; but Krebs, Weitz and Worms (1955) made it from white phosphorus at ordinary pressure in the presence of mercury and a 'seed' of the black variety. Transformation was complete after 8 days during which the temperature was gradually raised from 220° to 370°. The atoms in black phosphorus are covalently linked in an extended network.

Although white phosphorus is partially converted to red by light and wholly by heat, the conversion is catalysed by some halides, particularly P_2I_4. Pauling (1952) suggested the change was caused by the rupture of one bond of the P_4 tetrahedron and the linking of the pairs of equilateral triangles so formed into long chains (Fig. 165). This structure is not, however,

Fig. 165. Arrangement of phosphorus atoms in red phosphorus.

consistent with the high vapour pressure of red phosphorus (Melville and Gray, 1936). When phosphorus vapour is cooled rapidly from 1000° to $-196°$ a dark brown solid is obtained (Rice, Potocki and Gosselin, 1953), stable indefinitely at that temperature and probably containing P_2 molecules. At $-100°$ the brown phosphorus changes irreversibly to a mixture of approximately 20% red and 80% white phosphorus; as the temperature is raised the rate of conversion increases but the ratio of the allotropes alters little. The high vapour pressure of red phosphorus may be due to evaporation as P_2 molecules followed by their immediate dimerisation to P_4.

Halides

Trihalides of nitrogen with fluorine and chlorine can be isolated, but with bromine and iodine only the ammonia complexes, $NBr_3(NH_3)_6$ and $NI_3(NH_3)$, are known.

NF_3 is a colourless gas (b.p. —119°) of normal vapour density, made by electrolysing fused NH_4HF_2 in a copper vessel. The crude gas which contains HF, N_2, H_2, N_2O, O_2, O_3, NH_2F and NHF_2 is passed over KF to remove HF, MnO_2 to remove O_3, frozen, distilled and then washed with NaOH to remove NH_2F and NHF_2 (Ruff, Fischer and Luft, 1928). An exothermic compound ($\Delta H_f = -26$ kcal), it is much more thermally stable and chemically inert than the other nitrogen halides. It is not hydrolysed by water or alkali and is non-explosive, though it reacts violently with hydrogen on sparking:

$$2NF_3 + 3H_2 \rightarrow N_2 + 6HF.$$

NCl_3 is a yellow, oily liquid made by the action of chlorine on NH_4Cl in concentrated aqueous solution. An endothermic compound, ($\Delta H_f = +55$ kcal), it explodes above its boiling point or on impact, and is easily hydrolysed:

$$NCl_3 + 3OH^- \rightarrow NH_3 + 3OCl^-.$$

Difluorodiazine, N_2F_2, a minor product of the electrolysis of NH_4HF_2, has well defined isomers (cis m.p. $\sim -195°$, b.p. $-105.7°$; trans m.p. $-172°$, b.p. $-114°$). The trans isomer is converted to the cis on heating; it is appreciably less reactive than the cis with glass and mercury.

Tetrafluorohydrazine, N_2F_4, is produced when NF_3 is passed over hot copper and other metals which abstract fluorine. The compound boils at $-73°$, has a critical temperature of 36°, and has the structure

Monochloramine, NH_2Cl, is formed when NH_3 and NaOCl react in aqueous solution in equimolar quantities:

$$NH_3 + NaOCl \rightarrow NH_2Cl + NaOH.$$

Distillation at low pressure, followed by drying and condensing the vapour, gives colourless crystals m.p. —66°, unstable at higher temperatures when dry. Dichloramine, $NHCl_2$, is formed when chlorine is passed into ammonium sulphate solution buffered to pH 5 ±0.5, but has not been isolated. NH_2F can be made pure. It is more reactive than NF_3, being hydrolysed by alkalis; NH_2Cl, on the contrary, is less reactive than NCl_3.

Purple $NBr_3(NH_3)_6$, resulting from the action of bromine vapour on an excess of ammonia (Schmeisser, 1940), and black $NI_3(NH_3)$, made by treating iodine with strong aqueous ammonia, are both highly explosive solids.

The halides of phosphorus are, with the exceptions stated in Table 70, colourless.

TABLE 70

PHOSPHORUS HALIDES

	Trihalides	Pentahalides	Others
Fluorides	PF_3 b.p. $-95°$	PF_5 b.p. $-85°$	
Chlorides	PCl_3 b.p. 76°	PCl_5 sublimes 163°	P_2Cl_4 b.p. 180°
Bromides	PBr_3 b.p. 173°	PBr_5 m.p. 100°	
		(yellow)	
Iodides	PI_3 b.p. 61°		P_2I_4 m.p. 124°
	(dark red)		(orange)

The trihalides are usually prepared by direct combination under controlled conditions, but PF_3 is best made by the action of AsF_3 on PCl_3:

$$AsF_3 + PCl_3 \rightarrow AsCl_3 + PF_3.$$

Hydrolysis gives phosphorous acid and the halogen hydracid; the ease of hydrolysis increases with molecular weight:

$$PX_3 + 3H_2O \rightarrow H_3PO_3 + 3HX.$$

They all react with oxygen and sulphur:

$$2PX_3 + O_2 \rightarrow 2POX_3, \qquad PX_3 + S \rightarrow PSX_3,$$

and with halogens except when $X = I$:

$$PX_3 + X_2 \rightarrow PX_5.$$

By using their lone pairs, the molecules can act as ligands in complexes:

$$Ni(CO)_4 + 4PCl_3 \rightarrow Ni(PCl_3)_4 + 4CO.$$

Mixed halides such as PF_2Br have been made; they decompose on heating:

$$3PF_2Br \rightarrow 2PF_3 + PBr_3.$$

The pentahalides are produced by the addition of another molecule of halogen, one 3d orbital being now occupied. Solid PCl_5 is made by dropping liquid PCl_3 into dry chlorine. The thermal stability of the pentahalides decreases with molecular weight. PCl_5 dissociates on slight heating, $PCl_5 \rightleftharpoons PCl_3 + Cl_2$, and is readily reduced by some metals on warming, $PCl_5 + Cd \rightarrow PCl_3 + CdCl_2$.

In the vapour phase PF_5 (b.p. $-75°$) and PCl_5 (subl. 163°) have trigonal bipyramidal molecules. In PF_5 the bonds are all equal in length (1.57 Å), but in PCl_5 three are said to be 2.01 Å and two 2.07 Å (Fig. 166) (p. 105, 138).

Solid PCl_5 contains tetrahedral PCl_4^+ and octahedral PCl_6^- ions (Clark, 1942), but PBr_5 has PBr_4^+ and Br^-. A solution of PCl_5 in methyl nitrite conducts electricity.

Hydrolysis occurs in two stages:

$$(i) \quad PX_5 + H_2O \rightarrow POX_3 + 2HX,$$
$$(ii) \quad POX_3 + 3H_2O \rightarrow H_3PO_4 + 3HX.$$

P_2Cl_4 is a colourless, oily, fuming liquid made by passing a silent discharge through a mixture of PCl_3 and hydrogen. It decomposes at its b.p., 180°, to P and PCl_3; it is hydrolysed to HCl, H_3PO_3 and phosphorus, and is liable to

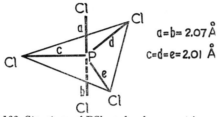

Fig. 166. Structure of PCl_5 molecule present in vapour.

inflame spontaneously in air. P_2I_4 is deposited as orange crystals when CS_2 solutions of phosphorus and iodine in CS_2 are mixed. It decomposes to PI_3 and P on heating and is hydrolysed to H_3PO_3, H_3PO_2 and HI.

Oxides of nitrogen and phosphorus

It is convenient to classify the oxides in the traditional manner in terms of the formal charge on the nitrogen or phosphorus, when electrons are regarded as transferred to the more electronegative oxygen atoms to give them a -2 charge number. The charge numbers of nitrogen and phosphorus in the oxides are then:

+1	+2	+3	+4	+5
N_2O	NO	N_2O_3	N_2O_4	N_2O_5
		P_4O_6	$(PO_2)_n$	P_4O_{10}

The oxides of nitrogen, except N_2O_5, are gases at room temperature, whereas all those of phosphorus are solid.

Nitrous oxide

Nitrous oxide, N_2O, is made by heating NH_4NO_3. Colourless and unreactive at room temperature, the gas is, through decomposition, an oxidising agent above 600°: $2N_2O \rightarrow 2N_2 + O_2$. It is not the anhydride of hyponitrous acid and, though but slightly soluble, gives a neutral solution.

TABLE 71

PHYSICAL PROPERTIES OF THE OXIDES OF NITROGEN

	N_2O	NO	N_2O_3	N_2O_4	N_2O_5
Molecular weight	44	30	76	92	108
Melting point (°C)	−102.4	−163.6	−102.0	−9.3	+30*
Boiling point (°C)	−88.5	−151.8	+3.5*	+21.3*	+47*
Colour of solid	Colourless	Colourless	Light blue	Colourless	Colourless

* With decomposition

Bond lengths in the linear molecule are

$$\text{N} \xrightarrow{\ 1.12\,\text{Å}\ } \text{N} \xrightarrow{\ 1.19\,\text{Å}\ } \text{O}$$

If both the nitrogen and oxygen atoms are considered to use sp hybrid orbitals the structure can be explained in terms of two σ bonds and two pairs of non-localized π orbitals extending over all three centres. The lowest orbitals in each pair, which differ only by rotation through 90° about the axis, give two partial π bonds in each region, N—N and N—O (Fig. 167(a)). The higher orbitals will be weakly bonding in one link, N—N, and weakly anti-bonding in the other (Fig. 167 (b)). Each bond in the molecule will have some triple bond character, this being highest in the N—N link.

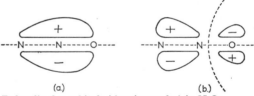

(a)   (b)

Fig. 167. Delocalised π orbitals (showing nodes) in N_2O:
(a) bonding in both regions, N—N and N—O;
(b) weakly bonding in N—N, weakly anti-bonding in N—O.

The molecule is isoelectronic and isosteric with CO_2 and the physical properties of the two compounds show similarities (crit. temp., N_2O, 36.5°; CO_2, 31.1°).

Nitric oxide

Nitric oxide, NO, is a colourless paramagnetic gas, having one odd electron in an antibonding π orbital. This is consistent with the fact that NO^+ (NO with the odd electron removed) has a shorter and stronger bond. Dulmage, Meyers and Lipscomb (1953) found the solid to be composed of rectangular dimers with the dimensions indicated, although the X-ray evidence did not distinguish between similar and opposite orientations of the N—O groups:

$$\begin{array}{ccc} & 2.40 \text{ Å} & \\ \text{N} & \cdots\cdots\cdots & \text{O} \\ 1.10\text{ Å}\Big| & 2.40\text{ Å} & \Big|1.10\text{ Å} \\ \text{O} & \cdots\cdots\cdots & \text{N} \end{array}$$

The liquid has a high Trouton constant and a low dielectric constant. The bond length in the monomer is 1.14 Å and the molecule very stable, so that association to N_2O_2 is endothermic at ordinary temperature. The gaseous molecule has a small dipole moment of 0.16 debye.

Nitric oxide is made on a large scale by oxidising ammonia with air on the surface of platinum above 500°:

$$4NH_3 + 5O_2 \rightarrow 4NO + 6H_2O.$$

The gas is oxidised to N_2O_4 by oxygen and to nitrosyl halides, NOX, by F_2, Cl_2 and Br_2. The reactions have empirical third-order kinetics but are probably bimolecular, involving the dimer even though there is no direct evidence for its presence:

(i) $\quad NO + NO \rightleftharpoons N_2O_2 \left(\text{with } K = \dfrac{N_2O_2}{[NO]^2}\right)$,

(ii) $\quad N_2O_2 + Cl_2 \rightarrow 2NOCl;$

thus rate $\quad \propto [N_2O_2][Cl_2],$ *i.e.* rate $\propto K[NO]^2[Cl_2].$

Compounds from nitric oxide

These are formed in three ways.

(i) Electron sharing, giving highly coloured, covalent substances, typified by the volatile, easily hydrolysed nitrosyl halides.

(ii) Electron gain, to form NO^-, as in sodium nitrosyl from the action of nitric oxide on the metal in liquid ammonia: $Na + NO \rightarrow NaNO.$

(iii) Electron loss, to form NO^+, the nitrosonium ion.

The covalent nitrosyl halides have bent molecules:

$$\text{Cl}\overset{1.95\text{ Å}}{\underset{116°}{-\!\!\!-\!\!\!-}}\text{N}\overset{1.14\text{ Å}}{\diagdown}$$
$$\text{O}$$

The N—X bonds are exceptionally long, suggesting considerable polar character. NOF is best made by allowing F_2 to mix with a twofold excess of NO in a copper tube. NOCl is conveniently produced by passing N_2O_4 over moist KCl at room temperature:

$$N_2O_4 + KCl \rightarrow NOCl + KNO_3.$$

NOBr can be got by passing NO into bromine at —15°. The iodide has not been made. Nitrosyl halides react with hydroxylic compounds to give nitrites:

$$NOCl + ROH \rightarrow RONO + HCl.$$

The ionisation potential for the process $NO \rightarrow NO^+ + e$ is 9.5 eV, much lower than for $N_2 \rightarrow N_2^+ + e$ (~ 16 e V) or $O_2 \rightarrow O_2^+ + e$ (~ 15 e V). As happens with the odd electron in an atom, the odd electron in NO is more readily lost than one from a doubly occupied orbital since it moves outside a closed shell which more effectively screens the nuclei (cf. p. 64). Nitrosonium compounds such as $NO^+ClO_4^-$, $NO^+HSO_4^-$ and $NO^+BF_4^-$, can be prepared in non-hydroxylic solvents. They are usually isomorphous with the corresponding hydroxonium and ammonium salts:

$$H_3O^+ClO_4^- \qquad NO^+ClO_4^- \qquad NH_4^+ClO_4^-$$

Klinkenberg (1938) has shown the ion to be intermediate in size between H_3O^+ and NH_4^+. The NO^+ ion causes a Raman displacement of 2330 cm^{-1}.

Though stable in non-hydroxylic solvents, nitrosonium compounds react with hydroxylic solvents:

$$NO^+ + OH^- \rightleftharpoons HNO_2 \rightleftharpoons NO_2^- + H^+.$$

In strongly acid media the equilibrium is displaced to the left.

Metal complexes of the NO group

In these nitrogen is the donor atom, and in most NO is bound as NO^+ which is isoelectronic with CN^- and CO. The NO group can thus donate one extra electron to the metal; this accounts for the stability of $Co(NO)(CO)_3$ which has the same electronic pattern as $Ni(CO)_4$ (p. 494). Co-ordination complexes of this type do not usually contain more than one NO group and they are generally of outer orbital (sp^3) type (p. 134).

Nitrosyls

Unstable metal nitrosyls are formed by Fe, Ru and Ni. Black $Fe(NO)_4$, made by heating iron carbonyl with NO under pressure at 50°, is the most stable. The structure is unknown, but the ionic formula $NO^+[Fe(NO)_3]^-$ has been suggested to explain its low volatility. Ruthenium tetranitrosyl, $Ru(NO)_4$, is made as cubic, red crystals when NO is passed into $Ru_2(CO)_9$. A compound of empirical formula $Ni(NO)_2$ is obtained as a blue powder when NO is passed into $Ni(CO)_4$ dissolved in $CHCl_3$.

The nitrosyl carbonyls such as $Co(NO)(CO)_3$ are much more stable than the nitrosyls themselves. Nitrosyl halides, $Fe(NO)_2X$, $Co(NO)_2X$ and $Ni(NO)X$ are known; their stability falls from Fe to Ni and from I to Cl. Fluorides are unknown. The most stable nitrosyl halide, $Fe(NO)_2I$, results from passing NO over FeI_2 at $100°$:

$$2FeI_2 + 4NO \rightarrow 2Fe(NO)_2I + I_2.$$

Dinitrogen trioxide

This, the anhydride of nitrous acid, exists only in the solid state, m.p. $-102°$; the liquid of the composition N_2O_3, produced from NO and N_2O_4 at $-20°$, is probably a mixture. Mason (1959) gives the structure of dinitrogen trioxide as $O_2N.NO$ with a π-only N—N bond:

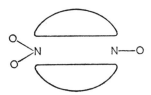

Molecular-orbital, spectroscopic and thermochemical considerations support the assignment of the band in the visible to an electronic transition between a lone pair on the nitroso nitrogen and an anti-bonding π^* orbital, and that of the near-ultraviolet band to a π—π^* transition in a nitroso-nitro molecule with a π-only N—N bond.

In concentrated H_2SO_4 the blue colour disappears as fully ionised nitrosonium hydrogen sulphate is formed:

$$N_2O_3 + 3H_2SO_4 \rightarrow 2NO^+ + H_3O^+ + 3HSO_4^-.$$

Dinitrogen tetroxide

This is colourless and diamagnetic in the dimeric form, N_2O_4, found pure only in the solid, m.p. $-9.3°$. The pale yellow liquid b.p. $21.3°$ contains about 1% of the brown, paramagnetic monomer, NO_2, with one unpaired electron. The vapour darkens progressively on heating and at $100°$ has about 90% of monomer. NO_2 is angular:

$$1.20\ \text{Å} \diagdown N \diagup 1.20\ \text{Å}$$
$$O \quad 132° \quad O$$

Its bonding energy is less than that of nitric oxide, which accounts for a greater tendency to dimerisation.

The monomer, NO_2, an odd-electron molecule, has many of the characteristics of a free radical since it (i) associates with other radicals, (ii) abstracts hydrogen from saturated hydrocarbons, (iii) adds to unsaturated hydrocarbons. Its photolysis, decomposition and oxidising action owe little, however, to its radical character.

N_2O_4 has the planar structure:

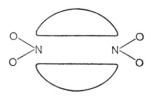

The distance between the nitrogen atoms is 0.27 Å greater than is normal for an N—N single bond. Coulson and Duchesne (1957) consider the bond to arise from a π-overlap only, as it is represented.

The ionisation of N_2O_4 is encouraged by (i) solvents of high dielectric constant such as H_2SO_4 and $HClO_4$, (ii) the removal of NO^+ as complexes by Lewis bases, (iii), the removal of NO_3^-, as, for example, when $Zn(NO_3)_2$ dissolves to form a complex ion:

$$Zn(NO_3)_2 + 2N_2O_4 \rightarrow 2NO^+ + Zn(NO_3)_4{}^{2-}.$$

Very many electron donors, such as amines and ethers, combine with N_2O_4 to produce compounds of the types

$$[\text{Base } NO^+] \ NO_3^- \qquad \text{and} \qquad [(\text{Base})_2 \ NO^+] \ NO_3^-.$$

Metals which react with liquid N_2O_4 (Na, K, Zn, Ag, Pb and Hg) all set free nitric oxide:

$$M + N_2O_4 \rightarrow MNO_3 + NO.$$

Salts react to produce nitrates:

$$N_2O_4 + KCl \rightarrow KNO_3 + NOCl,$$
$$2N_2O_4 + 2KI \rightarrow 2KNO_3 + 2NO + I_2,$$
$$N_2O_4 + NaClO_3 \rightarrow NaNO_3 + NO_2 + ClO_2.$$

Hydroxylic and amino solvents are usually nitrosated by N_2O_4:

$$N_2O_4 + 2ROH \rightarrow RONO + ROH_2^+ + NO_3^-,$$
$$N_2O_4 + 2R_2NH \rightarrow R_2N.NO + R_2NH_2^+ + NO_3^-;$$

but with primary amines nitrogen is evolved:

$$RNH_2 + N_2O_4 \rightarrow R.NH_2NO^+ + NO_3^-,$$

followed by

$$RNH_2NO^+ + RNH_2 \rightarrow RNH_3^+ + N_2 + H_2O.$$

Dinitrogen pentoxide

This is made by the dehydration of nitric acid with P_2O_5. The molecular structure in non-ionising solvents is

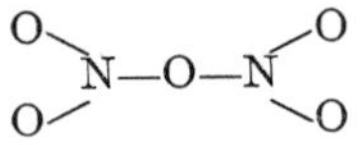

$$\begin{array}{c} O \\ \diagdown \\ O \diagup \end{array} N-O-N \begin{array}{c} O \\ \diagup \\ \diagdown O \end{array}$$

but in H_2SO_4 it ionises (Chedin, 1935):

$$N_2O_5 + 3H_2SO_4 \rightleftharpoons 2NO_2^+ + 3HSO_4^- + H_3O^+.$$

The solid also contains NO_2^+ and NO_3^- ions. The colourless crystals are stable in diffuse light below 8° but on warming, or exposing to sunlight, decomposition occurs. It dissolves in water with a hissing noise to give HNO_3. The oxide itself has a strong oxidising action, converting I_2 to I_2O_5.

Nitronium compounds

The NO_2^+ ion, with a Raman displacement of 1400 cm^{-1}, is present in sulphuric, selenic and perchloric acid solutions of HNO_3. The same Raman line is given by solid nitronium perchlorate, $NO_2^+ClO_4^-$, which can be separated from a solution made by dissolving HNO_3 and $HClO_4$ in nitromethane. Compounds such as $NO_2^+BF_4^-$ and $NO_2^+PF_6^-$ have been made by dissolving the appropriate fluoride or oxide in bromine and treating the solution with N_2O_4 followed by BrF_3. (Raman spectra, p. 120.)

Nitryl halides

Nitryl fluoride, NO_2F, is made when F_2 reacts with a 2:1 excess of NO_2, or when fluorine is passed over heated $NaNO_2$:

$$NaNO_2 + F_2 \rightarrow NaF + NO_2F.$$

NO_2Cl is got by treating $NOCl$ with ozone. Both are colourless gases. They have planar molecules with the structure shown, which is consistent with their hydrolysis to HNO_3 and HX.

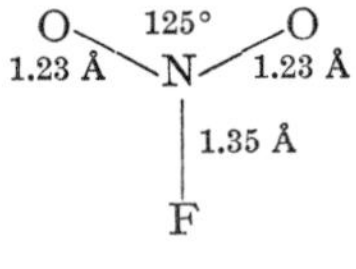

$$\begin{array}{c} O \diagdown \quad 125° \quad \diagup O \\ 1.23\,Å \quad \diagdown N \diagup \quad 1.23\,Å \\ \Big| \; 1.35\,Å \\ F \end{array}$$

Pernitryl fluoride

This compound, NO_3F, also known as fluorine nitrate, is formed as a colourless, explosive gas by the action of F_2 on concentrated nitric acid

(Cady, 1934). It is purified by freezing with liquid air followed by fractional distillation at $-42°$. NO_3F explodes to give NOF and O_2 when sparked, but the first-order decomposition proceeds slowly at $80–110°$. The gas hydrolyses slowly with water yielding oxygen, and fluoride and nitrate ions:

$$2NO_3F + 4OH^- \rightarrow 2F^- + 2NO_3^- + 2H_2O + O_2$$

It oxidises iodides:

$$NO_3F + 2I^- \rightarrow NO_3^- + F^- + I_2.$$

Oxides of phosphorus

The three oxides are P_4O_6, $(PO_2)_n$ and P_4O_{10}. The first and last have structures based on the P_4 tetrahedron (Fig. 164).

In P_4O_6 (Fig. 168) the P—O distance is 1.65 Å and the angles POP and OPO are 127.5° and 99°. In P_4O_{10} an extra O is attached to each P atom at a distance of 1.39 Å (Fig. 169).

A compound $P_4O_6S_4$, made by heating P_4O_6 with sulphur, has a similar structure.

Phosphorus trioxide, P_4O_6, is made by passing a mixture of oxygen and nitrogen, 3 : 1 by volume, over white phosphorus at $45–50°$. The white solid melts at $24°$. It is converted to phosphorous acid by cold water:

$$P_4O_6 + 6H_2O \rightarrow 4H_3PO_3;$$

but hot water produces a mixture of phosphoric acid, phosphorus and phosphine. When P_4O_6 is heated above $210°$ the polymeric $(PO_2)_n$ and red phosphorus are formed.

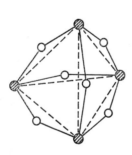

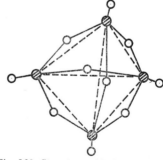

Fig. 168. Structure of P_4O_6 molecule.   Fig. 169. Structure of P_4O_{10} molecule.

The solid oxide $(PO_2)_n$ sublimes at about $180°$. The density of the vapour indicates a molecular formula P_4O_8. The oxide is not the anhydride of hypophosphoric acid, $H_4P_2O_6$.

Phosphoric oxide, P_4O_{10}, produced when phosphorus burns in an excess of oxygen, has three solid forms of increasing structural complexity, hexagonal, orthorhombic and tetragonal. It is the anhydride of the phosphoric acids:

$$P_4O_{10} \xrightarrow{\;2H_2O\;} 4HPO_3 \xrightarrow{\;2H_2O\;} 2H_4P_2O_7 \xrightarrow{\;2H_2O\;} 4H_3PO_4.$$

phosphoric oxide   metaphosphoric acid   pyrophosphoric acid   orthophosphoric acid

Oxoacids of nitrogen

Hyponitrous acid, $H_2N_2O_2$, has been made from its salts. A solution of sodium hyponitrite is produced by reducing concentrated aqueous $NaNO_2$ with sodium amalgam. The insoluble silver salt, precipitated from neutral solution, when treated with anhydrous HCl in dry ether gives the acid:

$$Ag_2N_2O_2 + 2HCl \rightarrow H_2N_2O_2 + 2AgCl.$$

The white crystals obtained by evaporating the ether solution decompose spontaneously:

$$H_2N_2O_2 \rightarrow N_2O + H_2O.$$

Nitroxylic acid, H_2NO_2, has not been made; but the yellow sodium salt Na_2NO_2 is produced by the electrolysis of $NaNO_2$ in liquid ammonia, or by the reduction of $NaNO_2$ with sodium in the same solvent. The salt decomposes at 100°, giving Na_2O, $NaNO_2$, $NaNO_3$ and nitrogen.

Nitrous acid, HNO_2, can be made in aqueous solution by dissolving a mixture of NO and NO_2 in ice-cold water. Though it is known only in solution, its salts and esters are moderately stable. The Gp.IA and Gp.IIA nitrites are thermally stable. Nitrous acid is a fairly strong acid ($pK_a = 3.3$ at 18°). The solution decomposes slowly:

$$3HNO_2 \rightarrow HNO_3 + 2NO + H_2O.$$

It is easily oxidised to nitric acid; but it is also easily reduced to NO, N_2O, $H_2N_2O_2$, NH_2OH, N_2 or NH_3, depending on the reducing agent used:

$$Fe^{2+} \text{ and } Ti^{3+} \rightarrow NO;$$
$$Sn^{2+} \rightarrow H_2N_2O_2;$$
$$H_2S \text{ (at pH 8–9)} \rightarrow NH_3.$$

The reaction

$$2HNO_2 + 2I^- + 2H_3O^+ \rightarrow 2NO + I_2 + 4H_2O$$

is quantitative and can be used for the determination of NO_2^-.

Nitrite esters can usually be made by treating the alcohols with acidified sodium nitrite at 0°.

Hyponitric acid, $H_2N_2O_3$, is very unstable, but its sodium salt can be made as the monohydrate by treating free hydroxylamine in methanol with ethyl nitrate in the presence of sodium methoxide:

$$NH_2OH + EtNO_3 \rightarrow HO.NH.NO_2 + EtOH$$
$$\downarrow$$
$$Na_2N_2O_3.H_2O.$$

On acidification decomposition occurs:

$$H_2N_2O_3 \rightarrow H_2O + 2NO.$$

Nitric acid, HNO_3, is made commercially from synthetic ammonia:

$$4NH_3 + 5O_2 \xrightarrow{\text{Pt}} 4NO + 6H_2O,$$
$$2NO + O_2 \longrightarrow N_2O_4,$$
$$3N_2O_4 + 2H_2O \longrightarrow 4HNO_3 + 2NO,$$

the nitric oxide formed in the process of solution being converted to more N_2O_4 by further aerial oxidation.

The pure acid exists as white cyrstals, m.p. $-41°$. Melting gives a faintly yellow liquid which shows weak Raman lines at 1050 cm^{-1} and 1400 cm^{-1}, indicating some dissociation to NO_2^+ and NO_3^-. The liquid, which has a density of 1.54 at 0°, boils at 83°. Two crystalline hydrates are formed; $HNO_3.H_2O$, m.p. $-38°$, sometimes called the ortho-acid, and $HNO_3.3H_2O$, m.p. $-18.5°$. Nitric acid forms a constant boiling mixture with water, of composition 68.4% HNO_3 and b.p. 121.9°. Concentration can be effected by distillation with H_2SO_4.

The molecule is planar:

$$\underset{O\underset{1.22\ Å}{\diagup}}{\overset{O\diagdown}{\underset{130°}{N}}}\underset{1.41\ Å}{\overset{115°}{-\!-\!-}}O\overset{\diagup H}{}$$

Bonding to the nitrogen atom is evidently through sp^2 hybrid orbitals, the remaining p electrons being used in π bond formation in which all the oxygens participate.

Liquid nitric acid and its strong aqueous solutions decompose, particularly on exposure to light, to give N_2O_4, oxygen and water. A solution of N_2O_4 in anhydrous nitric acid constitutes fuming nitric acid. When HNO_3 acts as an oxidising agent the usual products are NO from the dilute acid and N_2O_4 from the concentrated acid, but other products, such as N_2O, NH_2OH and NH_3, can be obtained under appropriate conditions. The oxidising action is catalysed by the presence of N_2O_4.

The oxoacids of phosphorus

These can be classified according to the formal charge number of the phosphorus (Table 72).

TABLE 72

OXOACIDS OF PHOSPHORUS

Charge number	Formula	Name
+1	H_3PO_2	Hypophosphorous acid
+3	HPO_2	Meta- ⎫
	$H_4P_2O_5$	Pyro- ⎬ phosphorous acids
	H_3PO_3	Ortho- ⎭
+4	$H_4P_2O_6$	Hypophosphoric acid
+5	HPO_3	Meta- ⎫
	$H_4P_2O_7$	Pyro- ⎬ phosphoric acids
	H_3PO_4	Ortho- ⎭

The peroxo-acids are dealt with elsewhere (p. 388).

Hypophosphorous acid, H_3PO_2, is made by acidifying, with dilute sulphuric acid, the barium hypophosphite solution obtained when white phosphorus is dissolved in hot baryta water:

$$Ba(H_2PO_2)_2 + H_2SO_4 \rightarrow 2H_3PO_2 + BaSO_4.$$

It can be separated as deliquescent colourless crystals, m.p. 26.5°. Raman spectra, X-ray analysis of its salts and a uniformly monobasic character show it to have the structure represented in Fig. 170. Its anion $H_2PO_2^-$ is tetrahedral. The acid ionises fairly strongly in water ($pK_a = 2$). Both acid and salts are strong reducing agents:

$$H_3PO_3 + 2H_3O^+ + 2e \rightleftharpoons H_3PO_2 + 3H_2O, \qquad E_h^\circ = -0.59 \text{ V,}$$
$$HPO_3^{2-} + 2H_2O + 2e \rightleftharpoons H_2PO_2^- + 3OH^-, \qquad E_h^\circ = -1.65 \text{ V.}$$

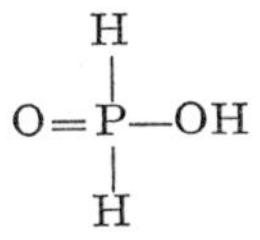

$$\begin{array}{c} H \\ | \\ O{=}P{-}OH \\ | \\ H \end{array} \qquad\qquad \begin{array}{c} H \\ | \\ O{=}P{-}OH \\ | \\ OH \end{array}$$

Fig. 170.
Structure of hypophosphorous acid.

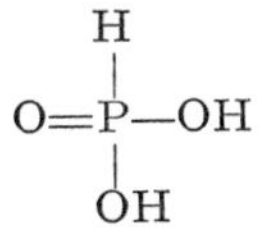

Fig. 171. Suggested structure of
orthophosphorous acid.

Orthophosphorous acid, H_3PO_3, can be made by hydrolysing PCl_3 with ice-cold water. The solid (m.p. 70°) can be crystallised from solution. Structural data are not available, but the dibasic character suggests the structure shown in Fig. 171.

The first ionisation constant is higher than that of H_3PO_4 ($pK_a = 2$). Both the acid and its salts are strong reducing agents:

$$H_3PO_4 + 2H_3O^+ + 2e \rightleftharpoons H_3PO_3 + 3H_2O, \qquad E_h^\circ = -0.20 \text{ V,}$$
$$PO_4^{3-} + 2H_2O + 2e \rightleftharpoons HPO_3^{2-} + 3OH^-, \qquad E_h^\circ = -1.05 \text{ V.}$$

Hypophosphoric acid, $H_4P_2O_6$, can be prepared as a dihydrate from the solution obtained when $Na_2H_2P_2O_6$ is poured through a column of cation-exchange resin in its hydrogen form:

$$2H\,(Resin) + Na_2H_2P_2O_6 \rightarrow 2Na\,(Resin) + H_4P_2O_6.$$

The sodium salt is made by the action of alkaline, aqueous NaOCl on red phosphorus.

The acid is tetrabasic, but the commonest salts are those in which only two of the hydrogens are replaced. Both acid and salts are remarkably stable towards oxidising and reducing agents. For the reaction

$$2H_3PO_4 + 2H_3O^+ + 2e \rightleftharpoons H_4P_2O_6 + 4H_2O, \qquad E_h^\circ = -0.8\ V,$$

and for

$$H_4P_2O_6 + 2H_3O^+ + 2e \rightleftharpoons 2H_3PO_3 + 2H_2O, \qquad E_h^\circ = +0.4\ V.$$

Support for the formula $H_4P_2O_6$ comes from cryoscopic and Raman evidence and from the diamagnetism of the salts. The probability of a P—P bond is indicated by X-ray diffraction.

Phosphoric acids

The system P_4O_{10}–H_2O is complex. Analysis of mixtures containing more than 72.4% P_4O_{10} shows that the relative amounts of condensed acids, such as $H_4P_2O_7$, $H_5P_3O_{10}$ and $H_6P_6O_{18}$, vary considerably with composition (Bell, 1948). The mixtures are not simply composed of H_3PO_4 and P_4O_{10}.

Orthophosphoric acid, H_3PO_4, a colourless solid, m.p. 42.4°, is made by removing water from syrupy phosphoric acid under reduced pressure. The arrangement of oxygen atoms round the phosphorus atom in this tribasic acid is only approximately tetrahedral (Furberg, 1955) (Fig. 172),

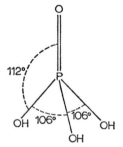

Fig. 172.
Structure of orthophosphoric acid.

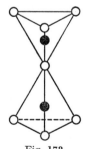

Fig. 173.
PO_4 tetrahedra in $P_2O_7^{4-}$ ion.

the $P{<}{}^{OH}_{OH}$ angles being 106° and the $P{<}{}^{O}_{OH}$ angles, 112°. The 'keto' oxygen is attached to an adjacent 'hydroxo' oxygen by a hydrogen bond.

Pyrophosphoric acid, $H_4P_2O_7$, is the colourless solid crystallised from an 80% P_4O_{10} solution which contains H_3PO_4 and $H_5P_3O_{10}$ in addition to $H_4P_2O_7$. The first dissociation constant is higher than that of the ortho acid ($pK_a = 0.8$, *cf.* $pK_a = 2.1$ for H_3PO_4). All the hydrogens are replaceable, but the commonest pyrophosphates are $M_2^IH_2P_2O_7$ and $M_4^IP_2O_7$, which contain the ion $P_2O_7^{4-}$ (Fig. 173).

Metaphosphoric acids of empirical formula HPO_3 may be obtained on further dehydration of H_3PO_4 by heating at 316°. Their nature is in doubt; the existence of a monomer is unlikely, for the vapour is believed to be dimeric even at white heat. The metaphosphates of sodium have been studied in some detail. The sparingly soluble Maddrells' salt, made by heating NaH_2PO_4 at 315°, is now thought to be a mixture of two salts of similar, but not identical, structures (Partridge, 1949) which have not been resolved. A trimetaphosphate $Na_3(PO_3)_3$ is obtained by heating $Na_2H_2P_2O_7$. The $P_3O_9^{3-}$ ion consists of three PO_4^{3-} tetrahedra joined through common oxygen atoms (Fig. 174).

A water-soluble tetrametaphosphate which crystallises with 4 or 10 molecules of water is prepared by treating P_4O_{10} with $Na_2CO_3.10H_2O$. The $P_4O_{12}^{4-}$ ion (Fig. 175) is made up of four PO_4 tetrahedra (Ketelaar, 1951).

The compound known as sodium hexametaphosphate is made by rapidly cooling molten metaphosphate. It does not contain $P_6O_{18}^{6-}$ ions and is best

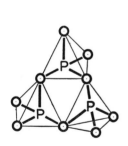

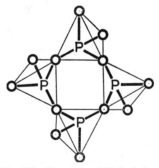

Fig. 174. Structure of $P_3O_9^{3-}$ ion.   Fig. 175. Structure of $P_4O_{12}^{4-}$ ion.

considered as a metaphosphate glass. It is soluble and acts as a water softener, removing Ca^{2+} ion from solution by chelation to the colloidal polyanions:

Sulphides

Tetrasulphur tetranitride, N_4S_4, is produced when dry NH_3 is passed into a solution of S_2Cl_2 in dry ether, separating as orange crystals, m.p. 178°.

$$6S_2Cl_2 + 16NH_3 \rightarrow N_4S_4 + 12NH_4Cl + 8S.$$

The compound is diamagnetic and strongly endothermic. It explodes on heating, is soluble in many organic solvents, and is attacked slowly by water which does not wet it easily. Boiling alkalis cause hydrolysis:

$$N_4S_4 + 6OH^- + 3H_2O \rightarrow S_2O_3^{2-} + 2SO_3^{2-} + 4NH_3.$$

Electron and X-ray diffraction show all the bonds to be equal in length and the interbond angles NSN = 104° and SNS = 113°. The probable form of the molecule is an eight-membered 'cradle' ring (Fig. 176). It is the

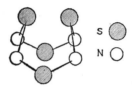

Fig. 176. Cradle-shaped structure of S_4N_4 molecule.

parent substance of other sulphur nitrides and derivatives of sulphur nitrides. Thus the ring can be split by heating to give white disulphur dinitride, N_2S_2, also soluble in organic solvents, which is converted into the insoluble yellow polymer, $(NS)_n$, at room temperature. Moreover, N_4S_4 can be reduced by tin (II) chloride to tetrasulphur tetraimide and halogenated by chlorine to the tetrachloride:

```
    H      H                         Cl
    |      |                         |
    N— S —N                       N—S—N
    |      |                       |     |
    S      S                    Cl—S     S—Cl
    |      |                       |     |
    N— S —N                       N—S—N
    |      |                         |
    H      H                         Cl
```

There are four sulphides of phosphorus, P_4S_5, P_4S_7, P_4S and P_4S_{10}. The structures of P_4S_7 and P_4S_{10}, the latter being the only sulphide with a structure similar to that of an oxide, were determined by Vos and Wiebenga

(1956), and those of P_4S_3 and P_4S_5 by Van Houten (1957). Their relationship to P_4 and to one another is illustrated:

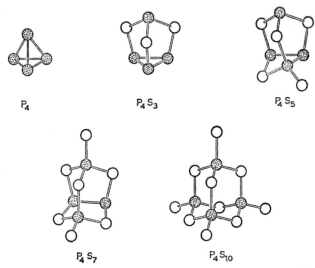

Fig. 177. Structures of phosphorus sulphides. (By courtesy of S. van Houten.)

P_4S_3, made by heating red phosphorus with sulphur in an atmosphere of CO_2, is the yellow crystalline solid, m.p. 174°, used in 'strike-anywhere' matches. The others have a similar physical appearance, somewhat higher melting points and much lower stability. P_4S_3 is attacked only very slowly by cold water and cold HCl, but decomposed by hot water to give H_2S, PH_3 and phosphorus oxo-acids. Cold HNO_3 converts it to H_3PO_4, H_2SO_4 and sulphur; aqueous KOH produces PH_3, hydrogen and the phosphite, hypophosphite and sulphide ions.

Nitrides

There are three types of nitride; ionic, covalent and interstitial. Ionic nitrides contain the N^{3-} ion, of radius 1.71 Å, the only simple ternegative ion known. Lithium nitride, Li_3N, with a heat of formation of 47.2 kcal, is the only exothermic nitride of Gp.I. The explosive Na_3N, K_3N and Rb_3N are made by passing an arc between a Pt cathode and an alkali metal anode under liquid nitrogen. Beryllium, magnesium and the other Gp.IIA elements form ionic nitrides when heated in nitrogen. Be_3N_2 and Ca_3N_2 have the highest heats of formation, 135.7 kcal and 103.2 kcal respectively. The ionic nitrides are hydrolysed to the hydroxides and ammonia.

Covalent nitrides include the volatile compounds with hydrogen, the halogens and carbon as well as the high-melting adamantine compounds of some Gp.III elements, typified by AlN. Boron nitride, BN, exists as the adamantine high-pressure form, borazon, as well as in the ordinary form similar in structure to graphite. The latter is used as an 'anti-sticking' compound in glass-maker's moulds and for coating crucible linings, since molten iron does not wet it. $Si_3N_4(\Delta H°_f = -179$ kcal) is a commercial product.

The transition metals, including those of Gp.IIIA, form true interstitial compounds (p. 147), many with the composition MN and the NaCl structure. Other interstitial nitrides, Mo_2N, W_2N, Fe_4N and Mn_4N, are hard, high-melting, good conductors of metallic appearance, commonly made by heating the powdered metal in nitrogen or ammonia at about 1200°. They vary considerably in thermal stability, reactivity and ease of hydrolysis, and are less thermally stable than the corresponding metal oxides. In some cases, an example being TiN, TiO and TiC, nitride, oxide and carbide are isomorphous Heats of formation are often high in spite of the high dissociation energy of N_2. Some interstitial nitrides are conveniently made by ammonolysis of halides in liquid ammonia, the amides first formed being converted to nitrides on heating. Another method is their simultaneous reduction and nitriding by heating in ammonia.

Phosphides

A mixture of sodium phosphides is made by direct combination of the elements. It appears to contain NaP_3 and Na_2P_5 and is used for sea flares. Also used for the same purpose are Mg_3P_2 and Zn_3P_2, made by warming intimate mixtures of the elements, and Ca_3P_2, by heating CaO in phosphorus vapour. The last is impure, containing some phosphate. Ferrophosphorus contains Fe_2P and FeP.

Hydrazoic acid

Hydrazoic acid, HN_3, is present in the aqueous distillate from NaN_3 with dilute H_2SO_4. Sodium azide for the purpose is made by the action of N_2O on sodamide at 190°.

$$N_2O + 2NaNH_2 \rightarrow NaN_3 + NaOH + NH_3.$$

The pure liquid, b.p. 37°, is obtained by fractionating the solution and drying the distillate over $CaCl_2$. It is colourless, mobile and exploded by shock. The vapour is monomeric. The ion N_3^- is linear. Fully ionised azides like those of the Gp.I metals and barium are non-explosive and yield N_2 and metal on heating. LiN_3 is an exception; it is converted to the nitride. The covalent azides, such as those of organic radicals and of Ag, Cu, Tl, Pb and Hg, are explosive. In these compounds the nitrogen atoms are arranged collinearly but the molecule is unsymmetrical:

$$N\overset{1.24\ \text{Å}}{\rule{1cm}{0.4pt}}N\overset{1.10\ \text{Å}}{\rule{1cm}{0.4pt}}N$$
$$\underset{\underset{CH_3}{1.47\ \text{Å}}}{\diagup}{}^{120°}$$

The acid dissociates only slightly in aqueous solution ($pK_a = 4.7$). Metals dissolve with the evolution of NH_3 and N_2:

$$Zn + 3\ HN_3 \rightarrow Zn(N_3)_2 + NH_3 + N_2.$$

Crystalline salts are formed with ammonia, $NH_4.N_3$ (empirically N_4H_4), and with hydrazine, $NH_2.NH_3.N_3$ (empirically N_5H_5). Other azides are the explosive chloroazide ClN_3 (gas), bromoazide BrN_3 (orange liquid), and iodoazide IN_3 (yellow solid). The first and second can be made from NaN_3 by treating it with sodium hypochlorite and bromine respectively.

Hydroxylamine

Hydroxylamine, NH_2OH, is a colourless solid, m.p. $33°$, very soluble in water and the lower alcohols, less so in other organic liquids. The hydrogen sulphate, $[NH_3OH]HSO_4$, is made commercially by adding concentrated H_2SO_4 to refluxing nitromethane at $110–120°$:

$$CH_3NO_2 + H_2SO_4 \rightarrow [NH_3OH]HSO_4 + CO.$$

This salt is converted to the sulphate $[NH_3OH]_2SO_4$ by the action of 85% methanol, and the sulphate is converted to the chloride by dissolving it in hot, concentrated HCl and crystallising from the solution:

$$[NH_3OH]_2SO_4 + 2HCl \rightarrow 2[NH_3OH]Cl + H_2SO_4.$$

When the chloride is added to sodium methoxide in methanol and the NaCl is filtered off, a solution is obtained from which free NH_2OH can be crystallised at $-10°$ to $-20°$. Before melting, the compound decomposes into NH_3, H_2O, N_2O and NO. It is a weak monoacid base without acidic properties. Like its aquo analogue, H_2O_2, and its ammono analogue, N_2H_4, hydroxylamine has both oxidising and reducing properties.

Phosphonitrilic compounds

Compounds of phosphorus and nitrogen based on the unit

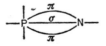

have attracted attention because they form polymers with properties useful at high temperatures. The materials range from fluids which may prove

useful for heat transfer and lubrication, to solids with the mechanical characteristics of organic polymers (Paddock, 1960). They show similarities to aromatic compounds, although the π-bonding is somewhat different.

Phosphonitrilic chlorides were prepared (Stokes, 1895) by the ammonolysis
of phosphorus pentachloride; dry distillation gives a mixture of $(PNCl_2)_3$ and
$(PNCl_2)_4$:

$$n\,PCl_5 + n\,NH_4Cl \rightarrow (PNCl_2)_n + 4n\,HCl.$$

Schenck and Römer improved the method by dissolving the PCl_5 in tetrachloro-
ethane; this increases the yield of higher polymers. The product is a liquid
mixture of polymers from which the excess of NH_4Cl is removed by filtration. The filtrate is mainly $(PNCl_2)_3$, but other polymers, up to $(PNCl_2)_6$,
are present. Concentrating the liquid under reduced pressure gives a material,
part of which is insoluble in petroleum ether and is believed to be a mixture
of linear polymers, $PCl_4(PNCl_2)_nCl$, but most of which is soluble and consists
of cyclic $(PNCl_2)_n$ polymers.

The preparative reaction is very versatile; the phenyls, $(PNPh_2)_{3,4}$, can be
obtained from Ph_2PCl_3 and the methyls, $(PNMe_2)_{3,4}$, from Me_2PCl_3. Bromides and mixed halides can also be made.

The trimeric compounds have a planar P_3N_3 ring

in which the hybrid P—N bonds are all equal in length (1.60 Å) and shorter
than the P—N bond (1.78 Å) in the phosphoramidate ion, $NH_2PO_3^{2-}$. They
are comparatively inert compounds, thermally stable and not readily hydrolysed; they can be steam-distilled without serious loss. The crystalline trimer
(and also the tetramer) can be futher condensed to rubrber-like materials,
of molecular weight $> 20,000$, by heating at $\sim 300°$. Unfortunately, however, the elastic properties are lost on exposure to damp air.

Although the chloro-compounds are much less reactive than is usual for
phosphorus–chlorine compounds, they react smoothly with alcohols and
alkoxides:

$$(PNCl_2)_3 + 6\,NaOC_2H_5 \rightarrow [PN(OC_2H_5)_2]_3 + 6\,NaCl$$

This product is a clear, viscous oil which changes to a gel on standing.
Ammonia and amines produce compounds such as $[PN(NH_2)_2]_3$ and
$[PN(NH.C_6H_5)_2]_3$, and some or all of the chlorine in $(PNCl_2)_3$ can be replaced
to give such compounds as $[PNCl(Me_2N)]_3$, $P_3N_3Cl_4Ph_2$, and $[PN(MeO)_2]_3$.

The bromo-compounds $(PNBr_2)_3$ and $(PNBr_2)_4$ are formed when NH_4Br replaces NH_4Cl in the preparative reaction; the fluoro-analogues are, however, made by the action of potassium fluorosulphite on $(PNCl_2)_3$ at 120°:

$$(PNCl_2)_3 + 6KSO_2F \rightarrow (PNF_2)_3 + 6KCl + 6SO_2.$$

The fluoro-trimer, m.p. ~ 18°, b.p. 51°, is insoluble in polar liquids, even in concentrated H_2SO_4. By contrast, $(PNMe_2)_3$, m.p. 195°, dissolves readily in water.

The tetramer formed in the preparative reaction with NH_4Cl is also cyclic, but the ring is puckered, not planar as with the trimer $(PNCl_2)_3$:

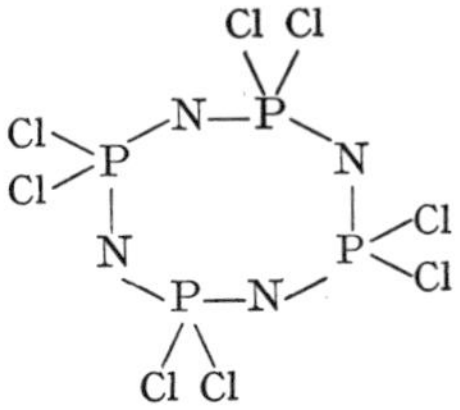

A chlorofluoro-polymer, $(PNFCl)_4$, is made by heating the trimer $(PNCl_2)_3$ with PbF_2. This is the only reaction yet reported by which a phosphonitrilic ring can be enlarged. Chlorine in the tetramer $(PNCl_2)_4$ can be substituted to give $(PNPhCl)_4$ by treatment with PhMgBr, $[PN(NHPh)_2]_4$ by treatment with $PhNH_2$, and $(PNF_2)_4$ by treatment with KSO_2F.

Bonding in the trimeric cyclic phosphonitrilic halides is interesting. Four electrons of the individual nitrogen atoms may be considered to occupy approximately sp^3 hybrid orbitals, one in every P—N bond and two in a lone pair. The fifth electron, in a p_z orbital, is available for π bond formation. The individual phosphorus atoms have four electrons arranged approximately tetrahedrally in σ bonds, leaving the fifth electron, in a d orbital, available for π bonding. Overlap results in $d\pi$–$p\pi$ bonding; this is unlike the π bonds in benzene which arise from an overlap of p orbitals only (Craig and Paddock, 1958).

Chapter 21

Arsenic, Antimony and Bismuth

GROUP VB

The elements of Gp. VB, like nitrogen and phosphorus, have the ns^2np^3 electron configuration and the ^4S ground state which indicates three singly-occupied orbitals. They differ from nitrogen and phosphorus, however, in their lower electronegativity, which decreases with increasing atomic number. The elements are dominantly tervalent and tend to form three electron pair bonds roughly at right angles, leaving an ns^2 lone pair; but some hybridisation occurs and results in distortion towards a more nearly tetrahedral form (p. 103). All five valence electrons may, nevertheless, participate in bonding, d-hybridisation yielding bipyramidal, square pyramidal and octahedral sets of bonds. In many of these compounds the metal is described formally as having charge number $+5$ or $+3$, but the bonding is often mainly covalent; only in bismuth compounds is there any real approach to a simple cation. In solution the only ions which occur are M^{3+}; they are hydrated.

TABLE 73

SOME PROPERTIES OF GROUP VB ELEMENTS

	As	*Sb*	*Bi*
Atomic number	33	51	83
Electron configuration	$4s^24p^3$	$5s^25p^3$	$6s^26p^3$
Covalent radius (Å)	1.21	1.41	1.52
Ionic radius, M^{3+} (Å)	0.69	0.90	1.20

The ionisation potentials are high, as would be expected from the electron configuration, and the standard electrode potentials are quite close together, diminishing ionisation potentials apparently being offset by the increasing ionic radii and reduced heats of hydration.

The 3rd, 4th and 5th ionisation potentials of bismuth are larger than those of antimony. This, coupled with the greater size of the Bi^{3+}, Bi^{4+} and Bi^{5+} ions, is the prime cause of the diminished stability of the $+5$ oxidation state of bismuth.

Although the metals are most commonly depicted with charge numbers $+5$ or $+3$, their tendency towards non-metallic character is revealed in compounds with true metals. In such compounds as Na_3As, Mg_3Sb_2 and K_3Bi, many of which resemble the corresponding phosphides, the GpVB metal apparently accepts electrons to achieve a formal charge of -3.

TABLE 74

IONISATION AND ELECTRODE POTENTIALS OF GROUP VB ELEMENTS

	As	Sb	Bi
Ionisation potential I (eV)	9.8	8.6	8.0
E_h° M^{3+}/M (V)	0.25	0.21	0.32

The elements well exemplify the trend towards more metallic character with increasing atomic number; but even bismuth is not a true metal in the structural sense. The metallic allotropes of As, Sb and Bi consist of puckered sheets in which each atom is covalently bonded to three neighbouring atoms, the different sheets being held together by metallic binding. The 8—N rule (p. 114), which applies to most non-metallic solid elements, continues to operate. It is significant too that the elements are polyatomic in the vapour. Arsenic, for example, exists principally as tetrahedral As_4 molecules at 800°; dissociation to As_2 occurs but is incomplete even at 1600°. Antimony behaves similarly. Bismuth vapour is an equilibrium mixture of Bi_2 and Bi, the former being appreciable even at 2000°.

TABLE 75

PHYSICAL PROPERTIES OF GROUP VB METALS

	As	Sb	Bi
Density (g/cc)	5.7	6.6	9.8
Atomic volume	13.3	18.5	21.3
Melting point (°C)	817 (36 atm.)	630	271
Boiling point (°C)	616 (sublimes)	1440	1420

Both arsenic and antimony have yellow cubic α-forms, soluble in CS_2. Yellow arsenic consists of tetrahedral As_4 units; the α-form of antimony is probably similar in structure but is yet to be studied, being unstable above $-90°$. Black β-forms, analogous to amorphous phosphorus, result from rapid cooling of the vapours. They are metastable, changing rapidly at 350–400° into the γ-forms which are moderately good conductors of heat and electricity and exhibit metallic lustre, though brittle, easily fractured and of low ductility. Antimony and bismuth differ from normal metals in having lower electrical conductivity as solids than as liquids; for Bi the conductivity of the solid is only 0.48 of the liquid conductance. Bismuth also has the lowest thermal conductivity of any metal at the ordinary temperature.

The physical properties given in Table 75 are for the metallic forms. Arsenic sublimes at the ordinary pressure; the m.p. as given is that for 36 atmospheres.

Occurrence, extraction and uses

The principal ore of arsenic (5×10^{-4} % of earth's crust) is arsenical pyrites, FeAsS, but the element occurs commonly with nickel, copper and tin; As_4O_6 is recovered from flue-dusts collected during the extraction of these metals. Sublimation in the presence of galena, which prevents the formation of arsenites, purifies the oxide; this is reduced to arsenic with carbon in a cast iron retort. The element itself has few uses; about 0.5% added to lead increases the surface tension of the molten metal and allows spherical lead-shot to be produced. The principal commercial form is the so-called white arsenic, As_4O_6. Arsenic compounds are used mainly for their toxicity; arsenical insecticides have been much used.

Antimony (5×10^{-5} %) occurs as stibnite, Sb_2S_3, which is converted to the volatile oxide by roasting in air:

$$2Sb_2S_3 + 9O_2 \rightarrow Sb_4O_6 + 6SO_2.$$

The sublimate can be reduced in a blast furnace similar to that used for smelting lead. The metal is alloyed with lead for battery plates and with tin in pewter, in both cases conferring greater hardness. It is also used with lead in corrosion-resistant piping, with lead and tin in type metals and with tin, copper and lead in bearing metals. The oxide, Sb_4O_6, is employed in vitreous enamels and as a pigment.

Bismuth (10^{-5} %) occurs as Bi_2S_3, associated with the sulphide ores of lead and copper and also with SnO_2. The flue-dusts from the roasting of lead, copper and tin ores, and the anode sludge from copper refining, are worked-up for bismuth. The oxide can be reduced at $\sim 500°$ with iron, carbon and a flux. Electrolytic purification is possible from a solution of $BiCl_3$ in HCl. The metal is used particularly in fusible alloys of which Wood's metal (4Bi, 2Pb, 1Sn, 1Cd), m.p. 71°, and type metal are examples. It and many of its alloys expand on solidification and give sharp impressions. The salts are used in pharmaceutical preparations, showing a marked contrast in toxicity to arsenic.

Reactions of the elements

The elements combine on heating with oxygen, sulphur and the halogens (X):

$$4\,M + 3\,O_2 \rightarrow M_4O_6\ (2\,Bi_2O_3),$$
$$2\,M + 3\,S \rightarrow M_2S_3,$$
$$2\,M + 3\,X_2 \rightarrow 2\,MX_3.$$

Antimony gives in addition to the trihalide some pentahalide with both F_2 and Cl_2, arsenic with fluorine only. The elements all dissolve in hot, concentrated H_2SO_4 with the evolution of SO_2. Antimony and bismuth yield sulphates, arsenic forms As_4O_6. Bismuth dissolves readily in nitric acid to give $Bi(NO_3)_3$; the other two elements are converted to mixtures of oxides. Hydrochloric acid has little action on any of the elements. Cold aqua regia dissolves antimony, producing a solution containing $SbCl_6^-$ ions. Arsenic dissolves in fused NaOH but the others do not:

$$2\,As + 6\,NaOH \rightarrow 2\,Na_3AsO_3 + 3\,H_2.$$

Halides

TABLE 76

HALIDES OF GROUP VB ELEMENTS

	F	Cl	Br	I
As	AsF_3	$AsCl_3$	$AsBr_3$	AsI_3
	AsF_5			
Sb	SbF_3	$SbCl_3$	$SbBr_3$	SbI_3
	SbF_5	$SbCl_5$		
Bi	BiF_3	$BiCl_3$	$BiBr_3$	BiI_3

AsF_3 is a colourless, fuming liquid made by heating As_4O_6 with CaF_2 and H_2SO_4 in a lead retort. The gaseous AsF_5 is the chief product of the treatment of arsenic with fluorine. In common with the known structure of all the corresponding halides of this group, the molecules are respectively pyramidal (Fig. 178a) and trigonal bipyramidal (Fig. 178b).

Other pentahalides of arsenic are unknown. $AsCl_3$, a colourless liquid, is formed by chlorination of arsenic. White crystalline $AsBr_3$ and red crystalline AsI_3 are conveniently obtained by treating the element with the halogen in a CS_2 solution. Kolditz (1955) succeeded in making the hygroscopic solid $AsCl_2F_3$ by passing chlorine into ice-cold AsF_3. The conductance rose with the addition of Cl_2, suggesting the formation of an ionic compound possibly

$[AsCl_4]^+[AsF_6]^-$. Hydrolysis of the arsenic trihalides becomes more difficult with increasing atomic weight of the halogen. Unlike phosphorus and antimony, arsenic forms no well-characterised oxohalide.

The white, solid SbF_3 hydrolyses but slightly and can be made by the action of HF on Sb_2O_3. It forms complexes such as K_2SbF_5. The viscous SbF_5, made by refluxing $SbCl_5$ with anhydrous HF followed by fractional distillation, gives a non-ionic solid (Ohlberg, 1954); unlike PCl_5 which con-

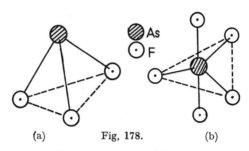

(a)　　　　　Fig, 178.　　　　　(b)

Fig. (a) Pyramidal structure of AsF_3 molecule.
Fig. (b) Trigonal bipyramidal structure of AsF_5 molecule.

tains PCl_4^+ and PCl_6^- ions in the crystal (p. 325), it is composed of covalent trigonal bipyramidal molecules in both solid and vapour states. The white crystalline $SbCl_3$, made by heating antimony with mercury(II) chloride and recrystallising from CS_2, forms complexes such as K_2SbCl_5. The trichloride hydrolyses in two stages to well-characterised oxide chlorides:

$$SbCl_3 + H_2O \;\rightarrow\; SbOCl \;+\; 2\,HCl;$$
$$4\,SbCl_3 + 5\,H_2O \;\rightarrow\; Sb_4O_5Cl_2 + 10\,HCl.$$

Unlike arsenic, antimony forms a pentachloride, $SbCl_5$, which is made in a similar way to PCl_5:

$$SbCl_3 + Cl_2 \;\rightarrow\; SbCl_5.$$

An acid $(HSbCl_6)_2.9H_2O$ can be crystallised from an HCl solution of $SbCl_3$ into which chlorine has been passed. The tribromide and tri-iodide of antimony are made from the elements. SbI_3 hydrolyses to give $Sb_4O_5I_2$.

The white powder BiF_3, like SbF_3, is made from the oxide and HF; with an excess of oxide, the oxide fluoride BiOF is formed. The trichloride, tribromide and tri-iodide of bismuth can all be made by direct combination. $BiBr_3$ is yellow and BiI_3, black. The last is hydrolysed by hot water to bronze crystals of BiOI.

Oxides

The trioxides of arsenic, antimony and bismuth are of structural interest, showing a transition from the molecular lattice characteristic of covalent compounds to an ionic lattice. Arsenic oxide contains As_4O_6 molecules, similar in structure to P_4O_6 and based on the As_4 tetrahedron. The cubic form of Sb_4O_6 is similar, but above 570° this is converted to the macro-molecular valentinite form containing infinite chains (Fig. 179).

Bismuth oxide has a number of forms of which two are important: the low-temperature α-form with a complex structure; and a simple cubic form obtained after the oxide has been fused for a long time in a porcelain crucible and probably stabilised by traces of impurities. The latter has the same ionic structure as Mn_2O_3, the bismuth being octahedrally co-ordinated (Fig. 180). The trioxides thus range in structure from the molecular, through the macromolecular to the ionic.

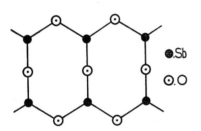

●.Sb

◉.O

Fig. 179. Valentinite structure of Sb_2O_3.

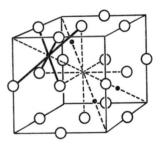

Fig. 180. Structure of Bi_2O_3.

There is no structural evidence for the existence of pentoxides of arsenic and antimony. Prolonged dehydration of a hydrated oxide of Sb^V gives a compound, Sb_2O_4, which is structurally analogous to $SbTaO_4$. Oxidation of Bi_2O_3 by chlorine, bromine and persulphates takes place, but the nature of the products is unknown. A non-stoichiometric, buff powder, called sodium bismuthate, is made by fusing Bi_2O_3 with NaOH and often formulated $NaBiO_3$. It is insoluble in water and moderately concentrated nitric acid, in which it will oxidise Mn^{2+} to MnO_4^-.

Arsenic, like phosphorus and vanadium, forms finite oxo-anions but the oxygen chemistry of Sb^V is quite different, being based not on the tetrahedral but the octahedral co-ordination of Sb^V by oxygen. There are two main groups of these oxo-complexes:

(i) Salts containing $Sb(OH)_6^-$ ions. A well-known example is $Na[Sb(OH)_6]$, formerly called sodium pyroantimonate. Spacu and Nisculescu-Schreher

(1948) have made several hexahydroantimony ammines by replacing K^+ from $K[Sb(OH)_6]$ with cobalt, chromium and copper ammines:

$$[Sb(OH)_6]_2 [Co(NH_3)_5Cl]. H_2O; \qquad [Sb(OH)_6]_3 [Co(NH_3)_6]. 3H_2O.$$

(ii) Mixed oxides based on SbO_6 octahedra, such as M^ISbO_3, $M^{II}Sb_2O_6$, $M^{III}SbO_4$ and $M_2^{II}Sb_2O_7$. Examples are $NaSbO_3$, structurally similar to ilmenite, $FeTiO_3$, and $FeSbO_4$, with a rutile structure. Obviously none of these compounds is an antimonate.

Sulphides

As with the oxides, there is a transition from molecular to ionic structure in passing from arsenic sulphide to bismuth sulphide. Realgar gives a vapour containing As_4S_4 molecules with a 'cradle' structure and As–S = 2.33 Å, As–As = 2.49 Å; $\angle$ As–S–As = 101°, $\angle$ S–As–S = 93° (Fig. 181). The vapour of orpiment contains As_4S_6 molecules with the P_4O_6 structure and As–S = 2.25 Å; $\angle$ As–S–As = 100°, $\angle$ S–As–S = 114° (Lu and Donohue, 1944). The compound is precipitated by passing H_2S into an acidified arsenite, and dissolves in aqueous alkali metal sulphides to give a solution from which thioarsenites, for instance Na_3AsS_3, may be crystallised:

$$As_2S_3 + 3 S^{2-} \rightarrow 2 AsS_3^{3-}.$$

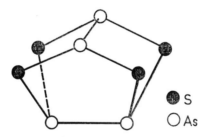

$\bullet$ S
$\bigcirc$ As

Fig. 181. Structure of As_4S_4 molecule.

Thioarsenates, such as $Na_3AsS_4.8H_2O$ and $(NH_4)_3AsS_4$, are obtained from solutions made by the action of alkali metal polysulphides on As_2S_3. Acidification of a thioarsenate solution gives a yellow precipitate containing a sulphide of arsenic, but there is no structural evidence that it is As_2S_5.

Antimony trisulphide occurs as stibnite. An orange form is precipitated when H_2S is passed into a solution of $SbCl_3$ in hydrochloric acid. When heated at 200° in CO_2, this changes to a dark grey, rhombic modification of greater density. Both forms dissolve in solutions containing sulphide ion to give thioantimonites; and, though they are soluble in polysulphide solutions, crystalline thioantimonates cannot be made from Sb_2S_3. The existence of a pentasulphide is doubtful.

Bi_2S_3 is formed as grey, rhombic crystals when Bi is fused with sulphur, and as a dark brown precipitate when H_2S is passed into the solution of a bismuth salt. It is insoluble in solutions containing sulphide ion. The compounds $KBiS_2$ and $NaBiS_2$ are made by fusing Bi_2S_3 with the appropriate Gp.IA sulphide; they oxidise rapidly in air.

Oxoacid salts of bismuth

Bismuth alone of the sub-group forms stable salts with oxo-anions. The deliquescent nitrate, $Bi(NO_3)_3.5H_2O$, can be crystallised from a solution of the metal or Bi_2O_3 in 20% HNO_3. It hydrolyses successively to $BiO(NO_3)$ and $BiO(OH).BiO(NO_3)$, the latter being stable in boiling water. There is no evidence of a significant quantity of $Bi(OH)^{2+}$ ion in solutions of these basic nitrates in $N/2$ to N HNO_3 (Swinehart and Garrett, 1951).

Bismuth sulphate, $Bi_2(SO_4)_3$, a white solid produced by evaporating a solution of the metal in concentrated H_2SO_4, gives on hydrolysis an insoluble hydroxide sulphate, $Bi(OH)_3.Bi(OH)SO_4$, which heating converts to the yellow bismuthyl sulphate $(BiO)_2SO_4$.

The addition of an ammonium carbonate solution to a bismuth nitrate solution precipitates the oxide carbonate, $[(BiO)_2CO_3]_2.H_2O$, which readily loses water and CO_2 on heating.

Chapter 22

Oxygen, Sulphur, Selenium, Tellurium and Polonium

GROUP VI B

As in the preceding group there is a gradual transition to a more metallic character with increasing atomic number. Oxygen resembles nitrogen in being the only member of its group to be a gas at room temperature. The small atomic radius of oxygen probably plays a major part in determining its chemical behaviour, by contrast with fluorine where the chief factor is the low dissociation energy (37.7 kcal/mole) of the molecule. For oxygen this is 117 kcal/mole. The elements have six electrons in their $ns^2 np^4$ valence shells and all show bivalence, with two covalent links and two lone pairs; but, beyond oxygen, d hybridisation commonly occurs, giving complexes in which the atom is usually shown with charge numbers +4 or +6.

TABLE 77

SOME PROPERTIES OF GROUP VIB ELEMENTS

	O	*S*	*Se*	*Te*	*Po*
Atomic number	8	16	34	52	84
Electron configuration	$2s^2 2p^4$	$3s^2 3p^4$	$4s^2 4p^4$	$5s^2 5p^4$	$6s^2 6p^4$
Atomic radius (Å)	0.74	1.04	1.17	1.37	1.64
Radius of M^{2-} (Å)	1.40	1.84	1.98	2.21	
,, ,, M^{4+} (Å)				0.89	1.02
,, ,, M^{6+} in MO_4^{2-} (Å)		0.34	0.40		

The first ionisation potential of oxygen is high. The electron affinity $O + 2e \rightarrow O^{2-}$, $A = -7.28$ eV, has a surprisingly large negative value; in other words, O^- resists the introduction of a second electron. Yet ionic oxides

TABLE 78

IONISATION POTENTIAL, ELECTRON AFFINITY AND ELECTRONEGATIVITY
OF GROUP VIB ELEMENTS

	O	*S*	*Se*	*Te*
Ionisation potential I (eV)	13.61	10.36	9.75	9.01
Electron affinity A (eV)	−7.28	−3.44	−4.21	
Electronegativity (Pauling scale)	3.5	2.5	2.4	2.1

are common, owing to the large lattice energy of the crystals (p. 142). The electronegativity ascribed to oxygen is extremely high, being exceeded only by that of fluorine. This accords with oxides having a more ionic character than the corresponding sulphides (p. 379).

Physical properties

The gradation of physical properties follows a similar pattern to that of the preceding group and is similarly related to the atomic structure. Oxygen consists of diatomic molecules, sulphur of 'puckered' rings of 8 atoms in the rhombic, and probably also in the monoclinic form. The red allotrope of selenium also contains 8-membered rings but the usual grey form has zig-zag chains of atoms. Tellurium (Fig. 182) is rather similar to grey Se. Polonium is dimorphic; the low-temperature α-form has a simple cubic lattice and the high-temperature β-form a simple rhombohedral one, the transition temperature being 75°. The density is similar to that of bismuth. Polonium has a low m.p., resembling that of Bi, but its b.p. is more in accord with a Gp.VI element.

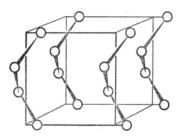

Fig. 182. Unit cell of tellurium, showing spiral arrangement of atoms.

TABLE 79

SOME PROPERTIES OF GROUP VIB ELEMENTS

	O	S	Se	Te	Po
Density of solid (g/cc)	1.27	2.06(α)	4.80(grey)	6.24(metal.)	9.51(β)
Atomic volume	12.6	15.56	16.45	20.24	22.2
Melting point (°C)	−218.9	114.5	217.4	450	254
Boiling point (°C)	−183.0	444.6	684.8	1390	962

The lithosphere contains about 47% oxygen by weight, and the oceans about 89%. The atmosphere has 20.95% oxygen by volume; the element is obtained by the fractional distillation of liquid air. Oxygen is decidedly reactive, its combination with other elements being often strongly exothermic:

$$2Ca + O_2 \rightarrow 2CaO \qquad \Delta H = -303.8 \text{ kcal,}$$
$$4Al + 3O_2 \rightarrow 2Al_2O_3 \qquad \Delta H = -800.6 \text{ kcal,}$$
$$Si + O_2 \rightarrow SiO_2 \qquad \Delta H = -210.3 \text{ kcal,}$$
$$4P + 5O_2 \rightarrow P_4O_{10} \qquad \Delta H = -720 \quad \text{kcal.}$$

The paramagnetism of molecular oxygen finds an explanation in molecular orbital theory (p. 95).

$$2O(1s^2\, 2s^2\, 2p^4) \rightarrow O_2[KK(z\sigma)^2(y\sigma)^2(x\sigma)^2(\omega\pi)^4(v\pi)^2]$$

The oxygen molecule contains two more electrons than N_2, and these are in the antibonding $v\pi$ orbitals. As there are two such orbitals, they are singly occupied by these electrons which have parallel spin. Valence-bond theory fails to account so readily for the paramagnetism.

Ordinary oxygen contains, in addition to ^{16}O, about 0.2% ^{18}O and 0.04% ^{17}O. Water can be enriched in ^{18}O by fractional distillation. Dostrovsky, Llewellyn and Vromen (1952) report the production of 20 ml 3.2% $H_2^{18}O$ per day by this method. The isotope has been used as a non-radioactive tracer, to show, for example, that the oxygen liberated when an aqueous solution of H_2O_2 is oxidised by Ce^{4+} or MnO_4^- comes wholly from the H_2O_2 (Cahill and Taube, 1952).

The solubility coefficient of oxygen in water is 0.029 at 20°. An optical study of hydrates has shown evidence for $O_2.H_2O$ and the less stable $O_2.2H_2O$ (Heidt and Johnson, 1957). The monohydrate is believed to have the ring structure:

The dihydrate may be a chain. The hydrogen bond shown in the diagram differs from that between water molecules in having a proton sharing three electrons instead of four, one from an oxygen atom of the biradical form of the oxygen molecule and two from the O—H bond.

Atomic oxygen is produced by the passage of an electric discharge through the gas at 1 mm pressure or by irradiation in ultraviolet light of wave length less than 1900 Å. The atoms constitute a very strong oxidising agent:

$$O + 2H^+ + 2e \rightarrow H_2O, \qquad E^\circ_h = + 2.2V$$

Ozone is made by passing a silent discharge through oxygen or by electrolysing strong aqueous perchloric acid at −50° between a lead cathode and a platinum anode (Putnam, 1948), when anodic oxidation of the water occurs. Microwave and electron diffraction studies show the molecule to be angular:

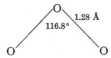

The binding may be considered as due to two σ bonds and a delocalised π orbital stretching over all three atoms. Every atom may be regarded as roughly sp^2 hybridised, the end atoms having two lone pairs and the central atom one.

Ozone is one of the strongest oxidising agents. In acid solution:

$$O_3 + 2H^+ + 2e \rightarrow O_2 + H_2O, \quad E_h^\circ = +2.07V.$$

Only fluorine, atomic oxygen and F_2O have higher redox potentials. The gas oxidises moist sulphur to $|H_2SO_4$, raises silver(I) compounds to the $+2$ state and converts olefinic compounds to ozonides. The reaction $2O_3 \rightarrow 3O_2$, which is catalysed by many metals and metal oxides, is exothermic and rapid above 200°. Gaseous ozone is deeper blue than oxygen; it condenses at $-112°$ to a dark blue liquid which freezes at $-193°$ to a dark purple solid. Surprisingly, the liquid is not completely miscible with liquid oxygen.

Oxygen at room temperature and pressure shows spectroscopic evidence of the diamagnetic species O_4; the equilibrium concentration decreases with rising temperature. The bond between the two O_2 molecules is weaker than an electron pair bond but stronger than a Van der Waals attraction (Wulf, 1928).

Sulphur (0.052% of the lithosphere) occurs mainly as the element and in sulphides and sulphates.

The element has several allotropes. The form stable below 98° is α-sulphur, whose rhombic crystals are built up from 8-membered rings of S atoms with S—S—S bond lengths of 2.12 Å and bond angles of 105.4°. They are packed into 'crankshafts' stacked in crossed layers (Warren and Burwell, 1935) as shown in Fig. 183a.

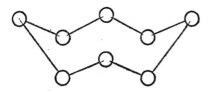

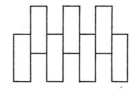

Fig. 183. 8-membered-ring of sulphur atoms.   Fig. 183a. Crankshaft stacking of 8-membered rings in α-sulphur.

Between 98 and 122°β -sulphur is stable. Its monoclinic crystals also contain 8-membered rings. The two modifications (with a range of stability and a definite transition temperature) are the best-known example of enantio-tropic allotropy:

$$S_\alpha \underset{98°}{\overset{}{\rightleftharpoons}} S_\beta$$

Conversion from S_α to S_β is accompanied by a small evolution of heat (0.1 kcal per g.atom) and a slight increase in volume. Although the crystal form is changed in β-sulphur, it is probably not very different in structure from α-sulphur. However, there is a second monoclinic form γ-sulphur, separating as needle-like crystals from certain solvents and also from melts cooled so as to avoid nucleation by α-sulphur. This has also 8-membered rings stacked in 'sheared-penny rolls' which give a close-packed hexagonal arrangement in two dimensions.

Fig. 183b. γ-Monoclinic sulphur showing 'sheared-penny rolls' stacking of 8-membered rings.

Ordinary sulphur, S_α, melts at 120° to a pale yellow liquid, S_λ, of low viscosity; it consists of S_8 rings, a structure which is maintained up to 160°. Above this temperature long spiral chains of S_μ are formed and increase in proportion up to the b.p. (444.5°). Above 160° there is also present a third form, S_π, probably S_6 and a precursor of S_μ; it increases to a maximum at about 180°. At this temperature the viscosity is at a maximum and the liquid almost unpourable, probably because of cross-linking between the chains.

When molten sulphur much above 160° is poured into water, plastic sulphur is formed. Much of it is in the viscous form of long spiral chains of S_μ. On standing it slowly hardens, becoming a mixture of S_μ and solid S_α, the latter amorphous and also containing S_8 groups.

Two paramagnetic forms have been made. When sulphur vapour at 500–700° and 1 mm, consisting mainly of S_2 molecules, is passed over a surface at −196°, a purple paramagnetic solid is obtained which may contain S_2 molecules. At −80° it reverts to S_α. In the same circumstances the vapour from liquid sulphur gives a green solid, less strongly paramagnetic, and possibly made up of chains of S atoms. It reverts to S_α when the temperature is raised (Freud, Adler and Sparrow, 1953).

Gaseous sulphur has been shown by vapour density measurements to contain S_8, S_4 and S_2, the relative proportions depending on the temperature; the last is paramagnetic, like O_2.

Selenium (9×10^{-6} % of the earth's crust) occurs in small quantities in sulphide ores, particularly FeS_2. It is extracted from the flue dusts produced in the roasting of sulphide ores and from the 'lead chamber mud' formed in sulphuric acid manufacture, as a solution in aqueous KCN. It is precipitated from the filtered solution by the addition of HCl.

$$KCN \ + Se \ \rightarrow KCNSe,$$
$$KCNSe + HCl \rightarrow Se + HCN + KCl.$$

It is used for decolorising glass and in photoelectric cells. The electrical conductance of Se in the metallic form is increased as much as 200 times by light. Another application is in the iron-selenium barrier-layer cell which generates a current when illuminated. This system also operates as a rectifier because current flows more readily from iron to selenium than in the opposite direction when an external potential is applied.

The selenium precipitated from KCNSe by acid and from H_2SeO_3 by SO_2 is red and amorphous. It dissolves in CS_2 and a slow evaporation of the solution below 72° gives red, α-monoclinic Se, whereas rapid evaporation gives red β-monoclinic Se. Se_α contains puckered Se_8 rings with Se—Se—Se bonds of 2.34 Å and angles of 105.5°. Hexagonal crystals of 'metallic' Se, the stable allotrope at room temperature, are made by keeping the other forms at 200–220° for a sufficient time. Present evidence suggests that liquid Se has only one form.

Tellurium (2×10^{-7} % of the lithosphere) occurs in sulphide ores, particularly those of copper, and as the tellurides of silver and gold. Its source is the anode sludge from the electrolytic refining of copper. The sludge is treated with fuming sulphuric acid and the tellurium precipitated from the diluted solution with zinc. The element is added to lead to improve resistance to heat, mechanical shock and corrosion. The stable metallic form consists of hexagonal grey crystals whose low electrical conductance is little affected by light. A black, amorphous form is precipitated from telluric acid by SO_2.

Polonium, known in trace quantities since 1898, is now made in the ^{210}Po form in milligram quantities by the neutron irradiation of ^{209}Bi.

$$^{209}_{83}Bi\,(n,\gamma)\,^{210}_{83}Bi \xrightarrow[\text{5 days}]{\beta^-} \ ^{210}_{84}Po\ (\alpha, 138.4 \text{ days}).$$

The isotope is virtually a pure α-emitter, but its high specific activity, 4.5 curies per mg., makes it a dangerous material, the maximum permissible body burden for ingested ^{210}Po being only 4×10^{-12}g. The 100 year ^{209}Po would be preferred for chemical work but its production is expensive. The element can be separated from Bi by electrochemical replacement with Ag from $0.5 - 2N$ HCl at 70–80°. $E_h^\circ Po^{4+}/Po = +0.75V$; Au, Hg, Pt and Te must first be removed by reduction with hydrazine. Polonium is obtained from the surface of the silver by vacuum sublimation, but, should the separation be delayed, it becomes more difficult, possibly through compound formation. The metal is conveniently obtained from solution by precipitation as PoS followed by the decomposition of the sulphide in a vacuum at 500°; the metal sublimes leaving a residue of decay lead sulphide (Bagnall, 1957). Polonium intimately mixed with beryllium forms a useful, weak source of neutrons.

Chemical properties of the elements

Because of the diversity displayed, tabulation of the properties of the whole of Gp.VIB is not very helpful; the elements range from the very electronegative, non-metallic oxygen to the metallic polonium. Reactivity towards metals and hydrogen decreases from oxygen to tellurium. Sulphur, selenium and tellurium react energetically with fluorine and chlorine, rather less activity with bromine:

$$X + 3F_2 \rightarrow XF_6; \qquad X + 2Cl_2 \rightarrow XCl_4; \qquad X + 2Br_2 \rightarrow XBr_4;$$

being the reactions when an excess of the halogen is present. Tellurium and, to a greater extent, polonium show the inert pair effect and form oxide sulphates and nitrates with quadripositive Te and Po.

Stereochemistry

The oxygen atom, with $1s^2 2s^2 2p_x^2 2p_y^1 2p_z^1$ electronic configuration, forms two bonds in nearly all its compounds; the next orbital (3s) lies too high in energy for promotion and increase in valency to be feasible. Most of the simple inorganic covalent oxides and the aliphatic ethers seem to owe their structure to approximately sp^3 hybrid orbitals, two of which are occupied by lone pairs. Examples are:

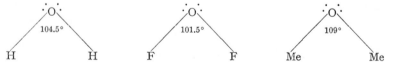

In ozone and in aromatic ethers, trigonal sp^2 hybridisation appears to be involved, the angle at the central oxygen being approximately 120°. The molecule $(SiH_3)_2O$ is linear, however, suggesting sp hybridisation at the oxygen. The ion O^+ is isoelectronic with N; it also forms three covalent bonds in H_3O^+, these being arranged similarly to the N—H bonds in ammonia and due basically to sp^3 hybridisation, with one position occupied by a lone pair. In the ion,

$$\left[\begin{array}{c} Cl \\ | \\ Hg \\ | \\ O \\ {}^{Hg}\diagdown {}^{Hg} \\ Cl \qquad Cl \end{array} \right]^+$$

however, the O—Hg—Cl groups are nearly linear and the whole structure is approximately planar (Scavnicar and Grdenic, 1955). There is no unambiguous example of 4-covalence in oxygen.

The stereochemistry of sulphur, selenium and tellurium is tabulated in Table 80. When it is two-bonded, sulphur differs from oxygen in having a valency angle less than the tetrahedral angle, 109.5°, except in SO_2. This remains true when aromatic groups are attached; in $(p\text{-}CH_3.C_6H_4)_2S$ the C—S—C angle is 109°. The small bond angle in H_2S (92.1°) suggests pure p orbitals, but nuclear quadrupole coupling constants (Burrus and Gordy, 1953) suggest both s and d contributions to the bonding orbitals.

TABLE 80

STEREOCHEMISTRY OF S, Se, Te

σ pairs	π pairs	Lone pairs	Hybrid	Shape	Examples
2	2	1	sp^2	V-shaped	*SO_2
3	3	0	sp^2	Triangular	*SO_3
4	2	0	sp^3	Tetrahedral	SO_2Cl_2, $[SeO_4]^{2-}$
3	1	1	sp^3	Trigonal pyramidal	$SOCl_2$, $SeOF_2$
2	0	2	sp^3	V-shaped	H_2S, Cl_2S, S_8
4	0	1	$sp^3d_{z^2}$	Distorted tetrahedral	$TeCl_4$
6	0	0	$sp^3d_{\gamma}^2$	Octahedral	SF_6, SeF_6, $Te(OH)_6$, S_2F_{10}
5	0	1	$sp^3d_{\gamma}^2$	Square pyramidal	$[MeTeI_4]^-$
6	0	1	$sp^3d_{\gamma}^2d_\varepsilon$	Distorted octahedral	$Cl_4Te(NMe_2Ph)_2$

*The breakdown here is slightly artificial, there are also π lone-pair and non-localised bonds.

The crystal structures of several polonium compounds have been determined. Both forms of PoO_2 have ionic lattices; $ZnPo$ has a zinc blende, and $PbPo$ a rock-salt structure. In $PoBr_4$, the Po is octahedrally co-ordinated with Br.

Ammonium hexachloropolonate(IV), $(NH_4)_2PoCl_6$, is isomorphous with $(NH_4)_2PtCl_6$: the Po–Cl distance, 2.38 Å, suggests a basically covalent bond.

Halides

TABLE 81

HALIDES OF GROUP VIB ELEMENTS

	O	S	Se	Te	Po
F	F_2O_2, F_2O	S_2F_2, SF_4, SF_6	SeF_4 SeF_6	TeF_4 Te_2F_{10}, TeF_6	
Cl	Cl_2O, ClO_2 Cl_2O_6, Cl_2O_7	S_xCl_2, S_2Cl_2, SCl_2, SCl_4	Se_2Cl_2, $SeCl_4$	$TeCl_2$ $TeCl_4$	$PoCl_2$ $PoCl_4$
Br	Br_2O, BrO_2, BrO_3	S_2Br_2.	Se_2Br_2, $SeBr_4$	$TeBr_2$ $TeBr_4$	$PoBr_2$ $PoBr_4$
I	I_2O_4, I_4O_9 I_2O_5			TeI_4	PoI_4

Sulphur, selenium and tellurium all form the hexafluoride by direct combination; other hexahalides are unknown. SF_6 and SeF_6 are chemically inert, colourless gases. The former is non-toxic and at once the most inert sulphur compound and possibly the most inert non-ionic fluorine compound; it resists fused KOH. The somewhat more reactive SeF_6 is reduced by NH_3 above 200°. TeF_6, also a colourless gas, is hydrolysed by water:

$$TeF_6 + 6H_2O \rightarrow 6HF + H_6TeO_6.$$

The difference in reactivity arises from the higher maximum covalence of Te. The hexafluoride molecules are octahedral, with six sp^3d^2 hybrid orbitals. The low b.p. are ascribable to the non-polarisable F atoms sheathing the molecules.

Tetrahalides are known. SF_4, b.p. —40.5°, is made by the direct fluorination of sulphur at —75° (Brown and Robinson, 1955). It is more conveniently prepared by the action of sulphur dichloride on a suspension of sodium fluoride in acetonitrile or tetramethylene sulphone at 70°. A medium offering some chance of ionisation is necessary.

$$3SCl_2 + 4NaF \rightarrow SF_4 + S_2Cl_2 + 4NaCl.$$

SeF_4 is conveniently made by passing diluted fluorine over a selenium surface at 0° (Aynsley, Peacock and Robinson, 1952). The liquid, b.p. 106°, gives with NaF, KF, RbF and CsF the complex fluorides M^ISeF_5, unlike the other halogeno complexes of selenium which are $M_2^ISeF_6$. Both SF_4 and

SeF_4 form solid $1:1$ addition compounds with BF_3, AsF_5 and SbF_5 (Bartlett and Robinson, 1956). Pure, crystalline TeF_4 is obtained by the reaction of TeO_2 with SeF_4 at $80°$ followed by evaporation of the excess of reagent and the $SeOF_2$ (Campbell and Robinson, 1956).

$$TeO_2 + 2SeF_4 \rightarrow TeF_4 + 2SeOF_2.$$

Tetrachlorides of S, Se, Te and Po are formed by direct chlorination. SCl_4 is a yellow liquid, stable only at low temperatures; $SeCl_4$ is a colourless, crystalline solid subliming at $196°$, and $TeCl_4$ a white, hygroscopic solid, m.p. $224°$. Fused $TeCl_4$ is an even better conductor of electricity than BrF_3 probably because

$$2TeCl_4 \leftrightharpoons TeCl_3^+ + TeCl_5^-.$$

It gives, with HCl, the acid H_2TeCl_6; K_2TeCl_6 is isomorphous with K_2SiF_6 and K_2SnCl_6. Actually $TeCl_6^{2-}$ is a regular octahedron. In common with the other Gp. VI tetrahalides whose structure is known, $TeCl_4$ is not a

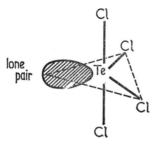

Fig. 184. Structure of $TeCl_4$ molecule.

regular, but a distorted tetrahedral molecule (Fig. 184), formed by sp^3d hybrid orbitals with one of the equatorial positions occupied by a lone pair which, by its large repulsion (p. 127), imposes the observed form.

Yellow $PoCl_4$ combines with NH_4Cl to give a compound which appears, from structural evidence, to be $(NH_4)_2PoCl_6$. A series of compounds M_2PoX_6 where $M = NH_4$ or Cs and $X = Cl$, Br or I have been made, and X-ray diffraction indicates that they are iso-structural with one another and with their tellurium analogues (Bagnall, D'Eye and Freeman, 1955).

Selenium, tellurium and polonium form tetrabromides. $SeBr_4$, a yellow solid, loses Br_2 to form Se_2Br_2 even at room temperature, and hydrolyses to a clear solution of H_2SeO_3 and HBr. Orange-red crystals of $TeBr_4$, along with green $TeBr_2$, result when tellurium reacts with bromine. Polonium forms carmine-red $PoBr_4$ at $200°$. A salmon-pink $PoBr_2Cl_2$ is also known. The diffraction pattern of $PoBr_4$ indicates a face-centred cubic cell of edge 5.6 Å; the intensities suggest this contains only one $PoBr_4$ unit with the Po atom randomly distributed over the sites normally occupied by four cations. The Po atom is surrounded octahedrally by six Br atoms at a Po–Br distance of 2.8 Å, which lies between the covalent octahedral distance (2.6 Å) and the theoretical ionic distance (2.97 Å).

Neither sulphur nor selenium forms an iodide; Te and Po form only tetra-iodides. TeI_4 consists of iron-grey crystals, made either by direct union or by reaction in aqueous solution:

$$TeO_2 + 4HI \rightarrow TeI_4 + 2H_2O.$$

PoI_4 is a black solid.

Of the dihalides the best-characterised are SCl_2, a red liquid made by saturating S_2Cl_2 with chlorine at room temperature, $TeCl_2$, a black solid made by the action of CCl_2F_2 on tellurium at 500° and $TeBr_2$, already mentioned. In SCl_2 the bond angle is about 103°, in $TeBr_2$ 98°, suggesting considerable p-character in the bonding orbitals of the centre atom. $PoCl_2$ has been made by reducing $PoCl_4$ with SO_2.

Sulphur and selenium form dimeric chlorides and bromides. S_2Cl_2, made by passing dry Cl_2 over molten sulphur, is an amber liquid whose vapour dissociates a little and becomes red. Hydrolysis by water is slow; HCl, sulphur, SO_2 and oxyacids, principally $H_2S_5O_6$, are formed. Electron diffraction by the vapour indicates a non-planar structure analogous to that of hydrogen peroxide (p. 381):

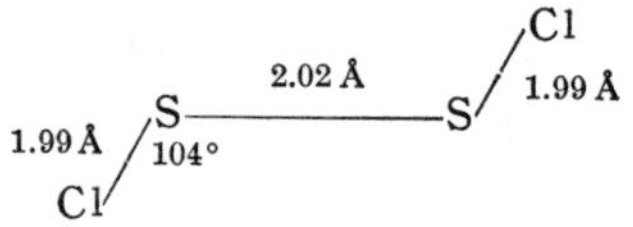

The S—S bond is appreciably shorter than in S_8 (2.08 Å). Se_2Cl_2 has a similar structure. It is made by the reaction between Se and $SeCl_4$, into which it disproportionates on warming.

$$2Se_2Cl_2 \rightarrow 3Se + SeCl_4$$

The brown, oily liquid hydrolyses readily to H_2SeO_3, Se and HCl. S_2Br_2 and Se_2Br_2, both red liquids, are products of direct combination of the elements.

Lower chlorides of sulphur, S_xCl_2, have been made with chains of up to five S atoms (Feher, Kraemer and Rempe, 1955) by reducing S_2Cl_2 vapour with hydrogen at a hot surface and passing the products over a cold surface.

Oxides

Disulphur monoxide, S_2O, is made by subjecting a mixture of S and SO_2 at 150–200° to an electric discharge, and has the structure SSO with S–S 1.88 Å, S–O 1.46 Å, and angle SSO 118°. It has many of the properties of a free radical, can exist for several days at 10 mm. pressure, and reacts immediately with Hg, Fe, and Cu. Alcoholic KOH converts it to K_2S, $K_2S_2O_4$ and K_2SO_3.

SO and SeO are unknown, but TeO is obtained as a black solid when $TeSO_3$ is heated. $PoSO_3$ produces on heating a black oxide believed to be PoO (Bagnall and Freeman, 1956).

Powdered sulphur reacts vigorously with liquid SO_3 forming a blue-green solid which decomposes slowly at room temperature, rapidly on warming, to give S, SO_2 and SO_3. Se and Te also dissolve in SO_3 producing solutions of green $SeSO_3$ and red $TeSO_3$. The four elements of the sulphur family

TABLE 82

OXIDES OF GROUP VIB ELEMENTS

S	Se	Te	Po
S_2O			
		TeO	PoO
S_2O_3			
SO_2	SeO_2	TeO_2	PoO_2
SO_3	SeO_3	TeO_3	
SO_4			

form dioxides; these are very different structurally. SO_2 is angular (119.5°), owing its shape to sp^2 hybrid orbitals about the sulphur, one occupied by a lone pair, but there is a little d-orbital contribution, too. SeO_2, made by burning Se in air, is colourless and crystalline, sublimes at 315° and, under pressure, melts to an orange liquid; the colour is lost on cooling. X-ray analysis shows it to contain macromolecular chains with oxygen atoms projecting alternately on opposite sides and at 90° to the plane of the chain (Fig. 185) (McCullough, 1937).

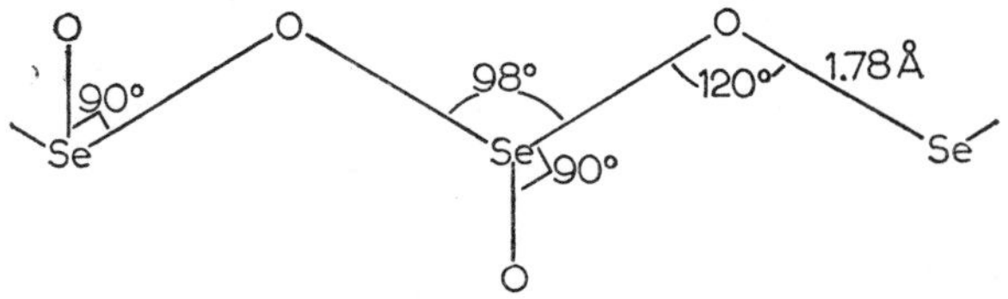

Fig. 185. Structure of SeO_2.

The links to the shared oxygen and to the projecting oxygen both possess some double-bond character. SeO_2 is used in organic chemistry to oxidise aldehydes and ketones containing the $-CH_2-CO-$ system to $-CO-CO-$, the SeO_2 being reduced to Se. The fact that only one $-CH_2-$ group is affected suggests that a complex is formed, but none has been isolated.

TeO_2, also made by combustion of the element, exists in two colourless forms, one having a rutile and the other a brookite type of structure, both indicating dominantly ionic character. PoO_2, of which there are two forms, red tetragonal and yellow face-centred cubic (Bagnall and D'Eye, 1954), surprisingly decomposes at 500° in a vacuum, leaving the metal.

The reactions of SO_2, SeO_2 and TeO_2 with water are of interest. Gaseous SO_2 dissolves, but the acid H_2SO_3 cannot be isolated. Liquid SO_2 is only partially soluble in water but completely miscible with benzene. SeO_2 gives an acidic aqueous solution from which colourless hexagonal H_2SeO_3 can be crystallised. TeO_2 is almost insoluble in water but dissolves not only in alkalis, but also in H_2SO_4, HCl and HNO_3. The rhombic oxide hydroxide nitrate, $Te_2O_3(OH)NO_3$, crystallises from a solution in the nitric acid, an indication of the amphoteric character of TeO_2.

SO_3, made by catalytic oxidation of SO_2 with oxygen, is a colourless, readily volatile solid. The vapour consists of planar, monomeric molecules of zero dipole moment, $O-S-O$ angle 120° and with bonds 1.43 Å. Moffitt (1950) ascribed the partly double-bond character to a d-orbital contribution, stronger than that in SO_2. Solid SO_3 exists in three forms; the two having asbestos-like structures with long chains of SO_2 groups linked by oxygen atoms probably owe their existence to traces of moisture; the ice-like variety is a cyclic trimer (Fig. 186). Bond lengths indicate the oxygens in the ring to be joined to the sulphur atoms by bonds which are essentially single. The projecting oxygens are held by double bonds.

SO_3 dissolves in liquid SO_2. There is exchange of oxygen (Nakata, 1943) but not of sulphur (Huston, 1951) between the two oxides, suggesting equilibria in the solution:

$$SO_2 + \ SO_3 \ \rightleftharpoons SO^{2+} + SO_4{}^{2-},$$
$$\text{or } SO_2 + 2SO_3 \ \rightleftharpoons SO^{2+} + S_2O_7{}^{2-}.$$

Though the means of comparing the strengths of Lewis acids is not entirely satisfactory, SO_3 is clearly one of the strongest.

SeO_3 is formed, together with much SeO_2, when an electric discharge is passed through selenium vapour in oxygen at 4 mm. pressure. The colourless, deliquescent solid is the anhydride of selenic acid. TeO_3 is an orange solid made by heating telluric acid, H_6TeO_6, very strongly.

Sulphur is the only element in the group to form a tetroxide. This white solid is produced when dry SO_2 and oxygen are passed through an ozoniser. There is cryoscopic evidence that it is monomeric. It decomposes at 3°, giving an orange liquid, empirically S_2O_7. SO_4 is a very powerful oxidising agent, converting aniline to nitrobenzene. It does not form H_2O_2 or a peroxo-acid.

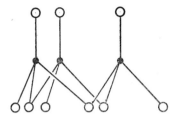

Fig. 186. Cyclic trimeric form of SO_3.

Oxoacids of sulphur

Sulphoxylic acid	H_2SO_2	Exists as salts
Sulphurous acid	H_2SO_3	Exists as salts and in solution
Disulphurous acid	$H_2S_2O_5$	Exists as salts
Dithionous acid	$H_2S_2O_4$	Exists as salts
Sulphuric acid	H_2SO_4	m.p. 10.5°
Disulphuric acid	$H_2S_2O_7$	m.p. 35°
Thiosulphuric acid	$H_2S_2O_3$	Solid stable at $\sim -78°$
Thionic acids	$H_2S_xO_6$	($x = 2-5$) Exist as salts and in solution.

Sulphoxylic acid is known with certainty in its cobalt salt, made by the action of sodium dithionite on cobalt(II) acetate, followed by treatment with ammonia:

$$CoS_2O_4 + 2NH_3 + H_2O \rightarrow CoSO_2 + (NH_4)_2SO_3.$$

Dithionites are made by reducing hydrogen sulphites with zinc, or by shaking sodium or potassium amalgam with dry SO_2 in the absence of oxygen. The salts reduce nitrocompounds to amines. An $Na_2S_2O_4$ solution is used to reduce and dissolve vat dyes such as indigo. X-ray analysis shows the $S_2O_4^{2-}$ ion in sodium dithionite to consist of two SO_2^- groups attached by a very long S—S bond (2.39 Å) (Dunitz, 1956).

Sulphurous acid cannot be isolated from aqueous SO_2. It ionises fairly strongly:

$$H_2O + H_2SO_3 \rightleftharpoons H_3O^+ + HSO_3^-, \qquad pK_a = 1.77$$

Standard redox potentials are:

$$SO_4^{2-} + 4H^+ + 2e \rightleftharpoons H_2SO_3 + H_2O, \qquad E_h^\circ = +0.20V;$$
$$H_2SO_3 + 4H^+ + 4e \rightleftharpoons S + 3H_2O, \qquad E_h^\circ = -0.45V.$$

It has thus rather strong reducing properties, being itself reduced to sulphur only by very strong reducing agents. The dibasic acid forms two series of salts. The hydrogen sulphites, $M^I HSO_3$, yield disulphites of the type $M^I_2 S_2 O_5$ on heating:

$$2NaHSO_3 \rightarrow Na_2S_2O_5 \text{ (the so-called sodium metabisulphite)} + H_2O.$$

The sulphite ion is pyramidal; the S—O bond (1.39 Å) is shorter than the S—O bonds in SO_2 or $SOCl_2$.

Sulphuric acid, commercially most important, is made by way of the catalytic oxidation of SO_2 to SO_3; this is done either at a surface, such as V_2O_5 or Pt in the contact process, or with NO as a homogeneous catalyst in the lead chamber process. Though a strong acid, the second ionisation is slight in any but the most dilute solutions. In the absence of water, the acid contains HSO_3^+ ions, the active sulphonating agent (p. 198). X-ray analysis shows the SO_4^{2-} ion to be almost tetrahedral and the dimensions indicate considerable double bond character. The ion often holds 'anion water' in crystal structures, examples being $CuSO_4.5H_2O$ and $FeSO_4.7H_2O$. In some complex compounds the SO_4 group is bound covalently to the central atom. Examples are

$$[(NH_3)_5 Co.SO_4]^+,$$

in which the SO_4 group is attached by a single bond, and

$$[(NH_3)_4 Pt : SO_4]^{2+},$$

in which the group is bound by two covalencies.

SO_3 dissolves in H_2SO_4 to give $H_2S_2O_7$, an excellent sulphonating agent. Sodium disulphate (pyrosulphate), $Na_2S_2O_7$, can be made by heating sodium hydrogen sulphate strongly:

$$2NaHSO_4 \rightarrow H_2O + Na_2S_2O_7.$$

The salt is hydrolysed in water to give HSO_4^- ions. Evidence for higher isopolysulphates exists in the compound $(NO_2)_2S_3O_{10}$ (Goddard, Hughes and Ingold, 1950).

Anhydrous thiosulphuric acid, which is very unstable, has been recently obtained by the reaction of H_2S with SO_3 at $-78°$, either alone or in a liquid such as freon. It can also be made by the action of H_2S on chlorosulphuric acid, HSO_3Cl, at the same temperature. Thiosulphates are made by boiling alkali metal sulphite solutions with sulphur:

$$SO_3^{2-} + S \rightarrow S_2O_3^{2-}.$$

Selenium also dissolves in sulphite solutions to give selenosulphates:

$$SO_3^{2-} + Se \rightarrow SSeO_3^{2-}.$$

Thiosulphates are numerous, fairly stable and usually very soluble in water
The $S_2O_3^{2-}$ ion is structurally analogous to SO_4^{2-} (Fig. 187).

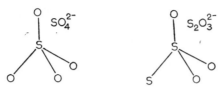

Fig. 187. Analogy between $S_2O_3^{2-}$ and SO_4^{2-} ions.

$Na_2S_2O_3$, made by boiling ^{35}S with inactive Na_2SO_3, yields a precipitate of
active sulphur on acidification but no activity remains in the SO_3^{2-} solution:

$$^{35}S + {}^{32}SO_3^{2-} \xrightarrow{boil} {}^{35}S{}^{32}SO_3^{2-} \xrightarrow{acid} {}^{35}S + {}^{32}SO_3^{2-}.$$

There is no exchange between the two S atoms, thus they cannot be equivalent in the molecule. Neyman (1952), employing $H_2{}^{35}S$ in the reaction:

$$4SO_2 + 2H_2S + 6NaOH \rightarrow 3Na_2S_2O_3 + 5H_2O.$$

obtained similar evidence on acidifying the salt produced. All the central S
atoms of the $S_2O_3^{2-}$ ions came from SO_2, but the ligand atoms partly from
SO_2 and partly from H_2S.

Addition of acid to a thiosulphate solution does not cause decomposition
until a pH of 4.6 is reached. The $HS_2O_3^-$ ion then formed, being much less
stable than the $S_2O_3^{2-}$ ion, decomposes quickly:

$$HS_2O_3^- \rightarrow HSO_3^- + S.$$

Thus thiosulphates exist only as neutral salts. If very dilute HCl is added
to sodium thiosulphate in the presence of As_4O_6, the pentathionate is formed:

$$6H^+ + 5S_2O_3^{2-} \rightarrow 2S_5O_6^{2-} + 3H_2O.$$

Dithionic acid appears in a solution of sulphurous acid oxidised by finely
divided MnO_2. From this, baryta precipitates all the sulphur-containing
anions except dithionate, and, when the excess of Ba^{2+} has been precipitated
by H_2SO_4, only $H_2S_2O_6$ is left in the solution. Although conductance measurements show the acid to be dibasic, acid salts are unknown. Dithionates are
soluble in water and, unlike salts of the higher thionic acids, are not decomposed by sulphites and sulphides.

Potassium trithionate, $K_2S_3O_6$, can be made by passing SO_2 into a solution
of $K_2S_2O_3$. The salt crystallises on standing, leaving in solution $K_2S_4O_6$ and
$K_2S_5O_6$ formed along with it. When aqueous $K_2S_3O_6$ is acidified, decomposition occurs:

$$H_2S_3O_6 \rightarrow H_2SO_4 + SO_2 + S.$$

Sodium tetrathionate, $Na_2S_4O_6$, is formed when $Na_2S_2O_3$ is oxidised with iodine. Although this, and other tetrathionates, can be isolated as solids, they are thermally unstable. Aqueous tetrathionic acid results from adding dilute H_2SO_4 to a solution of PbS_4O_6; attempts at concentration eventually cause decomposition:

$$H_2S_4O_6 \rightarrow H_2SO_4 + SO_2 + 2S$$

Sodium pentathionate, $Na_2S_5O_6$, is made by treating a concentrated $Na_2S_2O_3$ solution with HCl in the presence of As_4O_6 at $-10°$:

$$5S_2O_3{}^{2-} + 10H^+ \rightarrow 2H_2S_5O_6 + 3H_2O.$$

The liquid deposits crystals of $Na_2S_5O_6$ on standing. The acid itself is stable in fairly strong aqueous solution but eventually decomposes on concentration:

$$H_2S_5O_6 \rightarrow H_2SO_4 + SO_2 + 3S.$$

X-ray diffraction shows the dithionate ion to consist of two triangular pyramids joined at their apices (Fig. 188). In the trithionate ion the third sulphur atom lies between the other two with an S—S—S angle of 103° (Fig. 189). In the tetrathionate and pentathionate ions the additional sulphur atoms are attached to one another in simple chains (Fig. 190).

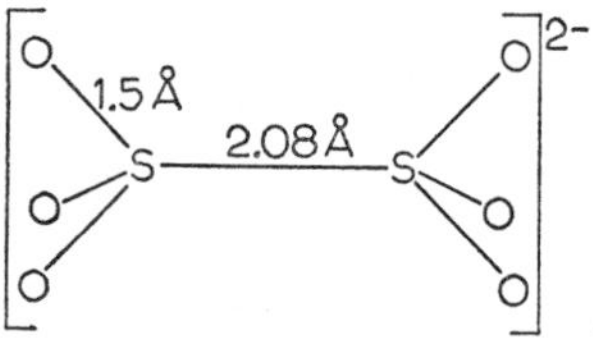

Fig. 188. Structure of dithionate ion.

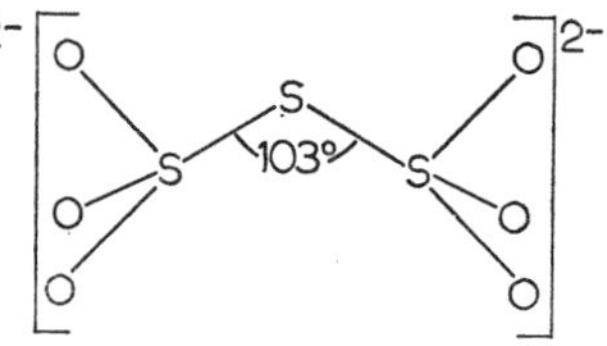

Fig. 189. Structure of trithionate ion.

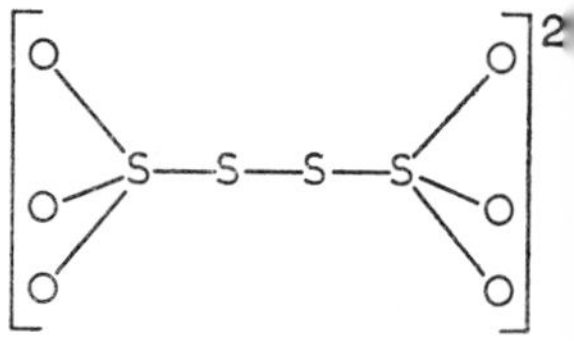

Fig. 190. Structure of tetrathionate ion.

Oxoacids of selenium

Selenium has two oxoacids:

Selenious acid, H_2SeO_3, colourless solid.
Selenic acid, H_2SeO_4, colourless solid, m.p. 59°.

When a solution of SeO_2 is evaporated the acid, H_2SeO_3, separates as hexagonal prisms. There are normal and acid selenites, and also superacid salts such as $KH_3(SeO_3)_2$. Heteropolyacids are formed with vanadic, molybdic and uranic acids.

Selenious acid is converted to selenic acid, H_2SeO_4, when refluxed with 30% H_2O_2. A 97.4% solution can be made by vacuum desiccation; the pure acid crystallises on cooling. This resembles sulphuric acid in (i) ionising strongly; (ii) forming selenates isomorphous with the sulphates; (iii) forming a nitroso-acid $(NO)HSeO_4$. It differs from H_2SO_4 by losing oxygen when heated above 200° and by oxidising chlorides to chlorine.

Telluric acid

Telluric acid, H_6TeO_6, can be made as white crystals by dissolving Te in aqua regia, adding a chlorate, evaporating in a vacuum, precipitating with HNO_3 and recrystallising from water. It is a very weak acid, quite unlike H_2SO_4 and H_2SeO_4. Pauling (1935) showed the TeO_6^{6-} ion to be octahedral.

Halogen derivatives of the oxoacids

Sulphur

Sulphinyl (thionyl) halides		Sulphonyl (sulphuryl) halides	
	b.p.		b.p.
SOF_2	$-30°$	SO_2F_2	$-52°$
$SOCl_2$	$78°$	SO_2Cl_2	$69°$
$SOBr_2$ (red)	$59°/40$ mm		

	Acids	
		b.p.
HSO_3Cl	chlorosulphuric	$151°$
HSO_3F	fluorosulphuric	$163°$

Sulphinyl chloride, $SOCl_2$, is made by the action of SO_2 on PCl_5:

$$SO_2 + PCl_5 \rightarrow SOCl_2 + POCl_3.$$
$$\text{b.p. }78° \qquad \text{b.p. }107°$$

The colourless liquid is obtained by fractionating the mixture. The molecule is pyramidal (Fig. 191), and owes its shape to the use of sp^3 hybrid orbitals round an S atom with one lone pair.

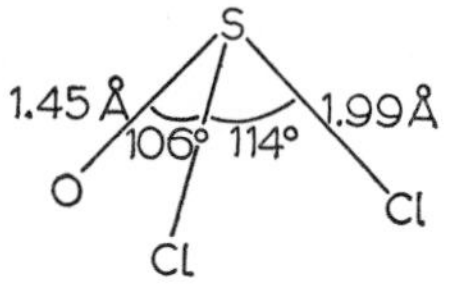

Fig. 191.
Structure of sulphinyl chloride.

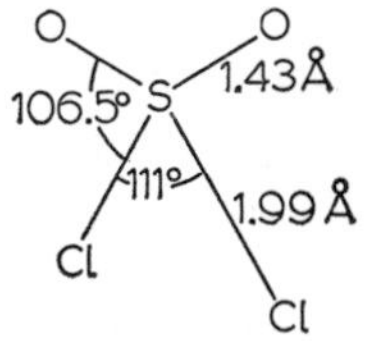

Fig. 192.
Structure of sulphonyl chloride.

Sulphinyl fluoride, SOF_2, a colourless gas which does not attack glass or mercury at room temperature, results from the action of SbF_3 on $SOCl_2$; the red liquid $SOBr_2$ is made by treating $SOCl_2$ with HBr. SOF_2 hydrolyses slowly in water, in which it is sparingly soluble; the chloride hydrolyses violently:

$$SOCl_2 + H_2O \rightarrow SO_2 + 2HCl.$$

When SO_2 and Cl_2 are passed alternately over camphor they combine to give sulphonyl chloride, SO_2Cl_2, which can be distilled from the product. The liquid is rather slowly hydrolysed by water. The molecule forms a distorted tetrahedron (Fig. 192). Sulphonyl fluoride, SO_2F_2, made by heating SO_2 and F_2 together, is an inert gas, unaffected by water but decomposed by hot alkalis:

$$SO_2F_2 + 4OH^- \rightarrow SO_4{}^{2-} + 2F^- + 2H_2O.$$

When dry HCl is passed into fuming H_2SO_4, which contains SO_3, the compound $HOSO_2Cl$, chlorosulphuric acid, is formed. Its relation to H_2SO_4 and SO_2Cl_2 is shown diagrammatically:

It is hydrolysed violently by water:

$$(HO)SO_2Cl + H_2O \rightarrow H_2SO_4 + HCl.$$

Fluorosulphuric acid, $(HO)SO_2F$, made by distilling fuming H_2SO_4 with CaF_2, is a colourless liquid hydrolysed incompletely by water.

Selenium

The element does not form selenonyl (SeO_2^{2+}) derivatives of H_2SeO_4, corresponding to the sulphonyl derivatives of H_2SO_4, or halogeno-acids corresponding to $HOSO_2Cl$.

The seleninyl (SeO^{2+}) compounds contain Se^{IV} and are thus related to H_2SeO_3.

> $SeOF_2$, colourless   b.p. 124°
> $SeOCl_2$, pale yellow   b.p. 176° (decomposition)
> $SeOBr_2$, orange   m.p. 42°

$SeOCl_2$ is made by heating SeO_2 and $SeCl_4$ together in a sealed tube. It is converted to $SeOF_2$ when passed over AgF, and to $SeOBr_2$ when distilled from NaBr.

Oxo-salts of tellurium and polonium

An oxide sulphate, $Te_2O_3.SO_4$, is obtained as white crystals when TeO is heated with concentrated H_2SO_4. A corresponding compound of polonium can be crystallised from a solution of $PoCl_4$ in $0.02-0.025N$ H_2SO_4. With stronger H_2SO_4, however, a colourless hydrate of $Po(SO_4)_2$ is formed. This loses water on standing or heating, becoming pink and finally purple. The purple anhydrous salt is stable up to $400°$.

Tellurium dissolves in concentrated nitric acid. On evaporation colourless rhombic $Te_2O_3(OH)_3NO_3$ crystallises. Polonium also forms a somewhat similar nitrate whose composition is as yet unknown.

Chapter 23

The Oxides

Of the known elements the inert gases alone are without oxides. Here are considered only what may be termed the normal oxides, namely those with separate oxygen atoms or ions attached directly and only to the atom or ion of another element. Besides these there are the peroxides (p. 383) and super-oxides (p. 384) in which the oxygen atoms are attached in pairs. In hydrogen peroxide (p. 381) they are connected by a single bond $H-O-O-H$; in ionic peroxides, such as Na_2O_2, they appear as O_2^{2-} ions; and in superoxides, such as KO_2, as O_2^- ions.

Normal oxides fall broadly into three classes according to their behaviour in water: (i) *basic* which are invariably those of metals and which, when soluble, give alkaline solutions; (ii) *acidic* which are roughly the soluble oxides of the non-metals and the higher oxides of the transition metals, and which give acidic solutions; (iii) *neutral* which include water and the relatively insoluble gases CO and N_2O.

The distribution through the Periodic Table of representative basic and acidic oxides is shown in Table 83; the oxides adjacent to the dividing line are commonly amphoteric.

Oxygen, owing to its high electronegativity, readily forms ionic compounds and most metallic oxides have simple ionic structures. Some, however, have considerable covalent character when the metal (*e.g.* transition metal) has a high charge number and a correspondingly greater electronegativity. The charge effect is well shown by manganese; MnO is an ionic solid with a rock-salt lattice and Mn_2O_7 a covalent liquid.

Oxides of the non-metals range from the volatile monomers (*e.g.* CO_2, N_2O, SO_2) to involatile macro-molecules (*e.g.* B_2O_3, SiO_2). Intermediately there are many oxides which are less volatile than might be expected through associa-tion (*e.g.* H_2O, SO_3, P_2O_5).

The classification of oxides as acidic and basic is not rigid. Generally the molecular oxides of the non-metals are acidic, many being acid anhydrides, and so too are the higher oxides of transition metals (*e.g.* CrO_3, Mn_2O_7). Such neutral oxides as H_2O, CO and N_2O are exceptional. The more or less covalent CuO is without acid character and the similar PbO is weakly alkaline. Although the ionic metal oxides are usually basic, ZnO and Al_2O_3 are am-photeric.

TABLE 83

DISTRIBUTION OF OXIDES THROUGH THE PERIODIC TABLE

Non-transition elements

Basic				*Acidic*			
Li_2O	BeO	B_2O_3	CO_2	N_2O_5			F_2O
Na_2O	MgO	Al_2O_3	SiO_2	P_2O_5	SO_3		Cl_2O
K_2O	CaO	Ga_2O_3	GeO_2	As_2O_3	SeO_2		Br_2O
Rb_2O	SrO	In_2O_3	SnO	Sb_2O_3	TeO_2		I_2O_5
Cs_2O	BaO	Tl_2O	PbO	Bi_2O_3	PoO_2		

Transition elements and Gps. IB and IIB

Basic			*Acidic*						*Basic*
Sc_2O_3	TiO_2	V_2O_5	CrO_3	Mn_2O_7	Fe_2O_3	CoO	NiO	Cu_2O	ZnO
Y_2O_3	ZrO_2	Nb_2O_5	MoO_3	Tc_2O_7	RuO_4	Rh_2O_3	PdO	Ag_2O	CdO
*Ln_2O_3	HfO_2	Ta_2O_5	WO_3	Re_2O_7	OsO_4	IrO_2	PtO	Au_2O	HgO
Ac_2O_3									

* Ln = lanthanide atom.

Methods of preparation

Many normal oxides are formed on burning the element in air or oxygen. This is true not only of the non-metals boron, carbon, sulphur and phosphorus, but also for the volatile zinc, cadmium, indium and thallium, the transition metals cobalt and iron, in finely divided condition, and the noble metals osmium, ruthenium and rhodium. With some elements, limiting the supply of oxygen produces the lower oxide (*e.g.* P_4O_6 in place of P_4O_{10} (p. 332)).

Lower oxides have been made by reducing a higher oxide with carbon or hydrogen (*e.g.* MnO_2 to MnO and V_2O_5 to V_2O_3 by hydrogen).

A few elements are oxidised by steam at red heat:

$$3Fe + 4H_2O \rightarrow Fe_3O_4 + 4H_2,$$
$$C + H_2O \rightarrow CO + H_2,$$
$$Mg + H_2O \rightarrow MgO + H_2.$$

In this reaction magnesium burns brilliantly.

Metal oxides are commonly prepared, and often manufactured, by the thermal decomposition of hydroxide, carbonate or nitrate:

$$Cu(OH)_2 \rightarrow CuO + H_2O,$$
$$CaCO_3 \rightarrow CaO + CO_2,$$
$$2Pb(NO_3)_2 \rightarrow 2PbO + 4NO_2 + O_2.$$

Certain precipitated hydroxides are easily converted to oxide, $Tl(OH)_3$ even in boiling water, but others, for instance $Cu(OH)_2$, which gives a hydrated black oxide, cannot be completely dehydrated. $Au(OH)_3$ is changed only to $AuO(OH)$ after prolonged standing over P_2O_5.

Precipitation by alkali from soluble salts usually gives a hydroxide:

$$Ca^{2+} + 2OH^- \rightarrow Ca(OH)_2.$$

Sometimes a complex hydrated oxide is formed:

$$2Pb^{2+} + 4OH^- \rightarrow Pb_2O(OH)_2 + H_2O,$$
$$H_2PtCl_6 + 6OH^- \rightarrow H_2Pt(OH)_6 + 6Cl^-.$$

But in other instances the oxide itself results:

$$Hg^{2+} + 2OH^- \rightarrow HgO + H_2O,$$
$$2Au^+ + 2OH^- \rightarrow Au_2O + H_2O.$$

Other oxidising agents, especially nitric acid and the oxides of nitrogen, convert some elements to oxides. Nitric acid, for example, oxidises sulphur to SO_2 and SO_3, and germanium and tin to GeO_2 and SnO_2, respectively.

The preparation of pure, single-phase oxides of true stoichiometry is often difficult, sometimes impossible. FeO and MnO_2 are examples, the former being always metal-deficient, the latter always oxygen-deficient (p. 429, 484).

Oxide structures

Metallic oxides of predominantly ionic character

Metal oxides of MO type are generally simple structurally, having O^{2-} and M^{2+} ions arranged in 4:4 or 6:6 co-ordination, depending on the ratio of the ionic sizes. The Be^{2+} ion (0.31 Å) has only four O^{2-} ions (1.40 Å) round it in BeO; but most MO-type ionic oxides, with M^{2+} ranging from 0.5 Å to 1.0 Å, have the 6:6 co-ordination and rock-salt lattices. Examples are MgO, CaO, SrO, BaO, CdO, VO, MnO and CoO. NiO has a slightly distorted version which gives it rhombohedral structure. The normal oxides of the Gp. IA metals are ionic oxides of the M_2O type. They have the antifluorite crystal lattice arising from 4:8 co-ordination; a structure so named because the position of anions and cations are the reverse of those in CaF_2 (p. 150).

There are two main types of ionic oxides which are empirically formulated MO_2. Where the metal ion is large (Th^{4+}, 0.95 Å; Ce^{4+}, 0.92 Å; U^{4+}, 0.89 Å) the crystals are built up of fluorite-type unit cells with 8:4 co-ordination. But where the metal ion is smaller (Sn^{4+}, 0.71 Å; Ti^{4+}, 0.68 Å) the structure is based on the rutile lattice with 6:3 co-ordination. Other examples of this structure are VO_2, RuO_2, PbO_2 and TeO_2. The rutile lattice is slightly deformed in MoO_2 and WO_2.

The structurally simplest MO_3-type oxide is rhenium oxide, ReO_3 (Fig. 255,

p. 485). WO_3 and CrO_3 are like it, but slightly deformed. The reason for these small deformations, those of MoO_2 and WO_2 (deformed rutile), and that of NiO (deformed rock-salt), is not known.

The usual lattices of the M_2O_3-group of ionic oxides are those of corundum and of the so-called A- and C-type lanthanide sesquioxides. The relationship of corundum to MgO appears in Fig. 193. In both structures O^{2-} ions are arranged octahedrally round the metal ions, but in α-Al_2O_3 one third of the metal ions are missing. The A-type lanthanide sesquioxides, La_2O_3 is an example, have a hexagonal lattice (Fig. 194) and unusual co-ordination. Each La^{3+} ion has, as nearest neighbours, four O^{2-} at 2.42 Å and three O^{2-} at 2.69 Å.

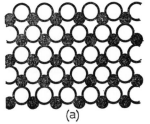

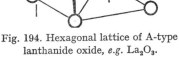

Fig. 193. Relation between MgO structure and α-Al_2O_3.
(a) MgO structure; (b) Al_2O_3 structure.

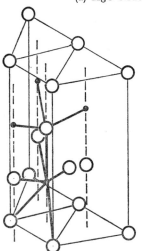

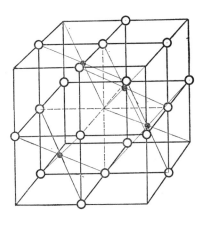

Fig. 194. Hexagonal lattice of A-type lanthanide oxide, *e.g.* La_2O_3.

Fig. 195. Cubic lattice of C-type lanthanide oxide, *e.g.* Sc_2O_3.

The C-type oxide (Fig. 195), Sc_2O_3 is an example, has the simpler symmetry of the cubic lattice and 6:4 co-ordination.

In oxides with the empirical composition M_3O_4, the metal necessarily appears with two charge numbers. As a result, the compounds often resemble complex oxides. Red lead, Pb_3O_4, which is isomorphous with $ZnSb_2O_4$, has a complicated structure. Octahedra of $Pb^{IV}O_6$ share opposite edges to form chains; these are linked by Pb^{II} atoms each forming three bonds, pyramidally arranged, with its nearest oxygen neighbours (Fig. 163, p. 314).

Metal oxides of more covalent character

In these oxides the number of bonds round the metal is smaller than size considerations alone suggest, and they are frequently arranged in the same manner as those present in complexes of the metal.

Silver(I) and copper(I) oxides are similar in structure (Fig. 270, p. 515), with the M—O bonds collinear and 2 : 4 co-ordination. But in PdO and PtO each metal atom has four coplanar bonds and each oxygen four tetrahedral ones in a tetragonal unit cell (Fig. 267, p. 507).

Layer lattices, which are uncommon among oxides, indicate a predominantly covalent character in the metal-oxygen bonds. SnO and PbO are solids of this type. Each metal atom is joined to four oxygens arranged in a square on one side of it (Fig. 196).

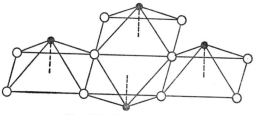

Fig. 196. Structure of PbO.

MoO_3 also has a layer structure; in it MoO_6 groups share two edges and two corners.

Complex oxides

These are sometimes considered under two heads, those with complex ions, such as CO_3^{2-} and NO_3^-, and those without complex ions. Only the latter will be discussed here. They are of two main types. In the first, the lattice structures are those of simple compounds in which random replacement of metal ions has occurred. Li_2TiO_3 has a random rock-salt structure with two thirds of the metal ion positions occupied by Li and one third by Ti. $FeSbO_4$ has a random rutile structure.

In the second, there occur structures not present in simple compounds. Three of these are of importance: they are respectively the *perovskite*,

$CaTiO_3$; the *ilmenite*, $FeTiO_3$; and the *spinel*, $FeAl_2O_4$. In perovskite the large Ca^{2+} and O^{2-} ions form a close-packed structure with smaller Ti^{4+} ions uniformly arranged in some of the interstices (Fig. 197).

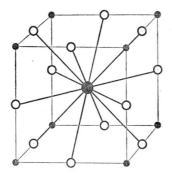

Fig. 197. Perovskite structure. Note relationship to ReO_3 (p. 485).

Other complex oxides with a perovskite structure are $SrTiO_3$, $CaZrO_3$ and $LaAlO_3$.

In ilmenite, the oxygen ions are in close-packed hexagonal arrangement with both the Fe^{2+} and Ti^{4+} ions severally occupying one third of the octahedral holes. The compounds $MnTiO_3$, $CoTiO_3$ and $NiTiO_3$ also have the ilmenite structure and there is no justification for calling them titanates. Ilmenite is isomorphous with α-Fe_2O_3 which has the corundum structure (Fig. 193 (b), p. 375). It differs from α-Fe_2O_3 only in having Ti^{4+} ions alternating with Fe^{2+} ions instead of the single type of metal ion, Fe^{3+}.

A slightly more complicated arrangement is that in the spinels. The oxide ions in $FeAl_2O_4$ are arranged in cubic close-packing with the Fe^{2+} ions in the tetrahedral, and the Al^{3+} ions in the octahedral interstices. Fig. 198 shows the arrangement of metal ions relative to two adjacent layers of oxygen ions.

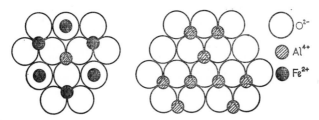

Fig. 198. Adjacent layers of O^{2-} ions with superimposed metal ions in $FeAl_2O_4$.

Other compounds with this structure include $CoAl_2O_4$ and $MnAl_2O_4$; these again have the M^{2+} ions in positions of tetrahedral, and the M^{3+} ions in positions of octahedral co-ordination. There is, however, a second rather more complicated type of spinel structure with a partly random arrangement of the metal ions. Examples are $Fe(MgFe)O_4$ and $Fe(TiFe)O_4$, so formulated because one half of the Fe atoms are symmetrically arranged in octahedral positions and the other half randomly arranged, with the ions of the second metal, in tetrahedral positions.

Oxides with chain structures

Some of the B sub-group elements form oxides with chain-like structures which can be considered as intermediate in valency character between the infinite three dimensional metallic oxides and the molecular non-metallic oxides. Examples are SeO_2:

and valentinite, a form of Sb_2O_3:

in which the Sb atoms form pyramidal bonds with bond angles about 90°.

Solid oxides containing individual molecules

The covalent oxides of non-metals form solids in which individual molecules are present, sometimes as the simple monomer, for instance CO_2 and SO_2, and sometimes as a dimer or trimer. Dimeric forms include P_4O_6 and As_4O_6. One of the forms of sulphur trioxide is trimeric (p. 365).

Comparison of oxides and sulphides

Oxides are generally more ionic in character than the corresponding sulphides. The electronegativity assigned to oxygen is 3.5, to sulphur only 2.5. Accordingly, elements of low electronegativity form markedly ionic bonds with oxygen but not necessarily with sulphur. This is brought out when the structures of oxides and sulphides are compared. The only unequivocally ionic sulphides are those of the Gp.IA and Gp.IIA metals and of a few of the transition metals, such as MnS. The existence of any truly ionic M_2S_3 sulphide is doubtful, although the ready hydrolysis of Al_2S_3 suggests that it may be one. No ionic MS_2 sulphide is known. The S^{2-} ion is evidently too easily polarised to exist in the neighbourhood of a small quadripositive cation. Instead, most of the solid disulphides have layer lattices, a type of structure very uncommon among the oxides:

$$TiO_2 \rbrace \ Rutile \qquad TiS_2 \rbrace \ Layer$$
$$SnO_2 \rbrace \ structure. \qquad SnS_2 \rbrace \ lattices.$$

Both the pyrities and marcasite forms of FeS_2 contain covalently bound S_2 units which are not ionic (Fig. 261, p. 494).

Non–stoichiometry

The solid oxides and sulphides all show, to a greater or lesser extent, homogeneous phases which vary in composition from that represented by the stoichiometric formula of the named compound. These phases often retain the same structure but, nevertheless, show a certain range of differences in their other properties (p. 158).

Thermochemistry of the oxides

In a series of oxides such as those of the metals of the second period (Fig. 199), differences between the heats of formation of its members depend largely on differences between the ionisation potentials of the elements combining with oxygen and the lattice energies of the oxides so formed. When a positive 'inert gas' ion is replaced by one of higher charge but of the same structure, the heat of formation, and consequently the stability,

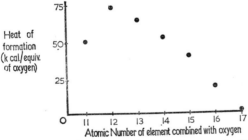

Fig. 199. Heat of formation $(-\Delta H)$ per equivalent of oxygen for Na_2O, MgO, Al_2O_3, SiO_2, P_4O_{10}, SO_3, Cl_2O_7.

decreases. The apparently anomalous increase in heat of formation per oxygen equivalent from Na_2O to MgO is understandable when the lower crystal energy of Na_2O, caused by the mutual repulsion between unipositive metal ions, is taken into account. The effect is demonstrated more emphatically by the nitrides, where the stable AlN has a large crystal energy and the unstable Na_3N a small one. Nevertheless, Li_3N is formed, because Li^+ is so small compared with N^{3-}.

Heats of formation of the oxides usually increase down a group in the Periodic Table:

$$CO_2 \quad SiO_2 \quad TiO_2 \quad ZrO_2 \quad HfO_2$$

Heat of formation
per oxygen equivalent (kcal) 23.5 49.5 54 64 83

Ionisation potentials decrease with increase in size of the M^{4+} ions. Lattice energies also decrease as the sum of the radii r^+ and r^- increases, but the effect is overshadowed by the change in ionisation potential, particularly where the radius of the positive ion (r^+) is small compared with that of the oxide ion (r^-).

Chapter 24

Peroxides and Peroxo-Compounds

Hydrogen peroxide

The geometry and probable electronic structure of H_2O_2 are shown in Fig. 200.

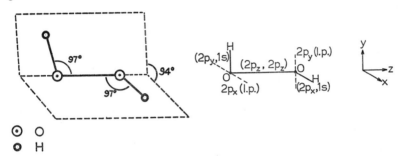

Fig. 200. Structure of H_2O_2.

The lengths of the O—O and O—H bonds are 1.48 ± 0.02 Å and 1.01 ± 0.03 Å, respectively (Abrahams, Collin and Lipscomb, 1951). The angles of 97° and 94° suggest only a slight distortion of the electronic structure shown; in which, for example, $(2p_x, 1s)$ indicates a localised bond involving the oxygen $2p_x$ orbital and the hydrogen 1s. This configuration would (i) minimise lone-pair—lone-pair repulsions and (ii) maximise small contributions to bonding which can arise from slight delocalisation of the lone pairs. It would therefore account for the observed lack of free rotation about the O—O bond.

The liquid is pale blue and syrupy in consistency, freezing at $-0.46°$ to tetragonal crystals, and is much denser than water (1.471 g/cc at 0°). The boiling point cannot be measured directly as the liquid decomposes explosively at a lower temperature, but extrapolation of vapour pressure data indicates 155.5°. The entropy of vaporisation (27.3 cals/deg/mole) is high, indicating the destruction of a considerable 'local order' (p. 232) which is characteristic of polar liquids. The dipole moment is in fact high (2.01 Debyes); the dielectric constant is large (89 at 0°); and the autoprotolysis constant (p. 196), $[H_3O_2^+][HO_2^-] = 1.55 \times 10^{-12}$, indicates that the liquid is a good ionising solvent.

The heat and free energy of formation are much lower than for water:

$$H_2(g) + O_2(g) \rightarrow H_2O_2(g) \qquad \Delta H_f = -33.3 \text{ kcal},$$
$$\Delta G_f = -29.3 \text{ kcal}.$$

Liquid hydrogen peroxide is thermodynamically unstable:

$$H_2O_2(l) \rightarrow H_2O(l) + \tfrac{1}{2}O_2(g) \qquad \Delta H = -23.5 \text{ kcal},$$
$$\Delta G^\circ = -29.3 \text{ kcal}.$$

but its decomposition at 25° is not rapid in the absence of catalysts. Catalysts are silver, the platinum group metals, cobalt, iron, copper, MnO_2 and several other oxides. As usual, the rate of reaction depends on their surface area.

Hydrogen peroxide is a strong oxidising agent in both acid and alkaline solutions:

$$H_2O_2 + 2H^+ + 2e \rightleftharpoons 2H_2O \qquad E_h^\circ = +1.77 \text{ V},$$
$$HO_2^- + H_2O + 2e \rightleftharpoons 3OH^- \qquad E_h^\circ = +0.87 \text{ V}.$$

But with some strong oxidising agents, such as Cl_2, or MnO_4^- in acid solution, hydrogen peroxide is itself oxidised:

$$2MnO_4^- + 5H_2O_2 + 6H^+ = 2Mn^{2+} + 8H_2O + 5O_2,$$
$$Cl_2 + H_2O_2 = 2HCl + O_2.$$

In acid solution:

$$2H^+ + O_2 + 2e \rightleftharpoons H_2O_2 \qquad E_h^\circ = +0.68 \text{ V},$$

but in alkaline solution

$$\tfrac{1}{2}O_2 + H^+ + e \rightleftharpoons OH \rightleftharpoons \tfrac{1}{2}H_2O_2 \qquad E_h^\circ = +0.22 \text{ V},$$

and oxidation can proceed more readily.

The standard redox potential of the cyanoferrate(III)–cyanoferrate(II) couple ($+0.356$ V) lies between these two values. As a result H_2O_2 will oxidise a cyanoferrate(II) in acid solution:

$$2Fe(CN)_6^{4-} + H_2O_2 + 2H^+ = 2Fe(CN)_6^{3-} + 2H_2O;$$

but in alkaline solution cyanoferrate(III) oxidises H_2O_2:

$$2Fe(CN)_6^{3-} + H_2O_2 + 2OH^- = 2Fe(CN)_6^{4-} + 2H_2O + O_2.$$

Production of hydrogen peroxide

Until recently its manufacture was based on the electrolysis of ammonium sulphate in an excess of sulphuric acid between platinum electrodes at high current density; this produces a solution of the ammonium salt of perdisulphuric acid by oxidation at the anode and liberates hydrogen at the cathode:

$$2NH_4HSO_4 \rightarrow (NH_4)_2S_2O_8 + H_2.$$

The solution, on heating at 40 mm pressure, hydrolyses and a distillate of water and H_2O_2 is obtained:

$$(NH_4)_2S_2O_8 + 2H_2O \rightarrow 2NH_4HSO_4 + H_2O_2.$$

The aqueous H_2O_2 is concentrated to 85–90% by low-pressure fractionation, water being more volatile than hydrogen peroxide.

Now an autoxidation process is used in which air is passed through a 10% solution of 2-ethyl anthrahydroquinol in a mixture of benzene and 7–11 carbon-atom alcohols, or an alternative mixed solvent of a safer character.

When the H_2O_2 reaches about 5.5 g/l., the solution is extracted with water to give an 18% aqueous solution which is concentrated as described above. The 2-ethylanthraquinone is reduced to the original compound with hydrogen in the presence of palladium on an inert support, the catalyst being suspended in the liquid by the stream of gas.

Hydrogen peroxide is used in the bleaching of textiles and in the preparation of organic peroxides. Peroxide ~85% has been employed in conjunction with hydrazine, methyl alcohol or certain other combustibles as a fuel for rocket motors. When catalytically decomposed it serves as a propellant for torpedoes.

Peroxides

A peroxide contains, by definition, the anion $(O—O)^{2-}$ (p. 372) and produces H_2O_2 when acidified. It is thus incorrect to apply the term to dioxides such as NO_2 and PbO_2. Peroxides are formed by all Gp.IA and several Gp.IIA metals: Li_2O_2, Na_2O_2, K_2O_2, Rb_2O_2, Cs_2O_2, and MgO_2, CaO_2, SrO_2, BaO_2.

The most common, Na_2O_2, is made by heating sodium in oxygen. The pale yellow commercial material contains about 10% NaO_2 (George, 1955). $Li_2O_2.H_2O_2.H_2O$ is precipitated when alcoholic H_2O_2 is added to LiOH; careful drying gives the anhydrous compound. The other peroxides of this group are made by controlled oxidation with either the calculated amount of air on the metal at 300°, or by passing the required amount of air through a solution of the metal in liquid ammonia at —50°. The compounds all give H_2O_2 on acid hydrolysis:

$$Na_2O_2 + H_2SO_4 \xrightarrow{\text{cold}} Na_2SO_4 + H_2O_2.$$

Belief in the existence of $(O{-}O)^{2-}$ ions in the Gp.I compounds is based on their reactions, not their crystal structure which is unknown.

Of the Gp.IIA peroxides, that of barium is most stable. It is made by heating BaO in air or oxygen at 400°. SrO_2 is made less easily; at 400° and 100 atmospheres the equilibrium mixture $2SrO + O_2 \rightleftharpoons 2SrO_2$ contains about 15% of the strontium as SrO_2. Octahydrates of these two peroxides, as well as $CaO_2.8H_2O$, are precipitated by adding H_2O_2 to the aqueous hydroxides. Dehydration to the anhydrous peroxide is possible with all of them. The monohydrate, $BaO_2.H_2O$, consists of Ba^{2+} ions and helical chains of peroxide groups, held together by hydrogen bonds. Anhydrous MgO_2 is made by adding $\sim 0.15M$ NaOH to $MgSO_4$ dissolved in 30% H_2O_2 and drying the precipitate over phosphorus pentoxide.

Of the Gp.IIB peroxides, anhydrous ZnO_2 is prepared in a similar way to MgO_2, and CdO_2 by the action of 30% H_2O_2 on an ammoniacal solution of $CdSO_4$ and drying the precipitate produced at 120°. Like MgO_2, the zinc and cadmium peroxides have the pyrites structure (p. 494) with an O—O distance, in the peroxide ion, of 1.50 Å.

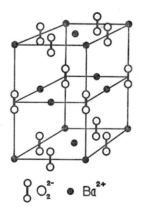

Fig. 201. Structure of BaO_2.

Superoxides

The alkali metals other than lithium form compounds of the formula MO_2, containing the anion O_2^- and termed superoxides (p. 372). NaO_2 is formed only at high oxygen pressures, those of the other metals more easily. In NaO_2 the arrangement of oxygens is disordered (Templeton, 1950). KO_2 and BaO_2 are similar in their geometry and stability:

Ionic radius		O—O distance	
K+	1.33 Å	O_2^-	1.28 Å
Ba^{2+}	1.35	O_2^{2-}	1.31

The paramagnetism of the superoxides suggests an ionic picture featuring the O_2^- anion; the moment of 2.04μ observed for KO_2 is characteristic of one unpaired electron.

Canisters containing potassium superoxide are a source of oxygen for high altitude climbing. In the presence of a little $CuCl_2$, it reacts with expired CO_2, one gram setting free 236 cc O_2 at S.T.P. The compound reacts even with ice-cold water:

$$2KO_2 + 2H_2O \rightarrow 2KOH + H_2O_2 + O_2;$$

and with acetic acid in diethyl phthalate solution:

$$2CH_3COOH + 2KO_2 \rightarrow O_2 + H_2O_2 + 2CH_3COOK.$$

BaO_2 combines with H_2O_2 to give $BaO_2.H_2O_2$, but there is no structural evidence for a Gp.II superoxide.

Potassium, rubidium and caesium also form oxides of the composition M_2O_3. When white K_2O_2 is heated in oxygen at very low pressure red K_2O_3 is produced. The magnetic susceptibilities of Rb_2O_3 and Cs_2O_3 are consistent with the presence of superoxide ions, O_2^-, and peroxide ions, O_2^{2-}, in the proportion $2:1$.

Hydroperoxides

When sodium peroxide is added to ethyl alcohol containing a little sodium ethoxide, sodium hydroperoxide is produced:

$$Na_2O_2 + EtOH \rightarrow NaOEt + NaOOH.$$

In the absence of NaOEt the compound reacts with the alcohol:

$$NaOOH + EtOH \rightarrow NaOEt + H_2O_2,$$

and further reaction occurs:

$$2NaOOH + H_2O_2 \rightarrow (NaOOH)_2.H_2O_2.$$

Potassium hydroperoxide peroxohydrate, $(KOOH)_2.3H_2O_2$, has been isolated.

Peroxoacids

A peroxoacid is one which contains the peroxide linkage and either (i) is formed by the action of H_2O_2 on the normal acid, or (ii) gives H_2O_2 on treatment with dilute H_2SO_4. The empirical Riesenfeld test involves the addition of the acid or a salt to a 30% KI solution buffered to pH 7.5—8 with $NaHCO_3$. It is claimed that only true peroxoacids oxidise the KI to iodine under these conditions. However, the only unambiguous evidence for the peroxide link must come from determinations of structure, but little information of this nature is available.

The peroxosulphuric acids

The best-characterised peroxoacids are those of Gp.VI. There are two peroxoacids of sulphur, peroxodisulphuric acid, $H_2S_2O_8$, and peroxomono-sulphuric acid, H_2SO_5. The former is made by the electrolysis of 50% H_2SO_4 at 0° with a Pt anode and a high current density; the HSO_4^- ions are oxidised at the anode to $H_2S_2O_8$ by a mechanism at present unknown. The acid can also be made by the action of 100% H_2O_2 on chlorosulphuric acid:

$$
\begin{array}{ccc}
\text{O—H} & \text{Cl.SO}_2\text{.OH} & \text{O—SO}_2\text{.OH} \\
| \quad + & \quad \rightarrow \quad & | \qquad\qquad + \text{ 2HCl} \\
\text{O—H} & \text{Cl.SO}_2\text{.OH} & \text{O—SO}_2\text{.OH}
\end{array}
$$

The HCl is removed in a vacuum, leaving the colourless, crystalline $H_2S_2O_8$, m.p. 65°, which is stable when dry but hydrolyses easily:

$$H_2S_2O_8 + H_2O = H_2SO_4 + H_2SO_5,$$
$$H_2SO_5 + H_2O = H_2SO_4 + H_2O_2.$$

Ammonium peroxodisulphate, $(NH_4)_2S_2O_8$, is produced at the anode when a mixture of $(NH_4)_2SO_4$ and H_2SO_4 is electrolysed. The less soluble potassium salt can be precipitated by adding $KHSO_4$ to the solution:

$$(NH_4)_2S_2O_8 + 2KHSO_4 = 2(NH_4)HSO_4 + K_2S_2O_8.$$

Peroxomonosulphuric acid, H_2SO_5, is made by
 (i) grinding $K_2S_2O_8$ with concentrated H_2SO_4, allowing the slurry to stand, and then pouring on ice:

$$H_2S_2O_8 + H_2O = H_2SO_4 + H_2SO_5;$$

(ii) treating SO_3 with 100% H_2O_2:

$$H_2O_2 + SO_3 = H_2SO_5;$$

(iii) adding the calculated amount of anhydrous H_2O_2 to well-cooled chloro-sulphuric acid:

$$
\begin{array}{ccc}
\text{OH} & & \text{O—SO}_2\text{.OH} \\
| \quad + \text{ Cl.SO}_2\text{.OH} & \rightarrow & | \qquad\qquad + \text{ HCl.} \\
\text{OH} & & \text{OH}
\end{array}
$$

Like $H_2S_2O_8$, it is a colourless crystalline solid, but differs in being mono-basic. The salts themselves are unstable, although a benzoyl derivative of the potassium salt has been made:

$$O — SO_2.OK$$
$$|$$
$$O — CO.C_6H_5.$$

Both acids give the Riesenfeld reaction and oxidise Fe^{2+} to Fe^{3+}. Unlike H_2O_2, neither has any action on $KMnO_4$, CrO_3 or TiO^{2+}. The two acids differ in their reactions with aniline and with KI at low pH:

	Potassium iodide	Aniline
$H_2S_2O_8$:	I_2 set free slowly.	Oxidised to aniline black.
H_2SO_5:	I_2 set free quickly.	Oxidised to nitrosobenzene.

Other Group VI peroxo-compounds

When hydrogen peroxide is added to a dichromate in dilute H_2SO_4 a blue colour is produced which fades rapidly unless extracted with ether. Schwarz and Elstner (1936) showed the ether extract contains $Et_2O{\rightarrow}CrO_5$. Bases give more stable co-ordination compounds such as $C_5H_5N{\rightarrow}CrO_5$. The addition of alcoholic H_2O_2 and KOH to an ethereal solution of CrO_5 yields a blue salt, $KCrO_6.H_2O$. The compound has 5 peroxo groups for every 2 chromium atoms and it has been suggested that the diamagnetic anion is

$$\begin{bmatrix} O_2 & O_2 \\ | & | \\ O—Cr—O—O—Cr—O \\ | & | \\ O_2 & O_2 \end{bmatrix}^{2-}$$

A series of red peroxochromates, $M_3^I CrO_8$, can be made by adding H_2O_2 to soluble chromates under slightly alkaline conditions. Red magnesium peroxochromate, $Mg_3(CrO_8)_2.13H_2O$, is also known, as are the double salts of calcium, strontium and barium peroxochromates with alkali metal peroxochromates, $K_2Ca_5(CrO_8)_4.19H_2O$ and $K_2Ca_2(CrO_8)_2.7H_2O$ (Beltrán Martínez and Roca Adell, 1955). The CrO_8^{3-} anion is described as having four peroxide ions, the centres of the O—O bonds being tetrahedrally arranged about the central Cr atom.

Hydrogen peroxide reacts with acidified molybdate solutions. Chaveau, Souchay and Tridot (1955) have shown the presence of the acid $H_2Mo_2O_{11}$ in solutions of molybdate in concentrated perchloric acid to which H_2O_2 has been added. The so-called 'permolybdic acid' is regarded as a salt of this acid with the cation $[HMo_2O_6]^+$, not itself peroxidic.

Group V peroxoacids

Peroxonitric acid, HNO_4, was reported by Schwarz (1948) who mixed anhydrous H_2O_2 with N_2O_5 at $-70°$. At high concentration the compound decomposes explosively below $0°$; a 70% aqueous solution is moderately stable and weaker solutions hydrolyse rapidly. Unlike solutions of HNO_3, H_2O_2 and HNO_2, those of HNO_4 liberate bromine from KBr. It oxidises aniline to nitrobenzene.

When HCl is added to sodium nitrite in 5% aqueous H_2O_2 a fugitive, light brown colour is produced which disappears with the evolution of oxygen. When the still brown liquid is run into NaOH, a bright yellow colour develops which may persist for upwards of 12 hours. The brown liquid is a dilute solution of peroxonitrous acid, $H—O—O—N = O$. Among other evidence for the presence of this compound is that the cold solution gives, with aromatic compounds, *o*-hydroxy and *m*-nitro derivatives. Their production can be explained by the following reactions (Halfpenny and Robinson, 1952):

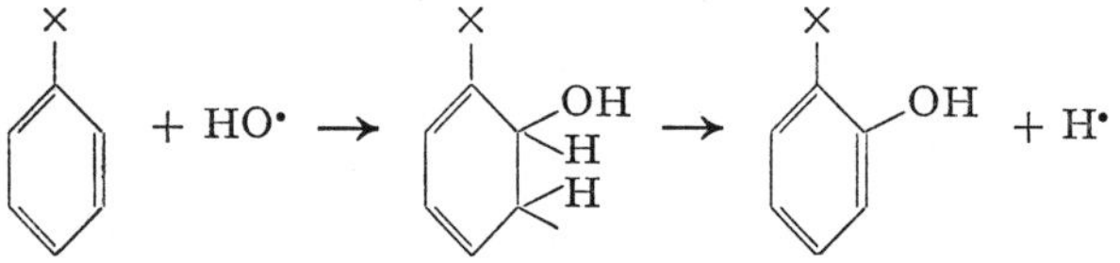

and

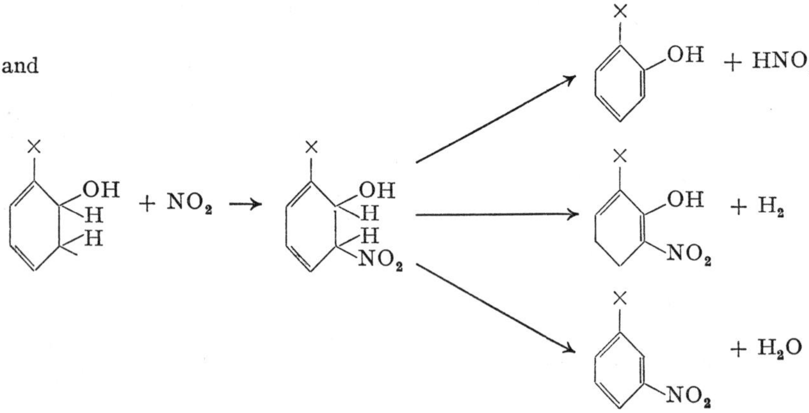

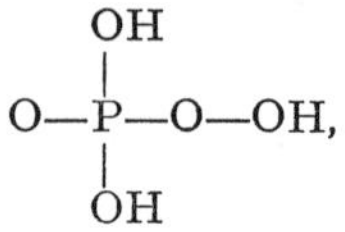

Schmidlin and Massini (1910) obtained a peroxomonophosphoric acid, H_3PO_5, presumably by the addition of $\sim 14\%$ H_2O_2 to P_2O_5 in acetonitrile which moderates the reaction. The aqueous solution oxidises aniline to a mixture of nitroso-benzene and nitrobenzene, and manganese(II) salts to permanganates in the cold. Salts of peroxodiphosphoric acid can be made by the electrolysis of concentrated solutions of orthophosphates: $2K_2HPO_4 \rightarrow K_4P_2O_8$.

Vanadates, niobates and tantalates react with alkaline H_2O_2 to give peroxo-salts formulated as $M_3^I VO_8$, $M_3^I NbO_8$ and $M_3^I TaO_8$. In strongly acid solution the vanadyl ion, VO^{3+}, gives a red colour with H_2O_2:

$$VO^{3+} + H_2O_2 \rightarrow VO_2^{3+} + H_2O.$$
$$\text{(red)}$$

In weaker acid:

$$VO_2^{3+} + H_2O_2 + 2H_2O \rightleftharpoons VO_6^{3-} + 6H^+.$$
$$\text{(yellow)}$$

Group IV peroxoacids

When a concentrated solution of K_2CO_3 is electrolysed, at about $-15°$, with a high current density, the pale blue peroxocarbonate, $K_2C_2O_6$, is deposited at a smooth platinum anode. The compound responds to the Riesenfeld test, reacts with dilute H_2SO_4 to give H_2O_2 and with MnO_2 to give oxygen, and oxidises PbS to $PbSO_4$. This electrolytically produced peroxocarbonate is believed to contain the ion

$$\left[\begin{array}{c} O-C-O-O-C-O \\ \parallel \qquad \parallel \\ O \qquad\quad O \end{array} \right]^{2-}$$

Wolffenstein and Peltner (1908) made several alkali metal peroxocarbo-nates by passing CO_2 into suspensions of their peroxides in ice-cold water. Later Partington and Fathallah (1950) produced many Gp.IA peroxocarbon-ates, for instance $M_2CO_4 \cdot xH_2O$, $MHCO_4$ and $M_2C_2O_6$, by treating saturated carbonate solutions with 30% H_2O_2 and precipitating with alcohol. Some of these liberate iodine and oxygen, some oxygen only, from a neutral solution of KI.

Titanium, zirconium and hafnium peroxo-compounds are produced by adding ammoniacal H_2O_2 to their salts. The oxide salt, $TiOCl_2$, gives a compound formulated $Ti(OH)_3OOH$. This, with KOH, produces $K_4TiO_8 \cdot 6H_2O$ which has been isolated as a solid; it does not, however, give the Riesen-feld reaction. In acid solution the $(TiO)^{2+}$ ion reacts with H_2O_2 to give the yellow colour ascribed to the hydrated $(TiO_2)^{2+}$ ion. The discharge of this colour by fluoride ions is almost certainly due to TiF_6^{2-} formation.

A solid, $K_2(TiO_2)(SO_4)_2.3H_2O$, has been isolated which gives the Riesenfeld reaction.

No peroxo-compound of lead or silicon has been reported but peroxo-germanates and peroxostannates, $Na_2Ge_2O_7.4H_2O$ and $Na_2Sn_2O_7.3H_2O$, have been made (Schwarz and Giese, 1930). These do not respond to the Riesenfeld test.

Peroxohydrates

Matthews (1911) obtained a compound of the empirical formula $NaBO_3.4H_2O$ by the action of Na_2O_2 on a cold borax, $Na_2B_4O_7.10H_2O$, solution and also by the electrolysis of a solution of borax and Na_2CO_3 with a platinum gauze anode. The compound did not set free iodine from KI (see below). Partington and Fathallah (1949) made the substances $LiBO_4.H_2O$ and $KBO_5.H_2O$ by adding $\sim 14\%$ H_2O_2 to metaborate solutions and precipitating with alcohol.

There are so many similarities in the physical properties of H_2O_2 and water that the existence of salts in which H_2O_2 forms peroxohydrates just as H_2O forms hydrates is not surprising. It is now known that Matthews' preparation is such a compound, correctly formulated $NaBO_2.H_2O_2.3H_2O$. The material is used in tooth powders and for rapid oxidation of vat dyes. A peroxohydrate of sodium carbonate, $2Na_2CO_3.3H_2O_2$, made by adding H_2O_2 to Na_2CO_3 solution, is used in washing powders.

Peroxohydrates can be distinguished from true peroxosalts by the ease with which ether extracts H_2O_2 from their aqueous solutions, and by their failure to give the Riesenfeld reaction. Distinctions based on such empirical tests cannot, however, be considered wholly satisfactory, and the chemistry of peroxo-compounds will not be fully understood until there is more structural information.

Chapter 25

The Halogens

GROUP VIIB

The feature dominating the chemistry of the halogens* is a tendency of their atoms to gain a single electron. Fluorine is always formally uninegative; the others sometimes exhibit positive charge numbers but only when combined with strongly electronegative elements. The uninegative halide ions are very much larger than the atoms from which they are derived.

TABLE 84

SOME PROPERTIES OF THE HALOGENS

	F	Cl	Br	I	At
Atomic number	9	17	35	53	85
Electron configuration	$2s^2\,2p^5$	$3s^2\,3p^5$	$4s^2\,4p^5$	$5s^2\,5p^5$	$6s^2\,6p^5$
Atomic radius (Å)	0.72	0.99	1.14	1.33	
Ionic radius (Å)	1.36	1.81	1.95	2.16	

Ionisation potentials in the group are generally high, but fall markedly with atomic number. Iodine appears as a unipositive ion in many of its reactions. Electron affinities show a maximum at chlorine. Nevertheless fluorine is the better oxidising agent in aqueous solution, and even when dry will usually replace chlorine from its compounds.

TABLE 85

IONISATION POTENTIALS AND ELECTRON AFFINITIES
OF THE HALOGENS

	F	Cl	Br	I
Ionisation potential I(eV)	17.4	13.0	11.8	10.4
Electron affinity A(eV)	3.74	4.02	3.78	3.44

The redox potential, $E_h^\circ\ X_2/2X^-$, measures a free-energy change, usually dominated by the ΔH term, but depending, as may be seen from the energy diagram, on (a) the energy needed to break the molecule into atoms (the heat of dissociation), (b) the energy liberated when the atom is converted into a

* For the pseudohalogens see p. 420.

negative ion (the electron affinity), (c) the energy set free on the hydration of the ion. For fluorine (b) is less than for chlorine but, the energy needed to break the F—F bond being also less and the hydration energy more, the total energy drop is much greater.

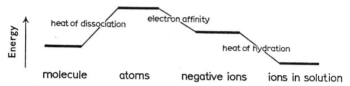

Fig. 202. Energetics of the change from free molecule to ion in solution.

Fluorine is, in fact, an extremely powerful oxidising agent. In spite of lower dissociation energies bromine and iodine are weaker oxiding agents than chlorine; this is due to their smaller electron affinities and smaller hydration energies.

TABLE 86

SOME PROPERTIES OF THE HALOGENS

	F	Cl	Br	I
Heat of dissociation of X_2 (kcal)	38	58	46	36
Hydration energy of X⁻ (kcal)	122	89	81	72
E_h° $X_2/2X^-$ (V)	2.87	1.36	1.07	0.53

The great reactivity of fluorine largely stems from the low energy of the F—F bond. The more acceptable figure of 38 kcal, derived from a study of its dissociation between 500° and 850° (Doescher, 1952), and from a Born-type treatment of heats of dissociation and heats of formation of alkali metal fluorides together with their heats of sublimation and those of the metals concerned (Barrow and Caunt, 1953), has replaced the earlier larger value (~ 70 kcal) which was based largely on extrapolations of data for chlorine, bromine and iodine. The F—F bond is weak because of repulsion between the non-bonding electrons; the stronger X—X bond, actually in Cl_2 and Br_2, and relatively in I_2, is due to hybridisation of p and d orbitals (Mulliken, 1955). The weakness of the σ bond between atoms of the first short period elements is also evident in the molecules H_2N—NH_2 and HO—OH, with bond energies N—N, 21 kcal and O—O, 36 kcal.

Another factor contributing to the exothermicity of many of the reactions of elementary fluorine is the short, strong bonds formed by its atoms with those of most other elements. When crystalline fluorides are formed their lattice energies are high because the F⁻ ion is comparatively small.

Stereochemistry of complexes

Halogens with positive charge numbers occur in complexes with co-ordination numbers ranging from 2 to 7. In compounds with oxygen, the halogen atom is surrounded by oxygen atoms; in interhalogen compounds the larger halogen atom has the smaller halogen atoms grouped round it. The number of bond pairs around the central atom can be increased by either (a) the use of some of its electrons to form π bonds with surrounding atoms, or (b) the promotion of some of its electrons to nd levels and the subsequent formation of σ bonds with the surrounding atoms.

The stereochemistry of such compounds is summarised in Table 87.

TABLE 87

STEREOCHEMISTRY OF HALOGEN COMPLEXES

Electron pairs round central atom	Hybrids	Electrons used in π bonding	Lone pairs	Charge number of central atom	Shape of molecule or ion	Examples
4	sp^3	1	2	3	V-shaped	ClO_2^-
		2	1	5	Trigonal pyramid	ClO_3^-, BrO_3^-, HIO_3
		3	0	7	Tetrahedron	ClO_4^-, IO_4^-
5	sp^3d_{z2}	0	3	1	Linear	ICl_2^-, I_3
		0	2	3	T-shaped	ClF_3
		1	1	5	Distorted tetrahedron	$IO_2F_2^-$
6	$sp^3d_\gamma^2$	0	2	3	Square	ICl_4^-
		0	1	5	Square pyramid	IF_5
		1	0	7	Octahedron	IO_6^{5-}
7	$sp^3d_\gamma^2d_\varepsilon$	0	0	7	Pentagonal bipyramid	IF_7

All the molecules and ions employing four electron pairs are basically tetrahedral (p. 125), those employing five pairs trigonal bipyramidal (p. 126), and those with six pairs, octahedral (p. 127). Bond directions are determined by the strong repulsive forces exerted by the lone-pair electrons on the bond pairs (Fig. 203).

In an unsymmetrical molecule some distortion of the simple shapes can occur. Thus ClF_3 is not exactly T-shaped. Microwave spectroscopy shows the bond lengths and inter-bond angles to be as in Fig. 204. This is consonant with the idea that lone pairs occupy two positions in a trigonal bipyramid arising from $sp^3d_{z^2}$ hybridisation.

The maximum group charge number of $+7$ is less stable in iodine than in the earlier members of the group; in this iodine resembles bismuth and tellurium, the two elements which precede it in the period. The most stable oxide of iodine is I_2O_5, whereas Cl_2O_7 is the only stable oxide of chlorine. Furthermore, the periodates can be reduced to iodates ($E_h^\circ \, IO_4^-/IO_3^- = +0.72$ V), but perchlorates are more stable than chlorates ($E_h^\circ \, ClO_4^-/ClO_3^- = +0.17$ V).

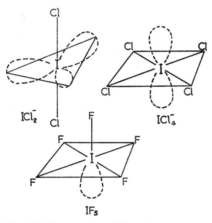

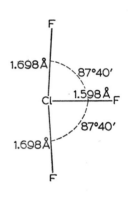

Fig. 203. Structures of ICl_2^-, ICl_4^- and IF_5, showing positions occupied by lone pairs.

Fig. 204. Bond lengths and interbond angles of ClF_3.

Occurrence and separation

The group is characterised by the molecules of all its elements being diatomic at the ordinary temperature. In this it is unlike Gp.V and Gp.VI in which only the first elements, the gaseous nitrogen and oxygen, are diatomic. The m.p. of Cl_2, Br_2 and I_2 are low compared with those of S, Se and Te,

TABLE 88

MELTING AND BOILING POINTS OF THE HALOGENS

	F	Cl	Br	I
Melting point (°C)	-233	-102	-7	113
Boiling point (°C)	-188	-35	59	183

because the cohesive forces in the solid halogens are essentially Van der Waals' forces between diatomic molecules.

The principal source of fluorine (0.08% of the lithosphere) is fluorspar, CaF_2, but much fluorine is recovered from industrial effluent gases arising from the aluminium, iron and other industries.

High grade fluorspar is used for the manufacture of anhydrous hydrofluoric acid. The anhydrous acid is a source of fluorine itself, of the fluorides of many metals, and also of freons such as CF_2Cl_2.

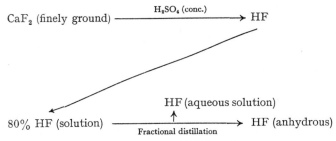

Fig. 205. Preparation of HF from fluorspar.

Industrial cells for preparing fluorine are rectangular steel vessels $4' \times 1\frac{1}{2}'$ and $2\frac{1}{2}'$ deep. The electrolyte, KHF_2 together with up to 0.6 molar parts of HF kept molten at 95–115°, is electrolysed by a current of about 0.5 amps/cm^2 between carbon anodes and sheet-steel cathodes. A monel metal diaphragm, perforated below the surface of the liquid but continuous above it, serves to keep separate the fluorine and hydrogen. Sealing and electrical insulation is provided by Teflon (CF_2 polymer). Small 10 amp cells convenient for laboratory work and very reliable in operation have been made (Leech, Rudge, 1949). Electrolysis depletes the cell of HF which is added from time to time in the anhydrous form. Liquid fluorine is now available in industrial quantities. Interest in the production of fluorine and its compounds has been stimulated by the use made of uranium hexafluoride for separating, by gaseous diffusion, the ^{235}U isotope from the 99.28% of ^{238}U in natural uranium, and of uranium tetrafluoride in the production of uranium metal.

Chlorine (0.19% of lithosphere) is produced mainly from NaCl which is either crystallised from brines or mined. The gas is a product of the electrolysis of aqueous sodium chloride for caustic soda production, with carbon anodes and a mercury cathode. It is also a by-product of the manufacture mainly of metallic sodium, but also of magnesium and calcium, by electrolysing the appropriate fused chloride. Its chief uses are as a bleach, a bactericide, and an industrial chemical.

Bromine (0.01% of lithosphere), once largely derived from salt deposits, is now obtained chiefly from sea-water, by passing chlorine into it at pH 3.5:

$$2Br^- + Cl_2 \rightarrow Br_2 + 2Cl^-.$$

The bromine is blown out with air and absorbed in Na_2CO_3 solution to give bromate and bromide. On acidification the element can be distilled off:

$$HBrO_3 + 5HBr \rightarrow 3H_2O + 3Br_2.$$

Iodine (10^{-4} % of lithosphere) is obtained mainly from iodates present in Chilean nitrates. Iodate-rich solutions are reduced with sodium bisulphite to liberate the element:

$$2IO_3^- + 5HSO_3^- \rightarrow 3HSO_4^- + 2SO_4^{2-} + H_2O + I_2.$$

Astatine has not been detected as a product of natural radioactive decay. ^{211}At was made (Corson, Mackenzie and Segrè, 1947) by bombarding a cooled bismuth target with high-energy α-particles. It was subsequently evaporated from the target under a low pressure, condensed and redistilled. Because of the short half-life (7.5 h) and consequent high activity, its chemistry has been studied by tracer methods only. This, so far as it is known, closely resembles that of iodine, the element being soluble in organic solvents and forming At^- and AtO_3^- ions. It may possibly differ from the rest of the halogens in having an insoluble sulphide, for it is co-precipitated with Bi_2S_3.

Reactions of the halogens

Most metals combine directly with all the halogens and particularly readily with fluorine. Some non-metals also react:

$$H_2 + X_2 \rightarrow 2HX;$$
$$2P(As) + 3X_2 \rightarrow 2PX_3(AsX_3).$$

The reactivity of the halogen decreases with atomic number. Fluorine, particularly, and chlorine to a lesser extent, often oxidise both metals and non-metals further than do bromine and iodine. Thus they raise the charge

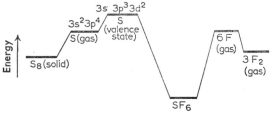

Fig. 206. Energetics of the formation of SF_6 from its elements.

number of phosphorus and arsenic to $+5$ in such compounds as PCl_5 and AsF_5. Sulphur is converted to SF_6 by fluorine, to SCl_2 by chlorine and to S_2Br_2 by bromine. Sharpe (1957) has discussed the basic energetics of such reactions. The formation of SF_6 from its elements may be pictured in terms of the energy changes shown in Fig. 206. The energy set free in the formation of SF_6 is large; except in the F_2 molecule itself, fluorine forms stronger bonds than any of the other halogens. On the other hand the dissociation energy of fluorine is only about 38 kcal/mole, and there is therefore a net binding energy in spite of the considerable height of the sulphur sp^3d^2 valence state (cf. p. 98). Chlorine is more difficult to dissociate into atoms and forms weaker bonds with sulphur. Insufficient energy is available to offset the valence state promotion energy for SCl_6 formation, and such a compound is not known.

A halogen of lower atomic number oxidises the ion of another of higher atomic number, both in solution and the crystal lattice.

$$Cl_2 + 2Br^- \rightarrow Br_2 + 2Cl^-.$$

The respective reactions of the halogens with water also illustrate the decrease in oxidising power with atomic number. For the reaction

$$4H^+ + O_2 + 4e \rightleftharpoons 2H_2O, \qquad E_h^\circ = +0.81 \text{ V}.$$

Since $E_h^\circ F_2/2F^-$ is $+2.87$ V, the redox potential for

$$2F_2 + 2H_2O \rightleftharpoons 4H^+ + 4F^- + O_2 \quad \text{is} \quad +2.06 \text{ V},$$

equivalent to a standard free energy change ΔG of -190 kcal. Fluorine accordingly sets free oxygen from water.

Since $E_h^\circ I_2/2I^-$ is $+0.53$ V, the redox potential for

$$2I_2 + 2H_2O \rightleftharpoons 4H^+ + 4I^- + O_2 \quad \text{is} \quad -0.28 \text{ V},$$

equivalent to a standard free energy change, ΔG, of $+25$ kcal. Here the reaction takes the opposite direction and oxygen oxidises the iodide ion to iodine. With chlorine and bromine the oxidation of water to oxygen is thermodynamically possible but has so high an activation energy that another course is followed:

$$X_2 + 2H_2O \rightleftharpoons H_3O^+ + X^- + HOX.$$

This reaction is naturally strongly dependent on pH; the addition of alkali favours the formation of halide and hypohalite.

Interhalogen compounds

These are made by direct combination in a nickel tube, the product depending on the conditions:

$$Cl_2 + F_2 \text{ (equal volumes)} \xrightarrow{200°} 2ClF;$$

$$Cl_2 + 3F_2 \text{ (excess } F_2) \xrightarrow{280°} 2ClF_3.$$

Bromine vapour diluted with nitrogen reacts with fluorine to give mainly BrF_3, unless an excess of F_2 is present, when BrF_5 is the chief product. There are eleven interhalogen compounds of the four types shown in Table 89:

TABLE 89

THE INTERHALOGEN COMPOUNDS

Type AX	AX_3	AX_5	AX_7
ClF (b.p. —100°)	ClF$_3$ (b.p. 12°)		
BrF (b.p. 20°)	BrF$_3$ (b.p. 127°)	BrF$_5$ (b.p. 40°)	
BrCl (b.p. 5°)			
ICl (solid, 2 forms)	ICl$_3$ (m.p. decomp. 101°)	IF$_5$ (b.p. 97°)	IF$_7$ (b.p. 4°)
IBr (m.p. 36°)			

For every class, the boiling points increase as the difference between the electronegativities of the two halogens increases. The greatest are those shown by iodine and bromine in their fluorides. No interhalogen compound is known containing either three or four of the elements, though the polyhalide ions ClIBr⁻ and FICl$_3$⁻ exist.

Long (1953) has discussed the stabilities in terms of net bond energy. The conversion of ICl to ICl$_3$ involves the promotion of two electrons of the iodine to orbitals of higher energy, and the consequent reduction of the net bond energy must largely determine the relative stabilities. ICl$_3$ is, in fact, stable as a solid but the vapour decomposes:

$$ICl_3 \text{ (g)} \rightarrow ICl \text{ (g)} + Cl_2 \text{ (g)}.$$

Neglecting the small entropy term in the free-energy change, $\Delta H - T\Delta S$, this implies that the net bond energy in ICl$_3$ is less than that in ICl. Since the bond energies in ICl and Cl$_2$ are 50 kcal and 58 kcal respectively, those in ICl$_3$ must be less than $\frac{1}{3}(50 + 58) = 36$ kcal. But if the bond energy of ICl$_3$ were greater than 38.3 kcal, the reaction

$$3 \text{ ICl (g)} \rightarrow ICl_3 \text{ (g)} + I_2 \text{ (g)}$$

would become thermodynamically feasible; it would proceed to a useful extent. The compatible range of bond energies is therefore small, as it is for any compound with a low heat of formation.

Compounds of the AX type resemble the halogens themselves in physical properties (Fig. 207); the divergences are naturally greatest where differences in electronegativity are marked. The b.p. of ICl is nearly 40° above that of Br_2 although it has the same molecular weight.

The AX compounds usually convert metals to mixed halides. Because the A—X bond energy is less than the X—X bond energy (X being the more electronegative element involved) the compounds are more reactive than the elements. Hydrolysis usually proceeds:

$$AX + 2H_2O \rightarrow HOA + H_3O^+ + X^- \quad \text{(X the more electronegative).}$$

Addition compounds are formed with olefines:

$$
\begin{array}{ccc}
-CH=CH- & & -CH-CH- \\
& \longrightarrow & \quad | \quad \quad | \\
A-X & & A \quad \quad X
\end{array} \quad ,
$$

and often with alkali halides:

$$NaBr + IBr \rightarrow NaIBr_2.$$

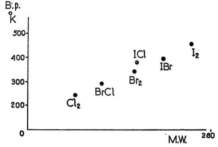

Fig. 207. Relation of boiling point to molecular weight in some halogen and interhalogen molecules.

Of the AX_3 compounds, ClF_3 is the most reactive but BrF_3 has greater value for preparative work. The liquid has a higher conductance:

$$2BrF_3 \rightleftharpoons BrF_2^+ + BrF_4^-.$$

It is a valuable fluorinating agent, converting many metals, their oxides and very many of their chlorides, bromides and iodides to fluorides. Some metal fluorides dissolve to give tetrafluorobromites (Sharpe and Eméleus, 1948):

$$KF + BrF_3 \rightarrow KBrF_4$$

or hexafluorobromates:

$$SbF_3 + BrF_3 \rightarrow SbBrF_6.$$

ClF_3 forms no corresponding compounds. Both BrF_3 and ClF_3 have high entropies of vaporisation, suggesting there is association in the liquid. ICl_3 is much less reactive than the other two AX_3 compounds.

Bromine pentafluoride is the most reactive of the AX_5 compounds, resembling ClF_3 in acting very violently, too violently to be used, undiluted, for the preparation of fluorides. Liquid IF_5 is a good conductor:

$$2IF_5 \rightleftharpoons IF_4^+ + IF_6^-.$$

It reacts with KI at its boiling point to give KIF_6.

Iodine heptafluoride, the only example of the AX_7 type, can be made by heating IF_5 with F_2 at 250–270°. It is comparable with ClF_3 and BrF_5 in its violent fluorinating action. In shape it is the unusual pentagonal bipyramid.

Several oxo-fluorides are known. ClO_2 reacts with F_2 to give chloryl fluoride, ClO_2F (Schumacher, 1956). The compound is produced by the action of BrF_3 on potassium chlorate:

$$6KClO_3 + 10BrF_3 \rightarrow 6KBrF_4 + 2Br_2 + 3O_2 + 6ClO_2F.$$

It forms solid additives with BF_3 and SbF_5, regarded as chloronium salts $ClO_2^+BF_4^-$ and $ClO_2^+SbF_6^-$ (Woolf, 1954). Perchloryl fluoride, ClO_3F, can be made by treating a perchlorate with fluorosulphuric acid. It is a colourless, inert, thermally stable gas in contrast with the reactive ClO_2F. Structurally

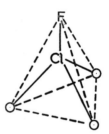

Fig. 208. Structure of ClO_3F molecule.

ClO_3F is a tetrahedral molecule centred on the chlorine atom (Fig. 208). BrO_2F can be made by the direct fluorination of BrO_2 at a low temperature. IO_2F and IO_3F are obtained by the reactions (Schmeisser, Pammer and Lang, 1955):

$$2I_2O_5 + 2F_2 \xrightarrow{\text{HF}} 4IO_2F + O_2,$$

$$2HIO_4 + 2F_2 \xrightarrow{\text{HF}} 2IO_3F + 2HF + O_2.$$

Halide ions, either in solution or in crystalline salts, frequently react with

halogens and interhalogen compounds. The best known example is the formation of polyiodides in solution,

$$KI + I_2 \rightleftharpoons KI_3.$$

Iodides, in the solid state, are also very ready to form these additions, particularly when the cations are large; evidently a low lattice energy is desirable:

$$CsI + I_2 \rightarrow CsI_3, \qquad\qquad CsI + Cl_2 \rightarrow CsICl_2,$$
$$(CH_3)_4NI + 4I_2 \rightarrow (CH_3)_4NI_9, \qquad CsI + BrCl \rightarrow CsIBrCl.$$

The ions I_3^-, ICl_2^-, IBr_2^- and $BrICl^-$ are linear, with I in the middle of the last three (Mooney, 1939) (p. 394). The ICl_4^- ion is planar (p. 394) by contrast with the fluorobromite ion, BrF_4^-, which is tetrahedral (Siegel, 1956). Fluorobromites and fluorobromates cannot be obtained by these methods; indeed very few fluorine polyhalides exist.

Cremer and Duncan (1933) have classified polyhalides according to their thermal stability and ease of hydrolysis. In general, stability increases with (a) symmetry: $(I—I—I)^- > (I—I—Br)^-$, (b) increasing difference in electronegativity between central atom and surrounding ones: $[Cl—I—Cl]^- > [Br—I—Br]^-$.

Acids formally corresponding to the polyhalide ions are not usually preparable, but the orange-yellow hydrate $HICl_4 \cdot 4H_2O$ can be crystallised from a solution of ICl_3 in aqueous HCl. The solution dissolves RbF and CsF to give $RbFICl_3$ and $CsFICl_3$ (Booth, 1932).

Oxides

There are ten oxides of the halogens. Chlorine forms the greatest and iodine the least number.

TABLE 90

SOME PROPERTIES OF THE HALOGEN OXIDES

F_2O (b.p. —145°)	Cl_2O (b.p. 2°)	Br_2O (m.p.—18°)	
F_2O_2 (b.p. decomp. —95°)	ClO_2 (b.p. 11°)	BrO_2 (stable as solid below —40°)	
	Cl_2O_6 (m.p. 4°)		I_2O_5 (m.p. decomp. 300°)
	Cl_2O_7 (b.p. —92°)	BrO_3 (stable as solid below —80°)	

The colourless gas, F_2O, is made by the action of F_2 on NaOH solution:

$$2F_2 + 2OH^- \rightarrow 2F^- + F_2O + H_2O.$$

Bonding is essentially covalent because of the similar electronegativities of oxygen and fluorine. The structure is shown in Fig. 209. The oxygen valence state is roughly tetrahedral (sp^3), but in difluorine oxide the F—O—F angle is less than the tetrahedral angle because the bond-pair–bond-pair repulsion is less than that caused by the lone pairs (p. 127). F_2O is neither explosive nor an acid anhydride; it reacts with bases to give F^- ions and free oxygen.

Orange dichlorine oxide, Cl_2O, is made by passing Cl_2 over precipitated HgO:

$$2Cl_2 + 2HgO \rightarrow HgO.HgCl_2 + Cl_2O.$$

The liquid can be distilled at its b.p. (2°) but at higher temperatures the gas explodes. The molecule is V-shaped (Fig. 210). Here the repulsion between the bond pairs is greater than in the fluorine compound, in accordance with the closer proximity of the electrons to the oxygen. The compound is formally the anhydride of hypochlorous acid.

Dibromine oxide, Br_2O, a dark brown liquid, is made in a similar way to Cl_2O; it is formally the anhydride of hypobromous acid.

Difluorine dioxide, F_2O_2, is an orange-red solid produced at $-165°$ by passing an electric discharge through an oxygen-fluorine mixture at low pressure. It decomposes into its elements at $-95°$, the boiling point.

Chlorine dioxide, ClO_2, is best made by treating silver chlorate at 90° with dry chlorine and condensing the ClO_2 by cooling:

$$2AgClO_3 + Cl_2 \rightarrow 2AgCl + 2ClO_2 + O_2.$$

The bonds are appreciably shorter than those in Cl_2O, having much more double-bond character (Fig. 211).

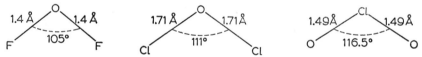

Fig. 209. Structure of F_2O. Fig. 210. Structure of Cl_2O. Fig. 211. Structure of ClO_2.

The odd-electron molecule is very reactive; the gas explodes unless diluted and it is a powerful oxidising agent since for

$$ClO_2 + 4H_3O^+ + 5e \rightleftharpoons Cl^- + 6H_2O, \qquad E_h^\circ = 1.50 \text{ V}.$$

The gas can be looked upon as a mixed anhydride:

$$2ClO_2 + 2OH^- \rightarrow ClO_2^- + ClO_3^- + H_2O.$$

Bromine dioxide, BrO_2, is a yellow solid below $-40°$; above it is unstable. Prepared in a similar way to F_2O_2, it is less explosive than ClO_2. Hydrolysis gives bromide and bromate:

$$6BrO_2 + 6OH^- \rightarrow Br^- + 5BrO_3^- + 3H_2O.$$

Dichlorine hexoxide, Cl_2O_6, results from mixing ClO_2 with ozonised oxygen at $0°$. It is a dark red liquid, less explosive than ClO_2, and reacts with alkalis to give chlorate and perchlorate:

$$Cl_2O_6 + 2OH^- \rightarrow ClO_3^- + ClO_4^- + H_2O.$$

Though the molecular weight in carbon tetrachloride agrees with the formula Cl_2O_6, the weak paramagnetism of the aqueous solution suggests some dissociation to ClO_3.

The action of a glow discharge on a mixture of bromine and oxygen between $-10°$ and $20°$ produces a white solid of crystalline appearance, stable below $-70°$, which is BrO_3 (Pflugmacher, Rabben and Dahmen, 1955).

The only true oxide of iodine is di-iodine pentoxide, I_2O_5, made by dehydrating iodic acid at $240°$ in a stream of dry air:

$$2HIO_3 \rightarrow I_2O_5 + H_2O.$$

The white powder decomposes to iodine and oxygen above $300°$. It is a fairly strong oxidising agent. The reaction

$$I_2O_5 + 5CO \rightarrow I_2 + 5CO_2$$

is quantitative at $70°$, and is used for determining CO in gaseous mixtures. The oxides, empirically I_2O_4 and I_4O_9, are of unknown structure, but are probably iodates of IO^+ and I^{3+} respectively, viz. $IO^+IO_3^-$ and $I^{3+}(IO_3^-)_3$.

Chlorine heptoxide, Cl_2O_7, is made by dehydrating perchloric acid with P_2O_5 at a low temperature and distilling the product. The colourless, oily liquid is not so strong an oxidising agent as the other oxides of chlorine. It is the anhydride of perchloric acid. Its structure is uncertain. Cl_2O_7 is the only exothermic oxide of chlorine ($\Delta H°_f = -63.4$ kcal).

Oxoacids

Fluorine does not form an oxoacid; the element is more electronegative than oxygen. In the chlorine, bromine and iodine compounds the halogen atom is positive in relation to the oxygen atoms, as indicated by the δ's:

$$H_2O + HClO_3 \rightarrow \begin{bmatrix} \overset{\delta^-}{O} \diagdown \quad \diagup \overset{\delta^-}{O} \\ Cl\delta^+ \\ | \\ \underset{\delta^-}{O} \end{bmatrix}^- + H_3O^+.$$

Increase of the charge number of the halogen atom from $+1$ to $+7$ is accompanied by (i) increasing thermal stability, (ii) decreasing oxidising capacity, (iii) increasing acid strength.

Periodic acid is exceptional in being more strongly oxidising than iodic acid:

	Cl	I
E_h° HOX/$\frac{1}{2}$X$_2$ (V)	+1.63	+1.45
E_h° HXO$_3$/$\frac{1}{2}$X$_2$ (V)	+1.47	+1.19
E_h° HXO$_4$/$\frac{1}{2}$X$_2$ (V)	+1.34	+1.38

Bromic acid is a particularly strong oxidising agent (E_h°HBrO$_3$/$\frac{1}{2}$Br$_2$ = +1.52 V), but perbromic acid is unknown. The increasing stability of the oxo-anions as the charge number of the halogen rises has already been discussed (p. 204).

Hypohalous acids

These are weak acids (pK_a ~ 8) which exist only in aqueous solution; indeed HOI is more correctly considered as iodine hydroxide (p. 407). Their aqueous solutions are made by shaking precipitated HgO in water with the particular halogen:

$$2X_2 + 2HgO + H_2O \rightarrow HgO \cdot HgX_2 + 2HOX.$$

Sodium hypochlorite, used commercially in cotton bleaching, is made by the electrolysis of brine, the electrolyte being agitated to mix the anode and cathode products. At the cathode, $2H^+ + 2e \rightarrow H_2$ increases the concentration of OH$^-$, while at the anode, $2Cl^- \rightarrow Cl_2 + 2e$ releases chlorine. These combine:

$$Cl_2 + 2OH^- \rightarrow OCl^- + Cl^- + H_2O,$$

and the solution becomes progressively stronger in NaOCl without chlorine being evolved.

Halous acids

Of these only chlorous acid, HClO$_2$, is known and that only in solution. It is a stronger acid than hypochlorous (pK_a ~ 2). Chlorites are best made by the reaction of ClO$_2$ with peroxides:

$$Na_2O_2 + 2ClO_2 \rightarrow 2NaClO_2 + O_2.$$

Heating converts an alkali metal chlorite to chloride and chlorate:

$$3NaClO_2 \rightarrow 2NaClO_3 + NaCl.$$

Halic acids and halates

Chloric and bromic acids are obtainable only in aqueous solution, but HIO$_3$ separates, as white crystals, when iodine is oxidised with fuming nitric acid. The acids are strong oxidising agents and fairly strong acids (pK_a ~ −2).

Chlorates, which are much more soluble than bromates and iodates, are conveniently made by the electrolysis of hot chloride solutions. Aqueous KCl (25%) is electrolysed at 70–75° till it is saturated with chlorate; it is then cooled and $KClO_3$ crystallises.

Chlorate crystals contain the pyramidal ClO_3^- ion (Fig. 212). Formally, the chlorine has charge number +5 and forms σ bonds like nitrogen. But a lone pair from each O ligand overlaps a chlorine 3d orbital and can form a π bond by donation; thereby charge returns to the chlorine. MacGillavry

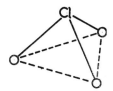

Fig. 212.
Pyramidal structure of ClO_3^- ion.

and Van Eck (1943) found $NaIO_3$ had orthorhombic symmetry, and discrete IO_3^- ions. Iodates follow the CsCl ionic arrangement (p. 249) and chlorates and bromates the NaCl (p. 141). However, HIO_3 itself, in its orthorhombic α-form, appears to exist as separate tetrahedral molecules.

The thermal decomposition of the halates is complex:

$$KClO_3 \longrightarrow KCl + oxygen$$
or $KClO_4 + KCl$ depending on temperature.
$$KBrO_3 \longrightarrow KBr + oxygen$$
(never perbromate, which is unknown).

Some bromates give mixtures of oxide, bromide and oxygen, others give oxide, bromine and oxygen. The iodates can give periodate and iodide and reactions allied to those of the bromates.

Perhalic acids

Only perchloric and periodic acids exist; neither perbromic acid nor perbromates occur. Perchloric acid distils as a colourless oily liquid when a perchlorate is heated with concentrated H_2SO_4 at 10–20 mm pressure. The hot, concentrated liquid is liable to detonate in the presence of a trace of reducing agent, particularly a carbon compound. The cold, aqueous acid gives hydrogen with Zn and Fe,

$$Zn + 2HClO_4 \rightarrow Zn(ClO_4)_2 + H_2,$$

without any reduction of the ClO_4^- ion. Ionisation is very strong ($pK_a \sim -11$); the tetrahedral ClO_4^- ion is the least polarised of anions. Of the many crystalline hydrates, the monohydrate is most interesting as the crystal is composed of H_3O^+ and ClO_4^- ions and is isomorphous with NH_4ClO_4 (Volmer, 1924).

Perchlorates can be made by heating chlorates under controlled conditions:

$$4KClO_3 \xrightarrow[\text{in silica flask}]{480°} 3KClO_4 + KCl;$$

and by the electrolytic oxidation of cooled chlorate solutions at high current densities. Any chlorate remaining can be decomposed by HCl which does not react with ClO_4^-, and the perchlorate separated by fractional crystallisation. Perchlorates are often isomorphous with the permanganates and perrhenates. Most of the salts are very soluble, but those of potassium, rubidium, caesium and ammonium are not.

When a stream of chlorine is passed through a boiling solution of iodine in an excess of caustic soda, a white precipitate of $Na_2H_3IO_6$ is formed:

$$18NaOH + I_2 + 7Cl_2 \rightarrow 2Na_2H_3IO_6 + 14NaCl + 6H_2O.$$

Treatment of a suspension of this with $AgNO_3$ solution gives a black precipitate of silver paraperiodate:

$$Na_2H_3IO_6 + 5AgNO_3 \rightarrow Ag_5IO_6 + 2NaNO_3 + 3HNO_3.$$

When chlorine is passed into a suspension of this salt, avoiding an excess of the gas, a solution of periodic acid is obtained from which, after filtration, paraperiodic acid, H_5IO_6, can be crystallised:

$$4Ag_5IO_6 + 10Cl_2 + 10H_2O \rightarrow 4H_5IO_6 + 20AgCl + 5O_2.$$

The colourless crystals contain octahedral molecules (Fig. 213), corresponding approximately to sp^3d^2 hybridisation with secondary π bonding (p. 106). HIO_4 is obtained by heating H_5IO_6 in a vacuum at 100°. The acid is a powerful oxidising agent.

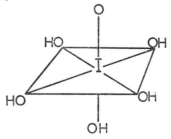

Fig. 213. Octahedral structure of H_5IO_6.

Periodates are of four formula types:

KIO_4 from metaperiodic acid, HIO_4;

$Na_4I_2O_9$ from dimesoperiodic acid, $H_4I_2O_9$;

$Pb_3(IO_5)_2$ from mesoperiodic acid, H_3IO_5 (hypothetical);

Ag_5IO_6 from paraperiodic acid, H_5IO_6.

The salts are also powerful oxidisers, converting Mn^{2+} ions to MnO_4^-, and iodides to iodine.

Compounds of cationic iodine

Molten ICl is a good conductor and molten ICl_3 an even better. In solution in nitrobenzene or anhydrous acetic acid, transport evidence suggests the ionisation of ICI to be:

$$2ICl \rightleftharpoons I^+ + ICl_2^-.$$

IBr behaves similarly. Non-aqueous ICl_3 solutions appear to contain ICl_2^+ and Cl^- ions.

IOH is better considered as iodine hydroxide than as an acid, though made in a similar way to hypochlorous acid:

$$K_b = \frac{\{I^+\}\{OH^-\}}{\{IOH\}} = 3.2 \times 10^{-10}, \text{ whereas } K_a = \frac{\{H_3O^+\}\{IO^-\}}{\{HOI\}} = 2.5 \times 10^{-11}.$$

The unipositive iodine ion is stabilised by complexing with pyridine. $I(py)_2NO_3$ and $I(py)_2ClO_4$ are made by the action of iodine on silver nitrate or silver perchlorate dissolved in pyridine (Carlsohn, 1935). $I(py)^+$ salts of benzoic, phthalic and p-nitrobenzoic acids have been prepared. There is spectrophotometric evidence for $I(py)^+$ and I_3^- ions in a pyridine solution of iodine (Zingaro, Van der Werf and Kleinberg, 1951). Compounds of I^{3+} with oxoanions do not require stabilisation by complexing. They are made by oxidising solutions of iodine in the particular anhydrous acid:

$$I_2 \text{ (in } CH_3 \cdot COOH) \xrightarrow{\;\;Cl_2O\;\;} I(OOC \cdot CH_3)_3,$$

$$I_2 \text{ (in } HClO_4) \xrightarrow{\;\;O_3\;\;} I(ClO_4)_3,$$

$$I_2 \text{ (in } H_3PO_4) \xrightarrow[\text{in acetic anhydride}]{\text{fuming } HNO_3} IPO_4.$$

Iodyl sulphate, $(IO)_2SO_4$, is made from iodine and I_2O_5 in concentrated H_2SO_4. It is yellow.

Chapter 26

The Halides

Types

Metals with large ions of low charge form saline halides* with three-dimensional ionic lattices. The salts have high m.p. and b.p. and are good conductors when fused. Most of the halides of the first three A sub-groups belong to this class.

Non-metals and many B sub-group metals form volatile, non-conducting halides which usually have molecular lattices.

Consideration of the chlorides of the first three elements in Gps.I–IV reveals sharp changes in volatility in passing along the periods (Table 91).

TABLE 91
BOILING POINTS OF SOME CHLORIDES (°C)

Monohalides		Dihalides		Trihalides		Tetrahalides	
LiCl	1380	$BeCl_2$	490	BCl_3	12.5	CCl_4	76
NaCl	1440	$MgCl_2$	1400	$AlCl_3$	183	$SiCl_4$	57
KCl	1380	$CaCl_2$	1600	$ScCl_3$	1000	$TiCl_4$	136

In the first period the changes are less abrupt, the b.p. of $BeCl_2$ being 890° below that of LiCl and 477° above that of BCl_3; whereas, in the other periods, the effect of the increasing covalent character is strikingly sudden. Equivalent conductance, measured at the melting points, shows similar discontinuities. Broadly speaking the least readily melted halides are the best conductors when fused, the transportation of current being usually mainly by the cations.

TABLE 92
EQUIVALENT CONDUCTANCES OF FUSED CHLORIDES
(AT THEIR M.P.) IN OHM^{-1}

Monohalides		Dihalides		Trihalides		Tetrahalides	
LiCl (614°)	166	$BeCl_2$ (405°)	0.086	BCl_3 (−107°)	0	CCl_4 (−23°)	0
NaCl (800°)	134	$MgCl_2$ (714°)	29	$AlCl_3$ (193°)	1.5×10^{-5}	$SiCl_4$ (−70°)	0
KCl (770°)	104	$CaCl_2$ (782°)	52	$ScCl_3$ (939°)	15	$TiCl_4$ (−30°)	0

* For pseudohalides see p. 420.

But, as $BeCl_2$ shows, a rigid division into saline and volatile halides is not possible. Many metals which form ions such as M^{2+}, M^{3+} or M^{4+}, give halides with intermediate properties. These compounds usually have layer lattice structures ($CdCl_2$, $FeBr_2$, BiI_3) or chain structures ($PdCl_2$). The covalence also increases with the size of the halogen atom; thus CaF_2 is an ionic crystal, and $CaCl_2$ has a very slightly deformed rutile structure, but CaI_2 has the CdI_2 layer lattice. Fluorides are frequently exceptional, for instance AuF_3, TiF_3 and PbF_4 are saline though the corresponding chlorides are volatile. Some of the intermediate halides combine saline and covalent characteristics; an example is iron(III) chloride which is volatile (b.p. 315°), soluble in organic solvents, dimeric in the vapour and readily hydrolysed, but, nevertheless, a good conductor when fused.

Halides frequently form hydrates which differ in proporties from the anhydrous materials. Many M^{III} fluorides (e.g. AlF_3) are quite insoluble when made by dry methods but the hydrates (e.g. $AlF_3 \cdot 3.5H_2O$) produced from solutions dissolve readily in water. The co-ordination of water molecules round cations greatly reduces the lattice energies.

Methods of preparation

Dry methods of preparation are obligatory when the product is easily hydrolysed.

(i) Direct halogenation is a particularly versatile method, useful for all types of halide:

$$2Fe + 3Br_2 \rightarrow 2FeBr_3,$$
$$Sn + 2Cl_2 \rightarrow SnCl_4,$$
$$S + 3F_2 \rightarrow SF_6.$$

(ii) Heating oxide or sulphide with carbon and chlorine, with carbon tetrachloride, or with phosgene, is usually a good method for non-saline metal halides:

$$Cr_2O_3 + 3C + 3Cl_2 \rightarrow 2CrCl_3 + 3CO,$$
$$ZrO_2 + 2C + 2Cl_2 \rightarrow ZrCl_4 + 2CO,$$
$$2BeO + CCl_4 \rightarrow 2BeCl_2 + CO_2.$$

(iii) A mixture of S_2Cl_2 and chlorine often converts an oxide, or even a sulphate, to a chloride. This is a common method of making the trichlorides of the lanthanides:

$$4Lu_2O_3 + 9Cl_2 + 3S_2Cl_2 \rightarrow 8LuCl_3 + 6SO_2.$$

(iv) Chlorine gives a mixture of chlorides with metallic uranium. The tetrachloride UCl_4 results from heating the dioxide UO_2 with CCl_4:

$$UO_2 + CCl_4 \rightarrow UCl_4 + CO_2$$

Probably UCl_6 is first formed and decomposes to give UCl_4.

(v) Fluorides are made by treating the chloride with anhydrous HF:

$$CrCl_3 + 3HF \rightarrow CrF_3 + 3HCl,$$
$$TiCl_4 + 4HF \rightarrow TiF_4 + 4HCl;$$

by treating covalent halides with SbF_3 in the presence of $SbCl_5$ as catalyst:

$$SiCl_4 \rightarrow SiF_4, \qquad BCl_3 \rightarrow BF_3;$$

or by heating the oxides with CaF_2 or a mixture of CaF_2 and H_2SO_4:

$$ZrO_2 + 2CaF_2 \rightarrow 2CaO + ZrF_4,$$
$$GeO_2 + 2CaF_2 + 2H_2SO_4 \rightarrow GeF_4 + 2CaSO_4 + 2H_2O.$$

Wet methods are feasible when the halide is not hydrolysed, either because it is truly ionic or because it is insoluble. The products are frequently hydrated:

(i) The metal may be dissolved in the aqueous halogen acid:

$$Zn + 2HCl \rightarrow ZnCl_2 + H_2.$$

(ii) The oxide or hydroxide may be dissolved in the halogen acid:

$$MgO + 2HCl \rightarrow MgCl_2 + H_2O,$$
$$Bi_2O_3 + 6HF \rightarrow 2BiF_3 + 3H_2O.$$

(iii) Precipitation methods are frequently useful for non-hydrated metal halides:

$$M(NO_3)_n + nX^- \rightarrow \downarrow MX_n + nNO_3^-.$$

The insoluble halides include the chlorides and bromides of the Ag^+, Cu^+, Au^+ and Tl^+ ions, of the Pb^{2+}, Pt^{2+} and the mercury(I) ion, Hg_2^{2+}. The iodides of these, together with HgI_2, PdI_2, BiI_3 and AuI_3, are also insoluble.

Certain ions are precipitated as fluoride from solutions of the corresponding chloride, for example, those of Mg^{2+}, Ca^{2+}, Sr^{2+}, Ba^{2+}, Pb^{2+}, and Cu^{2+} and Al^{3+}; but AgF, Hg_2F_2 and TlF are soluble.

The structures of halides

AB structures

The alkali metal halides have either NaCl type (6 : 6) or CsCl type (8 : 8) structures (p. 141). The ratios of the ionic radii in

KF	RbF	CsF
0.98	1.09	1.24

suggest that the structures should have 8 : 8 co-ordination (higher co-ordination is not consistent with overall electrical neutrality), yet they have the 6 : 6 NaCl structure. Ammonium chloride, bromide and iodide all possess two forms, that with the CsCl structure being stable below the respective transition temperatures and that with the NaCl structure above:

$$NH_4Cl \qquad NH_4Br \qquad NH_4I$$
$$184.3° \qquad 137.8° \qquad —17.6°$$

At a low temperature NH_4Br and NH_4I have a third form which is tetragonal. Hydrogen bonding imposes a wurtzite structure on NH_4F (Fig. 214). The copper(I) halides have the zinc blende structure.

AB_2 structures

Difluorides usually have fluorite or rutile structures. Large ions such as, Hg^{2+}, Sr^{2+}, Pb^{2+} and Ba^{2+} form a fluorite (8 : 4) lattice (p. 150); the smaller Ni^{2+}, Co^{2+} Zn^{2+} and Mn^{2+} cations give rise to the rutile (6 : 3) structure (p. 150). The crystals of some chlorides and bromides of metals with large bipositive cations are ionic. $CaCl_2$ has a deformed rutile structure with four Cl^- ions 2.76 Å, and two Cl^- ions 2.70 Å, from the Ca^{2+}. However, CaI_2 has the same layer lattice as CdI_2 (p. 147).

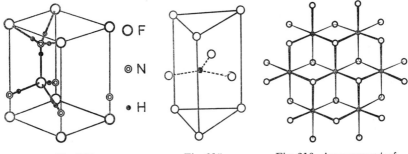

Fig. 214.
Hexagonal unit cell of NH_4F.

Fig. 215.
Structure of $PbCl_2$.

Fig. 216. Arrangement of octahedra in $CdCl_2$.

In $PbCl_2$ the lead ion occupies the centre of a trigonal prism with six Cl^- ions at the corners and three outside the face centres. $SrBr_2$ is similar (Fig. 215). But most dihalides form layer lattices. $CdCl_2$ can be considered as an NaCl structure (p. 141) in which half the octahedral holes between the Cl atoms are unoccupied (Fig. 216).

CdI_2 can be considered as being made up of hexagonally close-packed iodine ions in which only half the octahedral holes are filled with cadmium ions.

Other halides of these layer types are:

$CdCl_2$ type: $FeCl_2$, $CoCl_2$, $NiCl_2$, NiI_2, $ZnCl_2$, $MnCl_2$;
CdI_2 type: CaI_2, MgI_2, PbI_2, MnI_2, $MgBr_2$, $FeBr_2$.

The compounds $PdCl_2$ (Fig. 217), $CuCl_2$ and $CuBr_2$ have chain structures:

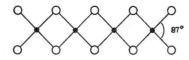

Fig. 217. Chain structure of $PdCl_2$.

AB_3 types

The trifluorides of many lanthanides and actinides have very slightly distorted rhenium trioxide structures (Fig. 218). Examples are CeF_3, PrF_3, NdF_3, ScF_3, EuF_3, AcF_3, UF_3 and NpF_3.

Bismuth trifluoride has the CaF_2 structure with twelve extra fluorine atoms at the mid-points of the edges and one at the centre of the unit cell (Fig. 219).

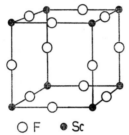

○ F   ● Sc

Fig. 218. Structure of ScF_3.

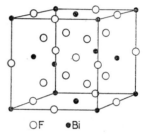

○F   ●Bi

Fig. 219. Cubic structure of BiF_3.

The chlorides and bromides of the lanthanides and actinides usually have the same structure as $PbCl_2$ but with one third of the prisms lacking metal ions. Examples are $LaCl_3$, $CeCl_3$, $NdCl_3$, $LaBr_3$, $CeBr_3$, $AcCl_3$, $NpCl_3$.

The structure of $CrCl_3$ (Fig. 220) is that of $CdCl_2$ (Fig. 216) with one third of the Cd atoms missing. $AlCl_3$ is similar.

BiI_3 is similarly related to CdI_2. It can also be considered as a structure of close-packed iodine atoms in which only one third of the octahedral holes are filled. Other examples of this structure are SbI_3, AsI_3, $FeCl_3$ and $CrBr_3$.

Halides containing individual molecules

The halides of B, C, N, O, Si and S and the Gp.IVB, VB and VIB elements consist of finite molecules. GeI_4 and SnI_4 also contain individual tetrahedral molecules. Al_2Br_6 molecules are present in aluminium bromide. PCl_5 and PBr_5 are interesting; the former contains tetrahedral PCl_4^+ ions and octahedral PCl_6^- ions, the latter tetrahedral PBr_4^+ ions and Br^- ions.

The hexachlorides of tungsten and uranium have a deformed hexagonal close-packing of chlorine atoms with metal atoms filling only one sixth of the octahedral holes.

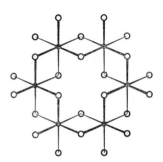

Fig. 220. Arrangement of octahedra in $CrCl_3$.

Halide molecules in the vapour state

The shapes of the free molecules in halide vapours are determined by mutual repulsion between electron pairs (p. 127) and may bear little relation to the disposition of atoms in the respective solid structures; the shapes depend largely on the electron configuration of the less electronegative element. Thus the PCl_5 molecule is trigonal bipyramidal, AsI_3 has a pyramidal molecule (Fig. 221), $AlCl_3$ exists principally as the dimer in the vapour just above the b.p. (Fig. 222), and $FeCl_3$ is probably the same. The trihalides of gold are planar dimers (Fig. 223):

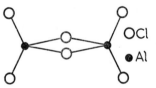

Fig. 221. Pyramidal structure of AsI_3.

Fig. 222. Structure of Al_2Cl_6.

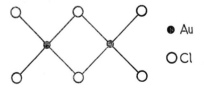

Fig. 223. Structure of Au_2Cl_6.

Heats of formation

Of the alkali metal halides, the fluorides have much the highest heats of formation. This is ascribed to the low heat of dissociation of the F_2 molecule and the high lattice energies of the compounds themselves. In the fluorides the heats of formation fall as the size of the cation increases, in the other halides they rise:

	Li	*Na*	*K*	*Rb*	*Cs*	
Fluorides	145	137	135	133	132	kcal.
Chlorides	97	98	104	105	107	kcal.

This is principally because the fraction $\dfrac{1}{r_{anion} + r_{cation}}$ which occurs in the lattice energy formula (p. 92) decreases more rapidly in the fluoride series on account of the small size of the anion; this change has more effect than have the decreasing ionisation potentials and sublimation energies of the respective metals.

Lattice energy considerations are important in fluorination by alkali metal fluorides:

$$\diagdown\!\!-\!\!C\!-\!Cl + MF \rightarrow \diagdown\!\!-\!\!C\!-\!F + MCl$$

Here $\varDelta G$ is largely dependent on the difference between the lattice energies of MF and MCl. As this difference is proportional to

$$\frac{1}{r_{M^+} + r_{F^-}} - \frac{1}{r_{M^+} + r_{Cl^-}} = \frac{r_{Cl^-} - r_{F^-}}{(r_{M^+} + r_{F^-})\,(r_{M^+} + r_{Cl^-})},$$

the greater the size of the M^+ ion the smaller the energy needed to produce MCl from MF and the less the energy which has to be supplied by the C–Cl → C–F change. Fluorine-exchanging ability therefore increases with

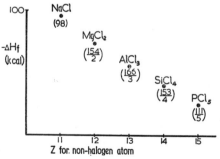

Fig. 224. Heats of formation per g atom of chlorine for chlorides of the second period.

cation size among fluorides which form isomorphous chlorides. Incidentally, the difference between the lattice energy of AgF and AgCl is very small because of the partly covalent bonding in AgCl and this accounts for the special fluorinating power of AgF.

Trends in heats of formation of halides through the Periodic Table are often surprisingly regular, as is shown for chlorides of elements of the second period in Fig. 224.

Kapustinskii (1948) found that the heat of formation (per halogen atom) of a halide plotted against the logarithm of the atomic number of its non-halogen atom displays a straight line relationship for compounds in which the maximum group valency is achieved. This is shown for the chlorides of Gps I to IV (Fig. 225).

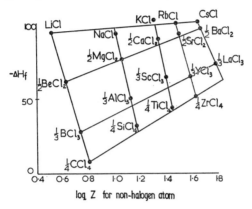

Fig. 225. Approximately linear relationships between heats of formation and log Z in some simple chlorides.

Heats of formation of chlorides, bromides and iodides increase in going down Gps.I, II, IIIA, IVA and VA. Elsewhere in the Periodic Table, heats of formation usually decrease down a group, but there are some irregularities, particularly in the first two periods.

$$BF_3 \quad 263 \text{ kcal} \qquad CCl_4 \quad 33 \text{ kcal}$$
$$AlF_3 \quad 311 \text{ kcal} \qquad SiCl_4 \quad 153 \text{ kcal}$$

The fluorides of Gp.VIB are interesting, their heats of formation being SF_6 262 kcal, SeF_6 246 kcal and TeF_6 315 kcal. Fluorine apparently forms particularly strong bonds with atoms having orbitals available for π-bonding, such as the 4f orbitals in Te; in this kind of situation the halogen lone pairs could make a small contribution to bonding by donation (*cf.* p. 106).

The heats of formation of hypothetical halides can be calculated by the

Born-Haber treatment. Van Arkel (1949) has discussed the heats of formation of halides for elements of variable charge number. The lowest curve in Fig. 226 is the type commonly found for bromides and iodides.

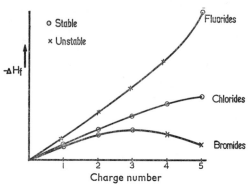

Fig. 226. Heats of formation of halides related to thermal stability.

According to simple theory, the increment to be expected in $-\Delta H_f$ between a bromide to a chloride, or a chloride to a fluoride, is proportional to the square of the charge number. This accounts for the form of the two higher curves. MBr_4 and MBr_5 are unstable and must liberate heat on conversion to MBr_3, whereas all the five chlorides are stable. When the curve becomes convex towards the charge number axis, as often happens for fluorides, the lower fluorides are metastable and heat must be liberated in the reaction

$$2MF_3 \rightarrow MF + MF_5.$$

It is stressed that in halides of the non-metals, the charge numbers shown by the non-metal change by steps of two because of the necessity of forming singly occupied orbitals. The implied promotion of electrons in the valence state will, of course, occur only when the formation of the bonds results in a net binding energy (p. 98).

Hydrolysis of halides

Most of the alkali metal and barium halides dissolve in water without changing the pH, although there is undoubtedly some hydration of the ions. The alkali metal fluorides give slightly alkaline reactions, however, because of the comparatively low ionisation of HF:

$$F^- + H_2O \rightleftharpoons HF + OH^-.$$

PbF_4 hydrolyses to give PbO_2 and HF. This reaction is made possible by the high lattice energy of the PbO_2 formed, and by the large energy of hydration of the four F^- ions.

Most covalent halides hydrolyse readily:

$$BCl_3 + 3H_2O \rightarrow H_3BO_3 + 3HCl,$$
$$SiCl_4 + 2H_2O \rightarrow SiO_2 + 4HCl,$$
$$3SiF_4 + 2H_2O \rightarrow SiO_2 + 2H_2SiF_6,$$
$$TeF_6 + 3H_2O \rightarrow H_6TeO_6 + 6HF.$$

Halides of layer-lattice type often hydrolyse reversibly:

$$FeCl_3 + 3H_2O \rightleftharpoons Fe(OH)_3 + 3HCl,$$

giving the solution a weakly acid reaction. Some hydrolyse reversibly to an oxide halide:

$$BiCl_3 + H_2O \rightleftharpoons BiOCl + 2HCl.$$

Hydrolysis is probably initiated by the donation of an electron pair to the central atom from the oxygen atom of the water molecule. Thus for example:

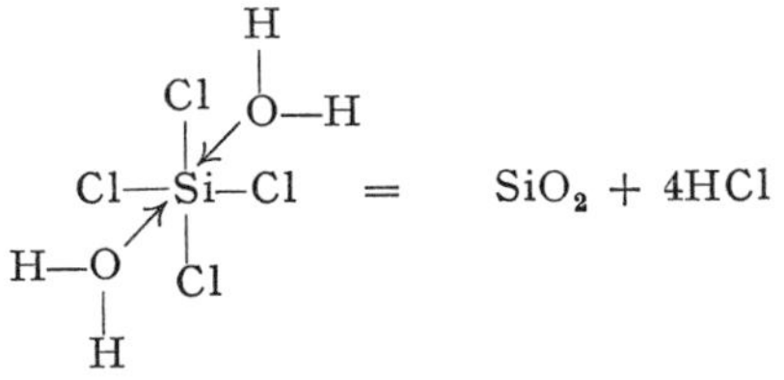

That Si—Cl bonds have some double bond character and involve the use of the 3d orbitals of Si, with donation from the chlorine lone pairs, is suggested by the high heat of formation of $SiCl_4$. One d orbital is occupied in sp^2d hybridisation, but the empty 3d orbitals can also accept electrons from the oxygen of water. CCl_4, with its lower heat of formation, is bound by simple σ-bonds and is not hydrolysed because there are no low-lying carbon orbitals of suitable symmetry to accept electrons from the water molecule.

The fluoride TeF_6 is much more readily hydrolysed than SeF_6; it also has a much greater heat of formation than SeF_6 which may be due, at least in part, to π-bonding in the Te—F bonds, made possible by the use of 4f electrons. For SeF_6, $-\Delta H_f = 246$ kcal, for TeF_6, 315 kcal.

The hydrolysis of covalent halides in which the central atom has attained its maximum covalency but still has one or more lone pairs is initiated by the donation of electrons to a proton of the water molecule:

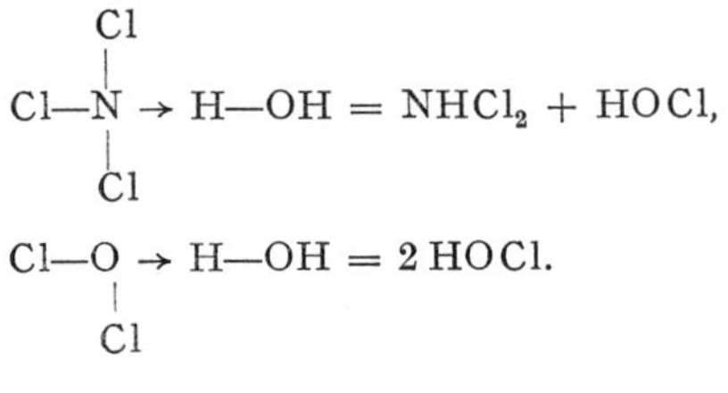

Such chlorides always yield HOCl instead of HCl on hydrolysis. NF_3 and F_2O do not hydrolyse because the fluorine is too electronegative to permit the donation of electrons to another molecule.

It should be noted that stability in the presence of water is not entirely dependent on the thermodynamic properties of a halide. The free energy changes for the following reactions show that they are thermodynamically feasible:

$$CF_4 \text{ (g)} + 2H_2O \text{ (g)} = CO_2 \text{ (g)} + 4HF \text{ (g)} \quad \varDelta G^0 = -36 \text{ kcal.}$$
$$SF_6 \text{ (g)} + 3H_2O \text{ (g)} = SO_3 \text{ (g)} + 6HF \text{ (g)} \quad \varDelta G^0 = -72 \text{ kcal.}$$

The failure of appreciable hydrolysis to occur under ordinary conditions must be due to the magnitude of the activation energies; this would be expected to be considerable since in each case the central atom is exhibiting its maximum valency, and the formation of an activated complex would require complete reorganisation of the electronic structure.

Colour of the halides

Halides, whether solid or in solution, are usually colourless unless the metal ion itself has a characteristic colour. The principal exceptions are certain anhydrous iodides: AgI, yellow; PbI_2, bright yellow; BiI_3, dark brown; HgI_2, scarlet.

Hydrates

NaF forms no hydrate. The hydrate of sodium chloride, $NaCl.2H_2O$, separates from a saturated solution only below $-10°$, NaBr and NaI form both di- and penta-hydrates at the ordinary temperature. CaF_2 is anhydrous but the other calcium halides form hydrates. By contrast, potassium and silver fluorides have hydrates, $KF.2H_2O$, $AgF.2H_2O$ and $AgF.4H_2O$, although their other halides are anhydrous. In $KF.2H_2O$ each K^+ and each F^- is surrounded approximately octahedrally by two H_2O molecules and four ions of opposite sign, each H_2O having two K^+ and two F^- ions arranged tetrahedrally round it.

In very few instances is the degree of hydration of fluoride and chloride the same; where it is, as in

$$FeF_2.4H_2O, \qquad FeCl_2.4H_2O,$$
$$CoF_2.2H_2O, \qquad CoCl_2.2H_2O,$$

the structures are not yet known.

Electrostatic considerations provide a useful guide to the likelihood of hydrate formation. For a pair of ions A^+ and B^- an over-all energy decrease is most likely to happen when r_{A^+} and r_{B^-} are large. Conversely when the ionic radii are small, as in LiF and NaF, a hydrate is not usually formed. As, however, the energy decrease in hydrate formation also depends on the energy change due to the hydration of individual ions, and as the smallest ions often have the greatest hydration energies, the formation of a hydrate depends on a rather fine energy balance. Thus AgF, for instance, with two small ions, forms a hydrate.

Many metallic dihalides form hexahydrates containing $M(H_2O)_6^{2+}$ ions. Examples are $MgCl_2.6H_2O$, $FeCl_2.6H_2O$, $CoCl_2.6H_2O$ and $NiCl_2.6H_2O$. The radius-ratio rule suggests that these hydrates should have a fluorite structure, but $Mg(H_2O)_6Cl_2$ is, in fact, less symmetrical. However, $Mg(NH_3)_6Cl_2$ has a fluorite lattice.

Solubilities are closely related to the ease of hydrate formation. In the ionic halides, solubilities increase with the size of the halide ion; fluorides are often particularly insoluble. In the more covalent halides this order of solubility is usually reversed.

Complex halides

These generally contain MX_4^{n-4} ions and MX_6^{n-6} ions, where n is the charge number of the metal. Many new fluoro-complexes containing metals with unusual charge numbers have been made recently, particularly by the use of BrF_3 as a non-aqueous solvent and fluorinating agent—Cs_2CoF_6, K_3CuF_6, $KIrF_6$.

Where the central metal ion is small the fluoro-complexes are less stable in solution than the chloro-complexes, perhaps because appreciable π-bonding is possible only in the latter. The complex fluorides of base metals with large positive ions are more stable than the corresponding complex chlorides. Hydration energies also play a part in determining relative stabilities in solution. The complex fluorides may be grouped into several structural types:

(i) Those with structures like simple halides:

$KLaF_4$ and K_2UF_6 have the CaF_2 structure (p. 150) with random arrangement of metal ions in the Ca^{2+} positions. $BaUF_6$ and $BaThF_6$ have the random lanthanum fluoride lattice (LaF_3 has the ReO_3 structure; see p. 485).

(ii) Those with perovskite-type lattices (p. 151):

$KMgF_3$, $KZnF_3$ and $KNiF_3$ are examples.

(iii) Uranium and thorium complexes with a fluorine deficiency:

Na_3UF_7 has a fluorite lattice with U^{4+} ions filling one quarter of the Ca^{2+} positions and Na^+ the other three quarters; one eighth of the F^-

positions are unoccupied. There are many uranium and thorium complexes with lattices of similar type.

(iv) Complexes of GroupIVA and VA elements of unusual formula: K_2NbF_7 contains $NbF_7{}^{2-}$ ions; $(NH_4)_3SiF_7$ contains octahedral $SiF_6{}^{2-}$ ions and discrete F^- ions.

(v) Fluoroaluminates:

These may contain AlF_6 octahedra linked in chains or layers, for instance Tl_2AlF_5 (Fig. 227).

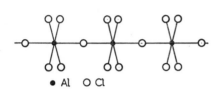

● Al   ○ Cl

Fig. 227. Chain ions in Tl_2AlF_5.

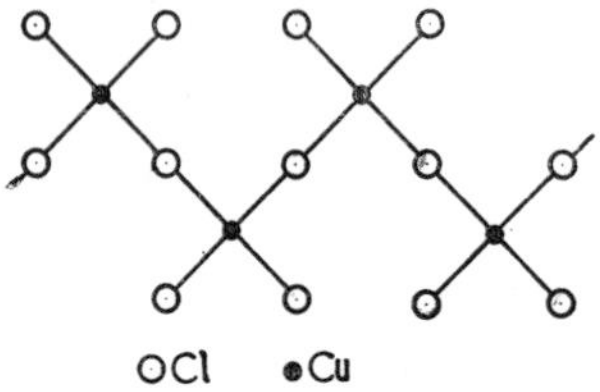

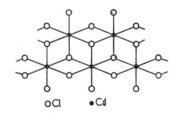

○Cl   ●Cu

Fig. 228. Double-chain ions in $CsCuCl_3$.

The chloro-complexes usually contain finite complex anions. None has the perovskite structure of $KMgF_3$. The complex $CsAuCl_3$ contains equal numbers of square $AuCl_4{}^-$ ions and linear $AuCl_2{}^-$ ions in addition to Cs^+ ions. Cs_2CuCl_4 contains finite $CuCl_4{}^{2-}$ ions, but $CsCuCl_3$ has a double chain (Fig. 228).

In K_2HgCl_4 and K_2SnCl_4 there are chains based on octahedral arrangement round the noble metal (Fig. 229), and in NH_4CdCl_3, double chains (Fig. 230).

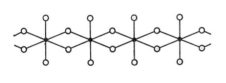

Fig. 229. Chain ions in K_2HgCl_4.

○Cl   ●Cd

Fig. 230. Double chain ions in NH_4CdCl_3.

THE PSEUDOHALOGENS AND PSEUDOHALIDES

Pseudohalides

Several uninegative groups show a similarity to halide ions in both their ionic and covalent compounds. The corresponding pseudohalogen covalent dimer of four of these entities has been isolated (Table 93). (The name is due to Birckenbach and Kellermann, 1925.)

TABLE 93

PSEUDOHALIDES AND PSEUDOHALOGENS

Pseudohalide	Ion	Pseudohalogen
Cyanide	CN^-	cyanogen $(CN)_2$
Cyanate	OCN^-	
Thiocyanate	SCN^-	thiocyanogen $(SCN)_2$
Selenocyanate	$SeCN^-$	selenocyanogen $(SeCN)_2$
Tellurocyanate	$TeCN^-$	
Azide	N_3^-	
Azidothiocarbonate	$SCSN_3^-$	azidocarbondisulphide $(SCSN_3)_2$
Isocyanate	ONC^-	

(1) With hydrogen, the uninegative groups form acids which are, however, very weak compared with the halogen acids.

$$\text{p}K_a \text{ for } HN_3, \text{ hydrazoic acid,} \quad = 4.4.$$
$$\text{p}K_a \text{ for } HCN, \text{ hydrocyanic acid,} = 8.9.$$

(2) The silver and mercury(I) salts are like the corresponding halides in being insoluble.

(3) The pseudohalogens are volatile and react with alkalis rather as do the halogens:

$$(CN)_2 + 2OH^- \quad \rightleftharpoons CN^- + OCN^- + H_2O$$
$$(SCSN_3)_2 + 2OH^- \quad \rightleftharpoons SCSN_3^- + OSCSN_3^- + H_2O$$
$$[cf. \ Cl_2 + 2OH^- \quad \rightleftharpoons Cl^- + OCl^- + H_2O]$$

(4) They form addition compounds with olefines and other unsaturated molecules:

$$C_2H_4 + (SCN)_2 \quad \rightarrow C_2H_4(SCN)_2$$
$$[cf. \ C_2H_4 + Br_2 \quad \rightarrow C_2H_4Br_2]$$

(5) Inter-pseudohalogen compounds and pseudohalogen-halogen compounds are known. Cyanogen chloride and bromide, CNCl and CNBr, result from the action of Cl_2 and Br_2 on HCN. Cyanogen fluoride, the existence of which has been in doubt, has been identified spectroscopically among products of the fluorination of cyanogen (Aynsley, Dodd and Little, 1959). Chloroazide, ClN_3, bromoazide, BrN_3, and iodoazide, IN_3, have also been made. In chloroform, thiocyanogen, $(SCN)_2$, combines with chlorine to give white crystals of SCNCl. Cyanogen bromide reacts with sodium azide to give $CN.N_3$:

$$CNBr + NaN_3 \rightarrow NaBr + CN.N_3.$$

Such compounds as CN(SCN) and CN(SeCN) have been obtained in crystalline form.

6) The pseudohalides form ions analogous to polyhalide ions:

$$NH_4(SCN)_3 \text{ and } K(SeCN)_3 \text{ resemble } KI_3.$$

The well-known complexes are similar to the less numerous halide complexes:

$$Fe(CN)_6{}^{3-} \quad [cf. \ FeF_6{}^{3-}].$$

(7) Certain lead(IV) compounds can be decomposed to give the lead(II) salt and the free pseudohalogen:

$$Pb(SCN)_4 \rightarrow Pb(SCN)_2 + (SCN)_2$$
$$Pb(SeCN)_4 \rightarrow Pb(SeCN)_2 + (SeCN)_2$$
$$[cf. \ PbCl_4 \rightarrow PbCl_2 + Cl_2]$$

Pseudohalogens

Cyanogen (p. 298) is made by heating AgCN alone or $Hg(CN)_2$ with $HgCl_2$:

$$2AgCN \rightarrow 2Ag + (CN)_2;$$
$$Hg(CN)_2 + HgCl_2 \rightarrow Hg_2Cl_2 + (CN)_2.$$

Thiocyanogen, $(SCN)_2$, is released by the action of bromine on AgSCN suspended in ether:

$$2 \ AgSCN + Br_2 \rightarrow 2AgBr + (SCN)_2.$$

The yellow solid polymerises irreversibly at room temperature giving an insoluble brick-red material. The dimer oxidises iodides to iodine and Cu^+ to Cu^{2+} ions.

Selenocyanogen, $(SeCN)_2$, also yellow and crystalline, is displaced by iodine from AgSeCN:

$$2 \ AgSeCN + I_2 \rightarrow 2AgI + (SeCN)_2.$$

Azidocarbondisulphide, $(SCSN_3)_2$, is formed as white crystals when $KSCSN_3$ is oxidised with hydrogen peroxide:

$$CS_2 + KN_3 \xrightarrow{40°} KSCSN_3 \xrightarrow{H_2O_2} (SCSN_3)_2.$$

The compound decomposes at room temperature:

$$(SCSN_3)_2 \rightarrow 2N_2 + 2S + (SCN)_2.$$

Chapter 27

The Lanthanides, Scandium and Yttrium

GROUP IIIA

The lanthanides, for which the general symbol Ln is used here, have electron configurations with $6s^2$ in common and a variable occupation of the 4f level. Classically called the Rare Earths, they are also referred to as the inner-transition elements because the 4f electron build-up takes place in the fourth quantum level, below the 5s, 5p and 6s electrons. As the electronic diversity between the atoms is at some 'depth' the elements are very similar chemically. The small differences in properties arise principally from the

TABLE 94

THE LANTHANIDES

	Symbol	Z	Electron configuration			Common ionic charges		M^{3+} radii
Lanthanum	La	57		$5d^1$	$6s^2$	3		1.06
Cerium	Ce	58	$4f^1$	$5d^1$	$6s^2$	3	4	1.03
Praseodymium	Pr	59	$4f^2$	$5d^1$	$6s^2$	3	4	1.01
Neodymium	Nd	60	$4f^3$	$5d^1$	$6s^2$	2 3	4	1.00
Promethium	Pm	61	$4f^4$	$5d^1$	$6s^2$	3		–
Samarium	Sm	62	$4f^5$	$5d^1$	$6s^2$	2 3		0.96
Europium	Eu	63	$4f^6$	$5d^1$	$6s^2$	2 3		0.95
Gadolinium	Gd	64	$4f^7$	$5d^1$	$6s^2$	3		0.94
Terbium	Tb	65	$4f^8$	$5d^1$	$6s^2$	3	4	0.92
Dysprosium	Dy	66	$4f^9$	$5d^1$	$6s^2$	3	4	0.91
Holmium	Ho	67	$4f^{10}$	$5d^1$	$6s^2$	3		0.89
Erbium	Er	68	$4f^{11}$	$5d^1$	$6s^2$	3		0.88
Thulium	Tm	69	$4f^{12}$	$5d^1$	$6s^2$	2 3		0.87
Ytterbium	Yb	70	$4f^{13}$	$5d^1$	$6s^2$	2 3		0.86
Lutetium	Lu	71	$4f^{14}$	$5d^1$	$6s^2$	3		0.85

'lanthanide contraction'. Since, for every proton added to the nucleus, the corresponding electron goes into a 4f orbital which is too diffuse to screen the nucleus as effectively as a more localised inner shell, the attraction of the nucleus for the outermost electrons increases steadily with the atomic number of the lanthanide. This causes a fall in atomic size from lanthanum to lutetium. The contraction is quite regular in Ln^{3+} ions but not in the

TABLE 95

PROPERTIES OF SOME LANTHANIDES

Element	Structure	Atomic radius	Density	Atomic volume
57 La	h.c.p.	1.69	6.2	22.4
62 Sm	h.c.p.	1.66	6.9	21.7
63 Eu	b.c.c.	1.85	5.2	29.2
64 Gd	h.c.p.	1.61	7.9	19.9
69 Tm	h.c.p.	1.56	9.3	18.2
70 Yb	f.c.c.	1.70	7.0	24.7
71 Lu	h.c.p.	1.56	9.7	18.0

atomic radii inferred from the structures of the metals, in which the outer electronic structure is strongly affected by the metallic bonding (pp. 75 and 81).

The first three lanthanides, La, Ce and Pr, are dimorphous metals, with h.c.p. and f.c.c. structures differing little in density. The others are h.c.p. except Eu (b.c.c.) and Yb (f.c.c.) in which two the interatomic distances are greater and the densities lower (Table 95). The physical constants of the lanthanides are known only approximately; the first ionisation potentials are about 6 eV and the second about 12 eV, comparable with those of calcium. The standard electrode potentials, $E_h^0 Ln^{3+}/Ln$, are all about -2.1 V.

The radii of the ions and the ionic charges are related to the electron configurations in Table 94; these result, as would be expected, in a dominant charge number of $+3$. But empty, half-filled and filled 4f shells are particularly stable and this charge is the only one displayed by La, Gd and Lu. Of the rest of the lanthanides, Ce, Pr, Nd, Tb and Dy show in addition a charge number of $+4$ and Nd, Sm, Eu, Tm and Yb one of $+2$. Only neodymium has so far produced compounds with $2+$, $3+$ and $4+$ ions. The $+4$ state is probably formed from the $+3$ state by the loss of a 4f electron, and the $+2$ state by the gain of one; for instance Pr^{4+} has $4f^1$ and Sm^{2+} has $4f^6$.

The chemical properties of the early members of the series are similar to those of calcium but, with increasing atomic number, these give place to other properties more like those of aluminium. At the same time there is a progressive increase in the solubility of the potassium double sulphates.

Cerium provides two notable exceptions to the scheme in Fig. 231; it combines with fluorine to give CeF_4 and with oxygen to give CeO_2. Some of the metals react with hydrogen to give non-stoichiometric hydrides ($H/Ln < 3$).

Sources of the lanthanides

Though called rare, the elements are not particularly so. According to

Goldschmidt (1937) three, namely Ce, La and Nd, are more common than lead, and thulium is about as abundant as iodine. These elements tend to crystallise late from a magma since their ions are too large to replace other terpositive ions, hence they separate in the pegmatites. The 'light' lanthanides are extracted chiefly from monazite sand (Travancore), predominantly phosphates of thorium, cerium, neodymium and lanthanum, but also from orthite. Monazite is a poor source of europium, which is more commonly associated as Eu^{2+} with alkaline earth minerals, and does not carry much of the 'heavy' lanthanides which are obtained from gadolinite, $FeBe_2Y_2Si_2O_{10}$, and xenotime, YPO_4.

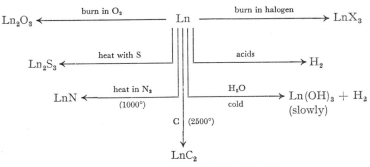

Fig. 231. The chemistry of the lanthanides.

Extraction from monazite

Monazite is digested with concentrated H_2SO_4 to produce a paste of the sulphates containing phosphoric acid and an excess of sulphuric acid. The paste, separated by centrifugation, is dissolved in cold water, the sulphates being less soluble in hot water. The solution is neutralised with a previously prepared mixture of lanthanide oxides to precipitate thorium, zirconium and titanium. The addition of Na_2SO_4 to the clear mother liquor throws down the light lanthanides (La to Sm) as double sulphates of variable composition; the heavy lanthanides (Gd to Lu), which comprise less than 4% of those present, remain in solution. Hot NaOH is added to the double sulphate precipitate of light fraction to give a mixture of hydrated oxides. This is washed free from Na_2SO_4 and dried in air at 100°, the cerium being thus completely oxidised to CeO_2. The composition at this stage is roughly: CeO_2 50%, Nd_2O_3 20%, La_2O_3 17%, Pr_2O_3 8%, Sm_2O_3 5%.

This mixture is extracted with dilute HNO_3 to dissolve the more basic sesquioxides, Ln_2O_3, and leave a residue of CeO_2. The crude CeO_2 is dissolved in 85% HNO_3 and added to an excess of dilute H_2SO_4, whereby the cerium is precipitated as red hydroxide nitrate, $Ce(OH)(NO_3)_3.3H_2O$. The dilute solution is used for leaching more of the dried hydroxides.

Separation of the light lanthanides, after removal of the Ce, has been accomplished in many ways, based mainly on solubility differences; fractional crystallisation of the double magnesium nitrates, $2Ln(NO_3)_3.3Mg(NO_3)_2.24 H_2O$, was an early method (James, 1908). The heavy lanthanides from the double sulphate solution (above) and from ores such as xenotime have been separated by fractional crystallisation of the bromates (James, 1908). Prandtl (1938) used double ammonium oxalates. Hartley (1952) obtained a 85% yield of mixed anhydrous lanthanide chlorides by direct chlorination of a mixture of monazite and carbon at 900°; most of the impurities are more volatile.

Separation by ion exchange

When a mixture of lanthanide ions is brought on to an exchange resin (p. 567) in its hydrogen form, the order of absorption follows the atomic numbers. Affinity for the resin decreases with radius of the hydrated ion:

$$3HR + Ln^{3+} \rightleftharpoons 3H^+ + LnR_3.$$

Early attempts to achieve an orderly displacement of the cations from the resin by a concentrated solution of an ammonium salt were not successful:

$$LnR_3 + 3NH_4^+ \rightleftharpoons Ln^{3+} + 3NH_4R.$$

However, the addition of an acid capable of complexing with the ions improved the separation. Harris and Tompkins (1947) found the distribution coefficients of adjacent lanthanides between citrate buffer solutions and Amberlite IR–1 to differ by a factor of about two. Spedding (1948) showed the eluants to be most efficient at low concentration and high pH. He absorbed light lanthanides on a cation resin in a 24 unit battery of Pyrex columns 10 ft by 4 in., and displaced them with 0.1% citric acid buffered to pH6 with ammonia. The eluate was collected in 40–50 litre fractions (about a day's run). It contained up to 0.4 g/l of Ln_2O_3 and upwards of 80% of each element was obtained in a high state of purity from a single passage through the columns. The elements were displaced in the reverse order of the atomic number.

Improvements in modes of complexing by Marsh (1950), who separated lanthanides by fractional crystallisation of the ethylenediaminetetra-acetic acid (EDTA) complexes, have been coupled with the ion exchange technique by Vickery (1952). EDTA proved an even more satisfactory complexing agent than citric acid and gave purer specimens than any other method.

Solvent extraction

A recent means of separation is a solution of tri-*n*-butyl phosphate in kerosene flowing counter to a nitric acid solution of lanthanides. Differences in the extraction coefficient are approximately equal from one element to the next. Weaver, Kappelmann and Topp (1953) separated Gd_2O_3 of about 95% purity on a kilogram scale in this way (p. 572).

The metals

Production

The various methods which have been used include:
  (i) electrolysis of the fused chlorides (*cf.* Ca),
  (ii) electrolysis of CeO_2 in fused CeF_3 (*cf.* Al),
  (iii) reduction of the anhydrous chlorides with Na (*cf.* Ti),
  (iv) reduction of the anhydrous fluorides with Mg (*cf.* U).
Spedding (1952) has made La and Ce in kg quantities, and Pr and Nd in smaller amounts, by reducing the anhydrous chloride in a refractory-lined crucible with calcium; the reactions are initiated with a little iodine. Gadolinium has been made similarly in a crucible of tantalum. It is noteworthy that Sm, Eu and Yb, which exhibit a reasonably stable $+2$ state, are reduced only as far as the dichlorides. Their removal is thus facilitated.

Physical properties

The metals are silvery-white but tarnish rapidly in air. The earliest members La and Ce are as soft as tin; hardness increases with atomic number, Sm being steel-hard. The m.p. of the first four are in the range 815°–930°, but samarium melts at about 1350°. They have the h.c.p., f.c.c. or b.c.c. structures typical of the true metals, and are good conductors of heat and electricity.

Nature and properties of the ions

All the lanthanides have Ln^{III} compounds, this being the principal form in which the elements occur; complexes and ions with charge numbers other than $+3$ are rather uncommon (p. 423, 424, 429).

Neither La^{3+} nor Lu^{3+} show absorption bands in the ultra-violet, visible or near infrared, but the rest do. The bands are narrow compared with those of the normal transition ions. The energy changes involved are probably due to excitations within the 4f shell, since complexing agents, which alter the absorption spectra of normal transition ions by modifying their outer structure, have little effect on the lanthanide ions. An ion with n

electrons in the 4f level generally has a similar absorption spectrum to one with $14 - n$, but the pairs Nd^{3+} ($4f^3$), Er^{3+} ($4f^{11}$), and Pm^{3+}, Ho^{3+} are anomalous.

The lanthanide ions, other than the $4f^0$ type, La^{3+} and Ce^{4+}, and the $4f^{14}$ type, Yb^{2+} and Lu^{3+}, are all paramagnetic, with both spin and orbital

TABLE 96

COLOURS OF LANTHANIDE $3+$ IONS

$4f^1$	Ce^{3+}	(colourless)	Yb^{3+}	(colourless)	$4f^{13}$
$4f^2$	Pr^{3+}	(green	Tm^{3+}	(green)	$4f^{12}$
$4f^3$	Nd^{3+}	(blue-violet)	Er^{3+}	(pink)	$4f^{11}$
$4f^4$	Pm^{3+}	(rose)	Ho^{3+}	(yellow)	$4f^{10}$
$4f^5$	Sm^{3+}	(cream)	Dy^{3+}	(cream)	$4f^9$
$4f^6$	Eu^{3+}	(colourless—	Tb^{3+}	(colourless—	
		u.v. absorption)		u.v. absorption)	$4f^8$
	$4f^7$ Gd^{3+}	(colourless—u.v. absorption)			

moments (p. 78). For the $J_0 \to J_1$ transition in Sm^{3+} and Eu^{3+}, $h\nu \sim kT$ and there is no simple expression for μ, the magnetic moment. But in all other cases μ is given to a near approximation by $\mu = \sqrt{J(J + 1)}g$ since $h\nu$ is much greater than kT, and the Curie law is closely obeyed. The moments of isoelectronic ions (Eu^{2+}, Gd^{3+}, Tb^{4+} — all $4f^7$) are very similar.

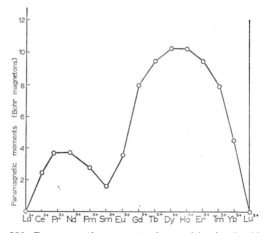

Fig. 232. Paramagnetic moments of terpositive lanthanide ions.

Compounds other than those of Lanthanide(III)

Bipositive state

Sm, Eu and Yb form 2+ ions. Their compounds are usually made by reduction with hydrogen:

$$2SmCl_3 + H_2 \rightarrow 2SmCl_2 + 2HCl$$

Solutions of Eu^{3+} can be reduced by amalgamated zinc (E_h^o $Eu^{3+}/Eu^{2+} =$ -0.4 V) and of Yb^{3+} by electrolytic reduction (E_h^o $Yb^{3+}/Yb^{2+} = -1.5$ V) but not Sm^{3+} since $SmCl_2$ decomposes water:

$$6SmCl_2 + 6H_2O \rightarrow 4SmCl_3 + 2Sm(OH)_3 + 3H_2.$$

Neodymium has recently been obtained in the $+2$ state: reduction of anhydrous $NdCl_3$ with Nd metal gives a dark green $NdCl_2$. A dark purple NdI_2 has also been made.

Quadripositive state

With the exception of Ce^{3+}, the Ln^{3+} ions resist oxidation in aqueous solution. The standard redox potential of the Ce^{4+}/Ce^{3+} couple varies greatly with the nature of the anion present.

TABLE 97

STANDARD REDOX POTENTIALS IN DIFFERENT MEDIA

Medium	E°_h Ce^{4+}/Ce^{3+}
HCl	$+1.28$ V
HNO_3	$+1.61$ V
$HClO_4$	$+1.70$ V

The figures suggest that the simple Ce^{4+} ion does not exist in aqueous solution, and the variations in redox potential seem too great to be caused merely by differences in its hydration. Because of its considerable charge and moderate size ($r = 0.92$ Å), the ion has appreciable polarising power and may well form complexes with suitable anions.

The $4+$ ion also occurs with praseodymium and terbium, but only in solids made by dry methods. When their nitrates, carbonates or hydroxides are heated in air the final products are empirically Pr_6O_{11} and Tb_4O_7; the corresponding cerium compounds give CeO_2. Pure PrO_2 is made by heating the Pr_6O_{11} to $300°$ under 50 atmospheres of oxygen (McCullough, 1950). Both PrO_2 and GeO_2 have fluorite lattices; Pr_6O_{11} has a defect lattice in which one twelfth of the oxygen positions of PrO_2 are empty. Dark colour is often associated with defect lattices of this type: Pr_6O_{11} is black and Tb_4O_7 brown.

Spedding (1952) attempted to make tetrafluorides of praseodymium and neodymium by treating Pr_6O_{11} and PrO_2, as well as Pr_2O_3 and Nd_2O_3, with ClF_3 but only trifluorides were formed. This is an exception to the general rule that metals exhibit their highest charge in fluorides.

Compounds of Lanthanide(III)

The anhydrous chlorides are best made by heating the oxides in carbonyl chloride:

$$Ln_2O_3 + 3COCl_2 \rightarrow 3CO_2 + 2LnCl_3.$$

They are non-volatile, usually deliquescent, very soluble in water and fairly soluble in alcohol. They form crystalline hydrates, generally with either 6 or $7H_2O$ ($LaCl_3.7H_2O$; $NdCl_3.6H_2O$). When these are heated in air an oxide chloride, $LnOCl$, is produced.

The hydroxides are precipitated by $NaOH$ from Ln^{III} solutions and are insoluble in an excess. Apart from the exceptions already mentioned, they are converted into the sesquioxides, Ln_2O_3, by heating in air. Lanthanum oxide, a very strong base, slakes like CaO on the addition of water and wil then take up CO_2. The oxides of the other elements become progressively weaker bases as the size of the Ln^{3+} ion diminishes. The lanthanide oxides have particularly high heats of formation:

La_2O_3	Pr_2O_3	Nd_2O_3	Sm_2O_3
458	444	442	430 kcal

The metals are therefore exceptionally strong reducing agents, comparable with the alkaline earth elements and aluminium.

Normal carbonates of the lanthanides can be precipitated from Ln^{III} solutions by $NaHCO_3$; in this the lanthanides resemble magnesium. Many of the carbonates form hydrates. The carbonates are soluble in alkali metal carbonate solutions, and compounds such as $K_2CO_3.Ce_2(CO_3)_3 3H_2O$ have been crystallised.

The nitrates are very soluble indeed and form double nitrates with magnesium, $3Mg(NO_3)_2.2Ln(NO_3)_3.24H_2O$; these were formerly used for separations within this series of elements. Their solubilities increase with molecular weight.

The sulphates do not form alums. Small ions such as Al^{3+} ($r = 0.50$ Å) can be surrounded octahedrally by six H_2O molecules, but the lanthanide ions ($r > 0.85$ Å) are too large to co-ordinate water molecules in this way.

Nevertheless there are many double sulphates, $(NH_4)_2SO_4.Ln_2(SO_4)_38H_2O$ being the commonest type.

The solubilities of lanthanide compounds resemble closely those of the Gp.IIA metals.

Soluble $LnCl_3$, $LnBr_3$, LnI_3, $Ln(NO_3)_3$, $Ln(ClO_4)_3$, $LnA\bar{c}_3$.
Insoluble Ln_2O_3, $Ln(OH)_3$, $Ln_2(O\bar{x})_3$, $Ln_2(CO_3)_3$, $LnPO_4$, LnF_3.
Variable $Ln_2(SO_4)_3$.

Complexes

In spite of a high charge, the ions are too large to cause much polarisation and few complexes are formed. Chelates with β-diketones, oxine and 'EDTA' acid (p. 263) can be made. Three types of ethylenediaminetetra-acetic acid complexes have been described.

(i) HLn(edta)   (Brintzinger, 1943),
(ii) $Ln_4(edta)_3$ (Brintzinger, 1948) and
(iii) NaLn(edta)   (Moeller and Brantley, 1950).

Lanthanide oxides react with the acid to give (i) and (ii), formulated by Moeller, Moss and Marshall (1955) as

H [Ln (edta)] xH_2O   — (strong acids),
and Ln [Ln (edta)]_3 yH_2O   — (salts).

The addition of NaOH gives $Na[Ln(edta)]3H_2O$. Evidence from X-ray diffraction, pH titration and ion migration studies suggests that in the $[Ln(edta)]^-$ ion the ethylenediaminetetra-acetate occupies only five coordination positions and possesses one uncomplexed —COO— group.

Promethium

Moseley's list of Atomic Numbers (1913) showed that there are 14 possible lanthanides. Attempts to find element 61, promethium, which lies between Nd and Sm, in natural occurrence have been unsuccessful because there is apparently no stable isotope.

The element was first produced artificially by Marinsky, Glendenin and Coryell (1947) who used ion exchange to separate the products of the slow neutron fission of ^{235}U. These contain 2.6% of promethium in the form of $^{147}_{61}Pm$, the isotope of longest half-life (2–3 years). It emits a soft β radiation (0.23 MeV) and no γ rays:

$$^{147}_{61}Pm \xrightarrow[\text{2.3 yr}]{\beta^-} {}^{147}_{62}Sm \text{ (stable)}.$$

The same nuclide results from an (n,γ) reaction on $^{146}_{60}$Nd in the pile, followed by β^- emission from the ^{147}Nd formed:

$$^{146}_{60}\text{Nd} \xrightarrow{\text{n, }\gamma} \,^{147}_{60}\text{Nd} \xrightarrow[\text{11 days}]{\beta^-} \,^{147}_{61}\text{Pm}.$$
(stable)

Though its specific activity is fairly high, the low β energy and the absence of γ radiation make it fairly safe to handle and chemical studies are possible. The chloride and nitrate have been made in mg amounts; their solutions are pink.

Scandium

Its $3d^1 4s^2$ structure gives element 21 properties similar to the lanthanides and to lanthanum $(5d^1 6s^2)$ in particular. The covalent and ionic radii, 1.44 Å and 0.68 Å, respectively, are however much smaller than those of the lanthanides. In consequence the Sc^{3+} ion has a greater polarising power and more readily forms complexes: for instance crystalline K_3ScF_6 can be obtained. The ionisation potentials 1st, 6.56 eV; 2nd, 12.9 eV; 3rd, 24.8 eV are not much larger than those of the lanthanides so far as they are known, and the metal itself is almost as reactive.

Scandium is present in some of the lanthanide minerals, but thortveitite, $ScSi_2O_7$, is the usual source. The metal is made by the electrolysis of a fused mixture of $ScCl_3$, KCl and LiCl on a zinc cathode followed by volatilisation of the Zn at low pressure from the Zn–Sc alloy so formed. The metal is dimorphous, with f.c.c. and h.c.p. forms. Its m.p. is rather high, $\sim 1400°$.

Some important differences between scandium and the lanthanides are

   (i)   the oxide is a weaker base,
   (ii) the chloride is more volatile,
   (iii) the nitrate, $Sc(NO_3)_3.4H_2O$, is more easily decomposed by heat;
   (iv) the sulphate, $Sc_2(SO_4)_3.5H_2O$, is very soluble in both cold and hot water.

Yttrium

Element 39, with $4d^1 5s^2$ electron configuration, is also similar to the lanthanides. It occurs with the lanthanides in minerals; the best source is xenotime, YPO_4. Yttrium has properties approximately midway between those of Sc and La; its compounds also resemble those of the heavy earths dysprosium and holmium, the ionic radius (0.90 Å) being similar.

Chapter 28

The Actinides

Characterisation

Before the properties of neptunium and plutonium became known (1941), actinium, thorium, protactinium and uranium had been considered to be the last members of their respective A sub-groups in the Periodic Table. There was some chemical evidence for this view; uranium forms complexes indicating variable charge and a particularly stable 6+ cation typical of molybdenum and tungsten, while thorium nearly always occurs with a 4+ charge. Thus they seemed to fit into Groups VI and IV. The little that was known about actinium, the existence of Ac^{III} and the isomorphism of its salts with those of lanthanum, suggested membership of Group III. Almost nothing was known of the properties of protactinium. With the production of neptunium by McMillan (1940), of plutonium and particularly of further trans-uranic elements by Seaborg and others (1944 to present), evidence for a different classification accumulated. The similarity of the elements from actinium onwards to those from lanthanum onwards became increasingly apparent, so that they are now accepted as a closely related family and known

TABLE 98

ELECTRON CONFIGURATION OF THE ACTINIDES

		Atomic no. (Z)	Probable electron configuration		
Actinium	Ac	89		$6d^1$	$7s^2$
Thorium	Th	90		$6d^2$	$7s^2$
Protactinium	Pa	91	$5f^2$	$6d^1$	$7s^2$
Uranium	U	92	$5f^3$	$6d^1$	$7s^2$
Neptunium	Np	93	$5f^4$	$6d^1$	$7s^2$
Plutonium	Pu	94	$5f^6$		$7s^2$
Americium	Am	95	$5f^7$		$7s^2$
Curium	Cm	96	$5f^7$	$6d^1$	$7s^2$
Berkelium	Bk	97	$5f^9$		$7s^2$
Californium	Cf	98	$5f^{10}$		$7s^2$

as the *actinides* (*cf.* the lanthanides which begin thirty-two places earlier in the Periodic Table). This classification is suggested by the
  (i) increasing stability of the 3+ ion with atomic number;
 (ii) isomorphism of trichlorides, dioxides and many salts with corresponding lanthanide compounds;
(iii) decrease in ionic radii with atomic number, analogous to the lanthanide contraction;
 (iv) character of the absorption spectra of the ions;
  (v) magnetic moments of the ions.

All the actinides are believed to have the electron configuration $(7s)^2$ and a variable occupation of the 5f and 6d shells (Table 98).

Ionic radii

TABLE 99

IONIC RADII OF THE ACTINIDES

	Ac	Th	Pa	U	Np	Pu	Am
M^{3+}	1.11	—	—	1.03	1.01	1.00	0.99 Å
M^{4+}	—	0.99	0.96	0.93	0.92	0.90	0.89 Å

These ionic radii, derived from X-ray diffraction data, should be compared with those of the lanthanides (p. 421). The size of an ion depends largely upon the quantum number of the outermost electrons and the effective nuclear charge (p. 89). In the 3+ ions of these elements the outermost electrons are in a completed 6p shell; the effective nuclear charge rises with atomic number because the screening effect of extra electrons in the 5f level fails to compensate entirely for the increased nuclear charge. The existence of a contraction, similar to the lanthanide contraction, affords further support for the idea that the 5f level is being filled in passing onwards from actinum. The contraction is more rapid in the actinides.

Separation of the metals

The principal source of thorium is monazite (p. 425), a phosphate of cerium and lanthanum with up to 15% of thoria. It is dissolved in concentrated sulphuric acid and the thorium phosphate precipitated with magnesium oxide. The washed phosphate heated with sodium carbonate gives crude thoria, ThO_2, which is converted to the soluble oxalate and separated from the insoluble oxalates of cerium and lanthanum. After ignition to oxide the nitrate is made, purified by recrystallisation, and again calcined to thoria.

An alternative separation of thoria, based on the low solubility of lanthanides in a mixture of phosphoric and sulphuric acids, is to treat monazite at 225° with concentrated sulphuric acid and to leave most of the lanthanide sulphates behind by extracting the semi-solid mass with water. The crude thorium sulphate is crystallised by concentrating the liquor, washed with cold concentrated sulphuric acid to remove phosphoric acid and redissolved in 25% sulphuric acid. The solution of the sulphate is boiled with ammonium carbonate to precipitate basic thorium carbonate. This is washed with a very little dilute nitric acid and calcined to thoria.

The pure uncontaminated metal is difficult to obtain because it readily combines with hydrogen, oxygen, nitrogen and carbon. In bulk, the metal is best made by preparing the tetrachloride, $ThCl_4$, by heating thoria in phosgene, and reducing it with calcium:

$$ThO_2 + 2\ COCl_2 \rightarrow ThCl_4 + 2\ CO_2,$$
$$ThCl_4 + 2\ Ca \rightarrow 2CaCl_2 + Th.$$

The metal may be purified (especially from ThO_2) by the thermal dissociation of ThI_4 on a hot filament (1100–1200°), the liberated iodine being recirculated to react with more crude metal powder (Van Arkel and De Boer).

Uranium is extracted from pitchblende, essentially U_3O_8. The ore is washed, then fused with sodium carbonate and sodium nitrate. From the mass, dilute sulphuric acid extracts uranyl sulphate, UO_2SO_4. The addition of ammonium carbonate enables ammonium uranyl carbonate, $(NH_4)_4UO_2(CO_3)_3$, to be crystallised which, on ignition, yields pure U_3O_8.

Uranium is separated from low-grade ores by treating them in dilute sulphuric acid with manganese dioxide which, in spite of its insolubility, is able to oxidise U^{IV} to U^{VI} in the presence of 0.4 g/l of an iron salt. The uranium forms a complex anion with the sulphate, presumably $[U^{VI}(SO_4)_5]^{4-}$, which is quite strongly absorbed on an anion exchange resin. The selectivity is very high and competition from other ions can be effectively eliminated. Elution may be with almost any salt other than a sulphate. Nitrates are best and give a liquor containing, typically, 20 g/l $UO_2(NO_3)_2$.

The reduction of UO_2 is carried out in the stages:

$$UO_2 \xrightarrow[\text{in HF vapour}]{\text{heat}} UF_4 \xrightarrow[\text{in pressure vessel}]{\text{heat with Mg}} \underset{\text{metal billet}}{U} + \underset{\text{slag}}{MgF_2}.$$

Two other ways are available for obtaining metallic uranium: (i) by the electrolysis of KUF_5 in fused $CaCl_2$ (80%) and NaCl (20%) at 900° with the graphite container as anode and a molybdenum cathode. The current density employed is 1.5 amp/cm² and the product better than 99.9%. (ii) by the hot-wire technique (Van Arkel and De Boer, 1925), also used for Ti (p. 449), Zr and W, applied to UI_4.

Transuranic elements from the nuclear reactor

Plutonium is produced almost entirely from uranium in a nuclear reactor. An air-cooled graphite pile consists essentially of a stack of blocks of very pure graphite through which run many parallel channels arranged in a pattern calculated to make the most effective use of the available neutrons. In the channels are placed metallic uranium slugs encased in aluminium or magnox cylinders and through the channels is blown cooling air. To control the neutron flux, rods of cadmium or other materials which absorb neutrons are automatically inserted into the pile, and thus the power output is governed. A thick shield of concrete surrounds the pile, with openings through which materials for irradiation may be introduced and placed in a required neutron flux. Through others the graphite protudes to form a 'thermal column' which makes the slower, 'thermal' neutrons available for experimental use. Both types of opening in the concrete are suitable shielded with cadmium and lead.

The sequence of nuclear changes is:

1. A single neutron is absorbed by a ^{235}U nucleus and causes instability leading to
   (i) fission fragments which lose most of their kinetic energy in the uranium metal itself,
   (ii) γ-rays which are absorbed mainly by the structure and shielding,
   (iii) fast neutrons with energies of 0.5 to 1 MeV.
2. The fast neutrons lose energy by every collison with a carbon nucleus; they are thus continuously retarded and deflected back into the uranium rods.
3. As the neutrons slow down their chance of capture increases. They are captured (i) by the structural materials of the pile and lost to the process; (ii) by the ^{238}U, through resonance absorption, leading to the production of ^{239}Pu; and (iii) by the ^{235}U ($\sim 0.7\%$ of natural uranium) leading to fissions which generate about 2.5 fresh neutrons for every neutron captured. The geometry of the pile ensures that one of the fresh neutrons is captured by another ^{235}U, thus maintaining a steady rate of fission of these nuclei and a steady neutron flux.

The sequence of nuclear reactions leading to the formation of $^{239}_{94}Pu$ is:

$$^{238}_{92}U + ^{1}_{0}n \longrightarrow ^{239}_{92}U + \gamma;$$
$$^{239}_{92}U \longrightarrow ^{239}_{93}Np + \beta^{-};$$
$$^{239}_{93}Np \xrightarrow[2.3\ days]{} ^{239}_{94}Pu + \beta^{-}.$$

The nuclide $^{239}_{94}Pu$ is an α-emitter with a half-life of 2.1×10^4 years.

Accumulation in the uranium of fission products, many of which absorb neutrons strongly, would eventually reduce the neutron flux below the intensity required to maintain the nuclear chain reaction. Accordingly the uranium is removed after a certain period and processed chemically, ^{137}Cs, ^{90}Sr and the plutonium being extracted (p. 573). Some neptunium, the long-life $^{237}_{93}$Np, is also obtained:

$$^{238}_{92}U + ^1_0n \longrightarrow ^{237}_{92}U + 2^1_0n;$$

$$^{237}_{92}U \xrightarrow[\text{6.8 days}]{} ^{237}_{93}Np + \beta^-.$$

This, too, is an α-emitter with a half-life of 2.25×10^6 years and, unlike the highly active β-emitter $^{239}_{93}$Np with a half-life of only 2.3 days, is particularly suitable for chemical work. Curium and americium also appear as the result of (n,γ) reactions involving plutonium:

$$^{239}_{94}Pu + ^1_0n \rightarrow ^{240}_{94}Pu \ (\alpha, \ 6000 \text{ years}) + \gamma;$$

$$^{240}_{94}Pu + ^1_0n \rightarrow ^{241}_{94}Pu + \gamma;$$

$$^{241}_{94}Pu \rightarrow ^{241}_{95}Am \ (\alpha, \ 500 \text{ years}) + \beta^-;$$

$$^{241}_{95}Am + ^1_0n \rightarrow ^{242}_{95}Am + \gamma;$$

$$^{242}_{95}Am \rightarrow ^{242}_{96}Cm \ (\alpha, \ 162 \text{ days}) + \beta^-.$$

The use of cyclotron-accelerated α-particles provides another method of producing plutonium, curium, americium, berkelium and californium:

$$^{241}_{95}Am + ^4_2He \rightarrow ^{243}_{97}Bk + 2^1_0n;$$
$$\text{(K capture, 4.8 h)}$$

$$^{246}_{96}Cm + ^4_2He \rightarrow ^{242}_{98}Cf + 8^1_0n.$$
$$(\alpha, \ 45 \text{ min})$$

Stripped carbon atoms (C^{6+}) accelerated in the cyclotron have recently led to some interesting transmutations. These particles have energies about 6 times those of deuterons under similar operating conditions. Examples are

$$^{238}U \ (^{12}C, \ 6n) \ ^{244}Cf, \text{ and } ^{238}U \ (^{12}C, \ 4n) \ ^{246}Cf.$$

Plutonium occurs in pitchblende to the extent of about 10^{-11} of the uranium present. The quantity, though extremely small, is nevertheless too high to be accounted for by neutrons from the ^{235}U present acting on ^{238}U. The extra neutrons required may result from (α,n) reactions on the lighter elements present.

Separation of transuranic elements by elution from ion exchange resins

Ion exchange resins provided the means of discovering elements beyond curium. A cationic resin, kept at 87° by boiling trichloroethylene, forms a column on which is poured 0.1 ml of a solution of the transuranic elements in $0.05\,M$ HCl. Elution with $0.4\,M$ ammonium citrate, or ammonium α-hydroxybutyrate, gives peaks of activity; the order of removal of the respective 3+ ions is the reverse of their atomic number (Fig. 233). In this way einsteinium, element 99 (1952), fermium, element 100 (1954) and mendelevium, element 101 (1955) were separated by Seaborg and his collaborators. The nuclide $^{256}_{101}$Md which undergoes spontaneous fission has a half-life of 3.5 hours. That this process could be studied so effectively on a sample consisting of 17 atoms gives an idea of the powerful experimental methods now available. More recently element 102 has been identified.

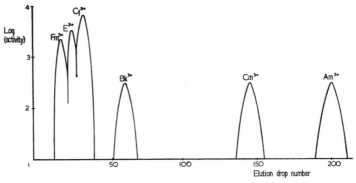

Fig. 233. Order of elution of trans-plutonium terpositive ions.

The metals

The actinides are base metals which require the reduction of a chloride or fluoride with sodium or barium for their isolation. Neptunium, for example, has been made by reducing its trifluoride with barium vapour at 1200°. The need for such drastic methods is understandable because the heats of formation of the M^{4+} ions are as much as three times greater than that of the Pt^{4+} ion. The metals are silvery white and, except thorium and americium, have high densities.

TABLE 100

ATOMIC VOLUMES OF THE ACTINIDES

Th	Pa	U	Np	Pu	Am
21	14.7	13	13.5	*12.1	23

* α-phase-monoclinic.

The sudden increase in atomic volume at americium is interesting and paralleled by a similar increase at the corresponding lanthanide, europium. It probably results from the change to close-packed M^{2+} ions, from the M^{3+} ions of the preceding elements.

Uranium is reactive chemically, igniting spontaneously in fluorine and, at about 250°, in chlorine, bromine and iodine vapour. It combines with sulphur at 500° and nitrogen at 1000°. The metal dissolves readily in hydrochloric and sulphuric acids giving U^{IV} salts; nitric acid renders the metal passive. In this uranium resembles the metals of Group VIA.

Oxides, hydroxides and oxoacids

For the actinide series up to curium, the ignition of the nitrate yields the dioxide, except for uranium where U_3O_8 is formed. Uranium dioxide is made by reducing U_3O_8 in hydrogen. The dioxides have the fluorite structure. The evidence for monoxides is limited to the identification of UO, NpO, PuO and AmO as films on the respective metals; they are reported to have NaCl lattices. Curium appears to have the oxide Cm_2O_3, and plutonium forms a similar compound. The neptunium oxide, Np_3O_8, corresponding to U_3O_8, is made by the action of NO_2 at $\sim 300°$ on the hydroxide precipitated from Np^V or Np^{VI} solutions. For plutonium, PuO_2 is the highest oxide yet produced. Non-stoichiometric phases (p. 158) are common among the actinide oxides.

The addition of ammonia to separate solutions of Np, Pu and Am salts precipitates respectively $Np(OH)_4$, a mixture of $Pu(OH)_4$ with $Pu(OH)_3$, and $Am(OH)_3$. Only for actinides beyond plutonium is the tri-hydroxide, $M(OH)_3$, sufficiently stable to be isolated.

Both uranium(VI) and plutonium(VI) form oxoanions. Uranium gives mono-, di-, tri-, tetra-, penta- and hexa-uranates; the common diuranates, $M_2U_2O_7$, correspond only formally to the dichromates. Barium hydroxide precipitates the triplutonate, $BaPu_3O_{10}$, from solutions containing PuO_2^{2+}.

Halides

Uranium hexafluoride is important because it is used to separate ^{235}U from ^{238}U by means of the diffusion of this compound. The pale yellow crystals melt at 69° under 2 atmospheres pressure and have a vapour pressure of 760 mm at 56°, so that they are very easily sublimed. The hexafluoride is made by the action of fluorine on the metal in the presence of some chlorine; otherwise UF_4 is formed. Fluorination by ClF_3 is also employed. UF_6 is stable to air, oxygen, chlorine and iodine, but is easily hydrolysed and readily reduced to the tetrafluoride by hydrogen at the ordinary temperature. The molecule is octahedral and the dipole moment zero. The hexafluorides of neptunium and plutonium, the first of which has an orange and the second a dark brown colour, have a similar molecular structure.

The uranyl halides UO_2X_2 are very stable, being salts of the UO_2^{2+} ion and not covalent molecules like SO_2Cl_2 and CrO_2Cl_2. The corresponding neptunium and plutonium compounds exist in solution.

TABLE 101

THE HALIDES OF SOME ACTINIDES

	Ac	Th	U	Np	Pu	Am	Cm
VI			UF_6, UCl_6	NpF_6	PuF_6		
V			UF_5, UCl_5	—			
IV		ThX_4	UX_4	NpF_4, $NpCl_4$, $NpBr_4$	PuF_4	AmF_4	CmF_4
III	AcF_3, $AcCl_3$, $AcBr_3$		UX_3	NpX_3		PuX_3	AmX_3	CmF_3
II	—		—	—	—	—	—

X = F, Cl, Br and I.

Substances empirically represented by UF_5 and UCl_5 are known but not their structures. UCl_5 disproportionates readily:

$$2UCl_5 \rightarrow UCl_6 + UCl_4.$$

The crystalline tetrahalides of uranium are all stable and are the normal result of either direct union of the elements or action of the halogen acid on the metal. Neptunium tetrafluoride, a pale green solid, is also known:

$$4NpF_3 + O_2 + 4HF \xrightarrow{500°} 4NpF_4 + 2H_2O.$$

The corresponding chloride and bromide are made by heating the dioxide with carbon tetrachloride and aluminium bromide respectively. The only tetrahalide of plutonium yet isolated is the fluoride, PuF_4, although the tetrachloride appears to exist in solution. Americium forms a tetrafluoride and also a complex fluoride, $KAmF_5$.

With the exception of thorium, the actinides form trihalides. For uranium and neptunium, reduction of the MX_4 compounds with hydrogen is necessary, but for the elements from plutonium onwards the action of the carbon tetrahalide or aluminium halide on the dioxide is usually employed. The trifluorides are insoluble but the rest dissolve to give solutions containing M^{3+} ions.

Other compounds

The sulphides are made by dry methods and are all compounds of lower charge number.

The disulphides of thorium and uranium are essentially covalent compounds; but materials of the formula M_2S_3 appear to be semi-metallic, except for Pu_2S_3 which is covalent. This again emphasises the increasing stability of compounds with the charge number $+3$ as the atomic number increases.

TABLE 102

THE SULPHIDES OF SOME ACTINIDES

Ac	Th	U	Np	Pu
Ac_2S_3	ThS Th_2S_3 ThS_2	US U_2S_3 UOS US_2	Np_2S_3 NpOS	Pu_2S_3

Plutonium, like uranium, forms both a mononitride and a monocarbide; all have the sodium chloride structure:

$$PuCl_3 + NH_3 \xrightarrow[\text{temp.}]{\text{high}} PuN + 3HCl.$$

Uranium also forms a dinitride, UN_2, with a fluorite structure.

Uranium usually dissolves in acids to give U^{IV} salts. The sulphate crystallises as the tetrahydrate which heating converts to the hemihydrate, but further loss of water leads to decomposition. Plutonium sulphate is similar. Double sulphates of formula $(M^I)_4 M^{IV}(SO_4)_4$ (where $M^I = NH_4$, K or Rb and $M^{IV} = Th^{IV}$, U^{IV} or Pu^{IV}) have been made. Migration experiments indicate that these are true complexes.

Plutonium forms a nitrate of Pu^{IV} but the only nitrates of uranium are those of U^V and U^{VI}, namely $UO_2(NO_3)$ and $UO_2(NO_3)_2$.

Actinide ions

Table 103 should be compared with that giving the charges associated with the lanthanide ions (p. 423). The comparison suggests that the 5f are more easily removed than the 4f electrons. However, Jørgensen (1959) concluded from the spectra of actinide ions that there are only 5f electrons outside the radon shell of the ions with a charge greater than $+3$. He holds there is no necessary connexion between the presence of f electrons and the dominant $+3$ charge number. This is very relevant in view of other oxidation states which are being found for the lanthanides (p. 429). The most common ion in both series is $3+$, once thought to be the only charge displayed by curium, and still the only one shown by gadolinium, the corresponding lanthanide. The ions shown in parentheses do not occur in solution, though all the elements, with the exception of protactinium, behave as base metals and produce simple hydrated cations.

TABLE 103

IONIC CHARGES SHOWN BY ACTINIDES

Ac	Th	Pa	U	Np	Pu	Am	Cm	Bk	Cf
	(2)								
3	(3)	(3)	3	3	3	3	3	3	3
	4	4	4	4	4	(4)	(4)	4	
		(5)	(5)	(5)	(5)	(5)			
			(6)	(6)	(6)	(6)			

Oxo-ions containing M^{VI} are UO_2^{2+}, NpO_2^{2+} and PuO_2^{2+} and those containing M^V are UO_2^+, NpO_2^+ and PuO_2^+.

TABLE 104

THE REDOX POTENTIALS OF THE VARIOUS ION COUPLES (v)

Couple	U	Np (in M HCl)	Pu (in M HCl)	Am
M^{IV}/M^{III}	−0.63	+0.14	+0.97	+2.4
M^V/M^{IV}	+0.55	+0.74	+1.13	
M^{VI}/M^V	+0.06	+1.14	+0.91	

The redox potentials of the various ion couples are interesting because they show an increase in the stability of ions of lower charge generally, and particularly of the Am^{3+} ion, with atomic number. The stability of Np^{5+} is also noteworthy.

In all known compounds, actinium appears as Ac^{3+} with the radon structure, the hydrated ion occurring in aqueous solutions of its salts. Thorium salts give Th^{4+} ions. The identification of halides of Th^{II} and Th^{III} is questioned; solids resulting from the thermal decomposition of ThI_4 liberate hydrogen from water, the thorium being oxidised to Th^{IV}, presumably, if a lower iodide is formed, by the reaction:

$$2\, ThI_3 + 2\, H^+ \rightarrow 2\, Th^{4+} + 6\, I^- + H_2.$$

The great stability of Th^{4+} has been urged against the concept of an actinide series; undoubtedly, if the reaction just mentioned is substantiated, the element is behaving more like hafnium than cerium. Furthermore, evidence for 5f electrons in the thorium atom in its ground state is lacking and an electronic configuration completely analogous to that of the corresponding lanthanide does not appear until uranium is reached. But this does not detract from the general usefulness of classifying these elements as an actinide series. The relative energies of the d and f electrons in the actinides and lanthanides are not the same, and the filling of the 5f level need not necessarily start at thorium because the filling of the 4f level begins at cerium.

Uranium forms stable uranyl salts which give the UO_2^{2+} ion in solution, as indicated by absorption and Raman spectra. Polarographic reduction of a uranyl salt gives (a) a first stage at a half-wave potential little affected by acidity, presumably representing a simple electron transfer:

$$UO_2^{2+} + e \rightleftharpoons UO_2^+;$$

(b) a second wave, with an inflexion at half its height, which is irregular below this point and logarithmic above it, indicating a stepwise reduction:

$$\text{(i)} \quad UO_2^+ + 4H^+ + e \rightleftharpoons U^{4+} + 2H_2O,$$
$$\text{(ii)} \quad U^{4+} + e \rightleftharpoons U^{3+}.$$

In support of this view, the reduction of U^{IV} at a mercury cathode is reversible, whereas that of U^V is irreversible, and also heavily dependent on the hydrogen ion concentration. Solutions containing both UO_2^+ and U^{3+} ions undergo rapid oxidation in air, as is to be expected from the redox potentials.

Neptunium gives a series of reactions analogous to those of uranium, but the individual stabilities are different, thus NpO_2^+ is particularly stable (Table 104). A reagent as powerful as cerium(IV) sulphate is required to oxidise NpO_2^+ to NpO_2^{2+}. Furthermore, the disproportionation of the NpO_2^+ ion occurs only very slowly in solution:

$$2NpO_2^+ + 4H^+ \rightleftharpoons NpO_2^{2+} + Np^{4+} + 2H_2O.$$

The product of the concentrations $[NpO_2^{2+}]$ and $[Np^{4+}]$ is only about 0.025 of the concentration of $[NpO_2^+]^2$ at $25°$.

Plutonium also forms a similar series of cations. In this instance the redox potentials indicate that Pu^{4+} is the most stable ion. Hot bromate solutions are required to oxidise it to PuO_2^{2+}, but reduction to the terpositive state is easier than with U^{4+} and Np^{4+} ions, being effected by sulphur dioxide, hydrazine or the iodide ion. In solution, the Pu^{3+} ion is not oxidised by air. PuO_2^{2+} ions behave similarly to UO_2^{2+} ions when reduced at a dropping mercury cathode. The readily crystallised complexes, sodium plutonyl, $Na[PuO_2A\bar{c}_3]$, sodium uranyl, $Na[UO_2A\bar{c}_3]$, and sodium neptunyl, $Na[NpO_2A\bar{c}_3]$, acetates are isomorphous. The $5+$ ion of plutonium is much less stable than that of neptunium, a well-defined compound of PuO_2^+ being unknown. Disproportionation occurs at all acidities:

$$2PuO_2^+ + 4H^+ \rightleftharpoons PuO_2^{2+} + Pu^{4+} + 2H_2O.$$

Because the redox potentials for the couples Pu^{IV}/Pu^{III} and Pu^V/Pu^{IV} are about the same in solutions of moderate acidity, the $6+$, $4+$ and $3+$ ions can coexist in about the same concentrations:

$$3Pu^{4+} + 2H_2O \rightleftharpoons PuO_2^{2+} + 4H^+ + 2Pu^{3+}.$$

This equilibrium is considerably upset by the α-particle emission of the plutonium.

Neither americium nor curium forms a series of ions similar to those of uranium, neptunium and plutonium. The redox potential of the Am^{IV}/Am^{III} couple, calculated from such thermodynamic data as the heats of reaction of the respective oxides with nitric acid, agree well with the observation that the Am^{3+} ion is not oxidised even by Ag^{2+} ions in $2N HNO_3$, for which the redox potential is in excess of $+2$ volts. Reduction of the Am^{3+} ion is brought about by sodium amalgam but not by zinc amalgam. Thus the $3+$ ion offers considerable resistance to both reduction and oxidation. The corresponding curium ion is, however, unaffected by reagents which oxidise or reduce terpositive americium.

Although the outermost electrons in the actinides are apparently more readily available for bonding than those in the lanthanides, even M^{VI} occurring, the preference for M^{III} increases with atomic number. Redox potentials indicate that this trend is still more rapid than in the lanthanides. The fact that Cm^{III} is dominant (cf. gadolinium in the lanthanides), and that berkelium gives also Bk^{IV}, lends support to the suggestion that these elements have a half-filled 5f shell with its characteristic stability.

Isomorphism in the actinide group

Isomorphism among compounds of the actinides is common and only a few examples need be given. The dioxides, MO_2, of thorium, uranium, neptunium, plutonium and americium all have a fluorite lattice. The trihalides of the transuranic elements are isomorphous not only with the corresponding trihalides of actinium and uranium but also with those of the lanthanides. Isomorphism is also exhibited in many complex halides; thus thorium, uranium and plutonium form the isomorphous series KMF_5, and, together with neptunium, they also form another, KM_2F_9. Plutonium has a number of complex nitrates $M_2^I Pu(NO_3)_6$, of which the ammonium salt $(NH_4)_2Pu(NO_3)_6$ is isomorphous not only with $(NH_4)_2Th(NO_3)_6$ but with $(NH_4)_2Ce(NO_3)_6$ too. Examples might be multiplied to show that similarities exist between the crystalline compounds of the actinides comparable with those displayed by the lanthanides.

Absorption spectra

Further evidence for structures based on 5f electrons is furnished by the absorption spectra of compounds of the elements. The absorption bands are sharply defined and may be explained, as for the lanthanides, by characteristic atomic transitions involving 5f electrons rather than those engaged more actively in bond formation. It is noteworthy that the spectra of the 3+ ions show particular resemblances to their lanthanide analogues, for example U^{3+} and Nd^{3+}, Pu^{3+} and Sm^{3+}, and particularly Am^{3+} and Eu^{3+}.

Magnetic properties

A comparison of the paramagnetism of appropriate ions of the transuranic elements with that of the corresponding lanthanide ions discloses a remarkable parallelism (Fig. 234).

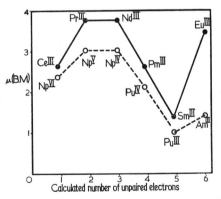

Fig. 234. Paramagnetism of transuranic and lanthanide ions.

The moments of the lanthanide ions agree closely with theoretical prediction (p. 78) but those of the transuranic ions are somethat lower than expected, possibly because the 5f electrons of the latter are less effectively screened from the crystal field which quenches the orbital contribution than the 4f electrons of the former. The variation of paramagnetic moment with the number of unpaired electrons differs radically from that which occurs in the first and second transition series where the maximum is five (p. 131). The magnetic properties lend credence to a 5f structure: those of UCl_3 indicate $5f^3$ for U^{III} (cf. Nd^{III}) and those of PuO_2^{2+}, with two unpaired electrons, indicate $5f^2$ for Pu^{VI}. Moments corresponding to a $5f^4$ configuration (Fig. 235) have been observed for Pu^{IV} compounds (Dawson, 1952). Some moments of U^{IV} compounds appear to be so close to spin-only values however, as to suggest an ion with a $6d^2$ (Fig. 235) rather than a $5f^2$ structure (cf. ligand field theory, p. 131). But more evidence is required before the absence of 5f electrons in U^{IV} can be safely accepted.

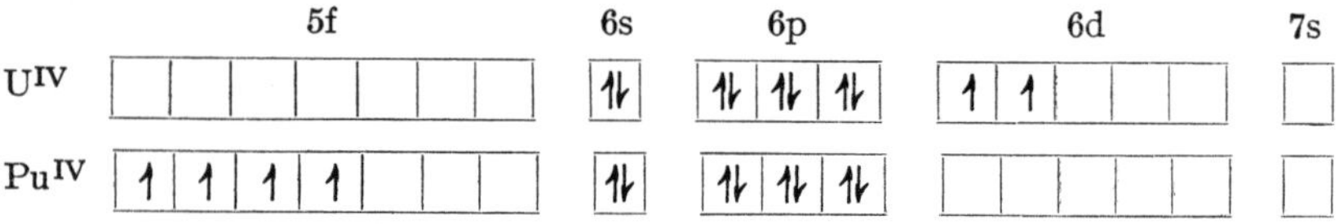

Fig. 235. Electron configuration of U^{IV} and Pu^{IV}.

Chapter 29

Titanium, Zirconium and Hafnium

GROUP IVA

The Gp. IVA transition elements, titanium, zirconium and hafnium all have the $(n - 1)d^2ns^2$ electron configuration. They differ from the transition elements of the later groups in their tendency to form M^{IV} compounds to the exclusion of those in which lower charge numbers occur; especially is this true of Zr and Hf.

TABLE 105

SOME PROPERTIES OF GROUP IVA ELEMENTS

	Ti	Zr	Hf
Electron configuration	$3d^24s^2$	$4d^25s^2$	$(4f^{14})5d^26s^2$
Atomic number	22	40	72
Atomic radius (Å)	1.32	1.45	1.44
Ionic radius, M^{4+} (Å)	0.68	0.74	0.75

The atomic and ionic radii of Hf are very close to those of Zr, in spite of the great increase in atomic number. This is a result of the lanthanide contraction (p. 75), which accompanies the filling of the 4f shell (completed at Lu, the element preceding Hf), and is largely responsible for the exceptional similarity between Zr and Hf, unmatched by a pair of elements in any other subgroup.

TABLE 106

IONISATION AND ELECTRODE POTENTIALS OF GROUP IVA ELEMENTS

	Ti	Zr	Hf
Ioniation potential I 1 (eV)	6.83	6.95	5.5
,, ,, 2 ,,	13.63	13.97	14.8
,, ,, 3 ,,	28.14	24.00	
,, ,, 4 ,,	43.24	33.8	
E_h° MO^{2+}/M (V)	—0.95	—1.53	—1.68

The first ionisation potentials are all fairly low and those for ionisation up to M^{4+} are known. As usual, the small $4+$ ion which is invoked in M^{IV} compounds does not exist as such, but takes a considerable share of the electron density of the ligands. Nor does the M^{4+} ion exist in aqueous solution; the most stable cation is the complex ion MO^{2+} and the redox potentials above refer to the MO^{2+}/M couples. The metals are evidently strongly reducing; but they are so easily rendered passive that they are not very reactive at room temperature and have a remarkable resistance to corrosion.

Ti^{4+}, the smallest of the M^{4+} ions, appears in tetrahedral molecules such as $TiCl_4$, although the bonds will really be predominantly covalent (as is suggested by the fact that $TiCl_4$ is a liquid at room temperature). Ti^{IV} is also found in complex ions such as the octahedral $TiCl_6^{2-}$. Ti^{III} compounds are known and the oxidation state occurs in aqueous solution as the $Ti(H_2O)_6^{3+}$ ion, an octahedral complex with a paramagnetic susceptibility which indicates a single d_ε electron. Aqueous solutions containing Ti^{III} are violet and result when titanium(IV) compounds are reduced; the redox potential for Ti^{4+}/Ti^{3+} is about 0.05 V. Such solutions may in turn be used for reducing Fe^{3+} to Fe^{2+}, chlorates and perchlorates to chlorides, and nitro-compounds to amines.

Zr^{IV} and Hf^{IV} salts also exist as tetrahedral and octahedral complexes; but, since their M^{4+} radii are larger than Ti^{3+}, the compounds are more ionic. $ZrCl_4$, for example, is a crystalline solid with considerable ionic character, subliming at 331°. When these compounds are reduced in aqueous solution they yield not simple M^{3+} ions but complex ions such as ZrO^+ and $ZrCl_2^+$. Examples of other complexes in which Zr^{IV} occurs are $Zr(OEt)_4$ and the anions ZrO_4^{2-} and ZrF_6^{2-}. Although various interstitial hydrides are known they are non-stoichiometric and there is no evidence for the existence of compounds in which the metals occur with charge number $+2$. The solids formulated as TiN, TiB, ZrN (p. 455) are also without exact stoichiometry and do not indicate the occurrence of a charge number of $+3$.

Preparation and properties of the elements

The elements, as many true metals, have h.c.p. lattices. Their atomic radii and atomic volumes are similar, especially those of zirconium and hafnium. As the atomic weight of Hf (178.6) is almost twice that of Zr (91.2) their densities differ by a factor of two. Titanium is not only much less dense than Zr but also than succeeding elements of the first transition series. The metals are typical transition elements in their high m.p. and b.p.

Titanium (0.6% of the earth's crust) is abundant but difficult to extract. It is commonly associated with siliceous rocks, but the principal workable ores are ilmenite, $FeTiO_3$, and rutile, a tetragonal form of TiO_2. Interest in the element has been stimulated by the need for a light, strong, corrosion-resistant metal for supersonic aircraft, but its manufacture has posed complex metallurgical problems. Reduction of TiO_2 with carbon is unsatisfactory because the very stable carbide is produced. The ease with which the metal combines with both oxygen and nitrogen at elevated temperatures makes other high-temperature reduction methods difficult. Only by the introduction of the following process (Kroll, 1940) has the commercial production of titanium become possible.

Chlorine is passed over ilmenite or rutile heated to $\sim 900°$ with carbon and the $TiCl_4$ vapour formed is condensed.

$$2TiO_2 + 3C + 4Cl_2 \rightarrow 2TiCl_4 + 2CO + CO_2$$

The liquid (b.p. 136°) is purified by fractional distillation. The vapour at atmospheric pressure is reduced with molten Mg at 800°, air being excluded by argon.

$$TiCl_4 + 2Mg \rightarrow Ti + MgCl_2 \quad (\triangle H = -115.6 \text{ kcal}; \quad \triangle G = -108.1 \text{ kcal})$$
(liquid) solid) (solid) (solid)

The molten $MgCl_2$ is tapped from the reactor when $\sim 60\%$ of the Mg has been used to allow the $TiCl_4$ to continue to attack the Mg until 85% of the metal has reacted. Further consumption of Mg is undesirable since its presence prevents the reactions:

$$3TiCl_4 + Ti \rightarrow 4TiCl_3; \qquad 2TiCl_3 + Ti \rightarrow 3TiCl_2.$$

The cold solid may be removed from the reactor mechanically and the Mg and $MgCl_2$ leached from the chips with dilute acid, or, without removal, the Mg and $MgCl_2$ may be distilled from the Ti under a high vacuum.

Reduction with molten sodium is also much employed:

$$TiCl_4 + 4Na \rightarrow Ti + 4NaCl \quad (\triangle H_{298} = -203.6 \text{ kcal}; \quad \triangle G_{298} = -194.0 \text{ kcal})$$
(liquid) (solid) (solid) (solid)

Arrangements are made for all the Na to be converted to NaCl and to end with a slight excess of $TiCl_4$. Most of the molten NaCl is forced out under argon pressure. The cold solid is removed from the reactor mechanically and treated with 2% HNO_3 to dissolve the impurities.

Ingots are made in a water-cooled copper crucible, by melting the metal with an arc struck between it and a compressed titanium sponge cathode, the operation being conducted in an atmosphere of argon. Very pure titanium can be made by the method of Van Arkel and De Boer in which TiI_4 vapour is decomposed on a hot wire.

The metal is unusual in igniting spontaneously in oxygen, at 25 atm. and room temperature, when a fresh surface is exposed by fracture. The reaction is self-propagating and leads to the complete combustion of massive pieces, through a superficial melting and rapid diffusion of the oxide into the metal leaving a new surface of metal for oxidation. Similarly ZrO_2 dissolves in molten Zr, and this metal also behaves like Ti; but Mg, Al, Nb and Ta, whose oxides have not this kind of solubility, do not show the phenomenon.

TABLE 107

SOME PROPERTIES OF GROUP IVA ELEMENTS

	Ti	Zr	Hf
Density (g/cc)	4.50	6.53	13.07
Atomic volume	10.64	14.0	13.7
Melting point (°C)	1725	1860	2200
Boiling point (°C)	3260	4750	

The mechanical properties of titanium are comparable with those of steel; it is more difficult to fabricate owing to the readiness with which it takes up, and is hardened and embrittled by, oxygen and nitrogen. Its strength, lightness, resistance to corrosion and the low thermal expansion have led to its employment in high-speed aircraft, naval and military projects and chemical research and industry.

The non-stoichiometric, interstitial cubic compounds TiB, TiB_2, TiC and TiN are very stable, strongly exothermic, and refractory. TiC is widely used in association with WC for tipping high-speed tools.

The principal ores of zirconium (0.025% of the lithosphere) are the silicate zircon, $ZrSiO_4$, and the oxide baddeleyite, ZrO_2. Treatment of these with carbon and chlorine at red heat gives $ZrCl_4$, which can be reduced with Mg in a modification of the Kroll process. For metal of higher purity the Van Arkel decomposition of ZrI_4 is used. The metal is much softer than titanium. Its principal uses at present are as a 'getter' to remove traces of oxygen and nitrogen from thermionic valves, in bullet-proof alloy steels and, because of its low cross-section for neutron capture, as the metal or one of its alloys for cladding metallic fuel elements in some atomic reactors. Hafnium must be separated as completely as possible (see below) from zirconium which is to be used in reactors, because of its high cross-section for neutron capture.

Hafnium, predicted from atomic number sequence, was the first element to be discovered by X-ray methods. Coster and Hevesy (1923) looked for and found it in zirconium minerals which usually contain about 0.1%, but occasionally up to 7%. Because of its very close resemblance to zirconium separation is difficult. Atomic weight determinations on zirconium made before 1923 were all too high through the presence of hafnium.

Both $HfCl_4$ and $ZrCl_4$ form surprisingly stable complexes with phosphoryl chloride, $(HfCl_4)_3(POCl_3)_2$ and $(ZrCl_4)_3(POCl_3)_2$, which afford a method of separating the elements because the boiling point of the first is 5° lower than the second. Fractional crystallisations of the hexafluoro-compounds, oxo-chlorides and oxalates have also been fairly successful, but a recent chromato-graphic separation (p. 569) has proved even better. Beyer, Jacobs and Masteller (1952) passed the chlorides in anhydrous methanol through a column of silica gel. A $1.9N$ solution of anhydrous HCl in methanol was used for elution, preferentially carrying forward the zirconium. The Hf was removed with $7N$ H_2SO_4. After two cycles a specimen of $HfCl_4$ 90% pure was obtained from a mixture which had contained only 2% of the hafnium compound. Solvent extraction (p. 572) from a acidified thiocyanate solution has also been successful (Fischer, 1947).

Reactions of the metals

Although unreactive at low temperatures, the metals combine directly at high temperatures with the halogens, oxygen, sulphur, nitrogen, carbon, boron and hydrogen. The interstitial hydrides are non-stoichiometric and not Ti^{II} or Zr^{II} compounds in a strict sense.

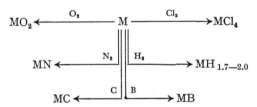

Fig. 236. The chemistry of Group IVA elements (M = Ti, Zr or Hf).

The metals decompose steam on strong heating. Titanium dissolves readily in cold H_2SO_4 and hot HCl to give Ti^{III} salts:

$$2Ti + 3H_2SO_4 \rightarrow Ti_2(SO_4)_3 + 3H_2.$$

Zirconium and hafnium dissolve rather less easily in these acids but all three metals dissolve in the presence of F^- ions, titanium giving salts of the Ti^{3+} ion, Zr and Hf salts of the MO^{2+} ion. The metals are remarkably resistant to corrosion by weakly acid solutions such as those of H_2S, SO_2, $FeCl_3$ (hot and cold) and even of H_2CrO_4. Hot and cold alkalis do not react with them.

Halides

The tetrachlorides are made by passing chlorine over the dioxides heated with carbon. $TiCl_4$ is a colourless, strongly fuming liquid but $ZrCl_4$ and $HfCl_4$ are solids. The vapours are monomeric. Water hydrolyses them:

$$ZrCl_4 + H_2O \rightarrow ZrOCl_2 + 2HCl.$$

This oxide chloride crystallises from the solution as the octahydrate, $ZrOCl_2.8H_2O$, which has a tetragonal structure containing $Zr_4(OH)_8^{8+}$ ions Phase studies of zirconium tetrachloride—alkali metal chloride systems indicate the formation of chlorozirconates, $M_2^IZrCl_6$. Ammonium chloro-titanate, $(NH_4)_2TiCl_6$, is precipitated when NH_4Cl is added to a solution of $TiCl_4$ in strong HCl.

Tetrafluorides result from the action of anhydrous HF on the chlorides:

$$TiCl_4 + 4HF \rightarrow TiF_4 + 4HCl.$$

The white solids form stable complexes:

$$ZrF_4 + 2KF \rightarrow K_2ZrF_6.$$

The bromides and iodides are made by direct combination of the elements. Some are coloured; $TiBr_4$ is yellow and TiI_4 red-brown, in accordance with the position of the ligands in the spectrochemical series (p. 134). They are solids of low m.p.; the crystals have a cubic lattice and contain tetrahedra molecules. Some bromo-complexes have been made, for instance $NH_4)_2TiBr_6.2H_2O$, but they are much less stable than the fluoro-compounds; iodo-complexes are unknown; the stability falls rapidly with the more easily polarisable halogens.

$TiCl_3$ is the most important trihalide. Its hexahydrate, like $CrCl_3.6H_2O$, (p. 546) has a green and violet form. Rubidium and caesium chlorides give complexes containing $TiCl_5^{2-}$ ions. The crystals, $M_2^ITiCl_5.H_2O$, are green but the solutions are violet. The colour change is associated with a change in the number of co-ordinated water molecules in the complex (cf. p. 469). TiF_3 is best made from titanium hydride and HF at 700°. It is a blue solid, stable to air, water and even concentrated H_2SO_4. Its magnetic susceptibility (1.75 B.M.) is appropriate to the Ti^{3+} ion with one d electron.

Pure $TiCl_2$ is a dark brown powder, spontaneously inflammable in air. The material is made (Gutmann, Nowotny and Ofner, 1955) by passing an electrode-less discharge through $TiCl_4$ mixed with hydrogen at low pressure. It sets free hydrogen from water.

Oxides

Both TiO_2 and ZrO_2 are manufactured for use as white pigments, TiO_2 from ilmenite by conversion to the sulphate, followed by hydrolysis (Fig.

237). Another method increasingly used is a vapour-phase oxidation of $TiCl_4$ attained by passing the vapour with air through a flame produced by burning a hydrocarbon in an excess of oxygen.

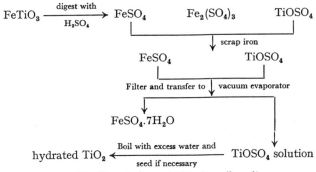

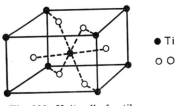

Fig. 237. Manufacture of TiO_2 from ilmenite.

The refractory oxide is normally white but resembles SnO_2 in becoming yellow when hot. It has three crystalline forms, the tetragonal rutile, the slender tetragonal prisms of anatase and the flat plates of orthorhombic brookite. The pigment grades are either anatase or rutile. Rutile has 6 : 3 co-ordination and is isomorphous with cassiterite, SnO_2 (Fig. 238). In anatase, linear molecules of TiO_2 are present (Fig. 239).

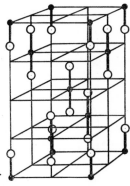

Fig. 238. Unit cell of rutile.

Fig. 239. Lattice of anatase.

Zirconia (m.p. 2700°) is used as a refractory and also as a pigment, mainly for white enamels. It is made from zircon (Fig. 240, (i)) or baddeleyite (Fig. 240, (ii)).

The hydrated oxides of titanium, zirconium and hafnium are soluble in acids, but heating produces oxides which resist solution, as it does with Al_2O_3 and Cr_2O_3.

White TiO_2 is converted to dark violet Ti_2O_3 by strong heating in hydrogen at atmospheric pressure. At very high pressures of hydrogen, the face-centred cubic, non-stoichiometric TiO is produced.

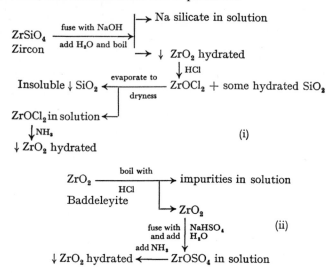

Fig. 240. Manufacture of zirconia, (i) from zircon, (ii) from baddeleyite.

A large number of sulphides, selenides and tellurides have been made by heating the elements together in evacuated silica tubes, and by the thermal decomposition of the higher compounds. The solids have compositions represented by MX, M_2X_3, MX_2, MX_3 and MX_4; not all the variants have been produced, and many of the phases are non-stoichiometric (p. 158).

Titanates

Hydrated TiO_2 is insoluble in alkalis but it reacts when heated with lithium, sodium and potassium carbonates to give compounds M_2TiO_3 and $M_2Ti_2O_5$:

$$K_2CO_3 + TiO_2 \rightarrow K_2TiO_3 + CO_2,$$
$$K_2CO_3 + 2TiO_2 \rightarrow K_2Ti_2O_5 + CO_2.$$

Some compounds formulated as titanates are complex oxides rather than salts. One of these, perovskite, $CaTiO_3$, gives its name to the perovskite structure (Fig. 239) of which other examples are $SrTiO_3$, $BaTiO_3$ and $CaZrO_3$. The barium compound, however, appears in four other crystalline forms: hexagonal, tetragonal, orthorhombic and trigonal. The tetragonal (s.g. 6.0) has a very high dielectric constant which varies markedly with temperature.

It is used for high value capacitances. One form has piezoelectric properties and is employed in transducers to convert electrical into mechanical energy, in ultra-sonic applications and in gramophone pick-ups. The material is made by heating $BaCO_3$ with TiO_2. It is ground, made to shape with a binding material, and fired like a ceramic.

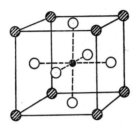

Fig. 241. Perovskite structure.

Nitrides

Both Ti and Zr form compounds of the M_3N_4 type. Ti_3N_4 is made by the reaction between $TiBr_4$ and KNH_2 in liquid ammonia. It decomposes on heating to give TiN and nitrogen. Zr_3N_4 is made by the following series of reactions:

$$ZrCl_4 + 4NH_3 \rightarrow Zr(NH_3)_4Cl_4 \xrightarrow{\;230°\;} Zr(NH_2)_4$$
$$\qquad\qquad\qquad\qquad\qquad\qquad\qquad\qquad \downarrow 300°$$
$$Zr_3N_4 \xleftarrow{\;350°\;} Zr(NH)_2$$

Although it is more stable than Ti_3N_4, strong heating converts it to ZrN. The interstitial nitrides, like the carbides TiC and ZrC, have the NaCl structure; alternatively they may be regarded as cubic close-packed arrangements of Ti atoms with nitrogens in the octahedral holes. As the metals have h.c.p. lattices, these have not been simply expanded to admit the N atoms.

Complexes

The tetrachlorides and tetrabromides of Ti and Zr (but not the fluorides) act as Lewis acids and give addition complexes particularly with oxygen compounds such as alcohols, ethers and carboxy compounds:

$$ROH + TiCl_4 \rightarrow \begin{array}{c} R \\ H \end{array}\!\!\!\!>\!\!O \rightarrow TiCl_4.$$

The Gp. IVA metals form chelates only with oxygen donors such as catechol and acetylacetone.

By far the most stable complexes are those which contain the anions TiF_6^{2-} and ZrF_6^{2-}; compounds containing the ZrF_7^{3-} anion are also known. This anion is an example of the rare 7 co-ordination.

Chapter 30

Vanadium, Niobium and Tantalum

GROUP VA

The atoms of these elements have five valence electrons in the configuration $(n - 1)d^3ns^2$ (V and Ta) or $(n - 1)d^4ns^1$ (Nb), the difference having no apparent effect on their chemistry.

TABLE 108

SOME PROPERTIES OF GROUP VA ELEMENTS

	V	Nb	Ta
Atomic number	23	41	73
Electron configuration	$3d^34s^2$	$4d^45s^1$	$5d^36s^2$
Atomic radius (Å)	1.22	1.34	1.34
Ionic radius, M^{4+} (Å)	0.64		
Ionic radius, M^{5+} (Å)	0.56	0.70	0.73

The first ionisation potentials lie in the usual range for transition metals (6—8 eV). The standard electrode potentials are, however, not accurately known because the metals are so easily rendered passive that the preparation of reversible electrodes is difficult. Although the approximate values show them to be strongly reducing, the metals are unreactive towards cold acids.

TABLE 109

IONISATION AND ELECTRODE POTENTIALS OF GROUP VA ELEMENTS

	V	Nb	Ta
Ionisation potential I (eV)	6.74	6.77	7.0
E°_h M^{4+}/M (V)	—1.5		
E°_h M^{5+}/M (V)		—0.6	—0.7

The close similarity of niobium and tantalum, especially in atomic and ionic radii, is reflected in their chemistry. In this respect they are rather like zirconium and hafnium. The elements resemble the rest of Gp. V only slightly, beyond showing (among others) valencies of 3 and 5, and are typical transition metals in the wide variety of their charge numbers. Thus, vanadium forms the halides VCl_2, VCl_3, VCl_4, VF_5. On the ionic or ligand field picture, vanadium appears with charge numbers rising from $+2$ to $+5$ as more electrons become involved in bonding. Charge number $+2$, with a d_ε^3 nonbonding group, occurs also in vanadium(II) oxide, an ionic crystal having the rock-salt lattice. Charge $+3$, with a d_ε^2 non-bonding group, is appropriate to octahedral complexes such as $V(NH_3)_6^{2+}$ which should, consequently, be slightly distorted (p. 133). Charge $+4$ in tetrahedral VCl_4 would leave one d_γ electron, again suggesting slight distortion, and charge $+5$ occurs in VF_5 which is a regular trigonal bipyramid (p. 126). Fluorine alone is sufficiently small and electronegative to produce the last condition.

Niobium and tantalum, although similar, are most commonly found with the charge number $+5$, forming pentahalides with all four halogens. With this charge tantalum is capable of 7 and even 8 co-ordination in the ions TaF_7^{2-} and TaF_8^{3-}. In most of these examples the actual bonding is largely covalent in character with a considerable return of electron density to the metal ion (p. 137). But in other compounds, such as the higher oxides, a purely covalent picture is appropriate. Thus in the series VO (rock-salt structure, p. 141), V_2O_3 (corundum structure, p. 375). VO_2 (rutile structure, p. 453), ending with V_2O_5 which has a structure composed of irregular tetrahedra sharing oxygen atoms, there is a steady fall in ionic character, the last member resembling the covalent (non-transitional) P_4O_{10}. This illustrates the general rule (p. 372) that as more electrons become involved in bonding the less complete is their transfer—the higher the charge number, the less the ionic character.

In solution, the most common ionic species of vanadium are V^{2+}, V^{3+}, VO^{2+} and VO_3^- and the stability of the last two ions is reflected in that of the metavanadates, which are usually more stable than the ortho-salts. Some representative information appears in Table 110.

TABLE 110

VANADIUM COMPOUNDS IN SOLUTION

Vanadium charge number	$+2$	$+3$	$+4$	$+5$
Most common corresponding species and appropriate reducing agents	$V^{2+} \xleftarrow[\text{or Cr}^{2+}]{\text{Zn}}$	$V^{3+} \xleftarrow[\text{or SO}_2]{\text{Sn}^{2+},\ Ti^{3+}}$	$VO^{2+} \xleftarrow{\text{Fe}^{2+}}$	VO_3^-
Colour in aqueous solution	Violet	Green	Blue	Colourless
Redox potential	-0.2 V	$+0.3$ V	$+1.0$ V	
Typical compounds	VSO_4	$V_2(SO_4)_3$	$VOCl_2$ $VOSO_4$	NH_4VO_3
Typical complexes	$V(CN)_6^{4-}$	$V(NH_3)_6^{3+}$	$VO(SCN)_4^{2-}$	

Although the most important charge number for both niobium and tantalum is $+5$, the ions Nb^{5+} and Ta^{5+} do not occur in solution. Reduction has been followed by a spectrophotometric examination of the liquid round a dropping mercury cathode: in $13N$ HCl the Nb^V probably appears in the complex ion $[NbOCl_4]^-$ or possibly $[NbOCl_5]^{2-}$; and reduction gives a charge number of $+4$ in the $[NbOCl_4]^{2-}$ ions of the orange solution. In $10N$ HCl, however, the colour on reduction is violet, suggesting a complex in which the charge number is lower (*cf.* V^{2+} which is violet). The reduced solutions readily oxidise in air but in an inert atmosphere they disproportionate to Nb^V and Nb^{III} compounds. Nb^{3+} ions do exist in the yellow solutions of the halides, in equilibrium with $NbCl_6^{3-}$:

$$Nb^{3+} + 6Cl^- \rightleftharpoons NbCl_6^{3-} \quad \text{(Cozzi and Vivarelli, 1955).}$$

The ease with which the three elements form a wide range of complex compounds and ions, not all of them thoroughly investigated, well illustrates the valence propensities of an incompletely filled d shell.

Preparation and properties of the elements

The elements all crystallise with the b.c.c. lattice. The small radius of the tantalum atom (inferred from measurements on the metal) is reflected in the high density of the element. The metals all have high m.p. (*cf.* iron, p. 490). In every transition series the m.p. rise to a maximum at the Gp.VIA element and then fall; and, as elements of the third transition series show the highest melting points, the m.p. of tantalum is exceeded by that of few other metals:

	Hf	*Ta*	*W*	*Re*	*Os*
°C	2200	2850	3370	3170	2700

Satisfactory figures for b.p. are not available.

TABLE 111

SOME PROPERTIES OF GROUP VA ELEMENTS

	V	*Nb*	*Ta*
Density (g/cc)	5.96	8.4	16.6
Atomic volume	8.4	10.8	10.9
Melting point (°C)	1700	2410	2850

Vanadium (0.02% of the lithosphere) is very widely distributed—more than 60 vanadium minerals have been described—but there are few workable ores. Carnotite, $K(UO_2)VO_4.xH_2O$, is a source of both uranium and vanadium; vanadinite, $Pb_5(VO_4)_3Cl$, isomorphous with apatite, is also worked-up for the element (Fig. 242).

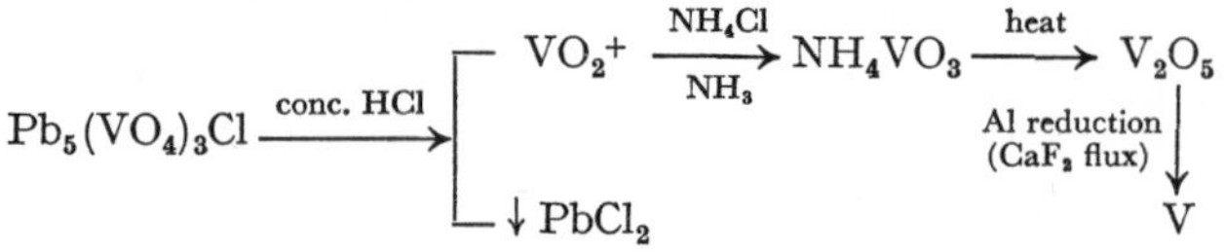

$$Pb_5(VO_4)_3Cl \xrightarrow{\text{conc. HCl}} \begin{cases} VO_2^+ \xrightarrow[\text{NH}_3]{\text{NH}_4\text{Cl}} NH_4VO_3 \xrightarrow[\substack{\text{Al reduction} \\ \text{(CaF}_2 \text{ flux)}}]{\text{heat}} V_2O_5 \\ \\ \downarrow PbCl_2 \end{cases} \qquad V$$

Fig. 242. Working-up of vanadinite.

Pure vanadium was made (Marden and Rich, 1927) by the reduction of V_2O_5 with calcium, some $CaCl_2$ being added to flux the lime formed:

$$V_2O_5 + 5Ca \rightarrow 5CaO + 2V.$$

McKechnie and Seybolt (1950) modified the process by adding I_2 instead of $CaCl_2$.

The metal forms a stable carbide, V_4C_3, and is used to refine the grain and carbide structure of steel and to improve its hardness at elevated temperatures. Amongst its numerous applications are incorporation in high-speed tool steels and exhaust-valve springs.

Niobium and tantalum (both rare, $\sim 3 \times 10^{-5}\%$) are extracted (Fig. 243) from a mineral which is a mixed niobate and tantalate of iron and manganese, (Fe,Mn) $(Nb,Ta,O_3)_2$. When it contains more niobium than tantalum it is known as columbite, otherwise as tantalite.

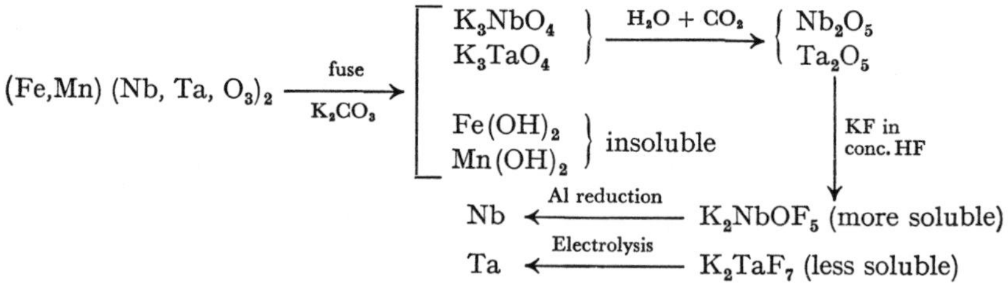

$$(Fe,Mn)\ (Nb,\ Ta,\ O_3)_2 \xrightarrow[K_2CO_3]{\text{fuse}} \begin{cases} \left.\begin{array}{l} K_3NbO_4 \\ K_3TaO_4 \end{array}\right\} \xrightarrow{H_2O + CO_2} \left\{\begin{array}{l} Nb_2O_5 \\ Ta_2O_5 \end{array}\right. \\ \\ \left.\begin{array}{l} Fe(OH)_2 \\ Mn(OH)_2 \end{array}\right\} \text{ insoluble} \end{cases}$$

$$\left.\begin{array}{l} Nb \xleftarrow{\text{Al reduction}} K_2NbOF_5 \text{ (more soluble)} \\ Ta \xleftarrow{\text{Electrolysis}} K_2TaF_7 \text{ (less soluble)} \end{array}\right. \xleftarrow{\substack{\text{KF in} \\ \text{conc. HF}}}$$

Fig. 243. Extraction of niobium and tantalum from columbite (tantalite).

Niobium and tantalum can also be separated by solvent extraction (p. 572); Nb is extracted almost quantitatively from HCl solution by methyldioctylamine in xylene while Ta remains in the acid. (Leddicotte and Moore, 1952). Chromatographic methods (p. 570) are also possible. Thus Mercer and Williams (1952) separated Nb and Hf from ores containing Ti and other metals. The fluorides were adsorbed on paper pulp; elution with methyl ethyl ketone saturated with water extracted the tantalum; equilibration of the column with a 1% solution of HF in the ketone arrested the movement of Ti, Zr and Sn; the niobium was then extracted with M.E.K. containing 12.5% of 40% aqueous HF.

Tantalum is resistant to corrosion and for this reason is employed both in chemical research and plant. The element has minimal foreign body reactions in human tissue and finds a place in surgery. It is used in electrolytic rectifiers and in capacitors. These applications are possible because of the thin anodic film that can be formed on the metal in oxoacid electrolytes.

Niobium is used to inhibit intergranular corrosion in austenitic steels and as carbide in hard carbide tool compositions. The metal is in commercial production and a more extensive use of it may be expected.

Reactions of the metals

Although unreactive at room temperature, the metals combine with other elements very readily on heating. All three burn in oxygen to the pentoxides. Vanadium combines on heating with chlorine to form VCl_4 and with nitrogen to give VN. The metals do not dissolve in cold mineral acids, but vanadium dissolves in perchloric acid and in ammonium persulphate to give metavanadic acid, HVO_3; it also dissolves slowly in hot concentrated sulphuric acid, hot HCl and hot dilute HNO_3. The metals all react with fused alkalis, hydrogen being liberated, vanadates and corresponding salts being formed.

Halides

Vanadium forms the halides and oxohalides tabulated in Table 112.

TABLE 112

HALIDES AND OXOHALIDES OF VANADIUM

Charge number	Fluorides	Chlorides	Bromides	Iodides
+2		VCl_2		VI_2
+3	VF_3	VCl_3	VBr_3	VI_3
	$VF_3.3H_2O$	$VCl_3.6H_2O$	VBr_36H_2O	VI_36H_2O
		VOCl	VOBr	
+4	VF_4	VCl_4		
	VOF_2	$VOCl_2$	$VOBr_2$	
+5	VF_5			
	VOF_3	$VOCl_3$	$VOBr_3$	

The only pentahalide, VF_5, is formed when VF_4 is heated to 600° in nitrogen.

Of the vanadyl trihalides, VOF_3 is a white solid, the other two are liquids:

$$2VF_3 + O_2 \xrightarrow{\text{heat}} 2VOF_3 \quad \text{solid m.p. } 300°$$

$$V_2O_5 + \text{carbon} \xrightarrow{\text{heat in Cl}_2} VOCl_3 \quad \text{liquid b.p. } 127°$$

$$V_2O_5 + \text{carbon} \xrightarrow{\text{heat in Br}_2} VOBr_3 \quad \text{liquid b.p. } 130°$$

Vanadyl trichloride is reduced to $VOCl_2$ on heating with zinc in a sealed tube, or on being passed with hydrogen through a red-hot tube; both are strongly reducing conditions. The brown liquid VCl_4 is made by direct combination of the elements, but VF_4 only by the action of dry HF on VCl_4:

$$4HF + VCl_4 \rightarrow VF_4 + 4HCl.$$

VBr_3 and VI_3 result from heating the respective elements together; VCl_3 is produced by the action of HCl gas on the metal. They are dark coloured solids which crystallise from water as green hexahydrates. The yellow crystalline VF_3 is obtained by prolonged heating of VCl_3 with dry HF.

When VCl_3 is heated to 800° in nitrogen, VCl_4 distils off leaving VCl_2:

$$2VCl_3 \rightarrow VCl_4 + VCl_2.$$

The residue dissolves in water to a violet solution which soon evolves H_2 and turns green. VI_2, obtained by heating the tri-iodide at reduced pressure, has been used in the preparation of pure vanadium by the Van Arkel method.

The important halides of niobium and tantalum are the pentahalides and the oxide halides $NbOCl_3$, $NbOBr_3$ and $TaOBr_3$. The pentahalides themselves are usually made by passing the halogen over the pentoxide heated with carbon; all of them have been prepared. Reduction of the pentachlorides is difficult. Heating with aluminium reduces $TaCl_5$ to the tetrachloride, the vapour of which deposits black crystals on cooling; these liberate hydrogen from water (Schäfer and Grau, 1954). The oxide fluorides NbO_2F and TaO_2F are of structural interest, having the ReO_3 lattice (p. 485) with a random distribution of O and F in the oxygen positions.

The halides form many complexes. In particular, fluorides and oxide fluorides combine with other metallic fluorides:

$$TaF_5 \rightarrow K_2TaF_7, Na_3TaF_8,$$
$$NbOF_3 \rightarrow Na_3NbOF_6, ZnNbOF_5.6H_2O.$$

Addition compounds with organic bases are also commonly formed, particularly by the pentachlorides:

$$NbCl_5 \rightarrow NbCl_5.6C_5H_{11}N \quad \text{(with piperidine)},$$
$$TaCl_5 \rightarrow TaCl_5.2C_5H_5N \quad \text{(with pyridine)}.$$

Oxides

Yellow, amphoteric V_2O_5 is used in the following surface catalyses: (i) oxidation of SO_2 to SO_3, (ii) oxidation of alcohol, (iii) hydrogenation of olefins.

The oxide dissolves in strong alkalis to form orthovanadates $M_3^IVO_4$. Some of these, ($Na_3VO_4.12H_2O$, $K_3VO_4.6H_2O$) can be crystallised from solutions at pH > 12. The addition of ammonium chloride to one of these solutions precipitates the metavanadate, NH_4VO_3, the heating of which gives the purest V_2O_5. When NH_4VO_3 is boiled for some time with 10% acetic acid, golden $NH_4V_3O_8$ separates. This is only one of a large number of polyvanadates, the commonest type being $M_4^IV_6O_{17}$. The formation of polyvanadate ions in solution is encouraged by lowering the pH.

A further lowering of the pH precipitates V_2O_5, but it redissolves to form the VO_2^+ ion. No simple salts of this ion have been isolated. Rossotti and Rossotti (1956) showed by spectrophotometric and potentiometric analysis that the VO_2^+ (aq.) ion alone existed in the pH range 0.5—1.3; between pH 1.3 and pH 6.5 the ions $H_2V_{10}O_{28}^{4-}$, $HV_{10}O_{28}^{5-}$ and $V_{10}O_{28}^{6-}$ were present in proportions dependent on pH.

The pentoxide is converted by reduction into the other oxides:

$$\underset{\text{(blue-black)}}{VO_2} \xleftarrow[\text{(heat)}]{SO_2} \underset{}{V_2O_5} \xrightarrow[\text{(heat)}]{H_2} \underset{\text{(black)}}{V_2O_3} \xrightarrow[\text{at low pressure}]{\text{heat with V}} VO$$

Glemser and Schwarzmann (1955) have identified by X-ray diffraction two compounds, $VO(OH)_2$ and $V_3O_5(OH)_4$. The rose-coloured crystals of the former are obtained on concentrating, in an inert atmosphere, the acid solution of a vanadate after reducing it with SO_2. Black crystals of the latter result from reducing vanadic acid with zinc in the presence of concentrated NH_4Cl. The basic trihydroxide $V(OH)_3$ is precipitated, green and flocculent, when ammonia is added to VCl_3 solution.

The pentoxides of niobium and tantalum are more difficult to reduce than V_2O_5.

$$Nb_2O_3 \xleftarrow[\text{(heat)}]{Mg} Nb_2O_5 \xrightarrow[\text{(high temp.)}]{H_2} NbO_2$$

$$Ta_2O_5 \xrightarrow[\text{(high temp.)}]{Mg} TaO_2$$

The pentoxides are more acidic than the dioxides ZrO_2 and HfO_2 of Gp.IVA. Fusion of Ta_2O_5 with caustic alkalis gives polytantalates of the type $M_8^ITa_6O_{19}$; meta- and pyrotantalates ($Ca(TaO_3)_2$, $Ca_2Ta_2O_7$) are also known.

Sulphides

The most stable sulphide of vanadium is V_2S_3, made by passing CS_2 over V_2O_5. It can be converted into V_2S_5 and VS.

$$V_2S_5 \xleftarrow[400°]{S} V_2S_3 \xrightarrow[1200°]{H_2} VS$$

Reduction of Ta_2O_5 with CS_2 at white heat gives TaS_2, the only sulphide of tantalum. NbS_2 is made by direct combination of the elements. The VS_4^{3-} ion is of interest because of its strong purple colour which is like that of MnO_4^-; yet neither of these ions involves partially filled d orbitals, to which strong colour can so often be ascribed.

Nitrides

The elements combine with nitrogen at high temperatures to give the hard, very stable nitrides VN, NbN and TaN. They are not attacked by cold acids, but steam reacts with them at high temperatures to give the oxides and NH_3. The unstable higher nitrides Ta_3N_5 and VN_2 are made by heating the appropriate halides with ammonia.

Carbides

Very hard carbides result from strongly heating the oxides with carbon. They are empirically MC and have the NaCl structure. Vanadium also forms V_4C_3 which has a defect structure, carbon atoms being missing from some of the lattice positions.

Oxoacid salts

There are no nitrates or carbonates of these metals, the only oxo-salts of importance being the sulphates of vanadium. A solid sulphate has not been obtained from a solution of V_2O_5, that is vanadium with charge number $+5$, in H_2SO_4, but reduction of the solution gives sulphates of vanadium with charge numbers $+4$, $+3$ and $+2$ respectively:

$$V_2^VO_5 \text{ in } H_2SO_4 \xrightarrow{SO_2} V^{IV}OSO_4 \xrightarrow[\text{sulphates}]{\text{alkali}} M_2^ISO_4.V^{IV}OSO_4.xH_2O$$

blue solution   dark blue double salts

$$\xrightarrow{Zn} V_2^{III}(SO_4)_3 \rightarrow \text{alums.}$$

$$\xrightarrow[\text{reduction}]{\text{cathodic}} V^{II}SO_4.7H_2O \text{ (isomorphous with } FeSO_4.7H_2O).$$

Chapter 31

Chromium, Molybdenum and Tungsten

GROUP VI A

Although the first two elements have the d^5s^1 electron configuration, chromium differs from the others in many respects, largely through its forming ions of lower charge (Cr^{2+}, Cr^{3+}) and of much lower radius (Cr^{4+}, Cr^{6+}). The ions Cr^{2+} and Cr^{3+} are related more closely to cations of the first transition series than to any derived from molybdenum and tungsten. Both the atomic and ionic radii of molybdenum and tungsten are, on the other hand, closely similar and, in consequence, the elements have many properties in common. The effect of the lanthanide contraction on the metals of the third transition series again is apparent, as it is in Gps. IVA and VA.

TABLE 113

SOME PROPERTIES OF GROUP VIA ELEMENTS

	Cr	Mo	W
Atomic number	24	42	74
Electron configuration	$3d^5\,4s^1$	$4d^5\,5s^1$	$5d^4\,6s^2$
Atomic radius M (Å)	1.17	1.29	1.30
Ionic radius M^{3+} (Å)	0.64		
M^{4+} (Å)	0.55	0.68	0.68
M^{6+} (Å)	0.52	0.62	0.67

The first ionisation potentials are not abnormally high for transition metals, but the metals are relatively inert since they easily become passive. Judged potentiometrically, chromium is a strong reducing agent, and molybdenum a moderate one; but again, as for the Gp VA metals, reactivity is inhibited by the formation of an adherent oxide film.

TABLE 114

IONISATION AND ELECTRODE POTENTIALS OF GROUP VIA ELEMENTS

	Cr	Mo	W
Ionisation potential I (eV)	6.76	7.18	7.98
E_h° M^{3+}/M (V)	−0.71	−0.2	
M^{4+}/M (V)			−0.05

Molybdenum and tungsten usually appear in their compounds with a formal charge $+6$, but the lower charge number $+3$ is preferred in chromium; salts containing the element in the state of higher charge are strong oxidising agents:

$$E_h^\circ \ Cr_2O_7^{2-}/Cr^{3+} = +1.3 \ V \ (pH, \ 0).$$

The value of the redox potential is strongly dependent on pH since the reversible electrode reaction is

$$Cr_2O_7^{2-} + 14H_3O^+ + 6e \ \rightleftharpoons 2Cr^{3+} + 21H_2O.$$

In alkalis the potential is much smaller and chromates can be made from Cr^{III} salts.

The Cr^{3+} ion is related in an interesting way to the other M^{3+} ions of the first transition series, namely Ti^{3+}, V^{3+}, Mn^{3+}, Fe^{3+} and Co^{3+}. The first two of these are reducing agents, the last three, following Cr^{3+}, are oxidising. Evidently Ti^{3+} with a $3d^1$ configuration, and V^{3+}, with a $3d^2$ configuration, tend to lose electrons to achieve an inert gas configuration; but Mn^{3+} ($3d^4$), Fe^{3+} ($3d^5$) and Co^{3+} ($3d^6$) tend to receive electrons and fill the 3d shell. The Fe^{3+} ion does this weakly because the half-filled d shell is rather stable; but Cr^{3+} ($3d^3$), between V^{3+} and Mn^{3+}, is less oxidising than even Fe^{3+}.

Chromium(II) ions are the strongest known reducing agents in aqueous solution,

$$E_h^\circ \ Cr^{3+}/Cr^{2+} = -0.4 \ V,$$

this redox potential being almost low enough to imply the reduction of water. A chromium(II) solution can remove oxygen completely from a mixture of gases.

The molybdenum compound with the empirical formula $MoCl_2$ does not possess the simple Mo^{2+} ion; its structure is $[Mo_6Cl_8]_4Cl_4$, the complex cation being cubic, with chlorine atoms at the eight corners and molybdenum atoms at the six face centres (Fig. 244). Tungsten forms a similar compound but, unlike the Mo complex which is stable in aqua regia, it is easily oxidised.

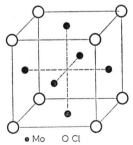

• Mo   O Cl

Fig. 244. Structure of $Mo_6Cl_8^{4+}$ ion.

There are compounds of terpositive molybdenum; they are strong reducing agents like those of Cr ^{I}. Corresponding simple compounds of tungsten are unknown, although complexes of W^{III} exist. Both Mo and W are quadripositive in chlorides, oxides and sulphides; MO_2 and WO_2 have a distorted rutile structure, and MoS_2 a layer lattice.

The +5 state is more common in molybdenum than in tungsten. $MoCl_5$, obtained by heating the metal in chlorine, is the highest chloride. Complex cyanides of both Mo and W, in which the charge number is +5, are exceptionally stable and cannot be oxidised even by $KMnO_4$. In these two elements, the +6 state is the one most readily assumed; it is exemplified by the hexafluorides, trioxides and acids (*e.g.* H_2MO_4). The hexachloride WCl_6 is unique in Gp. VIA, *cf.* UCl_6 formed by the actinide, uranium (p. 439).

The elements: separation and properties

TABLE 115

SOME PROPERTIES OF GROUP VIA ELEMENTS

	Cr	*Mo*	*W*
Density (g/cc)	7.1	10.4	19.3
Atomic volume	7.3	9.4	9.5
Melting point (°C)	1920	2620	3370

Molybdenum, like the common α-forms of chromium and tungsten, has a b.c.c. structure. In addition there are an h.c.p. β–Cr and a f.c.c. β–W. The metals are silvery-white and rather soft when pure, but their alloys can be particularly hard, *e.g.* stellite which contains Co, Cr and W. The m.p. are very high, every metal being at the peak of its own transition series and the m.p. of tungsten being consequently higher than that of any other metal.

Chromium (0.02% lithosphere) is produced from chromite, $FeCr_2O_4$. Direct reduction of this compound with carbon yields ferrochrome, an iron-chromium alloy used in making stainless steel. Chromium is obtained free from iron by converting the chromite first to a soluble chromate, then to the sesquioxide Cr_2O_3, and finally to metal:

$$FeCr_2O_4 \xrightarrow[\substack{heat\ strongly \\ in\ air}]{K_2CO_3} \begin{cases} K_2CrO_4 \xrightarrow[\substack{acidify,\ crystallise}]{dissolve\ in\ H_2O,\ filter,} K_2Cr_2O_7 \xrightarrow[\substack{NH_4Cl}]{heat\ with} Cr_2O_3 \\[2ex] Fe_2O_3\ (insoluble) \end{cases} \xrightarrow[\substack{reduce \\ with\ Al}]{} Cr$$

Electrolytic chromium is deposited from aqueous chromic acid acidified with sulphuric acid.

In the passive condition chromium is corrosion-resistant. It is therefore used as a protective electro-plating on ferrous metals and as a component of stainless steels. The metal dissolves slowly in cold dilute HCl and H_2SO_4, not at all in HNO_3, but rapidly in hot HCl and in hot conc. H_2SO_4. It reacts with Cl_2 and Br_2 when heated, with O_2 at the temperature of the oxy-hydrogen flame, and with H_2O at red heat:

$$Cr + 2HCl \rightarrow CrCl_2 + H_2; \quad 4Cr + 3O_2 \rightarrow 2Cr_2O_3;$$
$$2Cr + 3Cl_2 \rightarrow 2CrCl_3; \quad 2Cr + 3H_2O \rightarrow Cr_2O_3 + 3H_2.$$

Molybdenum ($10^{-4}\%$ of the lithosphere) occurs as molybdenite, MoS_2. The sulphide has a remarkably easy cleavage, similar to that of graphite; it also is used, suspended in oil, as a lubricant, particularly at high temperatures.

Molybdenite is the source of commercial molybdenum:

$$MoS_2 \xrightarrow{\text{roast in air}} MoO_3 \xrightarrow[\text{at high temperature}]{\text{reduce with } H_2, \text{ Al or C}} Mo.$$

The metal is used in toughening steel and for supporting tungsten filaments in electric lamps and other devices. It burns in oxygen at red heat:

$$2Mo + 3O_2 \rightarrow 2MoO_3;$$

and reacts with halogens to give the halides:

$$Mo + 3F_2 \rightarrow MoF_6,$$
$$2Mo + 5Cl_2 \rightarrow 2MoCl_5,$$
$$2Mo + 3Br_2 \rightarrow 2MoBr_3.$$

The metal dissolves in hot concentrated H_2SO_4 and aqua regia, but not in HF or in alkali solutions, though it reacts with fused alkalis.

Tungsten ($10^{-4}\%$ lithosphere) and its compounds are largely made from scheelite, $CaWO_4$, and wolframite, an isomorphous mixture of ferberite, $FeWO_4$, and huebnerite, $MnWO_4$. About 90% of the tungsten produced in the world (15,000 tons) is used in the manufacture of ferrous alloys, mainly tool steels. For this purpose ferro-tungsten is made by reducing high grade concentrates of ferberite, low in manganese, with aluminium powder (or ferro-silicon) in a thermit reaction:

$$3FeWO_4 + 8Al \rightarrow 3Fe + 3W + 4Al_2O_3.$$

Alternatively, wolframite or scheelite may be reduced with anthracite or coke in an arc furnace, with or without fluxing agents such as CaF_2.

A pure metal for lamp filaments (2–4% total production) is made by reducing pure WO_3 with hydrogen:

$$FeWO_4 \xrightarrow[\text{in air}]{\text{heat with Na}_2CO_3} \begin{cases} Na_2WO_4 \\ Fe_2O_3 \end{cases} \xrightarrow[\text{filter, acidify}]{\text{dissolve in H}_2O} H_2WO_4 \xrightarrow{\text{heat}} WO_3 \xrightarrow[\text{H}_2]{\text{reduce}} W$$

The reactivity is very similar to that of Mo but the chloride formed by the action of chlorine is the hexachloride, WCl_6, and the bromide by bromine is WBr_6.

Halides

The hexafluorides of molybdenum and tungsten are volatile liquids (respective b.p. 35.0°.and 19.6°), readily hydrolysed to molybdic and tungstic acids. WCl_6 is a solid. The metals form oxide chlorides, MO_2Cl_2. Chromyl chloride, familiar as a distinguishing test for a chloride, appears as a yellow distillate on heating a chloride with $K_2Cr_2O_7$ and concentrated H_2SO_4:

$$K_2Cr_2O_7 + 4KCl + 6H_2SO_4 \rightarrow 2CrO_2Cl_2 + 6KHSO_4 + 3H_2O.$$

The liquid is immediately hydrolysed by water, unlike the solid MoO_2Cl_2 which dissolves and ionises to MoO_2^{2+} and $2Cl^-$. The oxide fluorides $MoOF_4, MoO_2F_2$ and WOF_4 are solids; they form many oxofluoro-complexes $M_2^I(MoO_3F_2), M_2^I(MoO_2F_4), M_2^I(WO_2F_4)$.

The most stable pentahalides are $MoCl_5$ and WBr_5, both made by direct combination at high pressure.

Chromium forms trihalides with all four halogens. The colour of a $CrCl_3$ solution varies with temperature and chloride ion concentration. In cold dilute solution the octahedral $[Cr(H_2O)_6]^{3+}$ ion gives a violet colour. Addition of chloride ion, particularly if accompanied by heat, produces a green solution due to the $[Cr(H_2O)_5Cl]^{2+}$ ion:

$$[Cr(H_2O)_6]^{3+} + Cl^- \rightleftharpoons [Cr(H_2O)_5Cl]^{2+} + H_2O.$$

Three isomers of $CrCl_3.6H_2O$ can be crystallised from chromium(III) chloride solutions: (i) violet $Cr(H_2O)_6.Cl_3$ (Recoura, 1886), (ii) pale green $[Cr(H_2O)_5Cl.]Cl_2.H_2O$ (Bjerrum, 1906), (iii) darker green $[Cr(H_2O)_4Cl_2]Cl.2H_2O$ (Recoura, 1886). These are distinguished by *all* the chlorine from (i), *two thirds* from (ii) and *one third* from (iii) being precipitated by $AgNO_3$. Exchange between chlorine in the cation of (iii) and radioactive Cl^- ions is extremely slow (Van der Straaten and Aten, 1954).

Oxides

The trioxides MoO_3 and WO_3 are produced when the metals, their other oxides, or their sulphides are heated in air or oxygen. The dark red, crystalline CrO_3 is less stable, and is made by acidifying a saturated dichromate solution with concentrated H_2SO_4. No hydrate can be separated.

$$K_2Cr_2O_7 + 2H_2SO_4 \rightarrow 2KHSO_4 + H_2O + 2CrO_3.$$

MoO_3 has, surprisingly, a layer lattice; CrO_3 and WO_3 have the rhenium trioxide structure (Fig. 245).

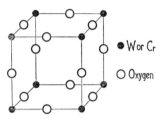

● W or Cr

○ Oxygen

Fig. 245. CrO_3 structure.

The slow decomposition of CrO_3, or of CrO_2Cl_2 in oxygen gives first a solid which X-ray analysis and magnetic measurements show to be Cr_5O_{13}. Further decomposition yields an oxide varying in composition from $CrO_{2.38}$ to $CrO_{2.48}$, and, finally, the ferromagnetic CrO_2, with a rutile structure, is produced.

At a high temperature, MoO_3 and WO_3 are reduced by hydrogen, through the violet Mo_2O_5 and blue W_2O_5, to the violet MoO_2 and brown WO_2. The blue compounds of molybdenum and tungsten, formed by reducing molybdic and tungstic acids with zinc, SO_2 and other reducing agents, are of unknown constitution.

When HCl is added to a hot solution of a tungstate the insoluble, yellow acid, H_2WO_4, separates. A cold solution yields soluble, colourless $H_2WO_4.H_2O$. The material which separates when nitric acid is added to a cold solution of ammonium molybdate is the hydrate $MoO_3.H_2O$. It is yellow when cold, but becomes colourless when heated, being converted to H_2MoO_4.

Chromium(III) oxide, Cr_2O_3, is a product of the oxidation of the metal and of the thermal decomposition of ammonium dichromate:

$$(NH_4)_2Cr_2O_7 \rightarrow Cr_2O_3 + N_2 + 4H_2O.$$

It resembles Al_2O_3 in having a corundum structure and in resisting solution particularly after having been heated. The ionic radii, Al^{3+} 0.50 Å and Cr^{3+} 0.64 Å, are similar enough to allow the formation of many isomorphous compounds, exemplified in the fluorides and the alums.

Black chromium(II) oxide, CrO, is most conveniently made (Dieckmann and Hauf, 1914) by dissolving the mercury out of chromium amalgam with dilute HNO_3 which, under these conditions, oxidises the chromium only as far as CrO.

Complexes

Molybdenum and tungsten show 8 co-ordination in many of their complexes. Octacyanomolybdic(V) acid, $H_3[Mo(CN)_8].3H_2O$, and octacyanomolybdic(IV) acid, $H_4[Mo(CN)_8],6H_2O$, can be isolated as crystals.

$$KCN + K_3MoCl_6 \text{ solution } \rightarrow K_4[Mo(CN)_8] \xrightarrow[HCl]{conc.} H_4[Mo(CN)_8].6H_2O$$

$$H_3[Mo(CN)_8].3H_2O \xleftarrow{KMnO_4}$$

Molybdenum(IV) has only one d electron. The arrangement of eight CN^- ligands around the metal atom in the $Mo(CN)_8^{4-}$ ion is such as to stabilise one d orbital relatively to all the others:

$$\text{Energy} \uparrow \quad \begin{array}{l} d_{xy}, \ d_{yz} \\ d_{z^2} \\ d_{x^2-y^2} \\ \\ d_{xy} \end{array}$$

The structure of the $Re(CN)_8^{3-}$ ion is similarly stabilised.

The free octacyanotungstic(V)acid, $H_3[W(CN)_8].6H_2O$, has also been prepared. Salts of all these acids are known and also some cyanotungstates, containing the complex $[W(CN)_8]^{4-}$. Wolfgang (1952), using the 66-hour isotope $^{99}_{42}Mo$, found transfer between $Mo(CN)_8^{3-}$ and $Mo(CN)_8^{4-}$ to be extremely rapid, suggesting the complexes to be of the spin-free type. Other complexes of 8-co-ordinated Mo and W are the fluoro-complexes M_2MoF_8 and M_2WF_8 (M = K, Rb and Cs, but not Na) made by condensing the appropriate hexafluoride on the alkali metal fluorides (Cox, Sharp and Sharpe, 1956).

Chromium forms many ammino complexes. The purple chloropenta-amminechromium(III) dichloride, $[Cr(NH_3)_5Cl]Cl_2$, is made by bubbling air through a solution of $CrCl_2$, NH_4Cl and NH_3 in water. It can be converted into hexa-amminechromium(III) trichloride, $[Cr(NH_3)_6]Cl_3$ (yellow), by treating its cold, concentrated solution with ammonia. A violet dichloro-tetra-amminechromium(III) chloride, $[Cr(NH_3)_4Cl_2]Cl$, exists and also the triammine, $Cr(NH_3)_3Cl_3$. Werner (1910) made the latter by the reactions:

$$CrO_3 \xrightarrow[\text{dilute } H_2SO_4]{H_2O_2, \text{ pyridine and}} \text{pyridinium perchromate} \xrightarrow{NH_3} CrO_4.(NH_3)_3$$

$$\downarrow \text{cold concentrated HCl}$$

$$Cr(NH_3)_3Cl_3$$

Cyano- and thiocyanato-complexes of chromium are also common. Among the more interesting of these is Reinecke's salt, $NH_4[Cr(NH_3)_2(SCN)_4]H_2O$, made by adding $(NH_4)_2Cr_2O_7$ slowly to melted NH_4SCN, washing with, and recrystallising from, alcohol. The octahedral ion has the form shown in Fig. 246.

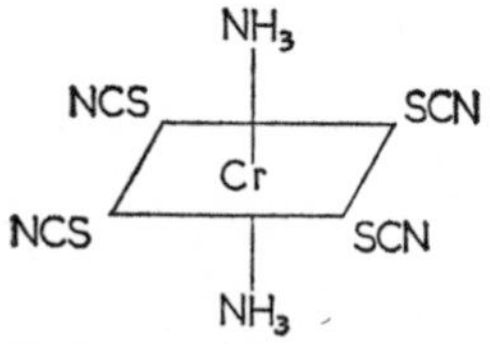

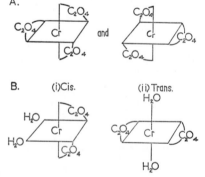

Fig. 246. Structure of $[Cr(NH_3)_2(SCN)_4]^-$ ion present in Reinecke's salt.

Some of the oxalato-complexes of chromium(III) are also of interest. Potassium trioxalatochromate(III), $K_3 Cr(C_2O_4)_3 3H_2O$, is obtained by adding potassium oxalate to the solution obtained by reducing $K_2Cr_2O_7$ with oxalic acid:

$$K_2Cr_2O_7 + 7H_2C_2O_4 \rightarrow \underbrace{K_2C_2O_4 + Cr_2(C_2O_4)_3} + 6CO_2 + 7H_2O$$
$$\downarrow 2K_2C_2O_4$$
$$2K_3[Cr(C_2O_4)_3].$$

The anion of the blue crystalline compound was resolved by Werner (1912) into dextrorotatory and laevorotatory forms (Fig. 247, A). Potassium dioxalatodiaquochromate, $K[Cr(C_2O_4)_2(H_2O)_2]$, exists in *cis*- and *trans*-forms, the former (Fig. 247, B (i)), showing purple-green dichroism and the latter (Fig. 247, B (ii)) being mauve.

A.

B.   (i) Cis.   (ii) Trans.

Fig. 247. A. *d*- and *l*-forms of $[Cr(C_2O_4)_3]^{3-}$ ion.
B. *cis*- and *trans*-forms of $[Cr(C_2O_4)_2(H_2O)_2]^-$ ion.

Chromium forms a cyclopentadienyl compound similar to ferrocene (p. 499). Cyclopentadienyl sodium reacts with anhydrous chromium(II) chloride in tetrahydrofuran to give red $(C_5H_5)_2Cr$. By oxidising this, compounds containing the $(C_5H_5)_2Cr^+$ ion are easily obtained (Cotton and Wilkinson, 1954). When cyclopentadiene mixed with molybdenum or tungsten carbonyl is passed through a tube heated to 300° the dicyclopentadienyl hexacarbonyl is formed (Wilkinson, 1954):

$$2C_5H_6 + 2W(CO)_6 \rightarrow (C_5H_5)_2W_2(CO)_6 + H_2.$$

The compounds are monomeric in the vapour state and diamagnetic. The present view of their structure is that they have the two C_5H_5 groups rather unsymmetrically placed beyond the metal atoms, which are directly bonded to each other. Three CO ligands spread out from each metal atom away from the C_5H_5 groups (Fig. 248).

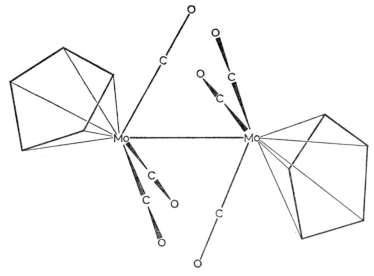

Fig. 248.   Structure of $(C_5H_5)_2Mo_2(CO)_6$.

The reaction between $(C_5H_5)_2Cr$ and CO is complex; in addition to a compound $(C_5H_5)_2Cr_2(CO)_6$, a salt, $[(C_5H_5)_2Cr]^+.[C_5H_5Cr(CO)_3]^-$, is obtained. At temperatures over 250°, the principal product is $Co(CO)_6$ (Fischer, 1955).

Chromates, molybdates and tungstates

Alkali metal chromates can be crystallised only from alkaline solutions; at low pH dichromates are obtained:

$$2CrO_4{}^{2-} + 2H_3O^+ \rightleftharpoons Cr_2O_7{}^{2-} + 3H_2O.$$

Insoluble chromates such as Ag_2CrO_4, $BaCrO_4$ and $PbCrO_4$ are, however, precipitated from acid solution, the last named being an important pigment, chrome yellow.

Alkali metal compounds of chromium of the formula MCr_3O_8 result from heating the dichromates with CrO_3 at $350°$ for a few hours (Suchow, Fankuchen and Ward, 1952).

Normal molybdates and tungstates are uncommon. When MoO_3 is dissolved in an excess of hot concentrated ammonia, $(NH_4)_2MoO_4$ crystallises on cooling, but the salt obtained from a near-neutral solution is $(NH_4)_6Mo_7O_{24}.4H_2O$. The tendency to form polyanions is even more marked with tungsten. When wolframite is roasted with sodium carbonate, the aqueous extract of the mass yields the compound $Na_{10}W_{12}O_{41}.28H_2O$.

Polyacids

The yellow precipitate obtained in the ammonium molybdate test for phosphate is $(NH_4)_2H(PMo_{12}O_{40})H_2O$ (Stockdale, 1958). When washed with dilute NH_4NO_3 it becomes $(NH_4)_3(PMo_{12}O_{40})$. This molybdophosphate is an example from the series of heteropolyacid salts formed by Mo and W. Some other members are

$$H_4(\ SiMo_{12}O_{40}), \quad \text{12-molybdosilicic acid;}$$
$$H_3(AsMo_{12}O_{40}), \quad \text{12-molybdoarsenic acid;}$$
$$H_5(BW_{12}O_{40}), \quad \text{12-tungstoboric acid.}$$

These are known, from the number of Gp.VI atoms, as 12-acids; the heteroatom may also be one of the following: Ti, Ge, Sn, Zr, Hf, Th and Ce. 6-acids of molybdenum and tungsten are also known; they possess the general formula,

$$H_n(MMo_6O_{24}),$$

where M can be I, Te, Fe, Cr, Al, Co, Ni, Rh, Cu or Mn, and its charge number $12 - n$.

Keggin (1934) suggested that the structure of a 12-acid anion could be represented as a tetrahedron round the central metal atom, surrounded by twelve MoO_6 or WO_6 octahedra; every tetrahedron corner is shared by three octahedra, every one of which shares an oxygen with its neighbours. The four resulting Mo_3O_{13} groups share corners to give $[XMo_{12}O_{40}]^{8-n}$ ions, where n = charge number of X. The large open spaces in this type of anion allow the inclusion of water molecules. Hydrates are, in fact, numerous.

Anderson (1937) proposed an analogous scheme for the 6-acids. Six MoO_6 octahedra are joined by sharing edges to form a hexagonal annulus, in the centre of which is an octahedral arrangement of bonds round the hetero-atom; the central atoms of the known 6-acids all show octahedral stereo-chemistry (Fig. 249). Evans (1948) found that potassium and ammonium molybdotellurates had this structure.

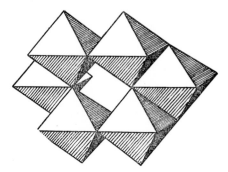

Fig. 249. Arrangement of MoO_6 octahedra in a 6-acid.

In addition to heteropolyacids there are isopolyacids, the commonest of which are the parent acids of the paramolybdates, $H_6[Mo_7O_{24}]$, and of the paratungstates, $H_5[HW_6O_{21}]$. The structure of the $[Mo_7O_{24}]^{6-}$ ion (Lindqvist, 1950) is like that of the 6-acid anions (above) but with a central, octahedrally co-ordinated Mo atom.

Work on the structure of polyanions is beginning to shed light on a former-ly intractable problem, yet there are still many unexplained anomalies. One of the most striking is the existence of surprisingly high ionic charges; the well-characterised $Fe_5^{III}H[SiW_{12}O_{40}]_2.52H_2O$ must contain an anion with a charge -8.

Tungsten bronzes

When alkali metal tungstates are reduced by heating with tungsten or by electrolysis in the fused state, intensely coloured, unreactive substances are obtained with semi-metallic properties; they are good conductors of electrici-ty. These *tungsten bronzes* have the general formula M_xWO_3 (M = Li, Na, or K; $x < 1$). The compounds have defect lattices with the alkali metal atoms occupying only a fraction of the places indicated in Fig. 250. When x is large (~ 0.9) the a dimension is large (3.85 Å) too, and the bronze is golden yellow. Reduction of x reduces a and intensifies the colour in this non-stoichiometric phase (p. 158).

The formula implies that tungsten exhibits a charge between $+5$ and $+6$

but it is most convenient to regard all the tungsten ions in the structure as
W^{6+}, the electrons from the sodium atoms being imagined as part of the free
'electron gas' of the whole lattice. This concept is in accord with the
electrical conductance, metallic appearance, and low paramagnetic susceptibilities of the tungsten bronzes.

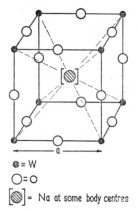

⊕ = W

◯ = O

▨ = Na at some body centres

Fig. 250. Structure of a tungsten bronze

Chapter 32

Manganese, Technetium and Rhenium

GROUP VIIA

Rapidly increasing knowledge of the chemistry of technetium shows that the last two members of Gp. VIIA resemble each other and differ considerably from the first, a relationship similar to that found in Gp. VA and Gp. VIA. The three elements have a total of seven s and d electrons and all may participate in bonding, but manganese has a stable d^5 group and it is commonly bipositive.

The structures of technetium compounds are insufficiently known to give satisfactory values for ionic radii. Its covalent radius is very little less than that of rhenium; both metals have the same crystal structure (h.c.p.) and the atomic volume of Re is very little greater (p. 480).

TABLE 116

SOME PROPERTIES OF GROUP VIIA ELEMENTS

	Mn	Tc	Re
Atomic number	25	43	75
Electron configuration	$3d^5 4s^2$	$4d^5 5s^2$	$5d^5 6s^2$
Atomic radius (Å)	1.17		1.28
Ionic radii (Å)	Mn^{2+} 0.91		Re^{7+} 0.68
	Mn^{3+} 0.62		

Though the first and second ionisation potentials of Mn are similar to those of Mg, the standard electrode potential E_h° Mn^{2+}/Mn is much less negative than that for magnesium because of the much greater heat of sublimation.

$$\text{Metal} \xrightarrow[\text{sublimation}]{\text{Heat of}} \text{Metal atom} \xrightarrow[\text{potential}]{\text{Ionisation}} \text{Metal ion} \xrightarrow[\text{hydration}]{\text{Heat of}} \text{Hydrated metal ion.}$$

The redox potentials given in Table 117 for technetium and rhenium are for the reactions:

$$MO_2 + 4 H_3O^+ + 4 e \rightleftharpoons M + 6 H_2O,$$
and
$$MO_4^- + 8 H_3O^+ + 7 e \rightleftharpoons M + 12 H_2O.$$

TABLE 117

IONISATION AND ELECTRODE POTENTIALS OF GROUP VIIA ELEMENTS

		Mn	Tc	Re
Ionisation potential I	1 (eV)	7.43	7.28	7.87
	2 ,,	15.46	15.26	
E_h° M^{2+}/M (V)		−1.05		
MO_2/M ,,			+0.27	+0.25
MO_4^-/M ,,		+0.79	+0.47	+0.34

Oxidation states

Unipositive manganese appears in the ion $[Mn(CN)_6]^{5-}$, obtained when yellow solutions of $[Mn(CN)_6]^{4-}$ ions are reduced with aluminium powder and alkali. When MnI_2 is treated with alkyl isocyanides, compounds are formed containing the $[Mn(RNC)_6]^+$ ion (Sacco and Naldini, 1956).

The Mn^{2+} ion has a $3d^5$ configuration and exhibits the stability associated with a half-filled d-level. The Mn^{3+} ion ($3d^4$) is a very strong oxidising agent:

$$E_h^\circ \; Mn^{3+}/Mn^{2+} = +1.51 \text{ V},$$

compared with E_h° $Fe^{3+}/Fe^{2+} = +0.77$ V, where it is the Fe^{3+} ion which has the $3d^5$ structure. Compounds of technetium and rhenium corresponding to the manganese(II) salts are not known.

Since for the reaction

$$MnO_2 + 4 H_3O^+ + e \rightleftharpoons Mn^{3+} + 6 H_2O, \quad E_h^\circ = 0.95 \text{ V},$$

disproportionation occurs in aqueous solutions of Mn^{3+}:

$$2 Mn^{3+} + 6 H_2O = Mn^{2+} + MnO_2 + 4 H_3O^+.$$

MnF_3, in fact, reacts with water to give MnF_2, HF and MnO_2. The existence of simple Re^{III} compounds is doubtful. The chloride of empirical formula $ReCl_3$ is probably a dimer.

Manganese with charge +4 exists only in such complex ions as MnO_3^{2-} and MnF_6^{2-}, and the oxide MnO_2 which is not, however, a true Daltonide compound. Pyrolusite never has more oxygen than represented by $MnO_{1.95}$. Technetium (IV) compounds are the black TcO_2 and TcS_2, the red $TcCl_4$ and the hexachlorotechnetate K_2TcCl_6, which is more readily hydrolysed than K_2ReCl_6. Rhenium forms ReF_4 and ReO_2 in addition to complexes, including the well-established chlororhenates, M_2ReCl_6.

Charge +5 is uncommon. A blue compound, $Na_3MnO_4.7H_2O$, obtained by reducing the manganate with sodium formate in alkaline solution (Scholder, Fischer and Waterstradt, 1954), disproportionates in neutral aqueous solution to MnO_2 and Na_2MnO_4. As yet, the $+5$ state has not been established for technetium, but rhenium(V) occurs in $ReCl_5$.

When MnO_2 is heated with potassium hydroxide and an oxidising agent, the green manganate(VI) is mainly produced together with some manganate (IV), respectively, K_2MnO_4 and K_2MnO_3. K_2MnO_4, isomorphous with the chromate(VI), is stable in solution only at high pH; an acid as weak as CO_2 converts a solution of it to permanganate and MnO_2:

$$3\ K_2MnO_4 + 2\ CO_2\ \rightarrow\ 2\ KMnO_4 + MnO_2 + 2\ K_2CO_3.$$

The technetates(VI) and rhenates(VI) are even less stable than the manganates; but Re^{VI} does occur in ReF_6, ReO_3 and $ReOCl_4$.

Charge number $+7$ is rather uncommon in manganese. The permanganates are strong oxidising agents:

$$MnO_4^- + 8\ H_3O^+ + 5\ e\ \rightleftharpoons\ Mn^{2+} + 12\ H_2O,\ E_h^{\circ} = 1.5\ V.$$

Free permanganic acid exists only in aqueous solution and the oxide Mn_2O_7 decomposes explosively above $0°$. The corresponding compounds of technetium and rhenium are, however, stable; the perrhenates are more weakly oxidising than the pertechnetates. The formal charge $+7$ is, in fact, dominant in technetium and rhenium.

The rhenide question

When a solution of $KReO_4$ is passed through a Jones' reductor, the oxidation state of the rhenium is reduced, apparently to -1 (Lundell and Knowles, 1937). A grey solid, thought to be $KRe.4H_2O$, was made (Griswold and Kleinberg, 1952) by reducing a solution of $KReO_4$ in moist ethylenediamine with potassium. A corresponding lithium compound, $LiRe.4H_2O$, was also claimed (Gross, 1953). The paramagnetic susceptibility of the solids is too low for the presence of even one unpaired electron, and Re^- might be expected to have at least four:

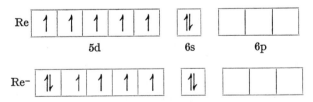

Pauling suggested the water molecules could be co-ordinated as the spin-paired, square complex anion, $[Re(H_2O)_4]^-$, with dsp^2 orbitals:

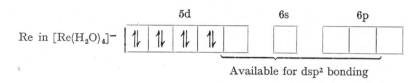

Re in [Re(H$_2$O)$_4$]$^-$

5d   6s   6p

Available for dsp^2 bonding

Since, however, nuclear magnetic resonance and infrared spectroscopy have recently shown that the materials have metal-hydrogen bonds, much doubt is thrown on these deductions about the charge state of the rhenium, indeed upon the nature of the compounds themselves. They have been variously formulated as $K_6Re_2H_{14}.6H_2O$, K_2ReH_8 and $KReH_4.xH_2O$, and remain a problem of interest.

Properties and preparation of the elements

The densities of the metals are normal for their respective periods and the m.p. characteristically high, that of rhenium being exceeded among the metals only by tungsten.

TABLE 118

SOME PROPERTIES OF GROUP VIIA ELEMENTS

	Mn	*Tc*	*Re*
Density (g/cc)	7.4	11.5	20.5
Atomic volume	7.4	8.6	8.8
Melting point (°C)	1260		3170

Manganese (0.08% of the earth's crust) occurs principally as oxides, pyrolusite, a tetragonal form of MnO_2, being the most important. The metal is made in small quantities by aluminothermic reduction of MnO_2, or by electrolysis of $MnSO_4$ solution. Pure manganese has three forms, an α- and β-cubic and a face-centred tetragonal with axial ratio 0.937. The metal is reactive; it combines with the halogens, oxygen, sulphur, carbon, nitrogen (Fig. 251) and with most of the metalloids. It liberates hydrogen from dilute HCl and H_2SO_4 in the cold and from steam at red heat.

Its most important use is for improving the mechanical properties of steel, almost every grade of which contains manganese. It combines with the sulphur which would otherwise make the steel brittle when hot (hot short), thereby improving its rolling and forging properties. The MnS forms harmless inclusions and the rest of the manganese acts as a deoxidiser while the metal is molten and improves its strength, toughness and response to heat-treatment after solidification. For this purpose ferromanganese (80% Mn, 20% Fe) and spiegeleisen (25% Mn, 5% C, 70% Fe) are made by blast-furnace reduction of mixed oxides.

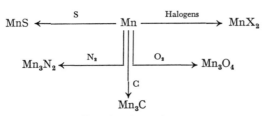

Fig. 251. The chemistry of manganese.

Pure manganese has three forms, an α- and β-cubic and a face-centred tetragonal with axial ratio 0.937. The metal is reactive; it combines with the halogens, oxygen, sulphur, carbon, nitrogen (Fig. 251) and with most of the metalloids. It liberates hydrogen from dilute HCl and H_2SO_4 in the cold and from steam at red heat.

Technetium does not occur terrestrially, but has been observed in the spectra of the sun and certain stars. Perrier and Segré (1937) made the 90-day $^{97}_{43}Tc$ by bombarding molybdenum with high-energy deuterons from a cyclotron. The isotope more useful as a tracer is the 60-day $^{95}_{43}Tc$. The long-lived $^{99}_{43}Tc$ is obtained (Motta, Boyd and Larsen, 1947) by long irradiation of molybdenum in an atomic pile:

$$^{98}_{42}Mo \ (n, \gamma) \ ^{99}_{42}Mo \ \xrightarrow[67 \text{ h}]{\beta} \ ^{99}_{43}Tc \ \xrightarrow[2.2 \times 10^5 \text{ yr}]{\beta} \ ^{99}_{44}Ru \text{ (stable)}$$

This isotope comprises about 6% of the fission products of uranium and a pile operating at 100 megawatts yields about 2.5 g per day; this is the principal source of the metal and Fig. 252 gives an early method of separation. It is now produced from fission-product waste by adding an excess of $HClO_4$ and precipitating the technetium as Ph_4AsTcO_4, along with the carrier Ph_4AsClO_4, by means of tetraphenylarsonium chloride. The precipitate is dissolved in C_2H_5OH and the TcO_4^- ion adsorbed on a strong-base ion-exchange resin, leaving the Ph_4AsCl_4 to be recovered from the solution. The TcO_4^- is eluted with $2N$ $HClO_4$ and precipitated from the eluate as Tc_2S_7 with H_2S.

The metal is made by heating Tc_2S_7 or NH_4TcO_4 in hydrogen, or by the electrolysis of NH_4TcO_4 in dilute H_2SO_4. It is a bright silvery metal which

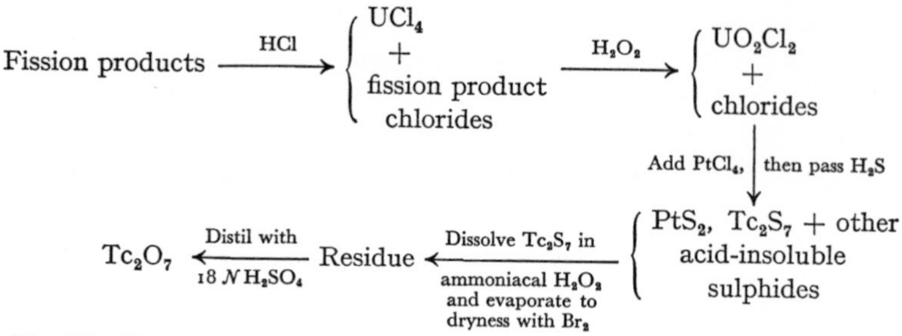

Fission products $\xrightarrow{\text{HCl}}$ $\left\{ \begin{array}{l} UCl_4 \\ + \\ \text{fission product} \\ \text{chlorides} \end{array} \right.$ $\xrightarrow{\text{H}_2\text{O}_2}$ $\left\{ \begin{array}{l} UO_2Cl_2 \\ + \\ \text{chlorides} \end{array} \right.$

Add PtCl$_4$, $\Big\downarrow$ then pass H$_2$S

Tc_2O_7 $\xleftarrow[\text{18 } N \text{ H}_2\text{SO}_4]{\text{Distil with}}$ Residue $\xleftarrow[\substack{\text{ammoniacal H}_2\text{O}_2 \\ \text{and evaporate to} \\ \text{dryness with Br}_2}]{\text{Dissolve Tc}_2\text{S}_7 \text{ in}}$ $\left\{ \begin{array}{l} PtS_2, \ Tc_2S_7 + \text{other} \\ \text{acid-insoluble} \\ \text{sulphides} \end{array} \right.$

Fig. 252. Early method of separating of Tc_2O_7 from fission products.

tarnishes in moist air and, like rhenium, burns in oxygen to the heptoxide; it dissolves in HNO_3 and concentrated H_2SO_4, but not in HCl.

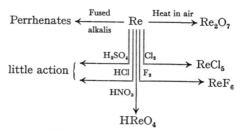

Fig. 253. The chemistry of rhenium.

Rhenium remained undiscovered till 1925 (Noddack, Tacke and Berg) largely because it was sought in manganese ores. In fact its only appreciable occurrence is in MoS_2, some Norwegian mineral containing as much as 20 p.p.m. of Re. The metal is usually made by reducing NH_4ReO_4 with hydrogen at 400° but the sulphide Re_2S_7, the chloride $ReCl_3$, and the oxide ReO_2 are also readily reduced. It is not employed industrially at present, but has possibilities as a hydrogenation catalyst:

$$CO \xrightarrow{\text{H}_2 \text{ over Re}} CH_4, \qquad C_2H_4 \xrightarrow{\text{H}_2 \text{ over Re}} C_2H_6.$$

Halides

MnF_3 is made by the action of F_2 on MnI_2. It is the only trihalide of manganese. With water it gives MnF_2 and MnO_2 (p. 478). MnF_2 is sparingly soluble but the other manganese(II) halides form soluble rose-pink tetrahydrates.

Rhenium combines with F_2 under a little pressure to produce a pale yellow solid, ReF_7, which is the highest binary metal fluoride known. At

$125°$ under atmospheric pressure the product is ReF_6 (m.p.19°). This hydrolyses: $3 ReF_6 + 10 H_2O \rightarrow ReO_2 + 2 HReO_4 + 18 HF$, and reacts with glass: $2 ReF_6 + SiO_2 \rightarrow 2 ReOF_4 + SiF_4$. It is reduced by H_2, SO_2, Re, Zn and Al to ReF_4 (m.p. 124.5°).

The chloride $ReCl_5$ is made by heating Re in Cl_2. When this is heated in an inert atmosphere, it is converted to the violet, crystalline $ReCl_3$. Direct combination of Re and Br_2 at 300° gives dark green $ReBr_3$. Technetium (IV) chloride has been made by heating Tc_2O_7 and CCl_4 in a closed tube.

The most common complex halides of Mn and Re are those in which the metal has a $+4$ charge; examples are M_2MnCl_6, M_2TcCl_6 and M_2ReCl_6 and, particularly, the corresponding fluoro-complexes. This state of Re is obtained from states of higher charge in the formation of these compounds:

$$2 ReCl_5 + 4 KCl \rightarrow 2 K_2ReCl_6 + Cl_2.$$

K_2ReF_6 is made in good yield by the action of anhydrous HF on K_2ReI_6, but the acid H_2ReF_6 cannot be isolated (Peacock, 1955). The Mn^{IV} complexes are spin-free with 3 unpaired electrons. The magnetic susceptibilities of the complex chlorides of Re^{IV} and Tc^{IV} increase with temperature and the moment approaches that expected for 3 unpaired electrons. Manganese (II) forms the complexes $MMnF_3$, $MMnCl_3$, M_2MnCl_4 and M_4MnCl_6, and manganese(III), M_2MnF_5 and M_2MnCl_5.

Rhenium forms many oxide-halides:

Re^{VI} $\quad ReO_2F_2$, ReO_2Cl_2, ReO_2Br_2, $ReOF_4$.
Re^{VII} $\quad ReO_3F$, ReO_3Cl, ReO_3Br.

The compound MnO_3F can be made by the action of anhydrous HF on $KMnO_4$ at low temperature (Engelbrecht and Grosse, 1954):

$$KMnO_4 + 2 HF \rightarrow MnO_3F + KF + H_2O.$$

The dark green crystals melt at $-38°$ and explode at 0°. As expected, ReO_3F (m.p. 147°) is a much more stable compound.

Oxides

Cubic MnO occurs as manganosite and the hydroxide, $Mn(OH)_2$, as pyrochroite. When made by thermal decomposition of the oxalate or carbonate, MnO is fairly easily oxidised. Heating in air at 250–300° converts it to Mn_2O_3. The precipitated hydroxide is oxidised by air even at room temperature.

Mn_3O_4 occurs as hausmannite, with a distorted spinel structure. It is formed when any other oxide is heated in air to 1000°.

Mn_2O_3 has α- and γ-forms, corresponding to those of Fe_2O_3 (p. 377). Another oxygen compound of Mn^{III} is manganite $MnO(OH)$.

MnO_2 exists principally as pyrolusite, a rutile-like structure. The ore is used, (a) for making ferromanganese and manganese itself, (b) in dry batteries, (c) in rendering glass colourless, (d) as a drier in paint, (e) for making $MnSO_4$ (used for treating manganese-deficient soils).

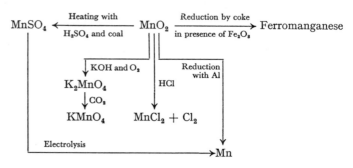

Fig. 254. Reactions of manganese dioxide.

The purest MnO_2 is made by decomposing $Mn(NO_3)_2$ at 200° followed by the dehydration of the residue at 500° in oxygen, but the product is always stoichiometrically deficient in oxygen.

Rhenium dioxide results from heating Re_2O_7 with the metal at 600°, or reducing $HReO_4$ with zinc and HCl. Heating ReO_2 to 750° at a low pressure converts it to Re_2O_7 and metal. Unlike MnO_2, it is only weakly paramagnetic. TcO_2 has been made by the ignition of NH_4TcO_4.

Rhenium trioxide, in almost quantitative yield, is given by the thermal decomposition of $Re_2O_7(C_4H_8O_2)_3$, the addition compound of Re_2O_7 with dioxan (Nechamkin, Kurtz and Hiskey, 1951). On heating, ReO_3 disproportionates:

$$3\,ReO_3 \rightarrow Re_2O_7 + ReO_2.$$

It has a very simple structure (Fig. 255).

Manganese, rhenium and technetium form the oxides M_2O_7. When powdered $KMnO_4$ is added to concentrated H_2SO_4 cooled to −20° a dark olive-green liquid is obtained, Mn_2O_7. It can be distilled below 0°, but explodes at 10°:

$$2\,Mn_2O_7 \rightarrow 4\,MnO_2 + 3\,O_2.$$

Tc_2O_7, a pale yellow hygroscopic solid (m.p. 119°), is obtained when the metal is heated to 600° in oxygen. Re_2O_7, also a pale yellow soluble solid (m.p. 300°), is made by heating the metal or the other oxides to 200° in air. It can be reduced with hydrogen at 300° to ReO_2, at 800° to the metal.

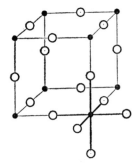

Fig. 255. Structure of rhenium trioxide.

Pertechnetic and perrhenic acids and their salts

A solution of pertechnetic acid, $HTcO_4$, is made by dissolving Tc_2O_7 in water; the dark red, anhydrous acid is obtained by evaporation. There are well-crystallised pertechnetates, such as NH_4TcO_4 and $KTcO_4$. The TcO_4^- ion is very stable in aqueous solution; interestingly, slight traces of it prevent the corrosion of iron in water containing dissolved air. The ReO_4^- ion is without this property.

Given the systematic name tetraoxorhenic(VII) acid (to distinguish it from pentaoxorhenic(VII) acid H_3ReO_5) perrhenic acid, $HReO_4$, is made in aqueous solution by the action of HNO_3 on Re_2S_7 or the metal, by dissolving Re_2O_7 in water, or by passing Cl_2 into a suspension of ReO_2:

$$2\,ReO_2 + 3\,Cl_2 + 4\,H_2O \rightarrow 2\,HReO_4 + 6\,HCl.$$

A syrupy yellowish solution containing 60% $HReO_4$ is obtained on the water bath; the anhydrous acid is colourless. Perrhenic acid is a strong monobasic acid, dissolving magnesium, iron and zinc with the evolution of hydrogen. Although not a strong oxidising agent, it oxidises HBr to bromine. The powerful reducing agents sodium amalgam, tin(II) chloride and hydrazine reduce $HReO_4$ to a mixture of ReO_2 and the metal.

Potassium perrhenate is precipitated when KCl is added to a solution of $HReO_4$, or when $HReO_4$ is neutralised with KOH. It is colourless and less soluble (1.2 g/100 g, 25°) than $KClO_4$. The sodium and ammonium salts are rather more soluble; $CsReO_4$ is less so. $AgReO_4$ and $TlReO_4$ are also made by precipitation:

$$AgNO_3 + NaReO_4 \rightarrow AgReO_4 + NaNO_3.$$

Other perrhenates are the crystalline $Cu(ReO_4)_2.5H_2O$ (pale blue), $Co(ReO_4)_2.5H_2O$ (deep pink), $Ni(ReO_4)_2.5H_2O$ (blue-green) and $Mn(ReO_4)_2.3H_2O$ (pink). Complexes are formed by some of these with ammonia and pyridine: $Cu(pyr)_4.(ReO_4)_2$, $Co(NH_3)_4(ReO_4)_2$, and $Co(NH_3)_6(ReO_4)_2$.

$KReO_4$ reacts with bromine trifluoride to give the compound $KReO_2F_4$ (Peacock, 1955).

Permanganates

$KMnO_4$ is one of the more important compounds of manganese (p. 479). It is used in oxidimetry, for the manufacture of saccharin and benzoic acid, and for bleaching waxes. The anhydrous acid $HMnO_4$ has not been isolated, but aqueous solutions can be made:

$$Mn_2O_7 + H_2O \rightarrow 2\ HMnO_4,$$
$$Ba(MnO_4)_2 + H_2SO_4 \rightarrow BaSO_4 + 2\ HMnO_4.$$

The acid is strongly dissociated in aqueous solution.

The permanganates exhibit weak temperature-independent paramagnetism though Mn^{VII} has no unpaired electrons.

Manganates

These are of three types, containing manganese with, respectively, $+4$, $+5$ and $+6$ charges. These are best indicated by the Stock notation of Roman numerals.

Manganates(IV). When H_2O_2 is added to a solution of $KMnO_4$ and $CuSO_4$ a compound of Mn^{IV}, $CuMnO_3$, is precipitated.

Manganates(V). Magnetic data suggest that blue $Na_3MnO_4.7H_2O$ contains Mn^V and not a mixture of Mn^{IV} and Mn^{VI} (Klemm; Scholder, 1954).

Manganates(VI). One of the most stable Mn^{VI} compounds is $BaMnO_4$, made by adding concentrated $KMnO_4$ to boiling saturated $Ba(OH)_2$:

$$4\ Ba(OH)_2 + 4\ KMnO_4 \rightarrow 4\ KOH + 4\ BaMnO_4 + 2H_2O + O_2.$$

It is a non-toxic green pigment. The magnetic moment indicates the presence of one unpaired electron (Jensen and Klemm, 1938).

Sulphides

Manganese(II) sulphide can be prepared in three forms with, respectively, the wurtzite, zinc blende and rock salt structures. The greyish-pink precipitate, obtained when $(NH_4)_7S$ is added to a solution of Mn^{2+} ion containing NH_3 and NH_4Cl, is a mixture of the two cubic forms, one rose-red and the other green. MnS_2, which occurs as hauerite, has a cubic structure.

Black Tc_2S_7 is precipitated by H_2S from an acidified technetate solution. When heated it gives TcS_2 and sulphur.

Brown Re_2S_7 is best made by boiling $KReO_4$ and $Na_2S_2O_7$ and then acidifying to give a precipitate contaminated with elementary sulphur. Boiling with toluene removes the sulphur, leaving dark brown Re_2S_7. When heated in nitrogen or carbon dioxide sulphur is lost and black ReS_2 remains.

Corresponding selenides, Re_2Se_7 and $ReSe_2$ can be made.

Complexes

Mn^I is present in $K_5Mn(CN)_6$ and in $Mn(RNC)_6^+$ compounds (p. 478). Corresponding rhenium compounds are unknown. The complex cyanide is diamagnetic, indicating that the approach of the cyanide ions causes a large splitting of the d levels (p. 132) and leaves two d_γ orbitals free for bonding in d^2sp^3 octahedral hybrids.

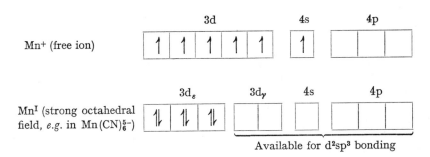

Mn^{II} occurs in both spin-free complexes, as in $Mn(H_2O)_6^{2+}$ with five unpaired electrons, and spin-paired complexes, as in $Mn(CN)_6^{4-}$ with one unpaired electron. The two cases are illustrated in Fig. 77 (p. 134), the CN^- providing a much stronger ligand field than H_2O—as indicated by its position in the spectrochemical series. In the former instance, the higher d orbitals ($4d_\gamma$) must be invoked, but in the latter d^2sp^3 could be employed.

Mn^{II} (weak octahedral field, *e.g.* in $Mn(H_2O)_6^{2+}$)

$3d_\varepsilon$			$3d_\gamma$		4s	4p			$4d_\varepsilon$			$4d_\gamma$	
↑	↑	↑	↑	↑									

Available for bonding (*e.g.* $sp^3d_\gamma{}^2$)

Mn^{II} (strong octahedral field, *e.g.* in $Mn(CN)_6^{4-}$)

↑↓	↑↓	↑											

Available for bonding ($d_\gamma{}^2sp^3$)

Complexes are unknown for Re^{II} and Tc^{II}.

Mn^{III} also occurs in both spin-free complexes such as $[Mn(acac)_3]^0$*, and in spin-paired complexes with two unpaired electrons such as $Mn(CN)_6^{3-}$. The Re^{III} complexes like $Re(NH_3)_6^{3+}$ and $ReCl_4^-$ are, however, diamagnetic.

All Mn^{IV} complexes are spin-free: K_2MnF_6 has a moment corresponding to the presence of three unpaired electrons; $ReCl_6^{2-}$ and $TcCl_6^{2-}$ have temperature-dependent moments which rise to maxima corresponding to three unpaired spins.

* acac = acetylacetone ligand.

Chapter 33

Iron, Cobalt and Nickel

GROUP VIII (FIRST TRIAD)

Group VIII comprises three A-type subgroups (Table 119). The A-type configurations run from ns^1 to $(n — 1)$ $d^l ns^m$, where $l + m = 10$, but the division of electrons between d and s shells is variable. There are three series which end, respectively, with Ni, Pd and Pt. Immediately following these are Cu, Ag and Au, the first elements of B-type configuration; they are always $(n — 1)d^{10}ns^1$ from which the three series continue regularly up to ns^2np^5. Although vertical similarities do exist between elements of the above subgroups, the practice of putting them together as Gp.VIII has persisted, mainly because of strong 'horizontal' relationships. In particular, the chemistry of Fe, Co and Ni in the First Triad differs considerably from that of their congeners in the Second and Third Triads.

TABLE 119

THE THREE A-TYPE SUBGROUPS

First Triad	Fe $(3d^6 4s^2)$	Co $(3d^7 4s^2)$	Ni $(3d^8 4s^2)$
Second Triad	Ru $(4d^7 5s^1)$	Rh $(4d^8 5s^1)$	Pd $(4d^{10})$
Third Triad	Os $(5d^6 6s^2)$	Ir $(5d^9)$	Pt $(5d^9 6s^1)$

Iron, cobalt and nickel are unlike the elements which precede them since they fail to form moderately stable oxo-anions like VO_3^-, CrO_4^{2-} and MnO_4^-. The unstable ferrate ion, FeO_4^{2-}, is a very strong oxidising agent; no oxo-anion of Co or Ni exists. In this, the metals illustrate the greatly reduced tendency of d electrons to function as valency electrons once the d level is more than half filled. However, the small ionic radii of the 2+ and 3+ cations, together with the presence of unfilled d orbitals, favour complex formation. The complexes of Co^{III}, anionic, cationic and neutral, are particularly numerous.

The radii, ionisation potentials and standard electrode potentials of the elements are summarised in Table 120.

TABLE 120

RADII, IONISATION POTENTIALS
AND ELECTRODE POTENTIALS OF Fe, Co AND Ni

		Fe	*Co*	*Ni*
Atomic number		26	27	28
Covalent radii (Å)		1.16	1.16	1.15
Ionic radii M^{2+} (Å)		0.83	0.82	0.78
M^{3+} (Å)		0.67	0.65	
Ionisation potential I 1 (eV)		7.90	7.86	7.63
2 ,,		16.16	17.3	18.2
E_h° M^{2+}/M (V)		−0.44	−0.28	−0.25
M^{3+}/M^{2+} ,,		+0.77	+1.84	

Separation and properties of the metals

The elements have typical metallic structures (Table 121). Their melting points, though somewhat lower than that of chromium in Gp. VI (p. 467), are characteristically high. The metals are ferromagnetic.

TABLE 121

THE METALLIC STRUCTURES OF Fe, Co AND Ni

Fe	α	b.c.c.	γ	f.c.c.
Co	α	h.c.p.	β	f.c.c.
Ni	α	h.c.p.	β	f.c.c.

TABLE 122

DENSITY, ATOMIC VOLUME AND MELTING POINT OF Fe, Co AND Ni

	Fe	*Co*	*Ni*
Density (g/cc)	7.9	8.7	8.9
Atomic volume	7.1	6.7	6.7
M.p (°C)	1535	1480	1455

Iron makes up 4.7% of earth's crust and may be the most important constituent of its interior. The principal ores are haematite, Fe_2O_3, magnetite, Fe_3O_4, limonite, $Fe_2O_3.3H_2O$, and siderite, $FeCO_3$. The metal is of the greatest economic importance, world output exceeding two hundred million tons per annum. Roasting of the ores converts them to Fe_2O_3 which is reduced in a blast furnace by carbon monoxide. The pig iron so made contains about 4% carbon and about 0.5% each of sulphur, phosphorus and silicon. Oxidation of the impurities by Fe_2O_3 in the open-hearth furnace, or by air in the Bessemer converter, leaves a purer iron which is made into steel by addition of a manganese-carbon-iron alloy.

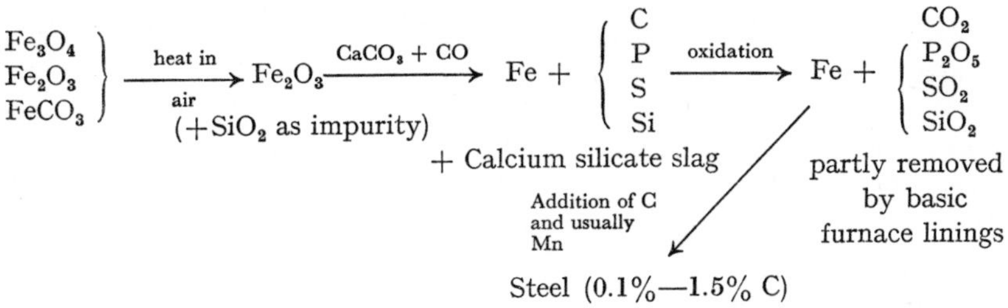

$$\left.\begin{array}{l} Fe_3O_4 \\ Fe_2O_3 \\ FeCO_3 \end{array}\right\} \xrightarrow[\text{air}]{\text{heat in}} Fe_2O_3 \xrightarrow{CaCO_3 + CO} Fe + \left\{\begin{array}{l} C \\ P \\ S \\ Si \end{array}\right. \xrightarrow{\text{oxidation}} Fe + \left\{\begin{array}{l} CO_2 \\ P_2O_5 \\ SO_2 \\ SiO_2 \end{array}\right.$$

(+SiO_2 as impurity)

+ Calcium silicate slag

partly removed by basic furnace linings

Addition of C and usually Mn

Steel (0.1%—1.5% C)

Fig. 256. Manufacture of iron and steel from iron ores.

Cobalt (4×10^{-3} % of the earth's crust) occurs principally as smaltite, $CoAs_2$, and cobaltite, CoAsS. The metal is used in corrosion-resistant alloys and magnets. Smelting involves oxidation of the ore to Co_3O_4, iron and arsenic being removed as slag, followed by alumino-thermic reduction of the cobalt oxide:

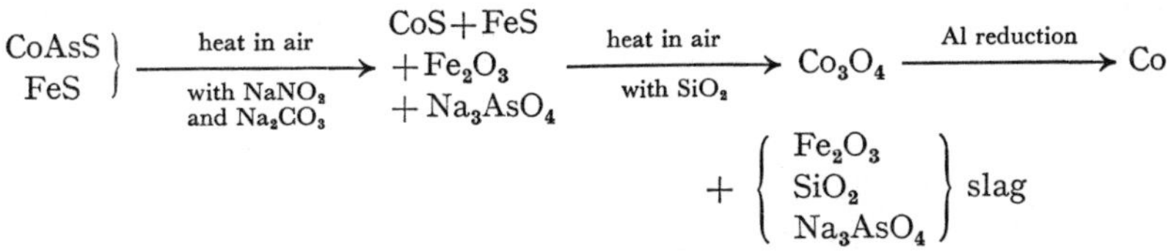

$$\left.\begin{array}{l} CoAsS \\ FeS \end{array}\right\} \xrightarrow[\substack{\text{with } NaNO_3 \\ \text{and } Na_2CO_3}]{\text{heat in air}} \begin{array}{l} CoS + FeS \\ + Fe_2O_3 \\ + Na_3AsO_4 \end{array} \xrightarrow[\text{with } SiO_2]{\text{heat in air}} Co_3O_4 \xrightarrow{\text{Al reduction}} Co$$

$$+ \left\{\begin{array}{l} Fe_2O_3 \\ SiO_2 \\ Na_3AsO_4 \end{array}\right\} \text{slag}$$

Fig. 257. Manufacture of cobalt from ores.

Nickel (10^{-2} % of the earth's crust) is found as pentlandite, NiS, with FeS as impurity. It is used in the fabrication of chemical plant, as an alloying metal to increase the corrosion resistance of steel, as a catalyst in hydrogenation reactions, and as a coinage metal. Alloyed with chromium it gives Nichrome for resistance heaters; with zinc and copper it forms German silver.

The sulphide ore is oxidised in the presence of silica which enables the iron to be removed as a silicate slag. The nickel oxide left is reduced at 350° by water gas to an impure metal leaving the iron as ferric oxide. Purification is based on the formation and decomposition of gaseous $Ni(CO)_4$. Carbon monoxide is passed over the impure metal at 60° and the gas containing a few per cent of the tetracarbonyl is brought into contact with agitated nickel pellets at 200°. The pellets grow as nickel is deposited on them; the CO is recirculated (Fig. 258).

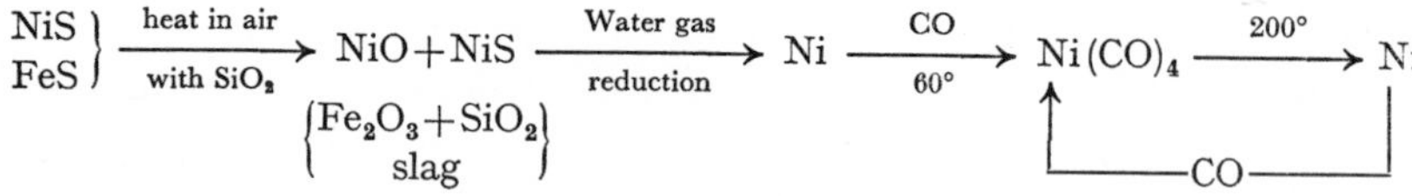

$$\left.\begin{array}{l} NiS \\ FeS \end{array}\right\} \xrightarrow[\text{with SiO}_2]{\text{heat in air}} \begin{array}{c} NiO+NiS \\ \left[\begin{array}{c} Fe_2O_3+SiO_2 \\ slag \end{array}\right] \end{array} \xrightarrow[\text{reduction}]{\text{Water gas}} Ni \xrightarrow[60°]{CO} Ni(CO)_4 \xrightarrow{200°} Ni$$

Fig. 258. Manufacture of nickel from ore.

The metals liberate hydrogen from dilute hydrochloric and sulphuric acids. Concentrated nitric acid renders them passive. They react on heating with oxygen, sulphur and the halogens. Hydrogen, boron, carbon, nitrogen, silicon and phosphorus combine with them, generally forming non-stoichiometric compounds, many of the interstitial-lattice type.

Halides

The metals all form dihalides. Anhydrous FeF_2 and $FeCl_2$ can be made by passing HF or HCl over the heated metal, CoF_2 by the action of HF on $CoCl_2$, and the others by direct combination of the elements. The colour deepens with increasing polarisability of the anion; both CoI_2 and NiI_2 are black. $CoCl_2$ forms blue crystals of the rhombohedral system with the cadmium chloride structure. The colour of a solution of $CoCl_2$ can vary with temperature and concentration from pink to blue, the latter being favoured by higher temperatures and concentrations and by the presence of concentrated HCl. The blue colour appears to be due to the $CoCl_4^{2-}$ ion (Percival and Wardlaw, 1929). The most common hydrate, $CoCl_2.6H_2O$, is red.

FeF_3 and $FeCl_3$ are formed by direct combination of the elements; CoF_3 is made by passing fluorine over $CoCl_2$ at 150°. Nickel forms no trihalide. The vapour density of iron(III) chloride shows some of the dimer to be present below 750°, but molecular weight determinations made in organic solvents indicate monomeric $FeCl_3$.

Oxides

FeO, γ-Fe_2O_3 and Fe_3O_4 are closely related structurally. In all, the oxygen atoms have c.c.p. arrangement. If stoichiometric FeO existed, all the octahedral spaces would be filled with Fe atoms, giving effectively a sodium chloride lattice of Fe^{2+} and O^{2-} ions. Pure FeO is, however, unknown. The atom ratio of the 'iron-rich' limit is 48.56% iron. Removal of Fe^{2+} ions from the ideal structure and replacement by two-thirds of their number of Fe^{3+} ions gives FeO deficient in iron—this is a more accurate picture than an excess of oxygen. When three-quarters of the original Fe^{2+} ions are replaced by Fe^{3+} ions the compound has the composition Fe_3O_4, that is $Fe^{II}(Fe^{III}O_2)_2$, and a spinel structure. Removal of more iron atoms gives γ-Fe_2O_3 in which all the original Fe^{2+} are replaced by Fe^{3+} ions. The addition of oxygen to iron and its lower oxides appears to take place by the formation of close-packed layers of oxygen atoms on the surface followed by diffusion of the iron atoms into these layers. The side of the unit cell containing 32 oxygen atoms decreases linearly as the proportion of iron to oxygen atoms decreases.

γ-Fe_2O_3 and Fe_3O_4 are both ferromagnetic. The rhombohedral, para-magnetic haematite, or α-Fe_2O_3, is the stable form; although it has only one crystal structure it occurs in three colours, grey, yellow and red.

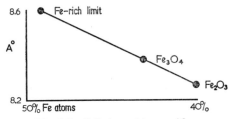

Fig. 259. Cell sizes of iron oxides.

CoO and NiO also have the sodium chloride structure. When dry, CoO is stable at room temperature but, when wet, is easily oxidised to CoO(OH); this compound is also obtained as a black precipitate when cobalt(III) complexes are decomposed by alkali. Dry CoO is oxidised to Co_3O_4 when heated in air, but further oxidation to Co_2O_3 does not occur. NiO is thermally stable and is made by strongly heating the carbonate or nitrate.

Only the hydrated oxides of cobalt(III) and nickel(III) are precipitated by alkali hypochlorites from cobalt(II) and nickel(II) solutions. Iron(III) hydroxide has two crystalline forms in the orthorhombic system, α-FeO(OH), dark brown needles, and γ-FeO(OH), thin red plates. All other hydrates of Fe_2O_3 are mixtures of these with either Fe_2O_3 or absorbed water.

A hydrate of NiO_2 is the depolarising agent in the Edison storage battery.

Sulphides

The monosulphides occur as hexagonal crystals which always show a deficiency of metal atoms without heterogeneity of structure (Fig. 260).

As Fe^{3+} ions oxidise H_2S, HS^- and S^{2-}, the precipitation of Fe_2S_3 free from sulphur is impossible. Monohydrated iron(III) oxide reacts with dry H_2S to give primarily Fe_2S_3 some of which disproportionates into FeS_2 and FeS (Pearson and Robinson, 1928). A cobalt(III) sulphide cannot be precipitated from aqueous solution and there is no unequivocal evidence for its formation or that of Ni_2S_3 in dry reactions. However, disulphides are known, of which the most important is FeS_2. In its commonest form, pyrites, Fe atoms and S_2 pairs are arranged in a sodium chloride-type structure with the axes of the sulphur pairs parallel to the four trigonal axes (Fig. 261).

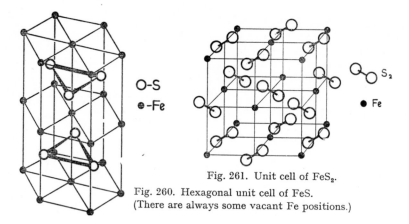

Fig. 261. Unit cell of FeS₂.
Fig. 260. Hexagonal unit cell of FeS.
(There are always some vacant Fe positions.)

Nature of complexes of iron, cobalt and nickel

The transition metals, with their partially filled d shells and small ionic radii, readily form stable complexes (p. 533) in which four or more ligands surround the central atom or ion. Gp. VIII elements are particularly effective in this respect, giving neutral compounds such as carbonyls, nitrosyls and pentadienyls as well as anionic and cationic species. In this triad of Gp. VIII, the compounds of cobalt(III) are the most stable and most abundant, much more so than, for instance, those with the iso-electronic Fe^{2+}. The charge on the metals range from 0 to $+6$ (-1 to $+6$ for cobalt) and provides a convenient basis for classification. But it must be remembered that the charge is formal (being the classical 'electrovalence') in that covalent character in the bonding returns electrons to the metal valence shell.

Uninegative cobalt is found in sodium tetracarbonylcobaltate($-$I), $NaCo(CO)_4$, which is a typical salt with the anion $[Co(CO)_4]^-$. This and the corresponding salts of potassium and calcium are related to cobalt carbonyl hydride (p. 303).

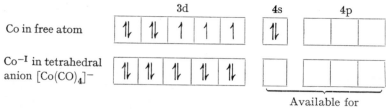

The atom with zero charge occurs in several nickel compounds; the diamagnetic carbonyl Ni(CO)$_4$, for instance, is tetrahedral. Under the ligand field (p. 134) the electrons fill up the d shell:

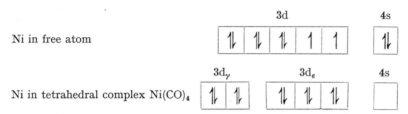

This leaves 4s and 4p orbitals available for dative bonding (in, for example, sp^3 hybridisation) with the CO lone pairs. Other diamagnetic complexes, also tetrahedral, result when the CO molecules are replaced by isonitriles (*e.g.* CNC$_6$H$_5$) or phosphorus trihalides, namely, Ni(CNR)$_4$ and Ni(PX$_3$)$_4$. The complex cyanide K$_4$Ni(CN)$_4$ also contains nickel in the Ni^0(d^{10}) state; and, although the neutral metal atom in an anion is rare, it appears in K$_4$Pd(CN)$_4$. Cobalt(0) occurs in K$_4$Co(CN)$_4$, a brown pyrophoric powder which liberates hydrogen from water (Hieber & Bartenstein, 1954). The weak paramagnetism is not inconsistent with Co^0(d^9), possibly with some dimerisation.

Charge $+1$ occurs on cobalt in Co(CNPh)$_5$ClO$_4$, the pentaphenyl *iso*-nitrile perchlorate, a diamagnetic bipyramidal complex. The electron configuration is Co^I(d^8)

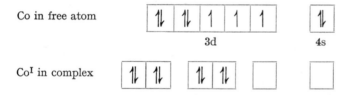

This leaves a 3d$_{z^2}$, a 4s, and the 4p orbitals free for bonding (*e.g.* by means of dsp^2 hybrids (p. 105). Of the several Co^I complexes known, none is spin-free. On the other hand K$_2$Ni(CN)$_3$, produced by reduction of K$_2$Ni(CN)$_4$ with sodium amalgam, might be expected to have the same triangular arrangement of CN groups but with one free electron in the d$_y$ orbital normal to their plane (*cf.* Fig. 262). The compound is, however, diamagnetic and

(i)
```
        N
 NC   C   CN
    Ni   Ni
 NC   C   CN
        N
```

(ii)
```
      CN        CN
      |         |
      Ni········Ni
    /    \    /    \
  CN   CN  CN    CN
```

Fig. 262. Possible structures for [Ni(CN)$_3$]$_2^{4-}$

dimerisation is suspected. Nast and Pfab (1952) suggested a structure with square-co-ordinated Ni atoms, bridged by two of the CN groups (i); but the infrared spectrum indicates only one type of C—N bond, and a direct Ni—Ni link (pairing the single d_γ electrons) may be more likely (ii).

Charge $+2$ is very common in Fe, Co and Ni, and both high- and low-spin complexes (p. 134) are known. All described Fe^{II} complexes are octahedral, but Co^{II} and Ni^{II} also engage in four and five co-ordination. A high-spin Fe^{II} complex is Fe(NH$_3$)$_6^{2+}$ in which the configuration $3d_\varepsilon^4\,3d_\gamma^2$ has four singly occupied orbitals, the 4s, 4p and 4d orbitals being left free for bonding. On the other hand, Fe(CN)$_6^{4-}$ in K$_4$Fe(CN)$_6$ is diamagnetic with a closed subshell, $3d_\varepsilon^6$, so that the $3d_\gamma$ is now also available for bonding. One example of a high-spin Co^{II} complex is CoCl$_4^{2-}$, which is tetrahedral: another is the octahedral Co(NH$_3$)$_6^{2+}$. Although all such complexes have three singly occupied d orbitals their magnetic moments vary from 4.3 to 5.6 μ_B, owing to orbital contributions (p. 78) which depend on ligand field strength. Similarly, the low-spin complexes with 4 co-ordination and only one singly occupied d orbital have moments of up to 2.9 μ_B, owing to large orbital contributions. In 6 co-ordination these drop to about 1.9μ_B. Nickel commonly forms square Ni^{II} complexes (p. 537) which are diamagnetic. They have the configuration Ni^{II}($3d_\varepsilon^6\,3d_\gamma^2$), with the d_γ orbital which lies in the plane free for bonding (e.g. with dsp^2 hybridisation (p. 106)), and the additional possibility of double-bond character (p. 106). High-spin Ni^{II} compounds also exist; for instance in the tetrahedral NiCl$_4^{2-}$ ion, present in solutions of nickel chloride in fused caesium chloride, and the same ion is present in the tetrachloronickelate, (Et$_4$N)$_2$NiCl$_4$, prepared from an alcoholic solution. They are usually formed with the more electronegative ligands and are green or blue, whereas the low-spin compounds are orange or red.

Charge $+3$ is also common. As Table 120 (p. 490) shows, Fe^{3+} is an electron acceptor ($E_h^\circ = 0.77$ V), and iron(III) salts are readily hydrolysed, the brown colour of their aqueous solutions being largely due to Fe(OH)$^{2+}$. The Co^{3+} ion is clearly an even more powerful oxidising agent ($E_h^\circ = 1.84$ V), and simple cobalt(III) salts are therefore difficult to make, since they liberate oxygen from water and are reduced to cobalt(II). It is only in co-ordination that Co^{III} becomes commonplace. There are many octahedral Fe^{III} complexes; FeF$_6^{3-}$ is of high-spin type with configuration $3d_\varepsilon^3\,3d_\gamma^2$ and Fe(CN)$_6^{3-}$, with a higher ligand field (p. 134), is low-spin with $3d_\varepsilon^5$ and both $3d_\gamma$ orbitals free for bonding. Interesting Co^{III} complexes include Co(NH$_3$)$_6^{3+}$, a diamagnetic octahedral complex with a filled d_ε shell and empty d_γ orbitals (again free for a d^{2}sp^3 description of the octahedral bonding). Nickel is less ready to form Ni^{III} complexes, though an interesting series has been made by treating the square nickel dioxime chelates with chlorine.

Charge $+4$ occurs much less commonly. Treatment of alcoholic $FeCl_3$ with o-$C_6H_4(AsMe_2)_2$ gives a brilliant red precipitate of $[Fe^{III}Cl_2.2C_6H_4(AsMe_2)_2]$ $FeCl_4$. Nyholm and Parish (1956) found that a nitrobenzene solution of this compound, when heated with $15NHNO_3$, gives $[Fe^{IV}Cl_2.2C_6H_4(AsMe_2)_2]$ $(FeCl_4)_2$ containing Fe^{IV} in the cationic complex. The perrhenate of the cation was also made in a fairly pure state and magnetic measurements suggested d_ϵ^4 (2 spin free) with two d_γ orbitals available for bonding. The Co^{IV} state is poorly represented, but Ni^{IV} exists in the oxide NiO_2 and in the $[NiCl_2.2C_6H_4 (AsMe_2)_2]^{2+}$ ion (Nyholm, 1951).

Charge $+5$ is unknown, but $+6$ occurs in the ferrates, which are made by hypochlorite oxidation of $Fe(OH)_3$ suspended in alkali:

$$2Fe(OH)_3 + 3OCl^- + 4OH^- \rightleftharpoons 2FeO_4{}^{2-} + 3Cl^- + 5H_2O.$$

The potassium and barium salts have been isolated. The carmine-red $BaFeO_4$ is structurally similar to $BaSO_4$ and $BaCrO_4$. The presence of two unpaired electrons in the compound was established by Hrostowski and Scott (1950) who succeeded in disentangling the ferro- and para-magnetic contributions to the susceptibility.

Miscellaneous complexes

1. Cyano-complexes of iron

Prussian blue, precipitated from potassium hexacyanoferrate (II) (ferro-cyanide), $K_4Fe(CN)_6$, solution by a little less than an equivalent of $FeCl_3$, is known to have the composition $KFe[Fe(CN)_6]$. Its structure (Fig. 263) is

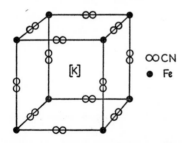

Fig. 263. Structure of soluble Prussian blue.

somewhat similar to that of a tungsten bronze. The cubic unit cell has an iron atom at each corner and a CN pair occupying the middle of each side. Half of the iron atoms have 6 carbon atoms as nearest neighbours and half have 6 nitrogen ones. There are potassium atoms at only half of the cube centres. Iron(III) cyanide has the same lattice with nothing at the cube centres; whereas $K_2Fe_2(CN)_6$, made by the action of $FeCl_2$ on $K_4Fe(CN)_6$, has potassium atoms at all the cube centres.

The pentacyanonitrosylferrates, (the 'nitroprussides') are of interest. Cyano complexes in general do not easily form mixed complexes by replacement of CN^- groups and, in the hexacyano-complexes of iron, only one CN^- can be replaced by NH_3, H_2O, CO, NO_2 (nitro) or NO (nitroso). Acidification of a $K_4Fe(CN)_6$–KNO_2 mixture gives first the pentacyanonitroferrate(II) ion, $[Fe(CN)_5NO_2]^{4-}$:

$$Fe(CN)_6^{4-} + NO_2^- \rightleftharpoons [Fe(CN)_5NO_2]^{4-} + CN^-,$$

and then the pentacyanonitrosylferrate(II) ion, the 'nitroprusside' ion:

$$[Fe(CN)_5NO_2]^{4-} + 2H_3O^+ \rightleftharpoons [Fe(CN)_5NO]^{2-} + 3H_2O.$$

The red sodium salt, $Na_2[Fe(CN)_5NO]2H_2O$, is diamagnetic; surprisingly since the NO group is an odd-electron group which must confer paramagnetism should it be co-ordinated in the normal way. If the group is considered as co-ordinating in the form NO^+, however, not only is the diamagnetism comprehensible but the charge on the iron becomes clear; it is, in fact, $+2$. The SH^- ion in alkaline solution converts the nitroprusside ion to purple $[Fe(CN)_5NOS]^{4-}$:

$$[Fe(CN)_5NO]^{2-} + OH^- + SH^- \rightarrow [Fe(CN)_5NOS]^{4-} + H_2O.$$

2. *Other iron complexes*

The trioxalatoferrate (III) ion, $[Fe(C_2O_4)_3]^{3-}$, is less stable than the hexacyanoferrate(III) ion, $[Fe(CN)_6]^{3-}$; in acid solution it gives the thiocyanate test for ferric ion. The ion is octahedral.

The salt made by the addition of oxalic acid to an iron(II) salt is probably $Fe[Fe(C_2O_4)_2].4H_2O$. Its magnetic moment (10.3 μ_B) is higher than can be accounted for in terms of either a tetrahedral or a square $Fe(C_2O_4)_2$ ion, however.

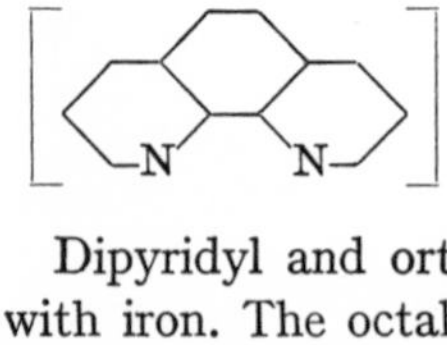

Fig. 264. The (phen)-group in octahedral $[Fe(phen)_3]^{2+}$-ion.

Dipyridyl and orthophenanthroline form particularly stable complexes with iron. The octahedral $[Fe(phen)_3]^{2+}$ ion (Fig. 264) is blood-red but is oxidised to pale blue $[Fe(phen)_3]^{3+}$ without any structural change. $E°$ for the system $= 1.14$ V, making the compound, also known as ferroin, a most useful redox indicator for the oxidation of Fe^{2+} ion ($E_h°$ $Fe^{3+}/Fe^{2+} = 0.77$ V) by cerium(IV) ion ($E_h°$ $Ce^{4+}/Ce^{3+} = 1.45$ V).

Dicyclopentadienyliron(II), or 'ferrocene' can be made by heating finely-divided iron with cyclopentadiene (Miller, Tebboth and Tremaine, 1952):

$$
\begin{array}{c}
\text{CH}_2 \\
\text{CH}\qquad\text{CH} \\
\text{CH}\!-\!\text{CH}
\end{array}
$$

or by treating $FeCl_2$ with a Grignard compound of cyclopentadiene (Kealy and Pauson, 1951):

$$2C_5H_5MgBr + FeCl_2 \rightleftharpoons (C_5H_5)_2Fe + MgBr_2 + MgCl_2.$$

The solid (m.p. 173°) is remarkably stable, and is unaffected by NaOH and HCl even at the boiling point. The complex is diamagnetic, has zero dipole moment, and all its CH bonds are alike: It has a 'sandwich' structure with the iron atom lying between two C_5H_5 pentagons (Wilkinson, Rosenblum, Whiting and Woodward, 1952).

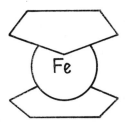

Fig. 265. Structure of ferrocene (dicyclopentadienyl iron(II)).

The rings show aromatic rather than olefinic reactivity; the existence of only three acetyl ethyl ferrocenes proves that the rings can rotate freely. Oxidation produces the blue cation $(C_5H_5)_2Fe^+$.

The dicyclopentadienyls of other metals are less stable than ferrocene. Wilkinson (1952) made $(C_5H_5)_2Ru$ and $(C_5H_5)_2Co^+$, the latter by the action of cobalt(III) acetonyl acetate on C_5H_5MgBr. Cyclopentadiene also reacts with metal carbonyls giving cyclopentadienyl carbonyls such as $Fe(CO)_4(C_5H_5)_2$. These yield dicyclopentadienyls on heating, and the method has enabled the Fe, Co and Cr compounds to be made (Wilkinson, 1954). Substituted cyclopentadienes have been used, too, and Pauson and Wilkinson (1954) have made di-indenyl derivatives of Fe^{II} and Co^{III}.

3. Cobalt (III) complexes

Although cobalt(II) salts are oxidised only with extreme difficulty $(E_h^\circ\ Co^{3+}/Co^{2+} = +1.84\ V)$, H_2O_2 or even air will oxidise Co^{II} to a complex of Co^{III} in the presence of cyanide or ammonia $(E_h^\circ\ Co(CN)_6{}^{3-}/Co(CN)_6{}^{4-} = -0.83\ V)$. Hexa-amminecobalt(III) chloride, $Co(NH_3)_6Cl_3$, is readily made by oxidising an ammoniacal $CoCl_2$ solution containing NH_4Cl in the presence of active charcoal as catalyst:

$$2 CoCl_2 + 2 NH_4Cl + 10 NH_3 + H_2O_2 \rightleftharpoons 2 Co(NH_3)_6Cl_3 + 2 H_2O.$$

This is a cobaltammine of the so-called 'luteo' series containing the $Co(NH_3)_6^{3+}$ ion. Treatment of $Co(NO_3)_2$, NH_4NO_3 and NH_3 with H_2O_2 in the absence of charcoal produces one of the 'purpureo' series, nitratopenta-amminecobalt(III) nitrate, $[Co(NH_3)_5NO_3](NO_3)_2$. Other series such as the 'roseo' aquopenta-amminecobalt(III) chloride, $[Co(NH_3)_5H_2O]Cl_3$, and 'vio-leo' chloroaquotetra-amminecobalt(III) chloride, $[Co(NH_3)_4H_2OCl]Cl_2$, can be made by suitable methods. The classical names, now falling into disuse indicate the colours. The colour changes observed in passing from one series to another conform nicely to the spectrochemical series (p. 134). In all, over two thousand cobaltammines are known.

Hexacyanocobaltates(III) contain the extremely stable $Co(CN)_6^{3-}$ ion. An excess of KCN added to a Co^{2+} solution gives potassium hexacyanocobal-tate(II), $K_4Co(CN)_6$, which is precipitated from aqueous solution by alcohol. When boiled with even a weak acid such as acetic, aerial oxidation to the hexacyanocobaltate(III), $K_3Co(CN)_6$, occurs:

$$4Co(CN)_6^{4-} + O_2 + 4H^+aq \rightarrow 4Co(CN)_6^{3-} + 2H_2O.$$

'Cobaltinitrites' are also complexes of Co^{III}. Addition of KNO_2 to a Co^{II} solution made acid with acetic acid gives a yellow precipitate of potassium hexanitrocobaltate(III), $K_3Co(NO_2)_6$:

$$Co^{2+} + 7NO_2^- + 2H^+aq \rightarrow Co(NO_2)_6^{3-} + NO + H_2O.$$

4. *Polynuclear complexes of cobalt*

When violet chloroaquotetra-amminecobalt(III) sulphate, $[Co(NH_3)_4(H_2O)Cl]SO_4$, is treated with cold alkali the asymmetric ion

$$\left(Co\left[\begin{array}{c} H \\ O \\ Co(NH_3)_4 \\ O \\ H \end{array} \right]_3 \right)^{6+}$$

is produced. The chloride of this ion was the first purely inorganic (non-carbon) compound to be resolved (Werner, 1914).

Another type of polynuclear cobalt complex is produced by aerial oxida-tion of ammoniacal $Co(NO_3)_2$ solution. This is the μ-peroxo-bis{penta-amminecobalt(III)} ion, $[(NH_3)_5Co-O-O-Co(NH_3)_5]^{4+}$. Further oxida-tion gives the ion $[(NH_3)_5Co-O-O-Co(NH_3)_5]^{4+}$ which Ebsworth and Weil have shown, by electron-spin resonance, to contain cobalt atoms of identical oxidation number, not Co^{III} and Co^{IV} as previously thought.

Chapter 34

The Platinum Metals

GROUP VIII (SECOND AND THIRD TRIADS)

The metals of the second and third triads of Gp. VIII resemble one another chemically and physically, as would be expected since both horizontal similarities (Fe, Co, Ni) and vertical similarities (Mo and W) (Tc and Re) are characteristic of this part of the Periodic Table.

These rather rare elements usually occur together and are called the platinum metals. Their ground-state electronic configurations are in doubt, but the tendency to complete the $(n - 1)$d level at the expense of the ns level increases across each triad. The almost uniform atomic radii are naturally accompanied by great physical similarity. Because the radii of Pd^{2+} and Pt^{2+} are so small, the metals rarely form uncomplexed cations.

TABLE 123

SOME PROPERTIES OF THE PLATINUM METALS

	Ru	Rh	Pd	Os	Ir	Pt
Atomic number	44	45	46	76	77	78
Electron configuration	$4d^7 5s^1$	$4d^8 5s^1$	$4d^{10}$	$5d^6 6s^2$	$5d^9$	$5d^9 6s^1$
Atomic radius (Å)	1.24	1.25	1.28	1.26	1.26	1.29
Ionic radius M^{2+} (Å)			0.65			0.52
M^{3+} (Å)		0.69				
M^{4+} (Å)	0.65			0.67	0.66	

Although the first ionisation potentials are not much greater than those of other transition elements and all are lower than that of zinc (9.4 eV), the standard electrode potentials are very high, being determined in part by the

TABLE 124

IONISATION AND ELECTRODE POTENTIALS OF THE PLATINUM METALS

	Ru	Rh	Pd	Os	Ir	Pt
I (eV)	7.5	7.7	8.3	8.7	9.2	9.0
E_h° M^{2+}/M (V)	$+0.45$	$+0.6$	$+0.85$	$+0.85$	$+1.0$	$+1.2$

sublimation energies which are high. A tendency to assume passivity also increases the noble character of some of the metals. Only platinum, osmium and palladium are soluble in aqua regia, and then, almost certainly, as complexes such as $PtCl_6^{2-}$.

Ruthenium and osmium bear a relation to iron rather similar to that of Mo and W to Cr. High charge numbers occur, in for instance OsO_4, but OsF_6 is the highest fluoride (Weinstock and Mahn, 1958). The maximum charge falls abruptly from ruthenium to rhodium and from osmium to iridium. Indeed, the general charge pattern of the preceding transition elements changes at this point in the Periodic Table; thereafter the elements tend to show less diversity of charge number. This is evident in the closer relationship between Ni, Pd, Pt than between both Co, Rh, Ir and Fe, Ru, Os. Nickel, palladium and platinum occur usually with charge $+2$; only in Pt is the $4+$ ion equally common. They all absorb hydrogen strongly, and their complexes are similar.

The following charge numbers are met, those in parentheses being rather uncommon:

Ru	3, 4, (5), 6, (7), 8	Rh		(1), 3		Pd	(0), 2, 4
Os	3, 4, (5), 6, 8	Ir	(0),	3, 4, (5), (6)		Pt	2, 4

But $+5$ occurs in ruthenium and osmium compounds, such as $CsRuF_6$ and $NaOsF_6$, and $+7$ in the per-ruthenates, $KRuO_4$. Rh^I is found in the ion $[Rh(PhNC)_4]^+$. Ir^{IV} and Ir^{VI} occur in Na_2IrF_6 and IrF_6 respectively, and Ir^0 and Pd^0 in Ir $(NH_3)_5$, (Watt, 1953) and $Pd(NH_3)_4$. Complexes in which the metal has charge $+4$ and a half-filled d shell increase in stability on passing downwards from Co through Rh to Ir; 6 co-ordination is usual.

Most of the common complexes are octahedral, being either high-spin or low-spin according to the ligand. But Pd^{II} and Pt^{II} appear exclusively, so far as is known, in square co-ordination (pp. 106 and 535).

The elements: preparation and properties

The six metals together comprise about 2×10^{-5} % of the lithosphere and are often found native. Osmiridium is a natural alloy of osmium and iridium. Important ores are sperrylite, $PtAs_2$, cooperite, PtS, and braggite, (Pt, Pd, Ni)S. The Sudbury (Canada) nickel and copper sulphide deposits contain about 2 ppm of the platinum metals, other than osmium. The metals, along with copper and gold, are segregated in the undissolved sludges from the electro-refining of Ni and Cu and in the involatile residues after the removal of $Ni(CO)_4$ in the carbonyl process. The separation (Fig. 266) begins with an extraction by hot aqua regia in which only platinum, palladium and gold dissolve.

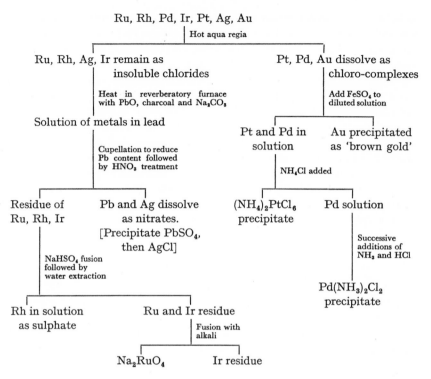

Fig. 266. Separation of the platinum metals.

The densities of the metals fall into two groups, those in the final triad being the highest of all the elements, nevertheless the atomic volumes are slightly greater than those of iron, cobalt and nickel. Ruthenium and osmium have h.c.p. structure, the rest f.c.c. Melting points decrease with atomic number rather quickly in each triad, but all are high.

TABLE 125

SOME PROPERTIES OF THE PLATINUM METALS

	Ru	Rh	Pd	Os	Ir	Pt
Density (g/cc)	12.2	12.4	11.9	22.5	22.4	21.4
Atomic volume	8.6	8.8	9.0	8.5	8.6	9.1
M.p. (°C)	2500	1970	1560	2700	2450	1770

Platinum and palladium are useful in catalysis. Many of the elements are resistant to corrosion: platinum is employed for electrodes and crucibles and extensively for spinnerets to extrude rayon, and rhodium provides a surfacing material for searchlight mirrors. Palladium is used for purifying hydrogen which diffuses rapidly and selectively through the warm metal.

The metals are relatively unreactive. Of them platinum does not react with oxygen, palladium alone dissolves in nitric acid, and platinum, osmium and palladium dissolve in aqua regia. Only osmium and ruthenium form volatile oxides, MO_4, or, when fused with alkalis and oxidising agents, compounds like the osmates and ruthenates, $M^I_2OsO_4$ and $M^I_2RuO_4$. Palladium and ruthenium acquire oxide coatings on heating to 600°–800°, but these decompose and leave bright metal at 1000°. The metals all react with chlorine at temperatures of 400° and above. The oxides and sulphides, a few of the sulphates, and some of the halides are the only uncomplexed compounds.

Halides

Many of the halides can be made by direct combination of the elements at 250°–800°. Temperatures are often critical; thus chlorine reacts with iridium at 770° to give principally $IrCl_2$, but IrCl is formed at 790°. The principal halides, many of them made by direct combination, are shown in Table 126.

TABLE 126

PRINCIPAL HALIDES OF THE PLATINUM METALS

	Ru	*Rh*	*Pd*	*Os*	*Ir*	*Pt*
F	RuF_5	RhF_3	PdF_2, PdF_3	OsF_6	IrF_4, IrF_6	PtF_4
Cl	$RuCl_3$	$RhCl_3$	$PdCl_2$	$OsCl_3, OsCl_4$	$IrCl, IrCl_2$	$PtCl_2, PtCl_3$
Br		$RhBr_3$				$PtBr_2, PtBr_3$
I						PtI_2, PtI_3

Lower halides are sometimes obtained from these by heating at very low pressures: $2OsCl_3 \rightarrow 2OsCl_2 + Cl_2$, by heating with the metal: $2IrF_6 + Ir \rightarrow 3IrF_4$, or by reducing with iodine or sulphur: $3RuF_5 + I_2 \rightarrow 3RuF_3 + 2IF_3$. Palladium trifluoride, PdF_3, is best made by the action of fluorine on $PdCl_2$. Pure PdF_2 has been obtained (Bartlett and Hepworth, 1956) by the following steps:

$$PdI_2 \xrightarrow{\text{BrF}_3} PdF_3.BrF_3, \qquad PdF_3.BrF_3 \xrightarrow{\text{SeF}_4} PdF_4.SeF_4,$$

$$PdF_4.SeF_4 \xrightarrow{\text{in SeF}_4 \text{ at } 220°} PdF_2 + SeF_6.$$

Platinum(IV) chloride, $PtCl_4$, is made from H_2PtCl_6. Platinum is dissolved in aqua regia and the liquid evaporated down several times with concentrated HCl to decompose nitrosyl complexes originally formed. The product is impure chloroplatinic acid, $H_2PtCl_6 . 6H_2O$, which, when heated in Cl_2 at 370°, gives the red-brown $PtCl_4$. A corresponding chloride of Pd is unknown.

Bromides and iodides are often made most satisfactorily by precipitation reactions, being generally much less soluble than the corresponding chlorides:

$$
\begin{aligned}
PdCl_2 &+ 2KI &\rightarrow PdI_2 &+ 2KCl, \\
PdCl_2 &+ 2KBr &\rightarrow PdBr_2 &+ 2KCl, \\
RhCl_3 &+ 3KI &\rightarrow RhI_3 &+ 3KCl, \\
H_2PtCl_6 &+ 4KI &\rightarrow PtI_4 &+ 4KCl + 2HCl.
\end{aligned}
$$

The method is not always applicable, however; OsI_4 is much more soluble than $OsCl_4$ and must be made from OsO_2 and HI. The preparation of $PtBr_4$ is similar to that of $PtCl_4$; platinum is dissolved in a mixture of nitric acid and bromine to give H_2PtBr_6 which, on drying, yields 2HBr and $PtBr_4$.

Most of the halides are highly coloured solids whose volatility usually increases with the charge number of the metal; some of the higher fluorides are easily vaporised:

IrF_6 (m.p. 44°. b.p. 53°) $\qquad OsF_6$ (m.p. 35°. b.p. 47°).

Halogen complexes

The principal chloro-ions are

	M^{II}	M^{III}	M^{IV}
Ru		$RuCl_6^{3-}$	$RuCl_6^{2-}$
Rh		$RhCl_6^{3-}$	
Pd	$PdCl_4^{2-}$		$PdCl_6^{2-}$
Os		$OsCl_6^{3-}$	$OsCl_6^{2-}$
Ir		$IrCl_6^{3-}$	$IrCl_6^{2-}$
Pt	$PtCl_4^{2-}$		$PtCl_6^{2-}$

Corresponding bromo- and iodo-complexes are known.

The chloro-complexes can sometimes be made by heating the metal with an alkali metal chloride in a stream of chlorine:

$$2Rh + 6NaCl + 3Cl_2 \rightarrow 2Na_3RhCl_6.$$

The reaction may be possible even when the corresponding simple halide is unknown:

$$Ir + 2NaCl + 2Cl_2 \rightarrow Na_2IrCl_6.$$

Another common method of preparation is to add NH_4Cl or KCl to the complex chloro-acid, ammonium and potassium salts being sparingly soluble as a rule:

$$H_2PtCl_6 + 2NH_4Cl \rightarrow (NH_4)_2PtCl_6 + 2HCl,$$
$$H_2OsCl_6 + 2NH_4Cl \rightarrow (NH_4)_2OsCl_6 + 2HCl.$$

The ammonium salt is frequently used in purification processes as it gives the metal on heating. The addition of KCl to a Na_3RhCl_6 solution precipitates the 5-co-ordinate K_2RhCl_5

Platinum resists attack by concentrated aqueous HCl except in the presence of KCl or RbCl which, by forming insoluble chloroplatinates, disturb the equilibrium which is normally in favour of the metal. Similarly, gaseous HCl reacts with Pt in the presence of KCl: von Wartenburg (1953) showed that K_2PtCl_4 is first formed and subsequently disproportionates to Pt and K_2PtCl_6, on cooling.

Of all the chloro-complexes, only the chloroplatinates(II) and (IV) are not hydrolysed in aqueous solution at pH 7. The rest give precipitates of hydrated oxides under these conditions.

Fluoropalladates of the type $M_2^IPdF_6$ (Sharpe, 1953), fluororuthenates (Hepworth, Peacock and Robinson, 1954) and fluoroplatinates (IV) (Perros and Naeser, 1953) of similar constitution have been made.

Oxides

The principal oxides are

	M^{II}	M^{III}	M^{IV}	M^{VIII}
Ru			RuO_2	RuO_4
Rh		Rh_2O_3		
Pd	PdO			
Os			OsO_2	OsO_4
Ir			IrO_2	
Pt	PtO		PtO_2	

The dominant charge $+2$ of Pd is shown in its oxide; this remains after heating $PdCl_2$ with $NaNO_3$ at 600° and leaching out the soluble sodium salts. In the tetragonal lattice (Fig. 267) the metal atoms have four coplanar bonds as in the Pd^{II} complexes; the oxygens are tetrahedrally co-ordinated. PtO is isomorphous with PdO but, as normally prepared by the cautious heating of black $Pt(OH)_2$ precipitated from H_2PtCl_6 by NaOH, is deficient in oxygen.

Yellow $Rh(OH)_3$ is thrown down when a very slight excess of alkali is added to an $RhCl_3$ solution. The black Rh_2O_3 is best prepared from it by first making the nitrate:

$$Rh(OH)_3 \xrightarrow{\text{HNO}_3} Rh(NO_3)_3 2H_2O \xrightarrow{\text{heat}} Rh_2O_3.$$

The oxide has the rhombohedral Fe_2O_3 structure. Dark green $Ir(OH)_3$ can be obtained by heating Na_3IrCl_6 to redness with NaOH and washing the solid with water.

$$Ir + NaCl \xrightarrow[\text{heat}]{\text{Cl}_2} Na_2IrCl_6 \xrightarrow[\text{reduction}]{\text{SO}_2} Na_3IrCl_6 \xrightarrow{\text{NaOH}} Ir(OH)_3.$$

This hydroxide is the best starting point for the Ir^{III} compounds; the corresponding oxide is not known.

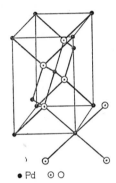

● Pd ⊙ O

Fig. 267. Structure of PdO, showing tetragonal unit cell.

Dark blue $Ir(OH)_4$ is precipitated when Na_2IrCl_6 solution is boiled with sodium bromate at pH 6. When heated in an inert atmosphere at 500° it is converted to black IrO_2, also obtainable by direct combination, as is RuO_2. But OsO_2, can only be prepared by the reduction of OsO_4. These three oxides have the rutile structure (p. 150). Platinum cannot be directly oxidised, being in this respect the most noble of the six metals; PtO_2 is made by fusing H_2PtCl_6 with $NaNO_3$ at 500° and washing the residue free of sodium salts.

The tetroxides of ruthenium and osmium are solids of low m.p. (RuO_4, 25°. OsO_4, 41°). RuO_4 volatilises when a stream of Cl_2 is passed through an alkaline solution of a ruthenate and is conveniently prepared by oxidising potassium ruthenate with periodic acid (Martin, 1952):

$$Ru \xrightarrow[\text{fuse}]{\text{KOH + KNO}_3} K_2RuO_4 \xrightarrow[\text{alkaline soln}]{\text{Cl}_2 \text{ in}} 2KCl + RuO_4.$$

It sublimes in a vacuum but decomposes explosively above 600°.

The much more stable OsO_4 is made by heating finely divided Os in oxygen: it can be boiled without decomposition.

These two metals form oxoanions similar to those of manganese and rhenium.

$$Os \xrightarrow[\text{fuse}]{Na_2O_2} \underset{\text{sodium perosmate}}{NaOsO_4} \xrightarrow[\text{solution}]{\text{MeOH to}} \underset{\text{sodium osmate}}{Na_2OsO_4.}$$

Violet crystals of K_2OsO_4 are precipitated when an excess of KOH is added to a solution of the sodium salt. Oxides corresponding to these oxo-anions are not known.

Sulphides

The platinum metals form the following sulphides:

Ru			RuS_2
Rh		Rh_2S_3	RhS_2
Pd	PdS		PdS_2
Os			OsS_2
Ir		Ir_2S_3	IrS_2
Pt	PtS		PtS_2

Although the six metals form disulphides, these are not the same structurally. RuS_2, RhS_2 and OsS_2 have a cubic, pyrites structure (Fig. 261, p. 494) containing S_2^{2-} ions; they are therefore compounds exhibiting the $+2$ state, but PtS_2 has the CdI_2 lattice (p. 150).

Both Rh and Ir form sulphides of the type M_2S_3 when their trichlorides are heated in H_2S.

PdS, made by direct combination, and PtS, by the reduction of PtS_2, have tetragonal structures.

Oxoacid salts

The sulphates of rhodium and iridium form yellow alums with the sulphates of K, NH_4, Rb, Cs and Tl^I. The salts themselves are formulated $Rh_2(SO_4)_3.15H_2O$ and $Ir_2(SO_4)_312H_2O$. Like palladium(II) sulphate, $PdSO_4.2H_2O$, they are made by the action of H_2SO_4 on the metals.

Palladium(II) nitrate, $Pd(NO_3)_2$, can be crystallised from a solution of palladium in nitric acid. In these salts, the metal again shows its dominant $+2$ charge and its similarity to nickel.

Complexes

Very many complexes are formed by the members of this family of metals. The square Pt^{II} complexes are all diamagnetic; this indicates a d^8 configuration with the one d_γ orbital left free for bonding lending itself to the formation of dsp^2 hybrids.

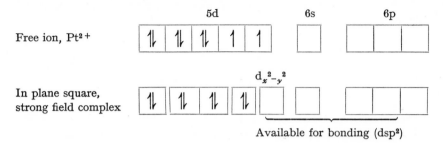

6-Co-ordinate complexes of Pd^{IV} and Pt^{IV} are formed with ligands which have low-lying orbitals available for π-bond formation. Secondary bonding of this kind facilitates the even distribution of electronic charge (p. 137) and helps to stabilise the complex. The majority of Pd^{IV} and Pt^{IV} complexes are regular octahedral and diamagnetic; the electron configuration of the cation is $(d_\varepsilon)^6$ with both d_γ orbitals available for d^{2}sp^3 bonding.

In Pd(diarsine)$_2$I$_2$ the iodine atoms are in trans positions (Fig. 268), and the Pd—I bonds are $\sim$ 30% longer than in the square [PdI$_4$]$^{2-}$ ion. This can be explained by the repulsion exerted on the iodine atoms by the filled d_{z^2} orbital of the Pd (p. 135).

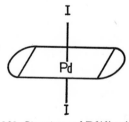

Fig. 268. Structure of Pd(diarsine)$_2$I$_2$.

Ru^{III} and Os^{III} complexes are all similar to the spin-paired Fe^{III} complexes but the orbital contributions to magnetic moment are smaller. Ru^{IV} and Os^{IV} complexes (K_2RuCl_6 and K_2OsCl_6) generally contain two unpaired electrons:

$(n-1)d$ ns np

Available for bonding (d^2sp^3)

An interesting exception occurs in $K_4[Cl_5Ru-O-RuCl_5]$ where, if the oxygen uses sp hybrid orbitals to give a linear bond between the rutheniums, it still has two unhybridised 2p pairs for secondary π-bond formation with the metal atoms. The d_ε level is split by the reduction in symmetry and both electrons fall into the same lower-energy orbital to give a resultant diamagnetism.

Ru^{IV} and Ir^{III} complexes are invariably diamagnetic and octahedral; they thus resemble spin-paired Co^{III} complexes.

The platinum metals sometimes show charges in complexes not found in their simple compounds. Thus Ir and Os are $+5$ in complex fluorides such as M^IOsF_6, where magnetic measurements indicate three unpaired electrons. When $K_2Pd(CN)_4$ is reduced with potassium in liquid ammonia the compound $K_4Pd(CN)_4$ is formed in which the metal is without charge. Zero charge also occurs in the carbonyls; these are formed by all this family of metals except Pt itself and Pd.

In addition to complex halides and cyanides, the metals form many ammines. Organic compounds of nitrogen, arsenic, sulphur, selenium and tellurium are other possible ligands. Many complexes with bidentate ligands are known. The various types of isomerism are common; thus $Pd(NH_3)_2Cl_2$ occurs as the pink $[Pd(NH_3)_4]$ $[PdCl_4]$ and as the yellow cis and trans isomers:

$$\begin{array}{ccc} NH_3 & Cl & \\ & \diagdown Pd \diagup & \\ NH_3 & Cl & \end{array} \qquad \text{and} \qquad \begin{array}{ccc} NH_3 & Cl & \\ & \diagdown Pd \diagup & \\ Cl & NH_3 & \end{array}$$

Wilkinson (1953) has made bis(cyclopentadienyl) cations, $Rh(C_5H_5)_2{}^+$ and $Ir(C_5H_5)_2{}^+$, but the yellow salts cannot be reduced in aqueous solution.

Of particular interest from the point of view of valency theory are the binuclear platinum-olefin complexes (Chatt, 1951):

$$\begin{array}{ccccc} C_2H_4 & Cl & Cl & \\ & \diagdown Pt \diagup & \diagdown Pt \diagup & \\ Cl & Cl & C_2H_4 & \end{array}$$

Infrared measurements show that (a) the olefin retains its double bond in the complex, and (b) the olefin is symmetrically bonded to the metal. Further, the olefin is found to be trans-directing. Chatt and Duncanson (1953) suggest that the metal is bound by both σ and π bonds, probably a σ-type bond between a Pt (dsp^2 hybrid) and the olefin π bond, together with a π-type bond between a Pt (dp hybrid) and the antibonding π^* orbital of the olefin (Fig. 269).

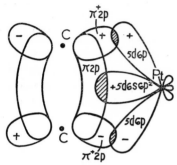

Fig. 269. Overlap of orbitals in [PtCl$_2$.C$_2$H$_4$]$_2$.

Chapter 35

Copper, Silver and Gold

GROUP IB

Copper, silver and gold, traditionally the 'coinage metals', all have the $(n-1)d^{10}ns^1$ electron configuration and ^2S ground state. They lie well to the right in the Periodic Table, have ionisation potentials about twice as large as the alkali metals which begin the periods, and show a considerable tendency to form covalent compounds. The d electrons frequently participate in bonding and the ions M^+, M^{2+}, and with copper and gold, M^{3+}, are recognised in various complexes.

TABLE 127

SOME PROPERTIES OF GROUP IB METALS

	Cu	Ag	Au
Atomic number	29	47	79
Electron configuration	$3d^{10} 4s^1$	$4d^{10} 5s^1$	$5d^{10} 6s^1$
Atomic radius (Å)	1.17	1.34	1.34
Ionic radius, M^+ (Å)	0.96	1.26	1.37

The hydrated ions occur in aqueous solutions and the standard electrode potentials are known:

TABLE 128

IONISATION AND ELECTRODE POTENTIALS OF GROUP IB METALS

	Cu	Ag	Au
Ionisation potential I (eV)	7.72	7.87	9.22
E_h° M^+/M (V)	$+0.522$	$+0.799$	$+1.68$
M^{2+}/M ,,	$+0.345$	$+1.39$	
M^{3+}/M ,,			$+1.42$

Although silver ions become less resistant to reduction with increasing charge, those of copper and gold become more so; this is due to a relatively high heat of hydration. Thus, although the second ionisation potential of copper is 20.2 eV, the large heat of hydration of Cu^{2+} compared with that of

Cu^+ makes the hydrated Cu^{2+} ion the more stable in aqueous solution. Thus soluble copper(I) compounds always disproportionate:

$$2Cu^+(aq) \rightarrow Cu + Cu^{2+}(aq).$$

The comparison with silver is striking:

$$\frac{\{Cu^{2+}\}}{\{Cu^+\}^2} = 1.2 \times 10^6 \qquad \frac{\{Ag^{2+}\}}{\{Ag^+\}^2} \simeq 10^{-17} \qquad \text{(at 25° C)}$$

Accordingly an appreciable concentration of Ag^{2+} does not occur in aqueous solution. Gold resembles copper in the instability of its unipositive ion,

$$3Au^+(aq) \rightarrow 2Au + Au^{3+}(aq),$$

and, on reduction, both Cu^{II} and Au^{III} salts usually give the metal.

The bonds in their simple unipositive compounds are largely covalent and the halides, oxides and sulphides are all, with the exception of silver fluoride, insoluble in water. The water-soluble compounds are those with complex ions, such as $Cu(CN)_3^{2-}$, $Cu(NH_3)_2^+$ and $Ag(NH_3)_2^+$, the solutions always being colourless. In these ions the metal is unipositive with a non-bonding d^{10} shell and the disposition of the ligands tends to be linear or trigonal planar as in non-transition metals.

The metals appear with charge $+2$ in many complexes, Cu^{II} compounds being particularly common. The d^9 configuration often gives square structures, with four ligands in the plane, and distorted octahedral structures in which two more ligands are attached, by somewhat longer bonds, above and below the plane (p. 135). Copper(II) compounds of both types occur. The most important silver(II) compound is the oxide AgO, but the solid is diamagnetic and confirms the artificiality of the ionic model, in which the $Ag^{2+}(d^9)$ would give a spin paramagnetism. On the other hand a solution of AgO in HNO_3 is paramagnetic, indicating bipositive silver in the resulting complex ion. Gold alone appears to have no M^{II} complexes.

Both copper and gold form M^{III} complexes. Copper appears with charge $+3$ in CuF_6^{3-}, whose paramagnetism indicates two singly occupied d orbitals; this is the high-spin case (p. 134) and the expected shape is regular octahedral, the non-bonding electrons being $d_z^6 d_{y^2}^2$. Gold, with its higher electronegativity, can obtain an adequate share of electrons from a smaller number of ligands (p. 137) and occurs more commonly in 4 co-ordination, examples being $AuCl_4^-$ and $AuBr_4^-$ which are square.

Properties and extraction of the metals

The metals are all very readily reduced, malleable and unaffected by clean air. Their densities are high, though not the highest of the elements in their respective atomic number range. Their atomic volumes are low, that of gold being particularly so as a result of the lanthanide contraction associated with the filling of the 4f shell. The metals have c.c.p. structure and their m.p. and b.p. are moderately high.

TABLE 129

SOME PROPERTIES OF GROUP IB METALS

	Cu	Ag	Au
Density (g/cc)	8.9	10.5	19.3
Atomic volume	7.1	10.3	10.2
Melting point (°C)	1083	960	1062
Boiling point (°C)	2310	1950	2600

The metals occur native. Their extraction from minerals is easy. Copper comprises about $7 \times 10^{-3}\%$ of the lithosphere as copper pyrites, $CuFeS_2$, cuprite, Cu_2O, and malachite, $Cu_2(OH)_2CO_3$; silver about $2 \times 10^{-5}\%$ as argentite, Ag_2S, horn silver, $AgCl$, pyrargyrite, Ag_3SbS_3; gold about $5 \times 10^{-7}\%$ as metal.

Copper oxide and carbonate ores are readily reduced by heating with coke and a flux:

$$CuCO_3 \xrightarrow{\text{heat}} CuO \xrightarrow{\text{C}} Cu.$$

The main source is copper pyrites which is relieved of volatile arsenic and antimony by roasting, after which it is slagged and reduced.

(i) Partial oxidation: $CuFeS_2 \xrightarrow{O_2} Cu_2S + FeS + SO_2.$

(ii) Slagging off iron: $Cu_2S + FeS + SiO_2 \rightarrow \begin{cases} FeSiO_3 \text{ slag (less dense).} \\ Cu_2S \text{ liquid sulphide (more dense).} \end{cases}$

(iii) Oxidation – reduction: (a) $Cu_2S \xrightarrow{O_2} Cu_2O + Cu_2S \xrightarrow{\text{heat alone}} Cu + SO_2.$

Copper is refined electrolytically, the silver and gold present separating as an anode sludge. The last two metals are also recovered during the purification of both lead (p. 310) and nickel (p. 502). Silver and gold are extracted by aqueous sodium cyanide which reduces the oxidation potential of the metals so that atmospheric oxygen brings them, or their salts, into solution as soluble complexes:

$$4Ag + 8NaCN + 2H_2O + O_2 \rightarrow 4NaAg(CN)_2 + 4NaOH;$$
$$Ag_2S + 4NaCN \rightarrow 2NaAg(CN)_2 + Na_2S.$$

The Na_2S is largely oxidised to Na_2SO_4 by the air and the 'back' reaction thereby impeded. Zinc precipitates the noble metals from the cyano-ion:

$$2Ag(CN)_2^- + Zn \rightarrow 2Ag + Zn(CN)_4^{2-}$$
$$2Au(CN)_4^- + Zn + 4CN^- \rightarrow 2Au + 3Zn(CN)_4^{2-}.$$

Oxides

The isomorphous Cu_2O and Ag_2O are of unusual structure. The metal atoms have two collinear bonds and the oxygens four tetrahedral bonds in a cubic structure similar to that of cristobalite. The low co-ordination, 4 : 2, is indicative of covalence. The structure represented in Fig. 270 is not the complete picture. An identical framework, in which the structure shown is moved forward so that the oxygens marked A take up the positions B, interpenetrates it without cross-connection by M—O bonds. The interpenetrating structure is unique in crystal chemistry. Both oxides form solid solutions with the metal.

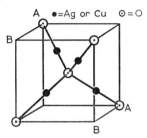

Fig. 270. Diagram illustrating how Ag_2O and Cu_2O are built up structurally.

Silver(I) oxide is made by heating finely divided silver at 300° under 15 atmospheres of oxygen:

$$4Ag + O_2 \rightleftharpoons 2Ag_2O.$$

The material precipitated by alkali from aqueous silver salts cannot be completely freed of water without decomposition; that precipitated from alcoholic solution is the hydroxide, AgOH, which can be made only in this way. The oxide is decomposed completely into silver and oxygen at 300° under normal pressure. It gives an alkaline reaction in water, the solubility though slight is in conformity with a low lattice energy. Its heat of formation is only 7.3 kcal.

Copper(I) oxide, more thermally stable and insoluble, is precipitated from aqueous solution without water of hydration. Its heat of formation, 40 kcal, though low for a metal oxide, is appreciably above that of Ag_2O.

Compounds of Cu^I in the solid, dry condition are not oxidised by air, but its soluble complexes are very readily converted to the Cu^{II} condition. A colourless solution of $Cu(NH_3)_2^+$ becomes blue immediately on exposure to air.

Gold(I) oxide is thermally unstable. A hydrate is precipitated from a KAuBr$_2$ solution by alkali, but attempts at dehydration are accompanied by loss of oxygen.

The copper(II) oxide structure involves 4 : 4 co-ordination with a tetrahedral bond arrangement round the oxygen and coplanar bonds round the copper atoms. The Cu—O distance of 1.95 Å indicates a large degree of covalency (Fig. 271).

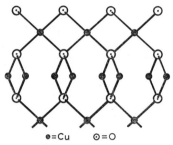

●=Cu   ⊙=O

Fig. 271. Arrangement of Cu and O atoms in CuO.

Crystalline Cu(OH)$_2$ is made by adding ammonia to boiling CuSO$_4$ solution until the green precipitate turns blue, washing, and digesting with NaOH solution. The hydroxide is converted by boiling water to black (CuO)$_4$.H$_2$O which loses all its water at dull red heat without further decomposition. Copper(II) oxide, and sulphide are less stable than the Cu^I compounds, to which they are converted at a higher temperature:

$$4\ CuO\ \xrightarrow{900°}\ 2\ Cu_2O + O_2, \qquad 4\ CuS\ \xrightarrow{1300°}\ 2\ Cu_2S + 2S.$$

The solution of Cu(OH)$_2$ in ammonia contains both [Cu(NH$_3$)$_2$](OH)$_2$ and [Cu(NH$_3$)$_4$](OH)$_2$.

Silver(II) oxide, AgO, which has the zinc blende structure (p. 525) is made by (i) the action of boiling water on Ag$_2$O$_3$ (black crystals formed on the anode when 10% AgNO$_3$ is electrolysed); (ii) precipitation from AgNO$_3$ with potassium persulphate; (iii) oxidising silver(I) oxide with hot alkaline KMnO$_4$. It is not a peroxide since it does not give hydrogen peroxide when acidified. Both Ag$_2$O$_3$ and a solution of AgO in concentrated HNO$_3$ are dark coloured and paramagnetic, suggesting the presence of the Ag^{2+} ion with a 4s^{2}4p^{6}4d^9 structure. Silver(II) oxide gives easily decomposed solutions in oxidising acids other than nitric acid. The couple Ag^{2+}/Ag$^+$ has the very high redox potential of 1.98 volts; thus a solution of Ag^{2+} ions in nitric acid is a particularly strong oxidising agent.

Anodic oxidation of silver nitrate in the presence of pyridine gives the orange red $[Ag(pyr)_4](NO_3)_2$. Dipyridyl compounds are also known, $[Ag(dipyr)_2]X_2$ where $X = NO_3$, HSO_4, ClO_4 and $\frac{1}{2}(S_2O_8)$; they are much more stable than AgO.

Gold(III) hydroxide is made by the action of MgO on $HAuCl_4$. Unlike $Cu(OH)_2$ it dissolves in hot alkalis; yellow crystals of potassium aurate, $KAuO_2.3H_2O$, can be recovered from such a solution.

Halides

The monohalides of the coinage metals, with the exception of AgF, are almost insoluble in polar solvents. Copper(I) halides all have the zinc blende structure; they show a predominantly covalent character in agreement with the observed lattice energies (p. 92) (Table 130).

TABLE 130

LATTICE ENERGIES OF COPPER (I) HALIDES

	$U_{expt.}$	U as calc. on ionic model	Difference
CuCl	221.9	216.0	+5.9
CuBr	216.0	208.0	+8.0
CuI	213.4	199.0	+14.4

Silver iodide is the only silver halide with an adamantine structure, the two elements having covalent radii in the ratio 1.34 : 1.33. Both AgCl (1.34 : 0.99) and AgBr (1.34 : 1.14) have a rock-salt structure and an ionic character. Gold (I) fluoride is unknown, and the chloride, bromide, iodide decrease in stability in that order, the formation of AuI being endothermic (ΔH, 5.52 kcal). With the exception of AuI, all are converted by water to the trihalide and metal, the chloride the most readily, possibly because the most soluble.

TABLE 131

LATTICE ENERGIES OF SILVER(I) HALIDES

	$U_{expt.}$	U as calc. on ionic model	Difference
AgF	217.7	219 (NaCl structure)	—1.3
AgCl	205.7	203 (NaCl structure)	+2.7
AgBr	201.7	197 (NaCl structure)	+4.7
AgI	199.2	190 (ZnS structure)	+9.2

For AgI the difference is sufficiently large to indicate considerable deviation from ionic bonding; its more covalent character is reflected in the insolubility of AgI in NH_3. Above 146°, AgI exhibits an unusual form of defect structure (p. 153). The suggestion that colour in AgBr and AgI is due to ionic deformation (increasing covalent character) is questionable as AgF is yellow. The fluoride alone forms a hydrate, $AgF.H_2O$.

Anhydrous CuF_2, made from fluorine and copper, is an ionic compound with the fluorite structure. But the covalent anhydrous chloride consists of infinite chains packed so that individual copper atoms show square 4-coordination (Fig. 272) and have, as nearest neighbours in the next chain, two chlorine atoms. In the hydrate $CuCl_2.2H_2O$ there are no chains. It probably has a distorted octahedral structure, the Cu—Cl (2.30 Å) and Cu—O (1.97 Å) lengths indicating predominant covalence. Anhydrous $CuBr_2$ has a structure similar to $CuCl_2$ and is without a stable hydrate.

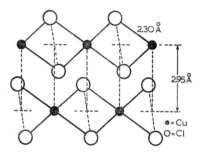

Fig. 272. Arrangement of Cu and Cl atoms in anhydrous $CuCl_2$.

Silver (II) fluoride, AgF_2, made by the action of fluorine on Ag or AgCl, is fairly stable, the equilibrium pressure of fluorine over the solid at 700° being only 80 mm. It is, nevertheless, a useful fluorinating agent.

Gold dissolves in aqua regia to a yellow solution which gives chloroauric acid trihydrate on evaporation:

$$Au \xrightarrow{\text{NOCl + Cl}_2} AuCl_3 \xrightarrow{\text{HCl + H}_2O} HAuCl_4.3H_2O \rightarrow AuCl_3 \rightarrow AuCl \rightarrow Au.$$

Heating gives first red $AuCl_3$, then yellow AuCl and finally gold. Gold(III) chloride results from the decomposition of AuCl in the presence of water:

$$3AuCl \rightarrow AuCl_3 + 2Au.$$

Probably the only sub-halide of the group is Ag_2F, made by the cathodic reduction of aqueous AgF at low current density. The bronze-coloured solid, which is electrically conducting, has successively the atom layers Ag, Ag, F; the Ag—Ag are metal bonds and the Ag—F ionic, giving a structure intermediate between that of a metal and a salt:

Ag   Ag   Ag   Ag
Ag   Ag   Ag   Ag
F   F   F   F
Ag   Ag   Ag   Ag
Ag   Ag   Ag   Ag
F   F   F   F

Layer structure of the sub-halide Ag_2F.

Complex halides

The M^I complexes are mainly of the type $M[CuX_2]$ in which the covalency of the metal is limited to two and of which all the elements provide examples. Of the M^{II} complexes, $K_2CuCl_4.2H_2O$ (Fig. 273) has a tetragonal unit cell with features deriving from both $CuCl_2.2H_2O$ and $CuCl_2$. In anhydrous Cs_2CuCl_4, the $[CuCl_4]^{2-}$ is not planar but a flattened tetrahedron (Helmholtz and Kruh, 1952); in solution the absorption spectrum is different from that of the solid, possibly because the anion reverts to a planar configuration on hydration.

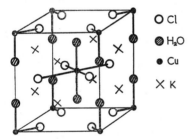

O Cl
◑ H_2O
● Cu
✕ K

Fig. 273. Structure of $K_2CuCl_4.2H_2O$.

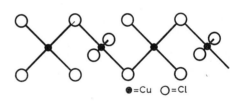

●=Cu O=Cl

Fig. 274. Spiral arrangement of atoms in $(CuCl_3^{2-})_n$ ions.

$CsCuCl_3$ consists of Cs^+ ions and infinite chain $(CuCl_3^{2-})_n$ ions. The co-ordination in these is planar but the sharing of corners by the $CuCl_3$ units gives them a spiral arrangement (Fig. 274).

K_3CuF_6 has been prepared; only the fluorine compound occurs, as so often happens, with the highest co-ordination number. Its paramagnetic moment corresponds to two unpaired electrons and suggests the $3d_s^6\, 3d_y^2\, Cu^{III}$ configuration with regular octahedral form.

Gold(III) complexes are particularly stable. The $AuBr_4^-$ ion in $K[AuBr_4]$.

$2H_2O$ is square. $CsAuCl_3$ contains both Au^I and Au^{III} and can be formulated $Cs_2[(AuCl_2) (AuCl_4)]$. The compound $(C_7H_7)_2S.AuBr_2$, made by the action of benzyl sulphide on $AuBr_3$, contains separate molecules of $(C_7H_7)_2S.AuBr$ and $(C_7H_7)_2S.AuBr_3$ in a highly disordered structure.

Sulphides

The sulphides Cu_2S and Ag_2S, and the corresponding selenides are known; copper also forms CuS and CuSe. All are insoluble in water. Gold gives Au_2S and Au_2S_3, the latter being hydrolysed by water.

Copper(I) sulphide has a high thermal stability; at a dull red heat it is very slowly attacked by chlorine and by sodium carbonate.

Oxoacid salts

Copper(I) sulphate is the only ionic Cu^I compound. It is made by heating Cu_2O with dimethyl sulphate and is decomposed immediately in water:

$$Cu_2O + Me_2SO_4 \rightarrow Cu_2SO_4 + Me_2O; \qquad Cu_2SO_4 \rightarrow Cu + CuSO_4.$$

This is expected from the redox potentials of the Cu^+/Cu and Cu^{2+}/Cu couples. The Cu^+ ion is, however, stabilised by complexing and appears as colourless crystals of $[Cu(NH_3)_2]_2SO_4$; these are produced from an aqueous solution of Cu_2O, NH_3 and $(NH_4)_2SO_4$ on the addition of ethyl alcohol.

Copper(II) sulphate pentahydrate, $Cu(H_2O)_4SO_4.H_2O$, has four water molecules and an oxygen from each of two SO_4^{2-} anions octahedrally arranged about the Cu^{2+} cation. The fifth water molecule is hydrogen-bonded to oxygen atoms. Bacon (1962) has determined the positions of all the water molecules and hydrogen bonds by neutron refraction. He found the H—O—H angles of all the water molecules near the tetrahedral angle, the O—H····O angles between 154–176°, and the O—O—O angles between 105–130°; so that some of the hydrogen bonds are bent, one by 26°. The corresponding ammine hydrate, $Cu(NH_3)_4SO_4.H_2O$, is known, but not a penta-ammine because the hydrogen bonding between NH_3 molecules is too weak to hold a fifth NH_3.

Copper(II) nitrate has the hydrates, $Cu(NO_3)_2.6H_2O$ and $Cu(NO_3)_2.9H_2O$. These, Guntz and Martin (1909) dehydrated by heating in a solution of N_2O_5 in nitric acid. Addison and Hathaway (1957) made anhydrous nitrate by dissolving copper in a mixture of N_2O_4 and ethyl acetate, separating the crystalline $Cu(NO_3)_2.N_2O_4$ formed, and decomposing it by heat. The N_2O_4 is driven off at 85° and further heating of the anhydrous $Cu(NO_3)_2$ in a vacuum at 150–200° enables it to be purified by sublimation on to a cold finger. The volatile nitrate is monomeric both in the vapour and in organic solvents such as dioxan, ethyl acetate and nitrobenzene. Some thermal decomposition of the solid to CuO begins at 150°, but the vapour is stable to 225°.

Its properties all indicate covalence and suggest a co-ordination complex—possibly formed by the overlap of π-orbitals of the NO_3^- group with d orbitals of the copper (p. 135), in which charge disparities are largely removed by the transfer of π-electrons to the metal ion.

Recently, Field and Hardy (1962) have shown that copper and other anhydrous, volatile nitrates can be prepared from the anhydrous chlorides of the respective metals by treating them with an excess of dinitrogen pentoxide. The chlorine is evolved as NO_2Cl and the excess of reagent and the co-ordinated oxides of nitrogen are removed by warming the product. The method is of general application and has enabled volatile $Zr(NO_3)_4$ to be made.

Silver nitrate is notable for a high solubility considerably increased by temperature (215 g per 100 g of water at 20° and 910 g at 100°). Attempts to volatilise $AgNO_3$ have failed.

The precipitation of a normal silver carbonate from solution,

$$2AgNO_3 + K_2CO_3 \rightarrow Ag_2CO_3 + 2KNO_3,$$

is in contrast with the formation of basic copper(II) carbonates under similar conditions, and conforms with the more basic character of Ag_2O.

Silver perchlorate is not only deliquescent and very soluble but also forms a monohydrate. It also dissolves in benzene and toluene, recrystallising from the latter as $AgClO_4.C_7H_8$. Solubility in organic solvents is thus shown to be an unreliable guide to covalent character, for silver perchlorate is considerably ionised both in water and nitromethane.

Oxoacid salts of gold are uncommon; one of the more stable, yellow $Au_2(SeO_4)_3$, crystallises from a solution of gold in hot selenic acid.

Other complexes

The metals form complex cyanides in which they are covalently bonded to the radical, e.g. $KM(CN)_2$. All complex with ammonia to give the ion $[M(NH_3)_2]^+$; and there are similar substituted ammonia and pyridine complexes. Copper(I) chloride dissolved in HCl absorbs CO, and the hydrated carbonyl derivative, $Cu(CO)Cl.H_2O$, has been recovered from the solution. A gold analogue is known. Copper(I) and silver solutions also absorb ethylene and substitued ethylenes. Manometric measurements (Vestin, 1954) have shown that two distinct complexes are formed by acetylene in HCl solution, $C_2H_2(CuCl)_3$ and $C_2H_2(CuCl)_2$.

The magnetic moments of many Cu^{II} complexes fall within the range $1.8-2.2\mu_B$ and are compatible with the presence of one unpaired electron with variable quenching of orbital moment. Most Ag^{II} complexes are also paramagnetic; otherwise paramagnetism is uncommon in complexes of metal ions with d^9 configurations, there being generally an interaction between the unpaired electrons of adjacent metal atoms.

The existence of 6-co-ordinate Cu^{II} complexes may generally be accounted for in terms of sp^3d^2 hybridisation.

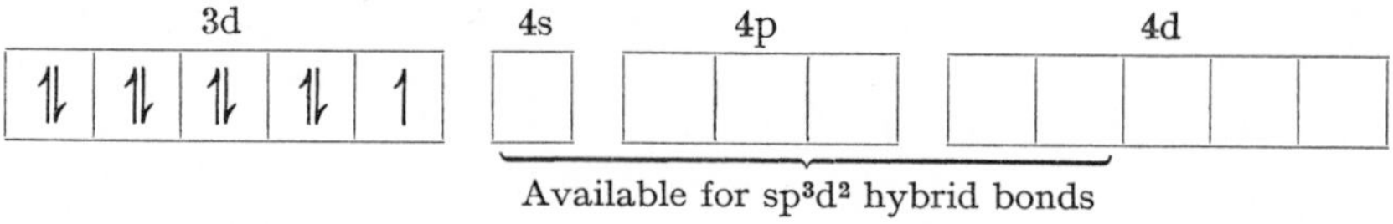

Since, however, the $3d_y$ orbital is singly occupied, the arrangement is tetragonal instead of regular octahedral. In $CuF_2.2H_2O$, for instance, there are two Cu—O bonds of 1.93 Å, two Cu—F bonds of 1.89 Å and two longer Cu—F bonds of 2.47 Å. The $3d_{z^2}$ orbital is doubly occupied but the $3d_{x^2-y^2}$ orbital contains only one electron; hence ligands along the z axis suffer greater repulsion than those along the x and y axes. In a few compounds the distortion is large enough to make the structure effectively square.

The Cu^{II} complex ions $CuCl_4^{2-}$ and $CuBr_4^{2-}$ have distorted tetrahedral structures. In the weak ligand field exerted by the halogen ions (p. 134), the metal has four electrons in d_y orbitals and only five in the three d_ε orbitals which point in the direction of the ligands; the ligands are thus able to approach more closely and form stronger bonds.

Copper(II) acetate monohydrate is one of the few complexes of bipositive copper which resembles, in its magnetic properties, the d^9 complexes of other metals. In it, there is interaction between the unpaired electrons of adjacent copper atoms; its paramagnetic moment is temperature-dependent and the complex is virtually diamagnetic at low temperatures.

Chelated Cu^{II} complexes are generally more stable than the simple complexes. Examples are the ethylenediamine, oxalato, catechol and β-diketone complexes; bis(acetylacetonato)copper(II) is shown:

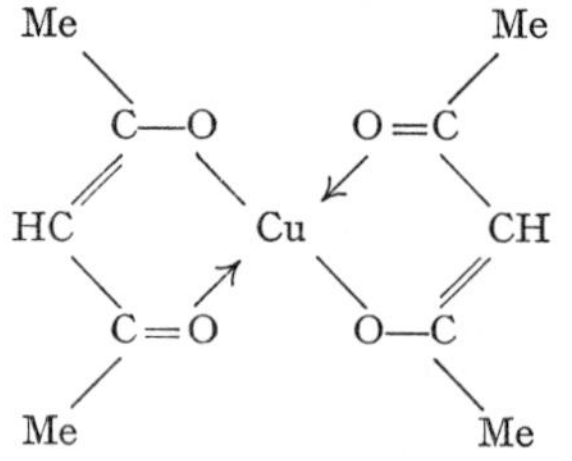

Substitution for halogen in $[AuX_4]^-$ groups gives a variety of complexes such as $[AuCl_3(OH)]^-$ and $[AuBr_2(Pyr)_2]^+$. Simple β-diketone and oxalato complexes are unknown but the dialkyl gold complexes are surprisingly stable:

$$\text{CH}_3 \diagdown \text{Au} \diagup \begin{array}{c} \text{O—C} \diagup \text{CH}_3 \\ \diagdown \text{CH} \\ \text{O=C} \diagdown \text{CH}_3 \end{array}$$

There is evidence that Au^{III} achieves a co-ordination number of six in complexes. The bromoaurate ion, $AuBr_4^-$, reacts with bromide ion in nitrobenzene and nitromethane to give the $AuBr_6^{3-}$, $AuBr_5^{2-}$ and $Au_2Br_{10}^{4-}$ ions.

The metals of Gp. IA have sometimes been compared with those of Gp. IB. This derives historically from the shorter form of the Periodic Table, once invariably used, in which the elements of the pairs of sub-groups are set side by side. In truth, these A and B families of elements are far removed from each other in properties, and, though each has a single s electron, the ions produced by the coinage metals are vastly different from the inert-gas type of ions formed by the alkalis. It is much more valuble to think of Cu in relation to Ni and Zn, of Ag in relation to Pd and Cd, and of Au in relation to Pt and Hg.

Chapter 36

Zinc, Cadmium and Mercury

GROUP II B

Individually these elements show many differences from Cu, Ag and Au which immediately precede them. Their electron configurations are $d^{10}s^2$, with ^1S ground states. The covalent radii are greater, but the bipositive ions, with their complete d shells, are smaller than the unipositive ions of Gp.IB.

TABLE 132

SOME PROPERTIES OF GROUP IIB ELEMENTS

	Zn	*Cd*	*Hg*
Electron configuration	$3d^{10}4s^2$	$4d^{10}5s^2$	$5d^{10}6s^2$
Atomic number	30	48	80
Atomic radius M (Å)	1.25	1.41	1.44
Ionic radius M^{2+} (Å)	0.74	0.97	1.10

The first ionisation potentials are larger than those of the coinage metals, the increased size of the s orbital being overshadowed by the greater effective nuclear charge. Unipositive ions are not observed, although the second ionisation potentials are large, because the d^{10} shell is inert enough to exist alone. In this the elements resemble those of Gp. IIA. The standard electrode potentials of the three metals show a remarkable range, evidently due to the high energies of hydration of the Zn^{2+} and Cd^{2+} ions, since the sum of the first and second ionisation potentials is about the same in all three.

TABLE 133

IONISATION AND ELECTRODE POTENTIALS
OF GROUP IIB ELEMENTS

	Zn	*Cd*	*Hg*
Ionisation potential I 1 (eV)	9.39	8.99	10.43
,, ,, 2 ,,	17.89	16.84	18.65
E_h° M^{2+}/M (V)	−0.763	−0.402	+0.854
E_h° $M_2^{2+}/2M$,,			+0.799

The individual metal is less dense than the corresponding coinage metal; its m.p. is distinctly lower, its b.p. strikingly lower. Mercury is the only metal liquid at room temperature, though liquid gallium can be supercooled below this point.

The elements have not the close-packing of atoms typical of true metals. Zinc and cadmium have distorted h.c.p. structure with axial ratios ~ 1.87 instead of the ideal 1.63 (Fig. 275). These are contributory factors to their low tensile strengths; the ultimate tensile stress of zinc is 7.5 tons per sq.in., of copper 15 tons. Mercury gives rhombohedral crystals with 6:6 co-ordination

TABLE 134

SOME PROPERTIES OF GROUP IIB ELEMENTS

	Zn	Cd	Hg
Density (g/cc)	7.1	8.6	13.6
Atomic volume	9.2	13.0	14.0
Melting point (°C)	419	321	−39
Boiling point (°C)	907	768	357

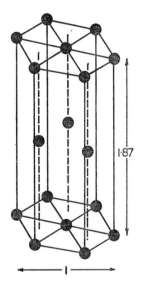

Fig. 275. Inter-atomic spacing in cadmium.

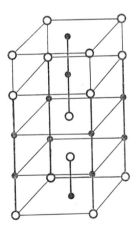

Fig. 276. Tetragonal unit cell of Hg_2Cl_2.

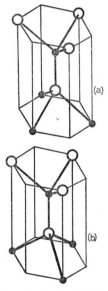

Fig. 277. Relation between (a) blende and (b) wurtzite in terms of arrangement of atoms.

Zinc and cadmium form simple bipositive cations only. Mercury displays in addition the cation Hg_2^{2+} in mercury(I) salts. The evidence for the form of this ion is:

(i) The cell

Hg | Mercury (I) nitrate 0.05M in $N/10$ HNO$_3$ ‖ Mercury (I) nitrate 0.005M in $N/10$ HNO$_3$ | Hg

has an e.m.f. ~ 0.029 V at 25°.

Since

$$E \sim \frac{RT}{ZF} \ln \frac{0.05}{0.005} = \frac{0.059}{Z},$$

Z, the charge on the cation reversible at the electrodes, equals 2 and the cation must be bipositive.

(ii) A simple cation does not produce a Raman spectral line (p. 120) because it is without vibrational energy. Woodward (1934) found mercury (I) salts gave a line, not ascribable to the anion, indicating that the cation is capable of vibration. Hence more than one atom is present.

(iii) The tetragonal unit cell of Hg_2Cl_2 contains linear Cl–Hg–Hg–Cl units (Fig. 276) (Havinghurst, 1926).

The Hg_2^{2+} ion involves an electron-pair bond. This type of metal-metal bonding is rare, but probably occurs in $[W_2Cl_9]^{3-}$ and in $[Ni_2(CN)_6]^{4-}$. The Hg_2^{2+} ion is but little more stable than the Hg^{2+} ion; hence the reduction of a mercury (II) salt normally yields the metal.

Zinc (0.02% of the earth's crust) occurs almost entirely as ZnS; this has two forms (Fig. 277), the much commoner cubic zinc blende or sphalerite, and the rarer, hexagonal wurtzite (p. 149). Iron and cadmium are nearly always present as substitutional impurities and the ore also serves to concentrate a number of much rarer elements such as indium, gallium and germanium. The sulphide is easily converted to oxide by roasting in air.

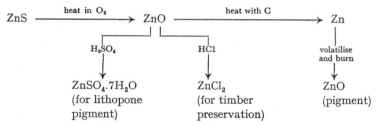

Fig. 278. The chemistry of Zn.

The metal is used for 'galvanising' steel. An alloyed with $\sim 4\%$ Al and 0.15—1.25% Cu is being increasingly employed for die-casting.

Cadmium ($2 \times 10^{-5}\%$ of the earth's crust) is derived exclusively from zinc ores; the mineral greenockite, CdS, is without economic importance. Its lower b.p. enables cadmium metal, which may amount to 0.5% of crude zinc, to be separated by distillation. It is used in electroplating, in bearing metals, in fusible alloys, and in atomic reactors to absorb neutrons.

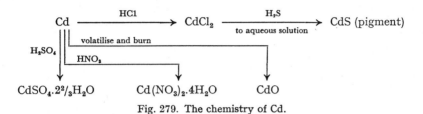

Fig. 279. The chemistry of Cd.

Mercury ($10^{-4}\%$ of the earth's crust) has only one important ore; red, rhombohedral cinnabar, HgS. Heating in air converts this to the metal and SO_2, the oxide being thermally unstable.

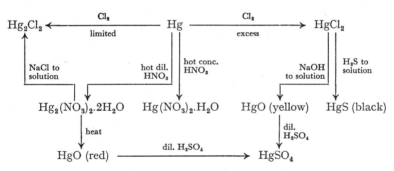

Fig. 280. The chemistry of Hg.

Halides

The chlorides of these elements show a sharp transition from ionic to covalent character. Fused $ZnCl_2$ is conducting, the chlorides of mercury are not. In solution, zinc chloride dissociates normally: $ZnCl_2 \rightleftharpoons Zn^{2+} + 2Cl^-$.

The halides of cadmium demonstrate the effect on structure of the easier polarisation of an anion by a smaller cation. CdF_2 has the cubic fluorite lattice but the chloride, bromide and iodide form hexagonal crystals based on layer lattices (p. 150). The distances between the layers increase from the chloride to the iodide, with a corresponding reduction in lattice energies.

TABLE 135

PROPERTIES OF CADMIUM HALIDES

Form		M.p. (°C)	B.p. (°C)	Solubility (25°)
CdF_2	Cubic (CaF_2)	1100	1758	4.5 g/100 g
$CdCl_2$	Hexagonal (layer)	568	964	120 g/100 g
$CdBr_2$	,,	567	960	115 g/100 g
CdI_2	,,	388	715	85 g/100 g

Cadmium halides form auto-complex ions in concentrated solution. The anomalous transport number of Cd in CdI_2 solution was noticed by Hittorf 1859) and correctly attributed to the equilibrium:

$$2CdI_2 \rightleftharpoons Cd^{2+} + CdI_4^{2-}.$$

The CdI_4^{2-} ion results from adding an excess of iodide ion to CdI_2 solution; the Raman spectrum of this and the similar $CdBr_4^{2-}$ ion have been examined. The latter has a pattern very like that of the isoelectronic $SnBr_4$.

Halogeno-zincates are much less stable in solution. The compound $KZnF_3$ has a perovskite structure and does not contain a complex ion.

Mercury(II) halides are too covalent to allow the free Hg^{2+} to appear; its presence must be associated with auto-complex formation. Thus $HgCl_2$ dissociates only slightly and then in an unusual way:

$$HgCl_2 \rightleftharpoons HgCl^+ + Cl^-.$$

But anionic complexes with halogens other than fluorine can be made by the addition of halide ion. Iodide solutions particularly, and bromide and chloride to a lesser extent, dissolve HgO:

$$HgO + 3I^- + H_2O \rightleftharpoons [HgI_3]^- + 2OH^-,$$
$$HgO + 4I^- + H_2O \rightleftharpoons [HgI_4]^{2-} + 2OH^-.$$

The solution can be made quite strongly alkaline without causing precipitation (Nessler's reagent). The complex ion $[HgI_4]^{2-}$ is tetrahedral. The similar $[CdI_4]^{2-}$ ion can also be made by dissolving CdO in an iodide solution, but less readily.

Mercury(I) fluoride is cubic, the other halides tetragonal (p. 139). Only the fluoride is appreciably soluble in water, the others resemble the Cu^I, Ag^I, Au^I and Tl^I compounds in their slight solubility. Hg_2Cl_2 and Hg_2Br_2 vaporise easily; though diamagnetic, the vapours have densities indicating HgCl and HgBr as the molecular formulae. The reason for this is probably disproportionation:

$$Hg_2Cl_2 \rightleftharpoons Hg + HgCl_2.$$

Oxides

Mercury(II) oxide is thermally unstable: $2HgO \overset{300°}{\rightleftharpoons} 2Hg + O_2$.

But ZnO and CdO sublime without decomposition; their heats of formation are fairly large.

TABLE 136

HEATS OF FORMATION OF ZnO, CdO AND HgO

	ZnO	*CdO*	*HgO*
$-\Delta H_f$	83 kcal	61 kcal	21.7 kcal

ZnO has the wurtzite, CdO the rock-salt lattice. Both the yellow and red forms of HgO are orthorhombic and indistinguishable in structure. A rhombohedral form of HgO, orange in colour, has been obtained as well-formed crystals by slow precipitation from aqueous solution (Laruelle, 1955). It is converted irreversibly to the orthorhombic form above 200°. When heated ZnO becomes yellow but without change in the structure of the phase. The hot oxide is bleached by oxygen and its colour is restored by zinc vapour. The coloured oxide has about 0.03% of zinc over the stoichiometric ratio; the zinc is present as atoms occupying interstitial sites (p. 147).

Of the three oxides only ZnO is amphoteric, the other two are purely basic. Thus zinc forms the most stable complex anion with oxygen, and mercury the most stable complex ions with the halogens. The hydroxides of zinc and cadmium are obtained as crystalline precipitates on the addition of alkali to solutions of the nitrates; a hydroxide of mercury is unknown. There is not a mercury(I) oxide.

Sulphides

Mercury(II) sulphide, HgS, exists in both zinc-blende and rock-salt structures, the red, hexagonal cinnabar, s.g. 8.18, being the stable and common form; the metastable, black, cubic metacinnabar, s.g. 7.60, is rare. Mercury(I) sulphide is unknown.

Cadmium sulphide varies from lemon yellow to deep orange through variation in composition within the CdS phase; there is no evidence of dimorphism.

Mercury-nitrogen compounds

Mercury forms direct covalent as well as co-ordinate links with nitrogen. Mercury(II) chloride reacts with gaseous ammonia to give 'fusible white precipitate':

$$HgCl_2 + 2NH_3 \rightleftharpoons Hg(NH_3)_2Cl_2.$$

Lipscomb (1953) suggests that $[Hg(NH_3)_2]^{2+}$ ions are arranged at the face centres of cubes of Cl^- ions with their axes randomly arranged along the a, b and c axes of the crystal. The crystal contains finite $[Hg(NH_3)_2]^{2+}$ ions (Fig. 281).

Treatment of $HgCl_2$ with aqueous ammonia gives 'infusible white precipitate', $HgNH_2Cl$, containing indefinitely long chains of $[—Hg—NH_2—]^+$ with Cl^- ions between them in an orthorhombic structure (Fig. 282). The infusibility and low solubility is ascribed to the chain structures.

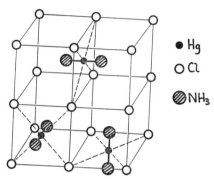

Fig. 281. Random arrangement of $Hg(NH_3)_2^{2+}$ ions in 'fusible white precipitate', $Hg(NH_3)_2Cl_2$.

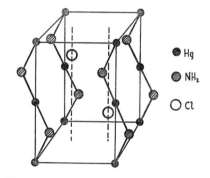

Fig. 282. Orthorhombic cell of 'infusible white precipitate' $HgNH_2Cl$, showing zig-zag chains $(—Hg—NH_2—)_n$.

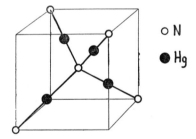

Fig. 283. Arrangement of Hg_2N^+ network in Millon's base, $Hg_2NOH.2H_2O$.

When HgO is warmed with aqueous ammonia the compound $Hg_2NOH.2H_2O$, Millon's base, is produced. This has a Hg_2N^+ network of cristobalite type with OH^- ions and water molecules held in the network by ionic, hydrogen bond and dispersion forces (Fig. 283).

The Hg—N distances in all these compounds are similar (~ 2.06 Å). The iodide corresponding to Millon's base, $Hg_2NI.H_2O$, is the precipitate produced from Nessler's reagent by ammonia. The nitrogen atom uses sp³-hybrid orbitals in these compounds; the collinear bonds of the Hg probably involve sp hybridisation.

When ammonia reacts with $Hg(ClO_4)_2$, a compound of much greater ionic character than $HgCl_2$ is formed, a complex tetra-ammine in which there are co-ordinate links between nitrogen and mercury:

$$Hg(ClO_4)_2 + 4NH_3 \rightleftharpoons [Hg(NH_3)_4]^{2+} (ClO_4)_2^-.$$

A mercury(I) compound reacts with aqueous ammonia to give free mercury together with the ammine formed by the corresponding mercury (II) compound under the same conditions. Thus Hg_2Cl_2 gives a black precipitate which is a mixture of finely divided mercury and infusible white precipitate.

Complexes

Of the oxygen complexes, those of zinc are the most stable; it alone forms imple oxoanions:

$$ZnO + 2OH^- \rightarrow ZnO_2^{2-} + H_2O.$$
$$\text{(zincate ion)}$$

Its chelate compounds include acetylacetone and dioxalato complexes, and a basic acetate, $Zn_4O(CH_3COO)_6$, very similar in properties to that of beryllium (p. 263), with a tetrahedral structure centred on the oxygen atom.

Sulphur forms more stable complexes than oxygen with these metals. In alkali metal polysulphide solutions, HgS gives the HgS_2^{2-} ion. The metal halides all form addition compounds with thioethers (Fig. 284).

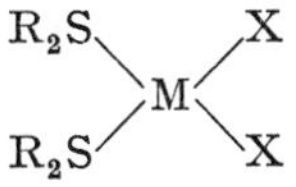

Fig. 284. Addition compounds with thioethers of metal halides of Group IIB.
R = alkyl, M = Zn, Cd or Hg, X = halogen.

Salts of the three metals form ammines, principally tetrahedral complex ions of the form $[M(NH_3)_4]^{2+}$, but in addition mercury salts form linear, diammine complexes, and zinc and cadmium octahedral hexa-ammines, $[M(NH_3)_6]^{2+}$. Ethylenediamine produces 6-co-ordinate complexes, $[M(en)_3]^{2+}$, with all three cations.

Oxoacid salts

The carbonates, nitrates, and even the sulphates are thermally unstable:

$$ZnSO_4 \xrightarrow{770°} ZnO + SO_3; \qquad ZnCO_3 \xrightarrow{300°} ZnO + CO_2;$$

$$2Zn(NO_3)_2 \xrightarrow{140°} 2ZnO + 4NO_2 + O_2.$$

Zinc carbonate is decomposed on boiling with an excess of Na_2CO_3 solution: the phosphate is much more stable, $Zn_2P_2O_7$ being used in the gravimetric determination of the metal.

Cadmium sulphate forms the hydrate $CdSO_4.2^2/_3H_2O$ with an interesting structure (Lipson, 1936). There are two sets of Cd^{2+} ions with slightly different environments; all are octahedrally surrounded by two H_2O molecules and four sulphate oxygens. There are four kinds of crystallographically non-equivalent H_2O molecules; three quarters are attached to Cd^{2+} ions, one quarter have as neighbours two other water molecules and two sulphate oxygen atoms.

Chapter 37

Complex or Co-ordination Compounds and Ions

GENERAL PRINCIPLES

The general nature of complexes has been discussed (pp. 131–137) and particular complexes have been considered elsewhere; here is a more systematic review of the subject.

Two or more compounds capable of independent existence often combine:

$$Fe(CN)_2 + 4KCN \rightarrow K_4Fe(CN)_6$$
$$2KCl + PtCl_4 \rightarrow K_2PtCl_6$$
$$K_2SO_4 + Al_2(SO_4)_3 + 24H_2O \rightarrow 2KAl(SO_4)_2.12H_2O$$
$$AgCl + 2NH_3 \rightarrow Ag(NH_3)_2Cl$$
$$KF + MgF_2 \rightarrow KMgF_3$$

These products differ widely in their behaviour, particularly in water; and, though there is no general agreement on what constitutes a complex or co-ordination compound the following definition is sufficient for the present purpose: a complex molecule or ion is one in which an atom (A) is attached to other atoms (B) or groups of atoms (C) to a number in excess of the charge or oxidation number of the atom (A).

(A) is the *central* or *nuclear atom* and (B) and (C) are *ligands*. An atom of (B) or (C) directly attached to (A) is a *co-ordinating atom*. A ligand (C) with more than one potential co-ordinating atom is *multidentate* (*uni-, bi-, terdentate*). A *chelate ligand* is one using more than one of its co-ordinating atoms. A complex with more than one nuclear atom is *polynuclear*. A *bridging group* is a group attached to two nuclear atoms in a polynuclear complex.

Potassium hexacyanoferrate(II), $K_4Fe(CN)_6$, dissolves in water to give a solution with none of the reactions of the Fe^{2+} ion; the metal is present as the $Fe(CN)_6^{4-}$ ion. A solution of K_2PtCl_6 contains $PtCl_6^{2-}$ ions, one of $Ag(NH_3)_2Cl$, $Ag(NH_3)_2^+$ ions. These are all complex ions. An alum solution, on the other hand, gives reactions characteristic of K^+, Al^{3+} and SO_4^{2-} ions. The brown caesium rhodium alum, $CsRh(SO_4)_2 \cdot 12H_2O$, behaves similarly in water, but it can be partially dehydrated to the red $CsRh(SO_4)_2 \cdot 4H_2O$ which does not produce a precipitate with $BaCl_2$ immediately after it is dissolved because $[Rh(H_2O)_4(SO_4)_2]^-$, not SO_4^{2-} ions, are formed. The alums and other hydrates are often distinguished from the complex salts and are called lattice compounds, but evidently a sharp distinction is not always possible.

In solid K_2PtCl_6 there are octahedral $PtCl_6^{2-}$ ions. In $KMgF_3$ there are no discrete complex ions; the compound has the perovskite structure (p. 151). There is thus no simple way of defining a complex in terms of solid structure.

Not all complexes contain complex ions. The well-known 'nickel dimethylglyoxime', bis(dimethylglyoximato)nickel(II), $[Ni(C_4H_7O_2N_2)_2]$, (p. 543, Fig. 288 (c)) and bis(acetylacetonato)copper(II) (p. 522) are uncharged molecules.

Oxo-anions can be considered as complexes. Calcium carbonate, for example, can be made from two stable, saturated compounds, $CaO + CO_2 \rightarrow CaCO_3$, and its crystals contain CO_3^{2-} ions in which one carbon atom is attached to three oxygen atoms. Potassium perchlorate, $KClO_4$, and potassium fluoroborate, KBF_4, both have the same structure with discrete complex ions. The compounds K_2SO_4 and Cs_2HgBr_4 have not only the same rhombic form but the same crystallographic axial ratios in which a : b : c = $= 1 : 0.74 : 0.57$.

Co-ordination number

The number of ligands (p. 131) grouped round the central atom in a complex is the co-ordination number of the complex.

6 Co-ordination is most common, such complexes being octahedral (Fig. 285). But a co-ordination number of four is fairly common and can be associated with either a square or tetrahedral structure. All complexes in which the ligands are attached by electron donation to sp^3 hybrid

Fig. 285. Example of 6 co-ordination.

orbitals (p. 103) are tetrahedral or approximately so. For instance BeF_4^{2-} is tetrahedral. We adopt the usual approach (p. 137), in which electrons are imagined to be transferred to the more electronegative atoms (or groups), leaving Be^{2+} in the field of four F^- ligands, and see that s and p orbitals are all available for bonding and partial return of charge to the cation:

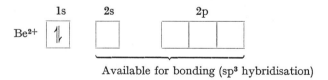

Available for bonding (sp^3 hybridisation)

An example of square co-ordination is the complex $Pd(NH_3)_4^{2+}$:

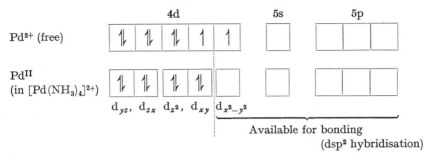

Here the 4d level is split by the ligand field (p. 134) and the higher orbital, $d_{x^2-y^2}$, is the one required for square hybridisation (p. 135).

Inner- and outer-orbital complexes

Chromium has the electron configuration $3d^54s^1$. In its 6-co-ordinate Cr^{III} complexes two 3d, one 4s, and three 4p orbitals are involved in the bonding MO's which accept electrons from the ligands:

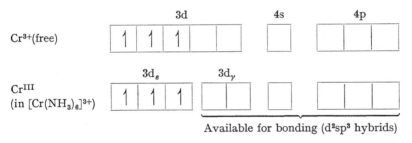

But chromium(II) also occurs in an octahedral complex, $Cr(CN_6)^{4-}$:

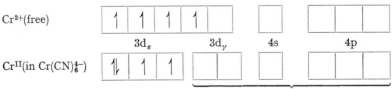

Here the ligand field is stronger (p. 134), the d_ε-d_γ splitting is larger, and an electron falls into a $3d_\varepsilon$ orbital, leaving two unpaired spins instead of the four of the free cation. Both complexes are of *inner-orbital* type, the hybrids involving d orbitals of lower principal quantum number than the s and p. But the second is 'low-spin' (spin-paired) and the first is 'high-spin' (spin-free) as there are three d orbitals and only three non-bonding electrons.

However, in the complex ion $Cr(H_2O)_6{}^{2+}$, the magnetic moment indicates four unpaired spins. This is because H_2O gives a weaker ligand field than CN^- (p. 134) and the splitting is not sufficient to make a d_γ electron fall into a d_ε orbital, with consequent spin-pairing. Octahedral hybridisation would then require the use of 4d orbitals, the 3d holding only non-bonding electrons:

Cr^{II}(in $Cr(H_2O)_6^{2+}$)

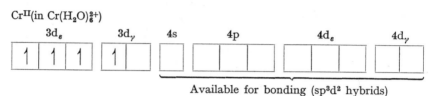

Available for bonding (sp^3d^2 hybrids)

This is again a spin-free complex, with the same magnetic moment as the free ion Cr^{2+}, but it is an *outer-orbital complex*. The spin-free type of complex was formerly classified as an ionic complex, the water and ammonia molecules being considered to be held by an ion-dipole interaction rather than by a covalent bond, the large permanent dipoles of the ligands providing the electrostatic attraction and being further polarised in the process. This is not an unreasonable description, but covalent character in the bonding is likely to be substantial.

Such evidence as is furnished by magnetic susceptibility, X-ray diffraction pattern and absorption spectrum rarely determines the type of bonding unequivocally. For instance, the $Fe(H_2O)_6{}^{2+}$ ion can be shown to be octahedral and to have the same magnetic moment as Fe^{2+}, but the octahedral shape is the system of maximum symmetry expected whatever the bond type. The magnetic evidence merely indicates the absence of spin-pairing. Again, it has been suggested that the similarity in colour of the Mn^{2+}, Fe^{2+}, Fe^{3+} and Co^{2+} ions, in their anhydrous salts and their corresponding $M(H_2O)_6{}^{2+}$ or $M(H_2O)_6{}^{3+}$ ions, is evidence for ion-dipole interaction; but that, on the other hand, the difference between yellow anhydrous NiF_2 and the green $Ni(H_2O)_6{}^{2+}$ in the hydrated sulphate indicates the presence of covalent bonds in the latter.

The present view is that the terms 'ionic' and 'covalent' when used to distinguish complexes of supposedly different bond type are misleading. There is no compelling reason to assume that any sharp transition occurs between ion-dipole and covalent linkages. Nyholm and Orgel have suggested

(1956) that where a cation such as Fe^{3+} produces complex ions of the two types, they should be classified respectively, as 'high-spin' and 'low-spin', since the magnetic evidence gives this information directly, and that the nature of the bonding be separately considered.

Conditions determining the formation of inner- and outer-orbital complexes

Inner-orbital complexes are formed by ions of the transition metals, regardless of the nature of the ligands, provided $(n-1)$d orbitals can be made available

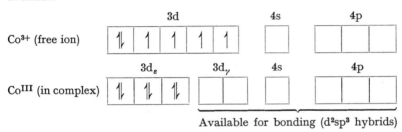

But 6-co-ordinate inner-orbital complexes of Co^{2+} and Ni^{2+} are unlikely since they would require the promotion of one or two electrons to the 4d level.

Ni^{II} (in octahedral complex)

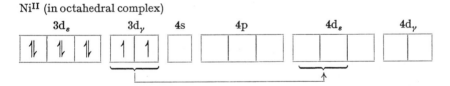

This ion can, however, form a spin-paired, square 4-co-ordinated type of complex using dsp^2 orbitals.

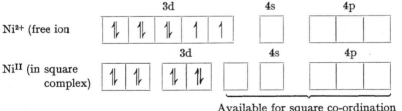

Available for square co-ordination
(dsp^2 hybrids)

Although Co^{II} does not form inner-orbital 6-co-ordinate complexes, it does produce a spin-paired 5-co-ordinate pentacyanocobaltate(II) ion of bipyramidal form (pp. 105 and 495):

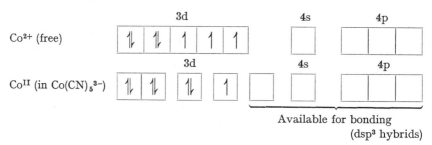

Copper(I) and zinc do not form inner-orbital complexes; the promotion of four electrons would be required in each case:

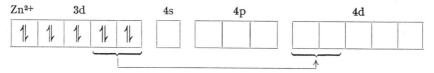

In those instances where a cation forms both an inner (spin-paired) and an outer (spin-free) orbital complex, the former usually appears with easily-polarisable ligands containing directed lone pairs such as H_2O, NH_3 and CN^-, and the latter with ligands such as F^- (p. 133).

Labile and inert complexes

Taube (1952) drew attention to the relationship between the electronic structure of a complex and the rates at which it underwent substitution reactions. A complex is labile when the ligands are rapidly replaceable by other groups:

$$M(NH_3)_6^{n+} + H_2O \rightarrow M(NH_3)_5H_2O^{n+} + NH_3.$$

Where substitution does not occur, or occurs only with difficulty, the complex is said to be inert.

Though the idea of lability in relation to a complex is vague, first because a quantitative definition is impossible and secondly because rates of substitution from which it stems depend, in part, on the substituting group, nevertheless certain types of electronic structure always produce inert complexes and other types always labile complexes.

Inner-orbital complexes

(a) Labile

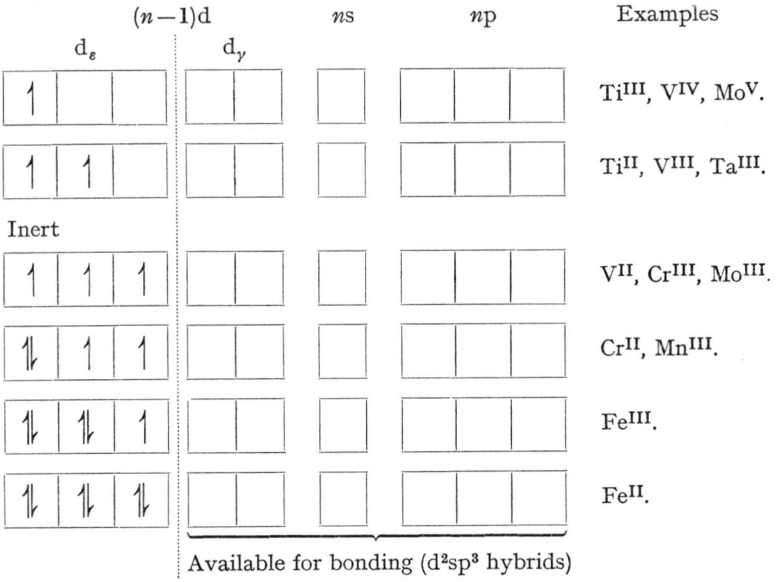

$(n-1)$d			ns	np	Examples

d_ε d_γ

| ↑ | | | | | | | | Ti^{III}, V^{IV}, Mo^{V}. |

| ↑ | ↑ | | | | | | | Ti^{II}, V^{III}, Ta^{III}. |

(b) Inert

| ↑ | ↑ | ↑ | | | | | | V^{II}, Cr^{III}, Mo^{III}. |

| ↑↓ | ↑ | ↑ | | | | | | Cr^{II}, Mn^{III}. |

| ↑↓ | ↑↓ | ↑ | | | | | | Fe^{III}. |

| ↑↓ | ↑↓ | ↑↓ | | | | | | Fe^{II}. |

Available for bonding (d^{2}sp^3 hybrids)

There is no connection between inertness and thermodynamic stability. Bjerrum (1941) showed the reaction

$$Co(NH_3)_6{}^{3+} + H_3O^+ \rightarrow Co(NH_3)_5H_2O^{3+} + NH_4^+$$

to have so large a negative free energy change at 25° that the equilibrium concentration of $Co(NH_3)_6{}^{3+}$, in the presence of H_3O^+ and NH_4^+ ions at unit activity, could be only 0.01% of the original concentration. For a further replacement ΔG was calculated to be even more negative. Yet the reaction is almost immeasurably slow. Similarly the reaction

$$Fe(CN)_6{}^{3-} + 6H_3O^+ \rightarrow Fe^{3+} + 6HCN + 6H_2O$$

is very slow at $[H_3O^+] = 1$, $[HCN] = 1$, in spite of the great negative free-energy change. These reactions obviously have very high energies of activation (p. 189).

Outer-orbital complexes

Here the division into labile and inert complexes is much less clear-cut. Where the central ion has a low charge the complex is generally labile, and in an isoelectronic series the lability decreases as the charge on the central ion increases:

$$\text{Order of lability: } AlF_6^{3-} > SiF_6^{2-} > PF_6^- > SF_6.$$

Some central ions which give labile outer-orbital complexes are Mn^{2+}, Fe^{2+}, Fe^{3+}, Co^{2+}, Ni^{2+}, Zn^{2+}, Cd^{2+}, Hg^{2+}, Ga^{3+}, In^{3+} and Tl^{3+}.

Central ions which give both inner- and outer-orbital types are Mn^{2+}, Mn^{3+}, Fe^{2+}, Co^{2+}, Co^{3+}. With these the spin-paired, inner-orbital form is invariably inert, for example:

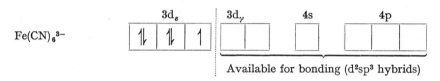

Available for bonding (d^2sp^3 hybrids)

Whereas the spin-free outer orbital form is invariably labile:

Available for bonding (sp^3d^2 hybrids)

The inner-orbital complexes show a sharp decrease in lability at the stage where no d orbital is left vacant. A pronounced difference in bond type cannot be expected in the following:

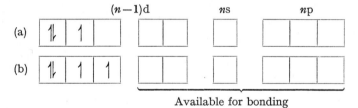

Available for bonding

But much more energy is likely to be needed to form a 7-co-ordinated activated complex in (b) than in (a). In (a) an orbital of low energy is available for this purpose and substitution can proceed by the bimolecular process:

$$MX_6 + Y \rightarrow [MX_6Y] \rightarrow MX_5Y + X.$$

For substitution in (b) there are three possible mechanisms all with high activation energy and correspondingly low probability; they are

(i) two odd electrons in $(n-1)$d orbitals must pair to leave one vacant orbital,

(ii) an odd $(n-1)$d electron must be promoted to the nd level,

(iii) the complex must undergo unimolecular decomposition, *i.e.* lose a ligand.

For outer-orbital 6-co-ordinate complexes, lability is associated with a charge of under four on the central ion, and inertness with one of four or over. These outer-orbital complexes probably undergo unimolecular dissociation and the ligand is easier to remove when the central charge is low. It is characteristic of the metals which give outer-orbital, 6-co-ordinate complexes readily, that they should also form 4-co-ordinate complexes.

Ingold, Nyholm and Brown (1954) have shown that the kinetic order in the substitution of the octahedral cobalt(III) complex 1-cis-$[Co(en)_2Cl_2]^+$ [en = $H_2N.CH_2.CH_2.NH_2$] depends upon the nucleophilic power of the substituting anion. Working in methanol solution and using polarimetric, spectrophotometric, titrimetric and, where necessary, radiochemical methods of following the kinetics, they found the rates of substitution of Cl^- by the other ions shown in Fig. 286. For the first three reagents the kinetic order

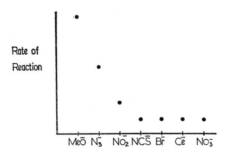

Fig. 286. Rate of substitution of Cl^- from 1-cis $[Co(en)_2Cl_2]^+$ by various other ions in methanol solution.

is second and the rate falls with their decreasing nucleophilic power. The evidence favours a bimolecular mechanism:

$$OMe^- + [CoCl_2(en)_2]^+ \rightarrow [CoCl_2(en)_2OMe] \rightarrow [CoCl(en)_2(OMe)]^+ + Cl^-$$

For the last four reagents the rates are the same and the kinetic order is first. The rate-determining stage is unimolecular:

$$[CoCl_2(en)_2]^+ \rightarrow [CoCl(en)_2]^{2+} + Cl^-.$$

Generalisations relating to stability

Although the idea of lability in relation to a complex is vague, first because a complex which is quite stable to one reagent may be decomposed by another, certain generalisations have emerged.

(i) The strongest co-ordination centres are the small cations of transition elements, such as Co^{3+}, Cr^{3+}, Pt^{2+}, Pd^{2+}. Large non-transitional metal ions like those of the alkalis and alkali earths seldom form stable complexes. The small non-transitional metal ions such as Zn^{2+} and Ag^+ give complexes of intermediate stability.

(ii) Molecules or ions capable of acting as electron donors can function as ligands. They are usually either (a) simple halogen ions, or (b) groups containing N, P, As, O, S or C atoms to provide the lone pairs. The strength of the co-ordination decreases along the two series as shown:

(a) $CN^- > SCN^- > F^- > Cl^- > Br^- > I^-$;

(b) $NH_3 > RNH_2 > R_2NH > R_3N > H_2O > ROH > R_2O > R_3As > R_3P > R_2S$.
   (R = alkyl or aryl)

Recently an increasing number of complexes have been prepared containing ligands which are not electron-pair donors. Typical of these are the ethylene and propylene complexes with Pd^{II}, Pt^{II}, Cu^I, Ag^I and Hg^{II}. The bonds involved have been discussed by Chatt and by Dewar (1951).

(iii) Ring formation is an important factor in stabilising complexes. A molecule such as ethylene diamine, $NH_2.CH_2.CH_2.NH_2$, can use the lone pairs of both nitrogen atoms for co-ordination to a single metal atom. The ion $Ni(en)_3^{2+}$ has the structure shown in Fig. 287.

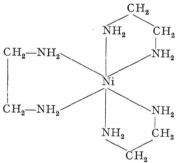

Fig. 287. Structure of the $Ni(en)_3^{2+}$ ion.

Such a ligand is described as bidentate. Dimethylglyoxime can act as a bidentate ligand in two ways: (i) as the whole molecule with a Cu^{2+} ion to form the bipositive bis(dimethylglyoxime)copper(II) ion (Fig. 288(a)); (ii) as the anion (b) with a Ni^{2+} ion to give the uncharged bis(dimethylglyoximato)nickel(II) (c).

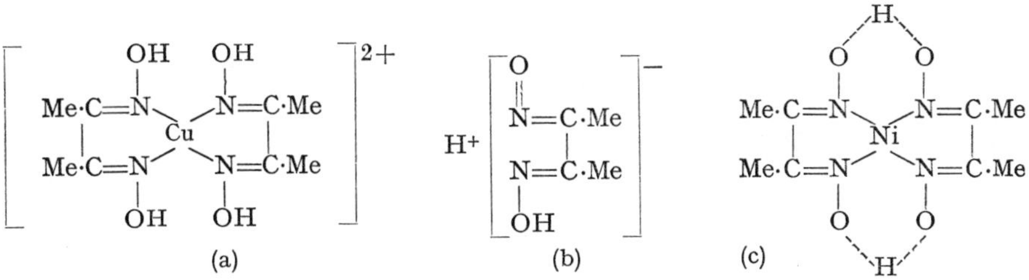

Fig. 288. Different behaviour of dimethylglyoxime towards Cu^{2+} (a) and Ni^{2+} ((b) and (c)).

Dibasic ions frequently form bidentate ligands, common examples being oxalate and phthalate. Such bidentate groups often confer great stability on complexes, particularly when 5- or 6-membered rings are formed. Thus simple ketones give few complexes with metals; but β-diketones many, by forming rings of the type

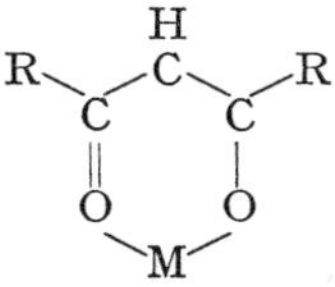

These complexes can often be distilled without decomposition. Morgan and Drew (1920) introduced the term chelation to denote the formation of rings of this type. Not all the 2 − anions co-ordinate with metal ions by chelation however; the sulphate ion, for example, occupies one co-ordination position only.

Terdentate groups such as $\alpha\beta\gamma$-triaminopropane (a) and tripyridyl (b)

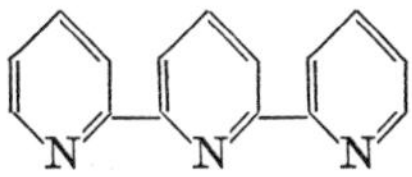

also form complexes.

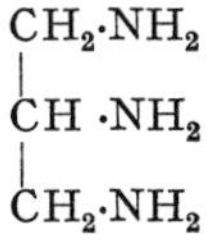

Chelating agents find much use in analysis. Many metals are precipitated by 8-hydroxyquinoline (oxine).

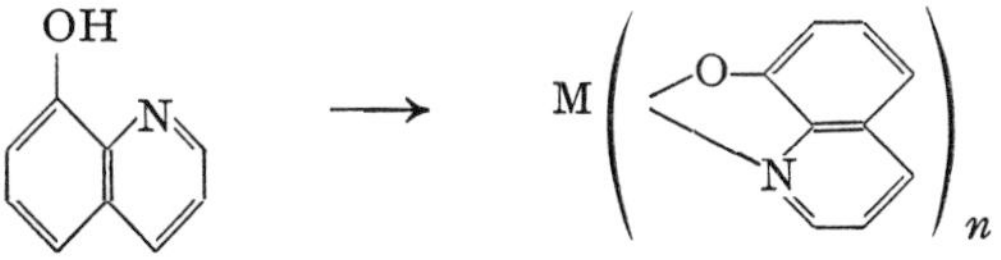

Schwarzenbach (1945) has developed the use of such chelating agents as nitrilotriacetic acid (a), ethylenediaminetetra-acetic acid (b) and 1 : 2 diaminocyclohexanetetra-acetic acid (c).

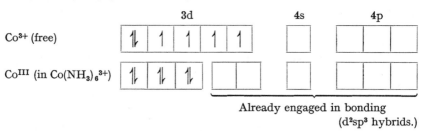

(a)   (b)   (c)

These *complexones*, as they are often called, form very stable water-soluble complexes with even the Gp. IIA metals (p. 263). With Gp. III metals the stability of the complexes is even more marked, indeed a pH of 13 can be reached without precipitating the rare earth oxides when (a) or (b) is present (p. 431). The stabilities are associated with the formation of chelate rings.

Stabilisation of ions by complex formation

Although a strong oxidising agent, the Co^{3+} ion frequently resists reduction when it occurs in an octahedral complex. The increase in stability occurs because the complex is far from truly ionic, the 4s and 4p orbitals being already engaged in bonding:

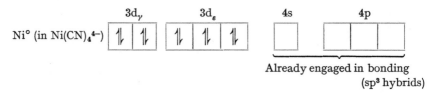

Nickel, with charge numbers both higher and lower than the normal $+2$, can be stabilised in a similar fashion. Thus $K_4Ni(CN)_4$ contains nickel with zero charge number:

Ni° (in $Ni(CN)_4^{4-}$)

Already engaged in bonding
(sp³ hybrids)

Whereas nickel in the compound

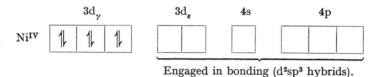

$(ClO_4)_2$

has charge number $+4$ with an electron configuration round the Ni atom similar to that of Co in the strong field (octahedral) Co^{III} complexes.

	$3d_\gamma$			$3d_\varepsilon$		4s	4p		
Ni^{IV}	⇅	⇅	⇅						

Engaged in bonding (d^2sp^3 hybrids).

In general, highly negative groups tend to stabilise higher charge numbers, and large groups tend to stabilise lower ones.

The complete filling of orbitals is not, however, essential to increased stability. Copper(II) iodide disproportionates rapidly into copper(I) iodide and iodine, but the ethylenediamine complex $Cu(en)_2I_2$ is quite stable even though it contains an unpaired electron in an inner d orbital.

Isomerism in complex compounds

Various types of isomerism occur in complex compounds.

1. *Ionisation isomerism*

This is due to an interchange of groups between the co-ordination sphere and ions outside it. Sulphatopenta-amminecobalt(III) bromide, $[Co(SO_4)(NH_3)_5]Br$, and bromopenta-amminecobalt(III) sulphate, $[CoBr(NH_3)_5]SO_4$, are such a pair of isomers. The former is red and in aqueous solution gives a precipitate of AgBr with $AgNO_3$ but no precipitate with barium chloride; the latter is violet and gives an immediate precipitate with $BaCl_2$. It should be noticed that in these compounds an SO_4 group occupies only one co-ordination position though it neutralises two ionic charges on the Co^{3+}; thus the number of co-ordinate links formed by a ligand ion is not necessarily the same as the number of charges it carries. An even more obvious example of ionisation isomerism is afforded by $[PtCl_2(NH_3)_4]Br_2$ and $[PtBr_2(NH_3)_4]Cl_2$.

2. Hydration isomerism

There are three isomers of $CrCl_3.6H_2O$. The violet-grey form is shown, by its conductance and the fact that all the chlorine is precipitated immediately with $AgNO_3$, to be the hexa-aquochromium(III) chloride, $[Cr(H_2O)_6]Cl_3$, The dark green substance obtained from hot solutions is the dichlorotetra-aquo-salt, $[CrCl_2(H_2O)_4]Cl \cdot 2H_2O$, from which $AgNO_3$ removes only one third of the chlorine. The third compound, the chloropenta-aquochromium(III) dichloride hydrate, $[CrCl(H_2O)_5]Cl_2.H_2O$, also green, yields two-thirds of its chlorine by precipitation with $AgNO_3$.

The exact nature of the bonds holding water molecules in the co-ordination sphere and outside it is not always known. In some hydrates those outside the co-ordination sphere are held in the interstices of the crystal lattice, in others they are attached to the simple ions.

3. Co-ordination isomerism

This occurs when both cation and anion are complex. Typical examples are (a) $[Co(NH_3)_6] [Cr(CN)_6]$ and $[Cr(NH_3)_6] [Co(CN)_6]$; and (b) $[Pt(NH_3)_4]$ $[PtCl_4]$ and $[PtCl(NH_3)_3] [PtCl_3(NH_3)]$. Co-ordination isomerism also occurs where an element is present in two states of different charge, as with $[Pt(NH_3)_4] [PtCl_6]$ and $[PtCl_2(NH_3)_4] [PtCl_4]$.

4. Geometrical isomerism

In the planar complexes of metals showing the co-ordination number four there is a possibility of cis- and trans- isomerism:

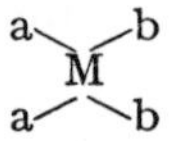

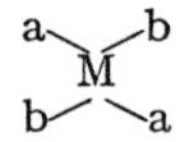

Examples are $Pt(NH_3)_2Cl_2$ and $Pd(NH_3)_2(NO_2)_2$; both have cis- and trans-isomers. The type of isomerism also arises in planar chelate compounds:

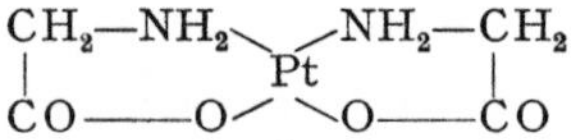

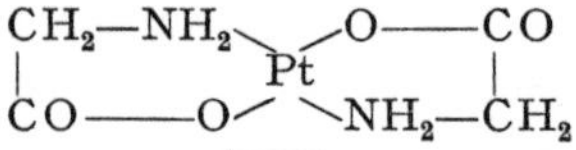

Geometrical isomerism cannot occur in the Ma_3b type of square complex, but the Mabcd type gives rise to three isomers:

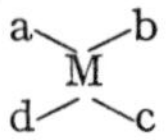

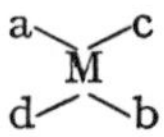

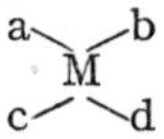

With 6-co-ordinate octahedral complexes, geometrical isomerism is also possible. Cis- and trans- isomerism is found in an ion such as $[CoCl_2(NH_3)_4]^+$

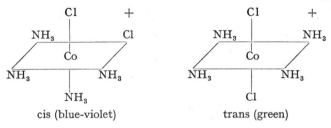

cis (blue-violet)   trans (green)

Complex ions of the type Ma_3b_3 exist in only two isomeric forms:

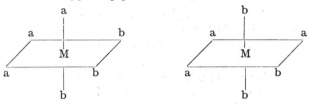

5. Optical isomerism

Werner showed (1908) that the element carbon is not a necessary constituent of an optical isomer when he resolved the compound

$$\left[Co \left\{ \underset{\diagdown OH \diagup}{\overset{\diagup OH \diagdown}{} Co(NH_3)_4} \right\}_3 \right] Br_6$$

This kind of isomerism occurs when a compound can be represented by two asymmetrical structures, one of which is the mirror image of the other. It is common in octahedral complexes involving bidentate groups; for, unless bidentate groups are present, there is always a plane of symmetry in complexes of this shape. The cation of $[CoCl_2(en)_2]Cl$ has two optically active cis-forms (Fig. 289(a) and (b)) in addition to an inactive trans-form (Fig. 289(c)). $[Co(en)_3]Br_3$ has also been resolved; Fig. 290(a) and (b) show the two enantiomorphs of the terpositive cation.

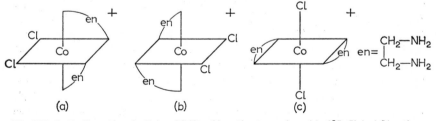

(a)   (b)   (c)

Fig. 289. Optically active cis- [(a) and (b)] and inactive trans-form (c) of $[CoCl_2(en)_2]^+$ cation.

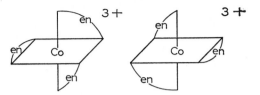

Fig. 290. Enantiomorphs of Co(en)$_3$ terpositive cation.

COMPLEXES IN AQUEOUS SOLUTION

Aquo-complexes

Dissolving a salt in water rarely gives unhydrated ions—ClO_4^- is a possible exception. The first step in the process is probably hydration of the ions; it will be assumed that the number of water molecules in the solvated shell corresponds with the co-ordination number of the ion, although this is not always true. Relatively few salts give neutral solutions, and when $FeCl_3$ or $CuSO_4$ dissolve they must do more than yield $Fe(H_2O)_6^{3+} + 3\ Cl_{aq}^-$ or $Cu(H_2O)^{2+} + SO_4{^{2-}}_{aq}$, for their solutions are acid. Sillén (1959) points out that the naive explanation of the acidity of a $FeCl_3$ solution as a simple hydrolysis,

$$2FeCl_3 + 6H_2O \rightleftharpoons 2Fe(OH)_{3aq} + 6H_{aq}^+ + 6Cl_{aq-},$$

implies the solubility of the hydroxide, since the solution is clear and non-colloidal; furthermore, the analytical data do not comply with the law of mass action. The Brönsted idea of the hydrated cation behaving as an acid is more probable:

$$Fe(H_2O)_6^{3+} + H_2O \rightarrow Fe(OH)(H_2O)_5^{2+} + H_3O^+$$

The loss of protons in this way will be the easier the greater the positive field about the cation. The Second Period exemplifies this: the electrostatic field about Na^+ being slight, it is only weakly hydrated; but the progressive increase in field about the following elements leads, successively, to $Mg(H_2O)_6^{2+}$, $Al(H_2O)_6^{3+}$, $Si(OH)_4$, $PO(OH)_3$, $SO_3(OH)^-$, ClO_4^- in acid solution, and to $Mg(OH)(H_2O)_5^+$, $Al(OH)_4(H_2O)_2^-$, $SiO_2(OH)_2^{2-}$, PO_4^{3-}, SO_4^{2-}, ClO_4^- in alkaline solution. These are mononuclear, but Bjerrum (1908) showed that $Cr_2(OH)_2^{4+}$ exists in solution, and polynuclear complexes have proved to be frequent products of hydrolysis. Indeed, mercury(II) is one of the few metals which always gives mononuclear species: $Hg(H_2O)_2^{2+}$, $Hg(OH)(H_2O)^+$, $Hg(OH)_2$. Beryllium produces mainly $Be_3(OH)_3^{3+}$ which is presumed to have a cyclic structure (Sillén). Iron(III) appears as the ions $Fe(OH)_2^+$ and

$Fe_2(OH)_2{}^{4+}$, the first being paramagnetic and the second diamagnetic (Mulay and Selwood, 1954).

Other complexes

The displacement of one ligand by another is a usual way of making a complex, for instance, when the light blue $Cu(H_2O)_4{}^{2+}$ ion becomes the dark blue $Cu(NH_3)_4^{2+}$ ion on the addition of ammonia, and when this, in turn, becomes the colourless $Cu(CN)_4{}^{2-}$ ion on the addition of sodium cyanide.

It is instructive to follow the behaviour of potassium alum which dissolves to give the ions $K_{aq}{}^+$, $[Al(H_2O)_6]^{3+}$ and $SO_4^{2-}{}_{aq}$. The hexa-aquoaluminium ion is immediately soluble but tends in time, especially when the temperature is raised, to hydroxylate in stages by proton loss:

$$[Al(H_2O)_6]^{3+} \rightarrow [Al(OH)(H_2O)_5]^{2+} + H_{aq}{}^+,$$
$$[Al(OH)(H_2O)_5]^{2+} \rightarrow [Al(OH)_2(H_2O)_4]^+ + H_{aq}{}^+.$$

A water molecule in these aquo-complexes can be replaced by SO_4^{2-}:

$$[Al(OH)(H_2O)_5]^{2+} + SO_4^{2-} \rightarrow [Al(OH)(SO_4)(H_2O)_4] + H_2O$$

The passage from solution to sol probably occurs by hydroxo-bridging

$$[Al(OH)(H_2O)_5]^{2+} + [Al(OH)(SO_4)(H_2O)_4] \rightarrow [(H_2O)_5Al\underset{\underset{H}{O}}{\overset{\overset{H}{O}}{<\quad>}}Al(SO_4)(H_2O)_4]^{2+}$$

This and similar kinds of bridging produce polymers of indefinite size which eventually separate as precipitates:

$$\cdots Al\underset{\underset{H}{O}}{\overset{\overset{H}{O}}{<\quad>}}Al\underset{\underset{H}{O}}{\overset{\overset{H}{O}}{<\quad>}}Al\underset{\underset{H}{O}}{\overset{\overset{H}{O}}{<\quad>}}Al(SO_4)(H_2O)_4$$

The change from soluble complexes, through sols, to precipitates is accelerated when the pH is raised. It is characteristic of the precipitate that repeated washing with water fails to remove all the SO_4^{2-} anions; this is because they occupy a place in the co-ordination sphere of the Al^{3+} cation and are not merely adsorbed on the surface of the particles.

Complex formation by replacement of molecules in the solvated shell of a metal cation in aqueous solution with, for example, unidentate ligands,

$$M(H_2O)_n + (n - x)L \rightleftharpoons ML_{(n-x)}(H_2O)_x + (n - x)H_2O,$$

usually produces an equilibrium of two or more complexes. The reaction proceeds stepwise with an equilibrium constant for every step:

$$k_1 = \frac{[M(H_2O)_{n-1}L];}{[M(H_2O)_n] \times [L]} \quad k_2 = \frac{[M(H_2O)_{n-2}L_2]}{[M(H_2O)_{n-1}L] \times [L]}; \quad k_n = \frac{[ML_n]}{[M(H_2O)L_{n-1}] \times [L]}$$

The constants k_1, $k_2 \ldots k_n$ are the *consecutive stability constants*; since a ligand already co-ordinated repels an incoming ligand of the same type, their values nearly always decrease in the order $k_1 > k_2 > \ldots > k_n$

Cation	Ligand	$\log k_1$	$\log k_2$	$\log k_3$	$\log k_4$
Cu^{2+}	NH_3	4.3	3.6	3.0	2.3
Cd^{2+}	NH_3	2.6	2.1	1.4	0.9

The product of the consecutive stability constants is the *cumulative stability constant, β*:

$$k_2 \times k_2 \times k_3 \times \ldots k_n = \frac{[ML_n]}{[M(H_2O)_n] \times [L]^n} = \beta$$

The symbol $p\beta$, that is $\log \beta$, is usually used as a measure of the stability of the ultimate complex. For $Cu(NH_3)_4^{2+}$, $p\beta$ is $4.3 + 3.6 + 3.0 + 2.3 = = 13.2$; and for $Cd(NH)_4^{2+}$, $p\beta$ is 7.0. A complex is regarded as stable when $p\beta$ exceeds 8.

Stability constants are calculated from the concentrations of the species present in equilibrium mixtures containing the metal ion and the ligand in a wide range of proportions. Activity coefficients are kept constant by appropriate additions of a salt, usually sodium perchlorate, whose ions do not compete with those of the cation and ligand. Concentrations at different ionic strengths are extrapolated to zero ionic strength. It may be necessary to find the number of water molecules displaced at each step; the total of these is not necessarily the same as the co-ordination number of the cation in the solid compound. Particularly in a polar solvent such as water, the ligands may not displace all the solvent molecules.

Ignoring hydration and charge, the equilibrium of a complex with its cation and ligands is expressed by:

$$M + nL \rightleftharpoons ML_n.$$

The total concentration of the metal, in the solvated cations and the complex, $[M]_t$, and the total concentration of the ligand, free and in the complex, $[L]_t$, can be found by analysis. The method of determining the concentration of the complex, $[ML_n]$, depends upon the system. When either the free ligand or the complex is coloured, or has a convenient absorption elsewhere in the spectrum, optical densities (log intensity of transmitted light/intensity of incident light) at a specific wave length are measured. Sometimes the concentrations of the uncomplexed metal ions are obtained potentiometrically with a suitable electrode. Polarography and extraction methods are also used, and occasionally the required information may be deduced from pH measurements.

To determine the stoichiometry of the reaction, Job's method of continuous variation is used: $[ML_n]$ is plotted against $[M]_t/\{[M]_t + [L]_t\}$ and a maximum in the curve indicates complex formation. Its composition corresponds to the position of the maximum.

With a complex of rather low stability, formation is not complete when M and L are in the proportion indicated by the plot and, as a result, the values of β drift as the ratio of metal to complexing agent is altered. But something very near the true value can be obtained by successive approximations.

Distribution methods for determining [M] depend on knowing the distribution coefficient for the metal ion or the ligand between two immiscible solvents. Thus free ammonia in equilibrium with the ammine complex of a metal can be determined from the ammonia concentration of a chloroform layer in equilibrium with the aqueous solution.

When the ligand is protonated, the equilibrium,

$$M + nHL \rightleftharpoons ML_n + nH^+,$$

may be set up, then:

$$\beta = \frac{[ML_n] \times [H^+]^n}{[M] \times [HL]^n}.$$

The equilibrium concentrations can be obtained from pH measurements. The method is applicable only when L is the anion of a weak acid; obviously it cannot be applied to the co-ordination of chloride and similar ions, for which the conjugate acid of the ligand is completely ionised before complex formation occurs.

Factors affecting the stability of complexes

What follows applies to solid complexes and is even more significant for dissolved complexes because these have to resist disruption by water.

1. Electrostatic field round the cation

Of the complexes formed by an individual ligand with a metal anion in two different oxidation states, those in which the anion has the higher charge number are nearly always the more stable, for instance with hexacyanoferrate(II), $Fe(CN)_6^{4-}$, $p\beta$ is 8.3, but with hexacyanoferrate(III), $Fe(CN)_6^{3-}$, $p\beta$ is 31.0. This follows if the ligands are held by the electrostatic charge on the central ion; the smaller, more highly charged, iron(III) ion extents a stronger attraction than the larger, lower charged, iron(II) ion.

Irving and Williams (1953) showed that the order of stability of complexes of these bipositive metal ions in the Third Period is related, irrespective of the ligand, to the ionic radius:

Cation	Mn^{2+}	<	Fe^{2+}	<	Co^{2+}	<	Ni^{2+}	<	Cu^{2+}	>	Zn^{2+}
Ionic radius (Å)	0.91		0.83		0.82		0.78		0.69		0.74

2. Distribution of charge

If complex formation be imagined to involve the donation of electron pairs from ligand to cation, and if the bonds were perfectly homopolar, then one unit of charge would be transferred for every bond formed. In these circumstances, a bipositive cation would accumulate a negative charge of four in becoming 6-co-ordinate, and the result would be a very unstable condition unlikely to persist. The stability of a complex increases as the Pauling 'postulate of neutrality' condition (p. 137) is approached, that is when each atom has a net charge between -1 and $+1$. Consequently ions such as Mg^{2+}, for which E_h° M^{n+}/M has a large negative value, attract electrons weakly and therefore form their strongest complexes with co-ordinating atoms of high electronegativity, for instance oxygen. At the other extreme, the noble metal ions with positive redox potentials accept electrons more readily, and form their strongest co-ordinate bonds with donor atoms such as sulphur and iodine which are easily polarised.

3. Occupation of low-energy orbitals

Although, as mentioned, iron(III) complexes are usually more stable than the corresponding iron(II) complexes, the tris(o-phenanthroline)iron (III) ion is much less stable than the tris(o-phenanthroline)iron(II) ion: $p\beta$ for $[Fe(phen)_3]^{3+}$ is 14, and for $(Fe(phen)_3]^{2+}$ is 21. Magnetic measurements show the former to be a high-spin complex and the latter to be a low-spin one. The additional stabilisation conferred on the complex by the filling of an $(n-1)d$ orbital of the cation more than overcomes the effect of the stronger electrostatic field.

4. Chelation

The stability of complexes is greatly increased by chelation; the formation of rings by polydentate ligands. Thus, for example, the stability constants of 6-co-ordinate Ni^{2+} with NH_3 and $NH_2CH_2CH_2NH_2$ are, respectively, 10^9 and 10^{19}. And the sexidentate EDTA ligand (p. 263) forms such stable soluble complexes that, for instance, the precipitation of Ca^{2+} by oxalate from alkaline solution is entirely prevented. Measurements of the free energy changes and the heats of reaction associated with chelation usually show that there has been a considerable increase in entropy. This occurs because several molecules of solvent in the solvated ion are replaced by a smaller number of multidentate ligands, or even by one:

$$M(H_2O)_n + L \rightleftarrows ML + nH_2O$$

The reaction represented increases the number of entities in the solution $n-1$ times; consequently it increases the disorder.

NOMENCLATURE OF COMPLEX COMPOUNDS

The formulae and names adopted for complex ions and compounds follow the main recommendations in *Nomenclature of Inorganic Chemistry*, 1959, issued by the International Union of Pure and Applied Chemistry; and in *Handbook for Chemical Society Authors*, 1960 which has much other useful information. Those referring to mononuclear complexes have been summarised.

Formulae

(i) Place the symbol for the nuclear atom first, follow with the symbols for the ligands, and enclose the complex in square brackets.

(ii) Indicate the charge number of the nuclear atom, when required, by Stock notation: Ni^0, Cu^I, Fe^{II}.

(iii) Place the ligands in the order (a) anionic, (b) neutral and cationic. Arrange within these classes in the sequences:
   (a) (1) H^-, O^{2-}, OH^-, I^-, Br^-, Cl^-, F^-;
       (2) other inorganic anions containing two or more elements, that with the smaller number of atoms first, and, when the number is the same, that with the central atom of larger atomic number first;
       (3) organic anions in alphabetical order.
   (b) (1) H_2O, NH_3;
       (2) other inorganic ligands in this order of their central atoms: B, Si, C, Sb, As, P, N, Te, Se, S, I, Br, Cl;
       (3) organic ligands in alphabetical order.

Names

(i) Cite names of ligands first, the name of the nuclear atom last.

(ii) Names of complex cations and neutral molecules have no distinguishing termination; names of complex anions end in -ate.

(iii) Cite ligands in their order in the formula. Names of the anionic end in -o; those of the neutral, except aquo for H_2O and ammine for NH_3, and the cationic are the same as the molecule or cation.

(iv) The anionic groups CN, O·NO, NO_2, NO_3, are named cyano, nitrito, nitro and nitrato. Anions derived from hydrocarbons are given the name of the radical, sometimes with an -o ending.

(v) The groups NO, NS, CO, CS are termed nitrosyl, thionitrosyl, carbonyl and thiocarbonyl, and are treated as neutral in computing the oxidation number of the nuclear atom.

(vi) The prefixes mono, di, tri, tetra, penta, hexa, hepta, octa, ennea, deca, hendeca and dodeca are used (without hyphen, except when two vowels are brought together as in the first example below) to indicate the numbers of the individual ligands in a complex. When, however, the name includes a numerical prefix with a different significance, then bis, tris and tetrakis are used, the group to which they refer being often placed in parentheses:

$[Ni(CO)_2(Ph_3P)_2]$ dicarbonyl-bis(triphenylphosphine)nickel;

and sometimes in cases like these:

$[Fe(C_5H_5)_2]Cl$ bis(cyclopentadienyl)iron(III) chloride, and
$Ca(PCl_6)_2$ calcium bis(hexachlorophosphate).

Details about formulae and names of polynuclear complexes can be found in *Nomenclature of Inorganic Chemistry*. It need only be mentioned here that a bridging group is indicated in the formula by separating it from the rest of the complex by hyphens, and in the name by prefixing it with μ-:

$[(NH_3)_5Cr{-}OH{-}Cr(NH_3)_5]Cl_5$

μ-hydroxo-bis{penta-amminechromium(III)} chloride.

Examples of formulae and names

$[Co(NH_3)_6]^{3+}$ the hexa-amminecobalt(III) ion.

$[Co(O·NO)_3]^{3-}$ the hexanitritocobaltate(III) ion.

$[Fe(CN)_6]^{-4}$ the hexacyanoferrate(II) ion.

$K_3[Fe(CN)_6]$ potassium hexacyanoferrate(III).

$[CoCl_2(NH_3)_4]Cl$ dichlorotetra-amminecobalt(III) chloride.

$K[Co(CN)(CO)_2NO]$ potassium cyanodicarbonylnitrosylcobaltate (0).

$[Co(NH_3)_2(en)_2]Cl_3$ diammine-bis(ethylenediammine)cobalt(III) chloride.

$[Co(NO_2)_3(NH_3)_3]$ trinitrotriamminecobalt(III).

$[Pt(NH_3)_6]Cl_4$ hexa-ammineplatinum(IV) chloride.

$[CrCl(H_2O)(en)_2]^{2+}$ the chloroaquo-bis(ethylenediamine)chromium(III) ion.

$$\left[(NH_3)_4Co \underset{\underset{OH}{\diagdown\diagup}}{\overset{\overset{NH_2}{\diagup\diagdown}}{}} Co(NH_3)_4 \right]^{4+}$$ the octa-ammine μ-amido μ-hydroxo-dicobalt(III) ion.

$$\left[\begin{array}{c} CH_3.C = N \diagup^{OH} \\ | \qquad \diagdown CoCl_2 \\ CH_3.C = N \diagdown_{OH} \end{array} \right]$$ dichlorodimethylglyoxime-N,N'cobalt(II).

Chapter 38

Catenation and Polymerisation in Inorganic Chemistry

The term *polymerisation* distinguishes the process whereby simple molecular units combine to give larger units. The phenomenon is very common. For instance *polymers* are frequently produced when salts dissolve in water. These often remain soluble and are limited in complexity to dimers and trimers; nevertheless, the properties of many of these solutions can be understood only in terms of these polymers and their interconversion (p. 549). This chapter deals, however, with much larger polymers, resembling those developed from purely organic materials, but of which the constituents are wholly or partly of inorganic origin.

Organic polymers include elastomers (rubber), hydraulic fluids, adhesives, coatings, thermoplastics and thermosetting plastics, materials showing a wide range of physical and chemical properties. They begin to oxidise or decompose in air above about 300°, hence a search in the inorganic field for alternative materials more resistant to heat and chemical action. Purely inorganic polymers have so far proved to be highly cross-linked with strongly directional bonds, so that their properties are rather circumscribed. Most progress has been made through the development of mixed organic–inorganic polymers; some of these have inorganic molecular skeletons, to enhance thermal stability, clothed with alkyl and aryl groups, to give flexibility. Of these, the silicones (p. 296) have been outstandingly successful.

As has been shown in earlier chapters, polymerisation occurs frequently in inorganic substances. Silicate and borate minerals, for example, contain polymeric anions (pp. 153 and 274), and compounds such as $CuCl_2$ and $PdCl_2$ (p. 412) have structures which arise from the polymerisation of neutral molecules. In silicon disulphide, the silicon atoms are linked in a chain of infinite length by double sulphur bridges (p. 298). Cyanide groups can act as bridges between metal atoms; silver(I) and gold(I) cyanides are linear polymers:

$$—Ag—C—N—Ag—C—N—Ag—C—N—Ag—C—N—.$$

On the other hand, metals which, in their bipositive states, can form four coplanar bonds (Pd, Pt, Ni, Cu) give cyanides with infinite layer lattices:

$$
\begin{array}{ccc}
\mid & & \mid \\
\text{C} & & \text{N} \\
\mid & & \mid \\
-\text{C}-\text{M}-\text{C}-\text{N}-\text{M}-\text{N}- \\
\mid & & \mid \\
\text{C} & & \text{N} \\
\mid & & \mid \\
\text{N} & & \text{C} \\
\mid & & \mid \\
-\text{N}-\text{M}-\text{N}-\text{C}-\text{M}-\text{C}- \\
\mid & & \mid \\
\text{N} & & \text{C} \\
\mid & & \mid
\end{array}
$$

Copper(II) and nickel(II) react with dithio-oxamide to produce insoluble compounds of high molecular mass (Jensen, 1944), which contain long chains of the type:

$$
\begin{array}{c}
\text{S}\!-\!-\!\text{C}\!=\!\text{NH} \\
\diagdown\text{M}\diagdown \qquad\qquad \diagup\text{M}\diagup \\
\diagup \quad \text{NH}\!=\!\text{C}\!-\!-\!\text{S} \diagup
\end{array}
$$

But, when the metal is capable of octahedral co-ordination, three-dimensional arrangements are possible, as in Prussian Blue (p. 497).

The metal chelate polymers contain metal ions joined to one another by polyfunctional chelating agents. Examples are the linear polymers prepared from Schiff bases by mixing a solution of the base with a soluble metal salt. The insoluble polymer is precipitated (Marvel and Tarköy, 1958):

$$
\left[
\begin{array}{c}
\text{(benzene)}-\text{O}\diagup\text{M}\diagdown\text{O}-\text{(benzene)}-\text{X}- \\
\text{CH}=\text{N}\diagup \quad \diagdown\text{N}=\text{CH}
\end{array}
\right]_n
\qquad \text{X}=\text{SO}_2 \text{ or } \text{CH}_2
$$

Viscosity measurements indicate that the products have molecular masses of about 10,000.

Catenation

The direct linking of like atoms, such an essential feature of carbon chemistry, occurs to only a limited extent with other elements. Metal–metal bonds are not uncommon but they are always weak; examples are found in the polynuclear carbonyls (p. 306) and compounds such as Sn_2R_6 and Pb_2R_6 (R = alkyl). Among the other non-metals catenation is displayed by boron, silicon, germanium, phosphorus and sulphur; none of the substances produced so far has, however, proved of value as a polymer. Nevertheless, there is sufficient of theoretical interest to warrant further consideration of catenation in these elements.

Bonds between boron atoms occur in halides such as B_2Cl_4, B_4Cl_4 and B_8Cl_8 (p. 271). In B_4Cl_4 the four boron atoms are arranged in a tetrahedron and the B–B bonds are of fractional order. In B_8Cl_8 every boron atom is attached to three others in a polyhedral molecule.

Fluorocarbon polymers are based upon the same carbon chains and rings characteristic of the hydrocarbon polymers, but the strength of the C–F bond and the absence of hydrogen makes them more resistant to oxidation. The increased stability is also due to the more effective shielding of the carbon atoms by the fluorine atoms which are so much larger than hydrogen atoms. Polytetrafluoroethylene, $(CF_2—CF_2)_n$, a colourless solid, is made by polymerising $CF_2 : CF_2$ in the presence of aqueous peroxodisulphates. The monomer itself is made by 'cracking' CF_2HCl at 800°. The polymer is thermoplastic; it has a transition point at 327° above which it can be fabricated. It is stable in air up to 300° and is insoluble in all common solvents. Because the material is difficult to fabricate industrially, fluorinated vinyl-type polymers, with a sufficiently low viscosity to allow them to be worked at the melting point, have been developed. The co-polymer of $CF_2 : CF_2$ and $CF_3CF : CF_2$, with the structure

$$(CF_2CF_2CF_2CF)_n,$$
$$|$$
$$CF_3$$

fulfils these requirements.

Fuorine reacts with graphite at 420–460° to give a solid varying in composition from $CF_{0.68}$ to $CF_{0.995}$. When low in fluorine the substance is grey; but, as the composition approaches C_nF_n, the solid becomes transparent and colourless. Its electrical conductance is very much less than that of graphite itself and it is chemically unreactive, not being attacked by concentrated acids or alkalis. The structure consists of a succession of puckered layers of carbon atoms with fluorine atoms attached to them so that the end-on view appears thus:

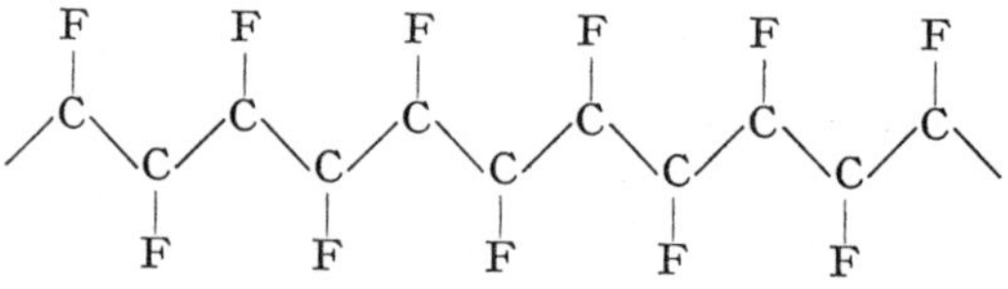

The distance between the carbon layers is 6.6 Å, almost twice the 3.34 Å possessed by graphite itself. At lower temperatures, graphite and fluorine react to give material with a composition varying from C_4F to $C_{3.6}F$; in this, every fourth carbon is believed to be covalently bound to fluorine. The solid is very inert but is a better electrical conductor than C_nF_n.

Silicon has a much smaller tendency to catenation than has carbon. Paraffin-like silanes are known up to Si_6H_{14} (p. 224), and a fully chlorinated decasilane, $Si_{10}Cl_{22}$, is a product of the 'cracking' of $SiCl_4$ at 1100°, in the presence of an inert gas. The iodide Si_2I_6 decomposes on heating to give, among other things, the polymer Si_nI_n. Drake and Jolly (1961) reported the production of germanes up to Ge_8H_{18} when monogermane, at about half an atmosphere pressure, is passed through a silent electric discharge.

Phosphorus has few compounds in which P atoms are directly linked to one another. Catenation occurs in the hydrides; thus diphosphorus tetra-hydride, P_2H_4, decomposes rapidly at 0° into phosphine and a mixture of hydrides represented by $P_xH_y(x > y)$. These yellow, amorphous solids attain the composition $P_{2n}H_n$ provided the reaction is allowed to proceed for a sufficient time. They are also produced when dry hydrogen chloride reacts with aluminium phosphide, AlP. Royen, using X-ray analysis, showed the solids to be amorphous; the available evidence suggests that they are high polymers. The solids are insoluble in all common solvents, but dissolve in molten phosphorus. They are reasonably stable in air at room temperature but are converted by slight heating into red solids of compositions such as P_9H_2 and P_5H_2, with the loss of PH_3.

Two unusual compounds of phosphorus, with surprisingly high thermal stability, are based upon the P_4 ring:

$$C_6H_5P—PC_6H_5 \qquad F_3CP—PCF_3$$
$$| \quad | \qquad \text{and} \qquad | \quad |$$
$$C_6H_5P—PC_6H_5 \qquad F_3CP—PCF_3$$

The latter is made by the reaction of CF_3PI_2 with mercury at room temperature or by the thermal decomposition of $P_2(CF_3)_4$ (Mahler and Burg, 1957):

$$4P_2(CF_3)_4 \rightarrow (PCF_3)_4 + 4(CF_3)_3P.$$

The thermal stability is probably due to $d_\pi—p_\pi$ bonding between the phosphorus atoms, similar in character to that between P and N atoms in the phosphonitrilic halides (p. 341).

Bonds between sulphur atoms occur in the hydrogen polysulphides or sulphanes (p. 234) and in the halides S_xCl_2 and S_xBr_2 (p. 362). Schmidt (1957) has made a series of acids, formulated $H_2S_xO_3$ and $H_2S_xO_6$, containing chains of sulphur atoms, by treating ethereal solutions of sulphanes with solutions of SO_3 in CF_2Cl_2 at $-78°$; instances are:

$$H_2S_5 + SO_3 \rightarrow HS_6O_3H$$
$$H_2S_5 + 2SO_3 \rightarrow HO_3S_7O_3H$$

Those with the shortest sulphur chains ($x = 3$) have a moderate thermal stability but this decreases with the length of the chain. Hydrolytic stability also falls, the compounds with longer sulphur chains being particularly susceptible to attack by alkalis and giving sulphur, SO_2 and thiosulphate ions.

Chains of like atoms have not yet provided a basis for the construction of stable, purely inorganic polymers. However, chains and rings of alternating atoms, $-X-Y-X-Y-X-Y-$, are formed by several pairs of elements. Some of the compounds derived from these chains and rings have theoretical and preparative interest, though, with the exception of the silicones, few are likely to be of technological importance.

Polymers based on boron

The B—O—B arrangement is present in the polyborate ions in borate minerals (p. 274). Boron–nitrogen polymers are based principally upon the borazole structure (p. 222), but the condensation of compounds such as $C_6H_5BCl_2$ and $C_4H_9NH_2$ has led to long-chain polymers of much higher molecular weight, probably because the formation of six-membered rings is prevented by steric hindrance:

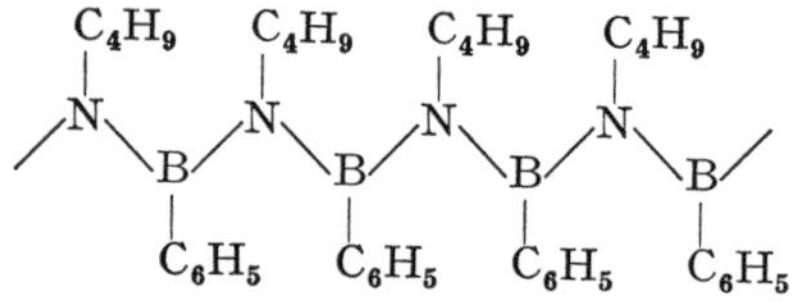

Boron–phosphorus polymers have been made by reactions similar to those for the boron–nitrogen compounds. Diborane forms addition compounds with phosphine and substituted phosphines at low temperature. Heating causes (a) disproportionation and (b) elimination of hydrogen, with polymer formation. The product of the reaction between diborane and PH_3 at 65° gives hydrogen and, finally, a white, insoluble polymer of composition $PBH_{3.75}$. The ideal formula is probably $(PBH_4)_n$, the lower figure for hydrogen is probably due to cross-linking between $-BH_2-PH_2-$ chains. The addition compound of diborane and dimethyl phosphine, when it is heated to 150°, gives mainly the very stable, chemically resistant $(Me_2P.BH_2)_3$, m.p. 86°, less of the somewhat less resistant tetramer, and a trace of a higher polymer which is convertible by heat into the trimer. Both tetramer and trimer hydrolyse slowly at 300° to give a molecule of H_3BO_3 and of Me_2PO_2H per $Me_2P.BH_2$ unit. Burg ascribed the stability of the trimer to π-bonding between B and P in which electrons of the B—H bonds enter d-orbitals of phosphorus. The B—P bond is thereby strengthened and the electron density on the hydrogen reduced, rendering it less susceptible to attack by electrophilic reagents. Dimethyl phosphine reacts with Me_2BBr in triethylamine to give the stable and inert trimer $(Me_2P.BMe_2)_3$.

The arsines are similar to the phosphines except that the bonds are weaker. Arsine and diborane do not react at —78°, but when the mixture reaches room temperature hydrogen is set free and an insoluble polymer, ideally $(AsBH_4)_n$, is produced. As the temperature is raised more hydrogen is lost, presumably by cross-linking between the —AsH_2—BH_2— chains similar to that in the phosphorus–boron polymers. The reaction between diborane and dimethylarsine completely parallels the dimethylphosphine reaction in giving trimeric, tetrameric and long-chain polymers of Me_2AsBH_2. With the initial product, however, there is appreciable hydrogen evolution at 50°, unlike the phosphine compound, which requires a temperature above 100°.

Polymers based on silicon

Silicate minerals contain —Si—O—Si— linkages in anions. The silicones have similar silicon–oxygen skeletons surrounded by alkyl and aryl groups in molecular polymers (p. 297). Partial hydrolysis of $SiCl_4$ at low temperatures gives a mixture of condensed siloxanes, $Si_nO_{n-1}Cl_{2n+2}$ with n up to six. They are oily liquids which can be separated by fractionation. The reaction probably proceeds through the formation of chlorosilanol, Cl_3SiOH, which then undergoes successive condensations with the elimination of HCl:

$$SiCl_4 + H_2O \rightarrow Cl_3SiOH + HCl$$
$$Cl_3SiOH + ClSiCl_3 \rightarrow Cl_3SiOSiCl_3 + HCl$$
$$Cl_3SiOSiCl_3 + HOSiCl_3 \rightarrow Cl_3SiOSiCl_2OSiCl_3 + HCl$$

The hydrolysis is carried out in diethyl ether; this withdraws the hydrogen chloride in the form of $Et_2O.HCl$. The chlorosiloxanes and the corresponding bromine compounds have also been made by passing an oxygen–halogen mixture over silicon at 700°. Under these conditions a crystalline cyclic tetramer $(SiOX_2)_4$ is another product of the reaction.

The —Si—O—Si—O— pattern characteristic of the silicones has been modified by replacing some silicon atoms by other Group IV elements such as titanium, and by introducing Group III elements such as aluminium. For instance, the controlled hydrolysis of mixtures of $RTiCl_3$ and $RSiCl_3$ produces cross-linked systems based on such units as

$$
\begin{array}{ccc}
R & & O \\
| & & | \\
-O-Ti-O-Si- \\
| & & | \\
O & & R \\
| & &
\end{array}
$$

Aluminium chloride and $RSiCl_3$ when suitably hydrolysed give

$$
\begin{array}{ccc}
& & R \\
& & | \\
-O-Al-O-Si- \\
| & & | \\
O & & O \\
| & & |
\end{array}
$$

Bradley, Gaze and Wardlaw (1955) made a series of polymers containing —Ti—O—Ti—O— skeletons by the hydrolysis of $Ti(OEt)_4$ in aqueous alcohol.

Germanium–oxygen linkages are also possible; Schumb and Smyth (1955) studied the partial hydrolysis of $GeCl_4$ in ether, chloroform or n-pentane by adding water in $GeCl_4 : H_2O$ molar ratios from 5 : 1 to 1 : 1. Solid polymers were obtained with compositions close to $Ge_2O_3Cl_2$, but an individual compound could not be isolated. Invariably hydrolysis ceased when the hydrochloric acid concentration of the aqueous phase reached about 6.5 M.

Polymers containing silicon–nitrogen bonds were made by Pflugmacher and Dahmen (1957) using an interesting reaction between molecular nitrogen and silicon tetrachloride in a glow discharge. The initial product is the fully chlorinated trisilylamine, $(SiCl_3)_3N$, but this lost $SiCl_4$ to give polymers with the formula $(Si_2NCl_5)_n$. A cyclic product:

$$
\begin{array}{ccccc}
SiCl_3 & & Cl & & SiCl_3 \\
\diagdown & & | & & \diagup \\
N & \!\!-\!\!-\!\!- & Si & \!\!-\!\!-\!\! & N \\
| & & | & & | \\
| & & Cl & & | \\
Cl-Si-Cl & & & & Cl-Si-Cl \\
| & & Cl & & | \\
| & & | & & | \\
N & \!\!-\!\!-\!\!- & Si & \!\!-\!\!-\!\! & N \\
\diagup & & | & & \diagdown \\
SiCl_3 & & Cl & & SiCl_3
\end{array}
$$

has been isolated as crystals, and the oily residue is believed to contain linear polymers of which the simplest is:

$$(Cl_3Si)_2N.SiCl_2.N(SiCl_3)_2$$

Silicon tetrachloride also reacts with ammonia in the vapour phase at 825° to give chlorosilazanes of low molecular weight such as:

$$Cl_3Si.NH.SiCl_3,$$

together with compounds of rather higher molecular weight such as the cyclic $Si_8N_4Cl_{20}$ shown above.

Polymers based on phosphorus

Because of the strong bonds it makes with oxygen, nitrogen and sulphur, phosphorus forms a large number of polymers. Polyphosphate anions have —P—O—P— linkages and so have the oxygen-linked compounds:

(i)

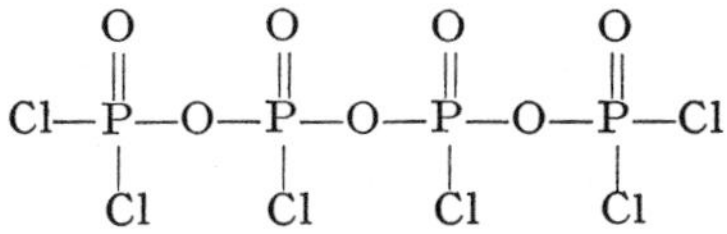

(ii)

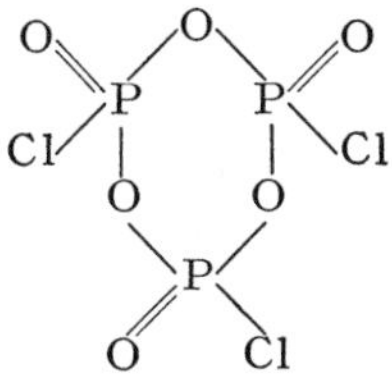

As in the oxygen-linked silicon compounds, the halogen atoms can be replaced by organic groups. When phosphorus trifluoride and oxygen are passed through an electrical discharge at —75°, a white solid with the composition $P_7O_{10}F_{15}$ is produced which loses POF_3, PF_5 and $P_2O_3F_4$ when allowed to warm to 0°, leaving a polymer $(PO_2F)_n$ with the probable structure (Wannagat and Rademachers, 1957):

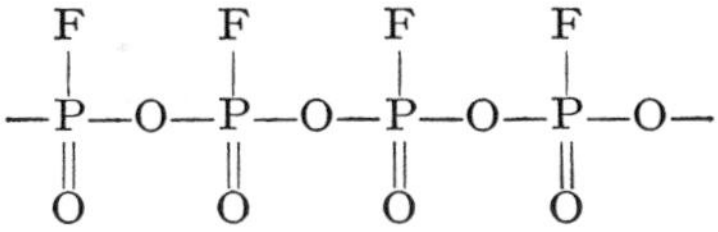

The compound has a rather simple X-ray pattern and is probably not of very high molecular weight; it is hygroscopic and easily hydrolysed.

The most numerous and best known phosphorus–nitrogen polymers are the phosphonitrilic halides (p. 343). Related to these are the phosphonitrilamides and phosphams. Moreau and Rocquet (1936) obtained phosphonitrilamides, $[PN(NH_2)_2]_n$, by adding PCl_5, dissolved in various solvents, to liquid ammonia. Audrieth and Sowerby (1959) made a trimer and tetramer of the same empirical formula by treating the corresponding phosphonitrilic chlorides with a large excess of liquid ammonia under pressure at room temperature:

$$(PNCl_2)_3 + 12NH_3 \rightarrow [PN(NH_2)_2]_3 + 6NH_4Cl;$$
$$(PNCl_2)_4 + 16NH_3 \rightarrow [PN(NH_2)_2]_4 + 8NH_4Cl.$$

These are white, slightly hygroscopic substances which lose NH_3 on heating. Their aqueous solutions react with formalin to give water-soluble substances which become glassy on drying. Prolonged heating of either the trimer or tetramer results in the formation of phosphams, high polymers formulated $(PN_2H)_n$, ammonia being liberated. The phosphams probably retain in their structures the 6- and 8-membered rings of the trimer and tetramer from which they are made.

The best known P—O—N polymer is the phosphoryl nitride, $(PON)_n$, first made by Gerhardt (1846) by raising phosphoryl imidoamide to red heat in the absence of air. The solid has a high melting point and is stable to heat and moderately stable to chemical attack, and it is only sparingly soluble in the common solvents. The probable structure is:

$$
\begin{array}{ccccc}
| & & | & & | \\
O & & O & & O \\
| & & | & & | \\
-P&-N-&P&-N-&P- \\
| & & | & & | \\
O & & O & & O \\
| & & | & & | \\
-P&-N-&P&-N-&P- \\
| & & | & & |
\end{array}
$$

in which there would be d_π–p_π bonding between the P and N atoms as in the phosphonitrilic halides (p. 343).

Polymers based on sulphur

When tetrasulphur tetranitride (p. 338) at low pressure is heated to 300° the ring is broken and a polymer, $(SN)_n$, is produced as fibrous crystals with a metallic lustre. The material, which is a semi-conductor, probably has the structure:

$$\diagup\!\!\begin{array}{c}S\\ \end{array}\!\!\diagdown\!\!\begin{array}{c}\\N\end{array}\!\!\diagup\!\!\begin{array}{c}S\\ \end{array}\!\!\diagdown\!\!\begin{array}{c}\\N\end{array}\!\!\diagup\!\!\begin{array}{c}S\\ \end{array}\!\!\diagdown\!\!\begin{array}{c}\\N\end{array}\!\!\diagup\!\!\begin{array}{c}S\\ \end{array}\!\!\diagdown\!\!\begin{array}{c}\\N\end{array}\!\!\diagup\!\!\begin{array}{c}S\\ \end{array}\!\!\diagdown\!\!\begin{array}{c}\\N\end{array}\!\!\diagup\!\!\begin{array}{c}S\\ \end{array}\!\!\diagdown$$

Reduction of S_4N_4 with tin(II) chloride gives the tetraimide:

$$
\begin{array}{ccc}
\mathrm{HN{-}S{-}NH} \\
| \qquad | \\
\mathrm{S} \qquad \mathrm{S} \\
| \qquad | \\
\mathrm{HN{-}S{-}NH}
\end{array}
$$

the infrared spectrum of which shows NH frequencies but no SH frequencies. $(SNH)_n$ does not exist in the chain form, but $(SNMe)_n$ chains have been produced by treating SCl_2 with CH_3NH_2 in hexane and removing the methyl ammonium chloride with methanol:

$$nSCl_2 + 2nCH_3NH_2 \rightarrow (SNCH_3)_n + nCH_3NH_3Cl + nHCl.$$

The polymer is thermally unstable.

Treatment of $S_4(NH)_4$ with ozone converts it into a linear polymer $(-SO-NH-)_n$; the brown, insoluble material has also been made by treating thionyl chloride with ammonia in the vapour phase. Thionyl fluoride, however, reacts with ammonia to give a volatile ether-soluble amide as the initial product:

$$SOF_2 + 2NH_3 \rightarrow SOF(NH_2) + NH_4F$$

which polymerises to a yellow material:

$$
\begin{array}{ccccc}
\mathrm{OH} & & \mathrm{OH} & & \mathrm{OH} \\
| & & | & & | \\
\mathrm{-S} & \!\!-\mathrm{N}-\!\! & \mathrm{S} & \!\!-\mathrm{N}-\!\! & \mathrm{S}- \\
| & & | & & | \\
\mathrm{F} & \mathrm{H} & \mathrm{F} & \mathrm{H} & \mathrm{F}
\end{array}
$$

Linear polymers are also obtainable from non-metal isocyanates such as sulphonyl isocyanate, which is itself prepared by the action of sulphur trioxide on potassium cyanate:

$$2KOCN + 4SO_3 \rightarrow OCNSO_2{-}O{-}SO_2NCO + K_2S_2O_7,$$
$$OCNSO_2{-}O{-}SO_2NCO \rightarrow OCNSO_2NCO + SO_3.$$

Complete hydrolysis of this compound gives sulphamide:

$$OCNSO_2NCO + 2H_2O \rightarrow H_2NSO_2NH_2 + 2CO_2.$$

But controlled hydrolysis with a smaller quantity of water results in the formation of gels:

$$OCNSO_2NCO + H_2O \rightarrow OCNSO_2NH_2 + CO_2,$$
$$nOCNSO_2NH_2 + nOCNSO_2NH_2 \rightarrow (-SO_2.NH.CO.NH.SO_2.NH.CO.NH-)n$$

Sulphamide has been used to form polymers by means of a reaction analogous to the urea–formaldehyde condensation (Wood and Battye, 1933). The products are resins containing the structural unit:

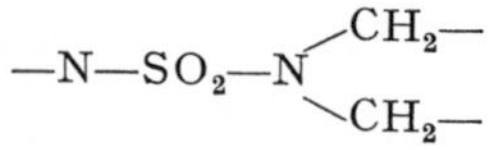

$$-N-SO_2-N\begin{smallmatrix}CH_2-\\[4pt]CH_2-\end{smallmatrix}$$

Appel and Gerber (1958) made polysulphourethane polymer by treating sulphonyl isocyanate with glycol:

$$H(-O-CH_2-CH_2-O-CO-NH-SO_2-NH-CO)_4O-CH_2-CH_2-OH$$

A polymeric sulphimidosulphonic acid is produced, together with trimeric and tetrameric sulphimide, when sulphur trioxide reacts with ammonia in nitromethane (Appel and Goehring, 1953).

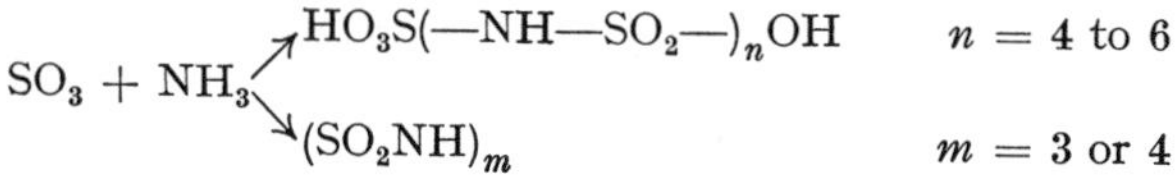

$$SO_3 + NH_3 \nearrow^{HO_3S(-NH-SO_2-)_nOH} \qquad n = 4 \text{ to } 6$$
$$\searrow_{(SO_2NH)_m} \qquad m = 3 \text{ or } 4$$

The trimer and tetramer are cyclic:

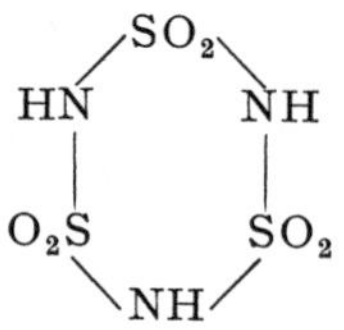

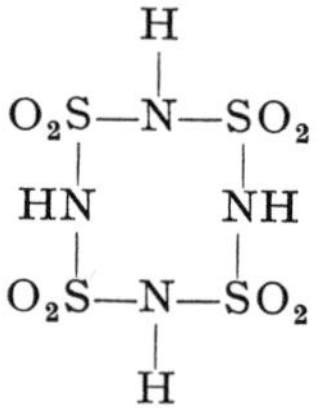

General conclusions

The difficulty of producing inorganic polymers stems mainly from two facts: (a) compounds of very high molecular weight cannot be produced through catenation of like atoms, since long chains or condensed rings are not formed by atoms other than carbon; (b) compounds containing chains and condensed rings of unlike atoms, —X—Y—X—, are sometimes thermally stable but always hydrolytically unstable. The difference between the electronegativities of X and Y contributes to this instability. However, there can be little doubt that polymers of higher stability and useful properties will eventually be produced from elements other than carbon, but they will probably be of the mixed inorganic–organic type.

Chapter 39

Ion Exchange, Partition Chromatography and Solvent Extraction

Three methods have come into general use for separating chemical species; they are ion exchange, partition chromatography and solvent extraction.

Ion exchange

The first ion-exchange materials were the hydrated alumino-silicates, known as the zeolites, employed for water softening. These had the disadvantage of adding silicate to the water and were of low exchange capacity; they were replaced by artificial materials with better characteristics. Another early exchanger was humic acid, a condensed aromatic system with carboxylic acid groups, made by treating soft coal with sulphuric acid. The hydrogens of these —COOH groups are replaceable by metal ions. Essential features of ion exchange are that the reactions are reversible, the equilibrium being governed by the concentration in the liquid, and that the solids do not disintegrate as the result of repeated exchange.

Later, synthetic exchange resins became important. They are of two kinds, cation exchangers and anion exchangers. The former are, as a rule, phenol formaldehyde or polystyrene resins in which there are extra $-SO_3H$, —COOH or —OH groups. A portion of a typical structure is:

The hydrogen atoms of the $-SO_3H$ groups ionise and are readily replaced by metal cations. Thus, when aqueous sodium chloride is passed down a column containing the resin, H^+ is largely replaced by Na^+.

$$\text{Resin H} + \text{NaCl} \rightarrow \text{Resin Na} + \text{HCl}$$
$$\text{(insol.)} \quad \text{(sol.)} \quad \text{(insol.)} \quad \text{(sol.)}$$

Such a cationic resin is a 'strong acid' exchanger and will furnish a strong acid from one of its salts. The 'weak acid' exchangers, with $-COOH$ and $-OH$ groups as sources of H^+ ions, do not do this, but they will set free a weak acid from its salt:

$$\text{Resin H} + \text{CH}_3\text{COONa} \rightarrow \text{Resin Na} + \text{CH}_3\text{COOH}.$$

In the sodium form they exchange with cations other than H^+.

Anion exchangers can also be made which have either a 'strong base' or 'weak base' character. The former are usually phenol-formaldehyde or polystyrene resins with extra quarternary ammonium groups. Ionisation occurs in both the salt and hydroxide form, and all kinds of anions are exchanged with reasonable ease:

$$2\text{R.N(CH}_3)_3\text{Cl} + \text{SO}_4{}^{2-} \rightarrow [\text{R.N(CH}_3)_3]_2\text{SO}_4 + 2\text{Cl}^-$$
$$\text{R.N(CH}_3)_3\text{OH} + \text{NaCl} \rightarrow \text{R.N(CH}_3)_3\text{Cl} \quad + \text{NaOH}$$
$$\text{R.N(CH}_3)_3\text{OH} + \text{HCl} \rightarrow \text{R.N(CH}_3)_3\text{Cl} \quad + \text{H}_2\text{O}.$$

The weak base type is without the hydroxide from. It contains tertiary amino groups and will absorb mineral acids, or release weak bases from their salts:

$$\text{R.N(CH}_3)_2 + \text{HCl} \rightarrow \text{R.N(CH}_3)_2\text{HCl}$$
$$\text{R.N(CH}_3)_2 + \text{C}_6\text{H}_5.\text{NH}_3\text{Cl} \rightarrow \text{R.N(CH}_3)_2\text{HCl} + \text{C}_6\text{H}_5.\text{NH}_2.$$

But these resins will not free a strong base from its salt, or absorb weakly ionised acids.

Ion exchange resins depend for success on their open structures which give ready access to the replaceable ions. They must also be insoluble, and structurally stable. Conditions during manufacture are controlled to give the cross-linking leading to optimum performance. The capacity for exchange of ions depends on the kind of resin, being generally about 3–5 milli-equivalents per gram of dry resin.

Applications of ion exchange

Exchange resins are taking the place of zeolites for certain water treatment. Thus, although a zeolite will replace calcium sulphate in water by sodium sulphate, a mixture of an anionic exchanger with a cationic one willr remove all the dissolved inorganic salts. This 'demineralisation', as it is termed, is being used increasingly in industry, particula rly for boiler-wate treatment.

Exchange resins are also employed for the concentration of ions present in very dilute solutions; instances are the recovery of silver from photographic residues, chromate from the waste liquor of chromium plating and magnesium from sea water. They have also been used for the separation of rare earths (p. 426), and of uranium, plutonium and radio-active fission products (p. 437), and for plutonium and uranium-233 purification. A striking application was the historic separation of single atoms of mendelevium on a sulphonated polystyrene resin and their elution therefrom, at 87°, with α-hydroxyisobutyrate (Seaborg, 1955).

They have many preparative and analytical uses. A cation can often be determined quantitatively by pouring a solution of it over a cation exchanger in its hydrogen form and then measuring the acidity of the liquid which emerges. Another method is to absorb the cation on the column, wash and then elute with a complexing agent which removes the cation as an anionic complex.

A partial separation of lithium isotopes has been effected by the use of a zeolite (p. 248), and a complete one of ^{15}N from ^{14}N by means of a cationic resin. Spedding, Powell and Svec (1955) found an equilibrium between the ammonium form of Dowex 50X12 resin and ammonium hydroxide with the separation factor (^{15}N resin/^{14}N resin $\times$ ^{14}N solution/^{15}N solution) $= 1.0257$:

$$^{14}NH_4Resin + {}^{15}NH_4OH \rightleftharpoons {}^{15}NH_4Resin + {}^{14}NH_4OH.$$

A band of NH_4^+ on a column of the resin in the hydrogen form, when eluted with NaOH, gave an enrichment of $^{15}NH_4^+$ at the rear edge, and of $^{14}NH_4^+$ at the leading edge, as the band moved downwards. The adsorbed band had, however, to be extended to about 39 times its length by elutriation in order to develop a tailing fraction containing 99% ^{15}N.

Newer synthetic inorganic exchangers include precipitated zirconium phosphate and zirconium tungstate. Amphlett, McDonald and Redman (1956) made a granular zirconium phosphate gel by mixing concentrated solutions of $Zr(SO_4)_2$, $ZrO(NO_3)_2$ or $ZrOCl_2$ in the appropriate $2N$ acid with 3% aqueous phosphoric acid. When washed and dried, the gel shrank and broke into lumps in a similar way to silica gel. This valuable cation exchanger is very insoluble in most reagents; it is made in its hydrogen form and will exchange H^+ with K^+, NH_4^+, Ca^{2+}, Sr^{2+}, Cu^{2+}, Ni^{2+}, VO_2^{2+}, Fe^{2+}, Fe^{3+} and La^{3+}. The material is hardly affected by hot aqueous solutions and is particularly effective in absorbing corrosion-product ions derived from metal surfaces. Kraus, Carlson and Johnson (1956) prepared a column from precipitated zirconium tungstate for the separation of Na^+, K^+, Rb^+ and Cs^+. The eluant was aqueous NH_4Cl whose concentration was increased as the elution proceeded.

A development is the production of membranes of ion exchange resin through which ions of only one sign can pass. Kressman (1949), condensing phenolsulphonic acid with phenol and formaldehyde, supported the resin on filter paper or fabric; other homogeneous ion exchange membranes have been made by the co-polymerisation of p-styrenesulphonic acid with styrene and divinylbenzene and by the chlorosulphonation of polyethylene and polyvinyl chloride. Heterogeneous membranes have been made by simply binding grains of a conventional resin with polyethylene, but they are less satisfactory as, on swelling, they develop voids which fill with electrolyte.

Fig. 291 which represents an electrolytic cell divided into three compartments, illustrates the use of these membranes. Cations cannot escape from the anode compartment because they cannot penetrate the anion exchange membrane A; both cations and anions can leave the centre compartment, but anions cannot pass from the cathode compartment. Thus the liquid in the centre compartment is demineralised. A process for separating electrolytes from non-electrolytes such as glycerol, sucrose or gelatin is based on this idea.

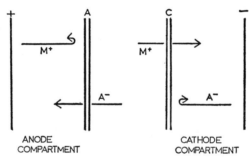

Fig. 291. Demineralisation by means of ion-exchange membranes.
A = anion exchange membrane. C = cation exchange membrane.

Partition chromatography

This means of separation is based on principles similar to those governing solvent extraction but here one solvent remains stationary in contact with an adsorbent in a column while the other solvent moves downward. The mobile phase carries solutes down at rates dependent on their relative partition coefficients.

Some of the first successful results were obtained with silica gel wetted with water as the fixed phase and chloroform as the mobile phase (Martin and Synge, 1941). Though much of the early work was on biochemical material, inorganic substances have also been separated by this method and the somewhat intractable problem of a clear-cut separation of hafnium from zirconium was solved by partition on silica gel with methanol as the moving solvent (p. 451).

Paper chromatography is a development of partition chromatography made possible because paper in moist air holds a small amount of water in equilibrium. Consden, Gordon and Martin (1944) used butanol as the moving phase to separate into its constituent amino-acids a drop of protein hydro-lysate placed on filter paper. The positions of the spots after some hours were indicated by spraying with ninhydrin solution and the amino-acids were characterised by colour and R_F values. (The ratio of the distance moved by the solute to that moved by the solvent front $= R_F$.) The method has been applied extensively to the separation of inorganic substances. Johnson and Kraus (1954) separated scandium from zirconium, titanium and thorium using methyl acetate and dilute nitric acid as solvents and quinalizarin to indicate the position of the spots. Pfrengle (1957) has separated condensed phosphates by elution on paper and subsequently identified them by the molybdenum-blue test, and Crowther (1954) has developed a method for separating any mixture of ortho-, pyro-, trimeta- and tetrameta-phosphates.

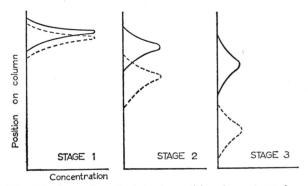

Fig. 292. Separation of solutes in partition chromatography.

James and Martin (1951) showed that partition chromatography of vapours was possible, using as the stationary phase a high-boiling liquid supported on kieselguhr and as the mobile phase nitrogen carrying the mixed vapours to be separated. In vapour-phase chromatography the arrival of the various fractions at the end of the column is indicated by variation in some physical property such as thermal conductance.

Adsorption chromatography

In the older technique of adsorption chromatography, a column of acti-vated alumina, magnesium carbonate or similar insoluble white solid fills a tube down which a solution of the materials to be separated is poured. A narrow band is produced which is eluted down the column with a suitable solvent, or displaced by adding a solution of a substance which is more strongly adsorbed. When the bands of different components have separated sufficiently the packing can be extruded from the column and cut into portions containing individual constituents which can then be dissolved out separately. In other instances, one band after another is eluted right out of the bottom of the column, the receivers being changed when necessary.

Solvent extraction

Ether extraction of an acidified solution of iron(III) chloride is an old way of removing iron. The principle of solvent extraction exemplified is extensively applied in research and industry where solutes are moved from aqueous to non-aqueous phases and *vice versa* to effect separation or purification. The distribution of a solute between two immiscible liquids is expressed by the partition coefficient, $K = [A]/[B]$; more precisely, when activities are substituted for concentrations in the two phases, $K = \{A\}/\{B\}$. This holds over a wide range of concentration provided the solute has the same form in each solvent, otherwise the coefficient changes markedly with concentration. The weight remaining in V_1 cc of a solution containing W g of solute after extraction by V_2 cc of a second liquid is

$$W_1 = \frac{WV_1}{KV_2 + V_1}, \text{ and after } n \text{ extractions } W_n = W\left(\frac{V_1}{KV_2 + V_1}\right)^n.$$

From this it follows that extraction is greater the higher the value of K and the larger the number of extractions. With $K = 10$ and $V_1 = V_2$ the amount remaining after 1 extraction and 3 extractions are respectively:

$$W_1 = \frac{W}{11} \text{ and } W_3 = \frac{W}{1331}.$$

Partition coefficients with values from 0.2 upwards find application.

Sometimes all of one solute can be removed from a solution containing two solutes by one extraction, but more often fractional extraction must be employed. Thus if K for organic/aqueous phase for A is 4 and for B 0.25, a single extraction removes 80% of A and 20% of B, and a second extraction raises this to 96% A and 36% B. Thus the increased yield of A has been secured at the expense of further contamination by B. This can be reduced by retrograde extraction, in which both A and B are recovered from the first extraction, brought into the aqueous medium again, and re-extracted. In these circumstances 64% of the original quantity of A is recovered but it carries only 4% of the original quantity of B, so that contamination is reduced at the expense of recovery. Excellent separation can often be effected, however, by combinations of multiple and retrograde extraction stages in apparatus specially designed for large numbers of equilibrations and transfers.

Extraction of inorganic solutes into organic liquids involves compound formation which is generally one of three kinds: (a) oxonium salts, (b) chelation complexes, (c) hydrogen-bonded solvates. The extraction of iron(III) chloride by ether is an example of the first of these, for ether is capable of forming $[Et_2OH]^+$ under acid conditions, whereby the oxonium salt $[Et_2OH]^+$ $[FeCl_4]^-$ is produced which dissolves in the ether. Hydrogen ions are necessary and the extraction is selective; thus, in $6N$ HCl, iron(III) chloride is taken up, but $MnCl_2$, $FeCl_2$, $CoCl_2$ and $NiCl_2$ are rejected. In the second, chelation complexes with metal ions are formed by cupferron (I), 8-hydroxyquinoline (II), dithizone (III) and thenoyl trifluoroacetone (TTA) (IV). They are generally used in a solvent such as chloroform or benzene, and the

(I)

(II)

(III) $S:C\begin{smallmatrix}NH\cdot NH\cdot C_6H_5\\N:NC_6H_5\end{smallmatrix}$

(IV)

chelate, being also soluble in the non-aqueous layer, takes the metal with it. Of materials forming solvates, the third class of compound, examples are ether and tributyl phosphate (TBP), $(C_4H_9)_3PO_4$, and the mode of attachment is the hydrogen bond. Uranyl nitrate, for instance, yields $UO_2(NO_3)_2 \cdot 3H_2O \cdot (C_2H_5)_2O$ and $UO_2(NO_3)_2 \cdot 2H_2O \cdot 2(C_2H_5)_2O$ on evaporation with ether, but their isolation need not be taken as indicating that these compounds actually exist in the solution. It is pretty certain, however, that the molecule $UO_2(NO_3)_2$ is involved. TBP, a viscous liquid, is used as a solution in refined kerosene. The solvates it forms with many molecules are also soluble in kerosene and are thus removed from the aqueous layer.

It is possible to recover the extracted material from these various organic phases by evaporation, but it is much more usual to back-extract them into a second aqueous phase by altering its acidity or making some other change. An example is afforded by the separation of plutonium from uranium present in a $1N$ HNO$_3$ solution as $UO_2(NO_3)_2$ and $PuO_2(NO_3)_2$. These form $MO_2(NO_3)_2 \cdot 2$ TBP and are extracted into the kerosene phase. By washing this loaded phase with $0.1N$ HNO$_3$ containing a reducing agent the Pu[VI] is reduced to Pu[III] and enters the aqueous phase, leaving the U[VI] still unreduced as the TBP solvate in the kerosene. From this it can be removed by washing with water in which the salt $UO_2(NO_3)_2$, essential to the TBP solvate, is ionised.

The Elements

ATOMIC WEIGHTS AND OTHER DATA

The scale of atomic weights has as its denominator the integral number 12 as the relative mass of the atom of the principal isotope of carbon, ^{12}C.

Name	Symbol	Atomic Number	Atomic Weight	Commonest natural isotope	
				Mass Number	Abundance in %
Actinium	Ac	89	(227)		
Aluminium	Al	13	26.982	27	100
Americium	Am	95	(243)		
Antimony	Sb	51	121.75	121	57.26
Argon	Ar	18	39.948	40	99.60
Arsenic	As	33	74.922	75	100
Astatine	At	85	(210)		
Barium	Ba	56	137.34	138	71.7
Berkelium	Bk	97	(247)		
Beryllium	Be	4	9.012	9	100
Bismuth	Bi	83	208.980	209	100
Boron	B	5	10.811	11	81.3
Bromine	Br	35	79.909	79	50.6
Cadmium	Cd	48	112.40	114	28.8
Caesium	Cs	55	132.905	133	100
Calcium	Ca	20	40.08	40	96.92
Californium	Cf	98	(249)		
Carbon	C	6	12.01115	12	98.9
Cerium	Ce	58	140.12	140	88.45
Chlorine	Cl	17	35.453	35	75.4
Chromium	Cr	24	51.996	52	83.7
Cobalt	Co	27	58.933	59	100
Copper	Cu	29	63.54	63	69
Curium	Cm	96	(247)		
Dysprosium	Dy	66	162.50	164	28.2
Einsteinium	Es	99	(254)		
Erbium	Er	68	167.26	168	26.9
Europium	Eu	63	151.96	153	52.2
Fermium	Fm	100	(253)		
Fluorine	F	9	18.998	19	100

Name	Symbol	Atomic Number	Atomic Weight	Commonest natural isotope	
				Mass Number	Abundance in %
Francium	Fr	87	(223)		
Gadolinium	Gd	64	157.25	158	24.8
Gallium	Ga	31	69.72	69	60
Germanium	Ge	32	72.59	74	36.5
Gold	Au	79	196.967	197	100
Hafnium	Hf	72	178.49	180	35.4
Helium	He	2	4.0026	4	99.9998
Holmium	Ho	67	164.930	165	100
Hydrogen	H	1	1.00797	1	99.985
Indium	In	49	114.82	115	95.8
Iodine	I	53	126.904	127	100
Iridium	Ir	77	192.2	193	61.5
Iron	Fe	26	55.847	56	91.6
Krypton	Kr	36	83.80	84	57.02
Lanthanum	La	57	138.91	139	99.91
Lawrencium	Lr	103			
Lead	Pb	82	207.19	208	52.3
Lithium	Li	3	6.939	7	92.6
Lutetium	Lu	71	174.97	175	97.5
Magnesium	Mg	12	24.312	24	79.0
Manganese	Mn	25	54.938	55	100
Mendelevium	Md	101	(256)		
Mercury	Hg	80	200.59	202	29.7
Molybdenum	Mo	42	95.94	98	24.0
Neodymium	Nd	60	144.24	144	23.9
Neon	Ne	10	20.183	20	90.0
Neptunium	Np	93	(237)		
Nickel	Ni	28	58.71	58	67.9
Niobium	Nb	41	92.906	93	100
Nitrogen	N	7	14.0067	14	99.6
Nobelium	No	102			
Osmium	Os	76	190.2	192	41
Oxygen	O	8	15.9994	16	99.76
Palladium	Pd	46	106.4	108	26.7
Phosphorus	P	15	30.974	31	100
Platinum	Pt	78	195.09	195	33.7
Plutonium	Pu	94	(242)		
Polonium	Po	84	(210)		
Potassium	K	19	39.102	39	93.08
Praseodymium	Pr	59	140.907	141	100
Promethium	Pm	61	(147)		

Name	Symbol	Atomic Number	Atomic Weight	Commonest natural isotope	
				Mass Number	Abundance in %
Protactinium	Pa	91	(231)		
Radium	Ra	88	226.05		
Radon	Rn	86	(222)		
Rhenium	Re	75	186.2	187	62.9
Rhodium	Rh	45	102.905	103	100
Rubidium	Rb	37	85.47	85	72.8
Ruthenium	Ru	44	101.07	102	31.5
Samarium	Sm	62	150.35	152	27
Scandium	Sc	21	44.956	45	100
Selenium	Se	34	78.96	80	49.9
Silicon	Si	14	28.086	28	92.18
Silver	Ag	47	107.870	107	51.35
Sodium	Na	11	22.9898	23	100
Strontium	Sr	38	87.62	88	82.56
Sulphur	S	16	32.064	32	95.0
Tantalum	Ta	73	180.948	181	100
Technetium	Tc	43	(97)		
Tellurium	Te	52	127.60	130	34.35
Terbium	Tb	65	158.924	159	100
Thallium	Tl	81	204.37	205	70.5
Thorium	Th	90	232.038	232	100
Thulium	Tm	69	168.934	169	100
Tin	Sn	50	118.69	120	32.9
Titanium	Ti	22	47.90	48	73.4
Tungsten	W	74	183.85	184	30.7
Uranium	U	92	238.03	238	99.28
Vanadium	V	23	50.942	51	99.75
Xenon	Xe	54	131.30	132	26.93
Ytterbium	Yb	70	173.04	174	31.8
Yttrium	Y	39	88.905	89	100
Zinc	Zn	30	65.37	64	48.9
Zirconium	Zr	40	91.22	90	51.6

Subject Index